JOHN A. BURNES

$1\mu = 10^{-3} mm$

SOIL MECHANICS
IN ENGINEERING PRACTICE

SOIL MECHANICS
IN
ENGINEERING PRACTICE

By

KARL TERZAGHI

Professor of the Practice of Civil Engineering,
Harvard University
Lecturer and Research Consultant in Civil Engineering,
University of Illinois

and

RALPH B. PECK

Research Professor of Soil Mechanics
University of Illinois

JOHN WILEY & SONS, *Inc.*
New York   *London*

PREFACE

Soil mechanics originated several decades ago under the pressure of necessity. As the practical problems involving soils broadened in scope, the inadequacy of the scientific tools available for coping with them became increasingly apparent. Efforts to remedy the situation started almost simultaneously in the United States and in Europe, and within a short period they produced an impressive array of useful information.

The initial successes in this field of applied science were so encouraging that a new branch of structural analysis appeared to be in the making. As a consequence, the extent and profundity of the theoretical investigations increased rapidly, and experimental methods were developed to a high degree of refinement. Without the results of these painstaking investigations a rational approach to the problems of earthwork engineering could not have been attempted.

Unfortunately, the research activities in soil mechanics had one undesirable psychological effect. They diverted the attention of many investigators and teachers from the manifold limitations imposed by nature on the application of mathematics to problems in earthwork engineering. As a consequence, more and more emphasis has been placed on refinements in sampling and testing and on those very few problems that can be solved with accuracy. Yet, accurate solutions can be obtained only if the soil strata are practically homogenous and continuous in horizontal directions. Furthermore, since the investigations leading to accurate solutions involve highly specialized methods of sampling and testing, they are justified only in exceptional cases. On the overwhelming majority of jobs no more than an approximate forecast is needed, and if such a forecast cannot be made by simple means it cannot be made at all. If it is not possible to make an approximate forecast, the behavior of the soil must be observed during construction, and the design may subsequently have to be modified in accordance with the findings. These facts cannot be ignored without defying the purpose of soil mechanics. They govern the treatment of the subject in this book.

Part A deals with the physical properties of soils and Part B with the theories of soil mechanics. These two parts are very short, but they contain all that engineering students and the average engineer need to know about soil mechanics proper at the present time. The heart of the book is Part C.

Part C deals with the art of getting satisfactory results in earthwork and foundation engineering at a reasonable cost, in spite of the complexity of the structure of natural soil strata and in spite of the inevitable gaps in our knowledge of the soil conditions. To achieve this goal the engineer must take advantage of all the methods and resources at his disposal—experience, theory, and soil testing included. Yet all these resources are of no avail unless they are used with careful discrimination, because almost every practical problem in this field contains at least some features without precedent.

Every discussion of practical problems in Part C starts with a critical survey of conventional methods and proceeds step by step to whatever improvements have been realized with the assistance of the results of research in soil mechanics. Therefore, the experienced engineer is advised to start reading the book at the beginning of this part. He should use Parts A and B only for reference, to get information about concepts with which he is not yet familiar. Otherwise he would be obliged to digest a considerable amount of material before he would be in a position to realize its function in his field of interest.

The details of the methods for coping with the practical problems covered by Part C may change as experience increases, and some of them may become obsolete in a few years because they are no more than temporary expedients. Yet the merits of the semiempirical approach advocated in Part C are believed to be independent of time. At the end of each article of Part C the reader will find a list of references. In their choice priority was given to those publications that are likely to foster the urge and capacity for careful and intelligent field observations. In connection with these references it should be emphasized that some of the discussions and closures may contain more important information than the articles themselves.

Since the field of soil engineering is too broad to be covered adequately in a single volume, various important topics such as highway, airport, and tunnel engineering had to be excluded. Brief references concerning these fields have been assembled in an appendix.

In its early stages, the manuscript was critically studied by Professor C. P. Siess, whose comments were especially helpful. The authors also appreciate the suggestions of the several practicing engineers who read various portions of the text. In particular, they are indebted to Mr. A. E. Cummings, Mr. O. K. Peck, and Mr. F. E. Schmidt for criticisms of Part C, to Dr. R. E. Grim for review of Article 4, and to Dr. Ruth D. Terzaghi for assistance in the preparation of Article 63.

Tables and figures taken in whole or in part from other sources are acknowledged where they occur in the text. The drawings are the work of Professor Elmer F. Heater. For his co-operative interest and skilful work the authors are indeed grateful.

KARL TERZAGHI

RALPH B. PECK

CONTENTS

ix

SYMBOLS

The symbols used in this text conform generally to those suggested in 1941 by the American Society of Civil Engineers (*Soil Mechanics Nomenclature*, Manual of Engineering Practice No. 22), although exceptions have been made wherever necessary to avoid confusion.

In the United States at the present time, it is customary to express the results of laboratory tests in terms of metric units, whereas the English system is used in the field and the design office. In conformity with this practice, the soil constants and test results contained in Part A are given in terms of metric units. In Parts B and C, which deal with theories and practical applications, only the English system is used. Fortunately, the values of quantities which enter most frequently into the computations involved in soil mechanics can be converted without mental effort from one system to the other by means of the closely approximate relation,

$$1 \text{kg/cm}^2 \approx 1 \text{ ton/ft}^2 \approx 1 \text{ atmosphere} = 34 \text{ ft of water} = 15 \text{ lb/in.}^2$$

In this relation, the ton is the short ton of 2000 lb. Other conversion factors which may be required are

$$1 \text{ lb} = 454 \text{ gm}$$
$$1 \text{ kg} = 2.2 \text{ lb}$$
$$1 \text{ ft} = 30.5 \text{ cm}$$

In the following list, the dimensions of the quantities are given in the metric (cm–gm–sec) system. If the numerical value of a quantity is given in this system, it can readily be expressed in the English (ft-lb-sec) system by means of the conversion factors just given. For example, we may express the value,

$$E = 120,000 \text{ gm/cm}^2$$

in the English system by introducing into the preceding equation,

$$1 \text{ gm} = \frac{1}{454} \text{ lb} \quad \text{and} \quad 1 \text{ cm} = \frac{1}{30.5} \text{ ft}$$

whence

$$E = 120,000 \, \frac{1}{454} \text{ lb} \times \frac{30.5^2}{\text{ft}^2} = 120,000 \, (2.05 \text{ lb/ft}^2)$$

$$= 245,000 \text{ lb/ft}^2$$

If no dimension is added to a symbol, the symbol indicates a pure number.

A (cm^2) = area

A_r = area ratio of sampling spoon

B (cm) = width

a_v (cm^2/gm) = coefficient of compressibility

C (any dimension) = constant

C (gm) = resultant cohesion

C_a (gm) = total adhesion

C_c = compression index for soil in field; creep ratio

$C_c{}'$ = compression index of remolded soil

C_s = swelling index

C_r = relative consistency

C_w = weighted creep ratio (failure by piping)

c (gm/cm^2) = cohesion

c (in) = constant in Engineering News formula

c_v (cm^2/sec) = coefficient of consolidation

D (cm) = grain size; depth; diameter; spacing between centers of piles

D_{10} (cm) = effective grain size

D_f (cm) = depth of foundation

D_r = relative density of cohesionless soil

d (cm) = diameter of pile; distance

E (gm/cm^2) = modulus of elasticity (If E refers to a definite state or range of stress, subscripts are used.)

E (volt) = difference in electric potential

e = void ratio

e (coulomb/cm^2) = electric charge per unit of area

e_o = void ratio in loosest state

$e_{\min}$ = void ratio in densest state

e_w = volume of water per unit volume of solid matter (for saturated soil $e_w = e$)

e_c = critical void ratio

F (gm) = reaction; resultant force

f_s (gm/cm^2) = sum of friction and adhesion between soil and pile or pier

f = coefficient of friction between soil and base of structure

f_0 (1/sec) = natural frequency (vibrations)

f_1 (1/sec) = frequency of impulse (vibrations)

G_a = air-space ratio (drainage)

G_s = factor of safety

H (cm) = thickness of stratum except when used in connection with consolidating layer. In this event, H = thickness of half-closed layer or half-thickness of open layer

H (cm) = height of fall of hammer (pile driving)

H_c (cm) = critical height of slope

ΔH (cm) = position head (hydraulics)

h (cm) = hydraulic head

h_1 (cm) = total hydraulic head

h_w (cm) = piezometric head

Δh (cm) = potential drop (hydraulics)

h_c (cm) = height of capillary rise; critical head for failure by piping

h_{cc} (cm) = height of complete saturation of drained soil

h_{cr} (cm) = critical head for failure by piping according to computation based on line of creep method

h_r = relative vapor pressure

h_{ra} = relative humidity

I_w = plasticity index

i = hydraulic gradient

i_c = critical hydraulic gradient

i_p (gm/cm^3) = pressure gradient

K = ratio between intensities of horizontal and vertical pressures at a given point in a mass of soil

K_0 = coefficient of earth pressure at rest (value of K for initial state of elastic equilibrium)

K_A = coefficient of active earth pressure

K_P = coefficient of passive earth pressure

K (cm^2) = permeability

K_s (gm/cm^3) = coefficient of subgrade reaction

k (cm/sec) = coefficient of permeability

k_I (cm/sec) = coefficient of permeability in direction parallel to bedding planes

k_{II} (cm/sec) = coefficient of permeability in direction perpendicular to bedding planes

k_r (cm/sec) = coefficient of permeability of remolded clay

k_h, k_v (gm/cm^3) = coefficients for computing pressure of backfill against retaining wall

L (cm) = length of line of creep; length

L_w = liquid limit

l (cm) = length

M_c (gm cm) = moment of cohesive forces

m_v (cm^2/gm) = coefficient of volume compressibility

N = dimensionless factor (N_c, $N\gamma$, and N_q = bearing capacity factors; N_s = stability factor in theory of stability of slopes); number of blows on sampling spoon during performance of standard penetration test

$N\phi$ = flow value = $\tan^2 (45° + \phi/2)$

N_d = number of equipotential drops (flow net)

N_f = number of flow channels (flow net)

n = porosity; number of piles in group

n_a = ratio between distance from bottom of lateral support to point of application of earth pressure, and total height of lateral support

n_d = depth factor (stability of slopes)

n_g = intensity of earthquake

P = per cent of grains smaller than given size

P (gm or gm/cm) = resultant pressure

P_A (gm/cm) = active earth pressure if arching is absent (retaining walls; active Rankine state)

P_a (gm/cm) = active earth pressure if arching is present (bracing in open cuts)

P_P (gm/cm) = passive earth pressure. May be subdivided into $P_P{}'$ which depends on unit weight of the soil, and $P_P{}''$ which depends on cohesion and surcharge. $P_P{}''$ may be further subdivided into P_c and P_q, respectively.

ΔP_A (gm/cm) = part of active earth pressure due to line load q'

P_w (gm/cm) = resultant water pressure

P_w = plastic limit

p (gm/cm^2) = pressure or normal stress; subgrade reaction

$p_{1,2,3}$ (gm/cm^2) = major, intermediate, and minor principal stresses

p_h (gm/cm^2) = horizontal pressure against vertical plane

p_v (gm/cm^2) = vertical pressure against horizontal plane

p_c (gm/cm^2) = confining pressure; all-around pressure

p_A (gm/cm^2) = intensity of active earth pressure

$\bar{p}$ (gm/cm^2) = effective pressure (bar may be omitted)

p_0 (gm/cm^2) = initial pressure; present overburden pressure

p_0' (gm/cm^2) = maximum consolidation pressure on soil in field

Δp_0 (gm/cm^2) = temporary excess overburden pressure

Δp (gm/cm^2) = change in pressure; consolidation stress

p' (gm/cm^2) = maximum consolidation pressure on shear test specimen

p_q (gm/cm^2) = increase in pressure on retaining wall due to surcharge q per unit of area

p_q' (gm/cm) = increase in pressure on retaining wall due to surcharge q' per unit of length parallel to crest

p_a (gm/cm^2) = initial consolidation pressure on shear test specimen; pressure of atmosphere

p_{cr} (gm/cm^2) = pressure corresponding to equal shearing resistance of given soil in slow and consolidated-quick tests

p_k (gm/cm^2) = capillary pressure

p_s (gm/cm^3) = seepage pressure

p_u (gm/cm^2) = pressure corresponding to point b, Figure 22a

Q (cm^3 or cm^2) = total discharge per unit of time

Q (gm) = concentrated load

Q_a (gm) = allowable load on pile

Q_c (gm) = ultimate bearing capacity of pile cluster

Q_d (gm) = ultimate static resistance of pile

Q_d (gm or gm/cm) = critical load on footing or pier resting on dense or stiff soil. May be subdivided into Q' due to weight of soil and Q'' due to cohesion and surcharge. Bearing capacity of circular footing is denoted by Q_{dr} and of square footing by Q_{ds}

Q_d' (gm or gm/cm) = critical load on footing or pier resting on loose or soft soil

Q_{dy} (gm) = dynamic resistance to penetration of pile

Q_f (gm) = skin friction (total)

Q_p (gm) = point resistance of pile

Q_{pr} (gm) = critical load on base of pier

Q_t (gm) = excess load on footing or raft, consisting of net dead load Q_{dn} and live load Q_l; load on pile, consisting of Q exerted by building, and $Q' + Q''$ due to negative skin friction

q (gm/cm^2) = uniformly distributed load; surcharge per unit of area; supplementary axial pressure (triaxial test)

q' (gm/cm) = uniformly distributed line load

q_a (gm/cm^2) = allowable soil pressure

q_c (gm/cm^2) = confined compressive strength

q_d (gm/cm^2) = ultimate bearing capacity for dense or stiff soil. Value for loose or soft soil denoted by q_d'. Bearing capacity of circular footing denoted by q_{dr}, of square footing by q_{ds}, and of oblong footing by q_{do}.

q_u (gm/cm^2) = unconfined compressive strength

r (cm) = radius

r_f (cm) = radius of friction circle (stability of slopes)

S (gm/cm) = total sliding resistance between base of dam and subsoil

S (cm) = settlement; penetration of pile under hammer blow

S_e (cm) = temporary elastic compression of pile under hammer blow

S_r = degree of saturation

S_t = degree of sensitivity

S_w = shrinkage limit

s (gm/cm^2) = shearing resistance

T (degrees centigrade) = temperature

T_s (gm/cm) = surface tension of liquid

T_v = time factor (theory of consolidation)

T_w = sticky limit

t (sec) = time

t (gm/cm^2) = shearing stress

U (gm/cm) = total neutral pressure on base of dam

U = degree of consolidation; uniformity coefficient = D_{60}/D_{10}

u (gm/cm^2) = excess hydrostatic pressure

u_w (gm/cm^2) = neutral stress, pore-water pressure

V (cm^3) = total volume

V_v (cm^3) = total volume of voids

v (cm/sec) = discharge velocity

v_s (cm/sec) = seepage velocity

W (gm or gm/cm) = weight

W_H (gm) = weight of ram of pile driver

W_P (gm) = weight of pile

W_s (gm) = effective weight of soil replaced by footing or basement

w = water content in per cent of dry weight

z (cm) = depth

z_c (cm) = depth of tension cracks

α = angle

β (degrees) = slope angle

γ (gm/cm^3) = unit weight (soil, water and air)

γ' (gm/cm^3) = submerged unit weight

γ_d (gm/cm^3) = unit weight of soil if water is entirely replaced by air

γ_{dr} (gm/cm^3) = unit weight of dry remolded soil sample

γ_{di} (gm/cm^3) = unit weight of dry intact soil sample

γ_w (gm/cm^3) = unit weight of water

γ_s (gm/cm^3) = unit weight of solid constituents

Δ = increment

δ (degrees) = angle of wall friction; angle between resultant stress on plane and normal to plane

ϵ = base of Naperian logarithms; unit strain

η (gm/cm^2 sec) = viscosity

θ (degrees) = angle; central angle

μ = Poisson's ratio; micron

Φ = velocity potential (flow net)

ϕ (degrees) = angle of internal friction; angle of shearing resistance in Coulomb's equation

ϕ_a (degrees) = angle of shearing resistance for partly saturated clay

ϕ_{cq} (degrees) = angle of shearing resistance corresponding to consolidated-quick test conditions

ϕ_s (degrees) = angle of shearing resistance corresponding to slow test conditions

$\log a$ = Naperian (natural) logarithm of a

$\log_{10} a$ = logarithm of a to the base 10

$\overline{ab}$ = distance ab measured along a straight line

$\overset{\frown}{ab}$ = distance ab measured along an arc

$\approx$ means approximately equal

15.3 indicates equation 3 in Article 15.   The article number appears at the top of
each page

INTRODUCTION

Soil Mechanics in Engineering Practice is divided into the following three parts:

A. Physical Properties of Soils.
B. Theoretical Soil Mechanics.
C. Problems of Design and Construction.

Part A deals with the physical and mechanical properties of homogeneous specimens of undisturbed and remolded soils. It discusses those properties which serve as convenient criteria for distinguishing between different soils and provides instructions for describing soils adequately. It also deals with those soil properties that have a direct bearing on the behavior of soil masses during and after construction operations.

Part B provides the reader with an elementary knowledge of the theories required for solving problems involving the stability or bearing capacity of soils or the interaction between soil and water. All these theories are based on radically simplifying assumptions regarding the mechanical and hydraulic properties of the soils. Nevertheless, when properly applied, the results obtained by means of these approximate procedures are accurate enough for most practical purposes.

Part C deals with the application of our present knowledge of soil behavior and of the theories of soil mechanics to design and construction in the field of foundation and earthwork engineering. The design of pavements for roads and airports is represented only by references in the Appendix because it constitutes an independent and highly specialized branch of earthwork engineering.

The physical properties of soils could be discussed quite properly in a general study of the engineering properties of materials, and the theories of soil mechanics constitute a part of the general subject of theoretical mechanics. However, design and construction in the field of foundation and earthwork engineering, which constitutes the third and largest part of this book, is an independent subject in its own right, because it involves methods of reasoning and procedure that have no counterpart in other fields of structural engineering. In all other fields, the engineer is concerned with the effect of forces on structures made of manufactured products such as steel and concrete or carefully selected natural materials such as timber or stone. Since the properties of these materials can be determined reliably, the problems associated with design can almost always be solved by the direct application of theory or the results of model tests.

On the other hand, every statement and conclusion pertaining to soils in the field involves many uncertainties. In extreme cases the concepts on which a design is based are no more than crude working hypotheses that may be far from the truth. In such cases the risk of partial or total failure can be eliminated only by using what may be called the observational procedure. This procedure consists in making appropriate observations soon enough during construction to detect any signs of departure of the real conditions from those assumed by the designer and in modifying either the design or the method of construction in accordance with the findings.

These considerations determine the subject matter and method of presentation of Part C. Instead of starting with instructions for applying theoretical principles to design, Part C deals first of all with the technique for securing information about the soil conditions at the chosen site by boring, sounding, sampling, and testing. In spite of the great amount of time and labor involved in such exploratory work, the results commonly leave much room for interpretation.

Subsequent chapters of Part C contain a discussion of the general principles of the design of structures such as retaining walls, earth dams, and foundations. The behavior of all such structures depends chiefly on the physical soil properties and the subsoil conditions. Because our knowledge of subsoil conditions is always incomplete, uncertainties inevitably enter into the fundamental design assumptions. These uncertainties require and receive continuous attention in the text. Similar discussions are not required in textbooks pertaining to other fields of structural design, because the reliability of the fundamental assumptions concerning the properties of the other common construction materials can almost always be taken for granted.

Part A

PHYSICAL PROPERTIES OF SOILS

The subject matter of Part A is divided into three chapters. The first deals with the procedures commonly used to discriminate between different soils or between different states of the same soil. The second deals with the hydraulic and mechanical properties of soils and with the experimental methods used to determine numerical values representative of these properties. The third chapter deals with the physical processes involved in the drainage of soils.

Chapter I

INDEX PROPERTIES OF SOILS

ART. 1. PRACTICAL IMPORTANCE OF INDEX PROPERTIES

In foundation and earthwork engineering, more than in any other field of civil engineering, success depends on practical experience. The design of ordinary soil-supporting or soil-supported structures is necessarily based on simple empirical rules, but these rules can be used safely only by the engineer who has a background of experience. Large projects involving unusual features may call for extensive application of scientific methods to design, but the program for the required investigations cannot be laid out wisely, nor can the results be interpreted intelligently, unless the engineer in charge of design possesses a large amount of experience.

Since personal experience is necessarily somewhat limited, the engineer is compelled to rely at least to some extent on the records of the experiences of others. If these records contain adequate descriptions of the soil conditions, they constitute a storehouse of valuable information. Otherwise, they may actually be misleading. In the field of structural engineering, an account of the failure of a beam would be of little value unless it contained, in addition to other essential data, a statement as to whether the beam was made of steel or of cast iron. In all the older records of foundation experience, the nature of the soils is indicated merely by such general terms as "fine sand" or "soft clay." Yet, the differences between the mechanical properties of two fine sands from different localities can be greater and more significant than those between cast iron and steel. As a consequence, one of the foremost aims in recent attempts to reduce the hazards in dealing with soils has been to find methods for discriminating between the different kinds of soil in a given category. The properties on which the distinctions are based are known as *index properties*, and the tests required to determine the index properties are *classification tests*.

The nature of any given soil can be altered by appropriate manipulation. Vibrations, for example, can transform a loose sand into a dense one. Hence, the behavior of a soil in the field depends not only on the significant properties of the individual constituents of the soil mass, but also on those properties which are due to the arrangement of the parti-

3

cles within the mass. Accordingly, it is convenient to divide index properties into two classes: *soil grain properties* and *soil aggregate properties.* The principal soil grain properties are the size and shape of the grains and, in clay soils, the mineralogical character of the smallest grains. The most significant aggregate property of cohesionless soils is the relative density, whereas that of cohesive soils is the consistency.

The discussion of the soil grain and aggregate properties will be preceded by a description of the principal types of soil, and it will be followed by a condensed review of the minimum requirements for adequate soil descriptions to be incorporated in the records of field observations.

ART. 2. PRINCIPAL TYPES OF SOILS

The materials that constitute the earth's crust are rather arbitrarily divided by the civil engineer into the two categories, *soil* and *rock.* Soil is a natural aggregate of mineral grains that can be separated by such gentle mechanical means as agitation in water. Rock, on the other hand, is a natural aggregate of minerals connected by strong and permanent cohesive forces. Since the terms "strong" and "permanent" are subject to different interpretations, the boundary between soil and rock is necessarily an arbitrary one. As a matter of fact, there are many natural aggregates of mineral particles that are difficult to classify either as soil or as rock. In this text, however, the term soil will be applied only to materials that unquestionably satisfy the preceding definition.

Although the terminology described in the preceding paragraph is generally understood by civil engineers, it is not in universal use. To the geologist, for example, the term rock implies all the material which constitutes the earth's crust, regardless of the degree to which the mineral particles are bound together, whereas the term soil is applied only to that portion of the earth's crust which is capable of supporting vegetation. Therefore, if the civil engineer makes use of information prepared by workers in other fields, he must be certain that he understands the sense in which the terms soil and rock are used.

On the basis of the origin of their constituents, soils can be divided into two large groups, those which consist chiefly of the results of chemical and physical rock weathering, and those which are chiefly of organic origin. If the products of rock weathering are still located at the place where they originated, they constitute a *residual soil.* Otherwise they constitute a *transported soil,* regardless of the agent which performed the transportation.

The depth of residual soils depends primarily on climatic conditions and on the time of exposure. In some areas, this depth amounts to hundreds of feet. In temperate zones residual soils are commonly stiff and stable. Exceptions to this rule are very rare. On the other hand, many deposits of transported soil are loose and soft to a depth of several hundred feet. Therefore, difficulties with foundations and other types of construction are associated almost exclusively with transported soils.

Soils of organic origin are formed chiefly *in situ*, either by the growth and subsequent decay of plants such as peat mosses, or by the accumulation of fragments of the inorganic skeletons or shells of organisms. Hence a soil of organic origin can be either organic or inorganic. The term *organic soil* ordinarily refers to a transported soil consisting of the products of rock weathering with a more or less conspicuous admixture of decayed vegetable matter.

The soil conditions at the site of a proposed structure are commonly explored by means of test borings or test shafts. The foreman on the job examines samples of the soil as they are obtained. He classifies them in accordance with local usage and prepares a boring log or shaft record containing the name of each soil and the elevation of its boundaries. The name of the soil is modified by adjectives indicating the stiffness, color, and other attributes. At a later date the record may be supplemented by an abstract of the results of tests made on the samples in the laboratory.

The following list of soil types includes the names commonly used by experienced foremen and practical engineers for field classification.

Sand and *gravel* are cohesionless aggregates of rounded subangular or angular fragments of more or less unaltered rocks or minerals. Particles with a size up to $\frac{1}{8}$ in. are referred to as sand, and those with a size from $\frac{1}{8}$ in. to 6 or 8 in. as gravel. Fragments with a diameter of more than 8 in. are known as *boulders*.

Hardpan is a soil that offers an exceptionally great resistance to the penetration of drilling tools. Most hardpans are extremely dense well-graded somewhat cohesive aggregates of mineral particles.

Inorganic silt is a fine-grained soil with little or no plasticity. The least plastic varieties generally consist of more or less equidimensional grains of quartz and are sometimes called *rock flour*, whereas the most plastic types contain an appreciable percentage of flake-shaped particles and are referred to as *plastic silt*. Because of its smooth texture, inorganic silt is often mistaken for clay, but it may be readily distinguished from clay without laboratory testing. If shaken in the palm of the hand, a pat of saturated inorganic silt expels enough water to make its surface appear glossy. If the pat is bent between the fingers, its surface again becomes dull. This procedure is known as the *shaking test*. After the pat has dried, it is brittle, and dust can be detached by rubbing it with the finger. Silt is relatively impervious, but if it is in a loose state it may rise into a drill hole or shaft like a thick viscous fluid. The most unstable soils of this category are known locally under different names, such as bull's liver and quicksand.*

Organic silt is a fine-grained more or less plastic soil with an admixture of finely divided particles of organic matter. Shells and visible fragments of partly decayed vegetable matter may also be present. The soil ranges in color from light to very dark gray, and it is likely to contain a considerable quantity of H_2S, CO_2, and various other gaseous products of the decay of organic matter which give it a characteristic odor. The permeability of organic silt is very low and its compressibility very high.

Clay is an aggregate of microscopic and submicroscopic particles derived from the chemical decomposition of rock constituents. It is plastic within a moderate to wide range of water content. Dry specimens are very hard, and no powder can be detached by rubbing the surface of dried pats with the fingers. The permeability of clay is extremely low. The term *gumbo* is applied, particularly in the western United States, to clays which are distinguished in the plastic state by a soapy or waxy appearance and by great toughness. At higher water contents they are conspicuously sticky.

Organic clay is a clay that owes some of its significant physical properties to the presence of finely divided organic matter. When saturated organic clay is likely to be very compressible, but when dry its strength is very high. It is usually dark gray or black in color, and it may have a conspicuous odor.

Peat is a somewhat fibrous aggregate of macroscopic and microscopic fragments of decayed vegetable matter. Its color ranges between light brown and black. Peat is so compressible that it is entirely unsuitable for supporting foundations or earth embankments.

If a soil is made up of a combination of two different soil types, the predominant ingredient is expressed as a noun, and the less prominent ingredient as a modifying adjective. For example, silty sand indicates a soil which is predominantly sand but contains a small amount of silt. A sandy clay is a soil which exhibits the properties of a clay but contains an appreciable amount of sand.

The aggregate properties of sand and gravel are described qualitatively by the terms *loose*, *medium*, and *dense*, whereas those of clays are described by *hard*, *stiff*, *medium*, and *soft*. These terms are usually evaluated by the boring foreman on the basis of several factors, including the relative ease or difficulty of advancing the drilling and sampling

---

* The term *quicksand* is also commonly applied to fine or very fine sands that have passed into a semiliquid state under the influence of a rising current of seeping water. Therefore, the term may indicate either a material or a state.

tools and the consistency of the samples. However, since this method of evaluation may lead to a very erroneous conception of the general character of the soil deposit, the qualitative descriptions should be supplemented by quantitative information whenever the mechanical properties are likely to have an important influence on design. The quantitative information is commonly obtained by means of laboratory tests on relatively undisturbed samples, Article 8, or by suitable field tests, Article 44.

A record of the color of the different strata encountered in adjacent borings reduces the risk of errors in correlating the boring logs. Color may also be an indication of a real difference in the character of the soil. For example, if the top layer of a submerged clay stratum is yellowish or brown and stiffer than the underlying clay, it was probably exposed temporarily to desiccation combined with weathering. Terms such as mottled, marbled, spotted, or speckled are used when different colors occur in the same stratum of soil. Dark or drab colors are commonly associated with organic soils.

Under certain geological conditions soils form which are characterized by one or more striking or unusual features such as a root-hole structure or a conspicuous and regular stratification. Because of these features, such soils can easily be recognized in the field, and, as a consequence, they have been given special names by which they are commonly known. The following paragraphs contain definitions and descriptions of some of these materials.

Till is an unstratified glacial deposit of clay, silt, sand, gravel, and boulders. It covers part of the rock surface in those regions which were glaciated during the ice age.

Tuff is a fine-grained water- or wind-laid aggregate of very small mineral or rock fragments ejected from volcanoes during explosions.

Loess is a uniform cohesive wind-blown sediment. The size of most of the particles ranges between the narrow limits of 0.01 and 0.05 mm, and the cohesion is due to the presence of a more or less calcareous binder. The prevalent color is light brown. Loess is characterized by vertical root holes and the ability to stand with nearly vertical slopes. True loess deposits have never been saturated. On saturation the bond between particles dissolves, and the surface of the deposit may settle.

Modified loess is a loess that has lost its typical characteristics by secondary processes, including temporary immersion, erosion, and subsequent deposition; chemical changes involving the destruction of the bond between the particles; or chemical decomposition of the more perishable constituents such as feldspar. Thorough chemical decomposition produces *loess loam*, characterized by greater plasticity than other forms of modified loess.

Diatomaceous earth (kieselguhr) is a deposit of fine, generally white, siliceous powder, composed chiefly or wholly of the remains of diatoms. The term diatom applies to a group of microscopic unicellular marine or fresh-water algae characterized by silicified cell walls.

Lake marl or *boglime* is a white fine-grained powdery calcareous deposit precipitated by plants in ponds. It is commonly associated with beds of peat.

Marl is a rather loosely used term for various fairly stiff or very stiff marine calcareous clays of greenish color.

Adobe is a term applied in the southwestern part of the United States and other semiarid regions to a great variety of light-colored soils ranging from sandy silts to very plastic clays.

Caliche refers to layers of soil in which the soil grains are cemented together by carbonates such as lime. These layers commonly occur at a depth of several feet below the surface, and their thickness may range between a few inches and several feet. A semiarid climate appears to be necessary for their formation.

Varved clay consists of alternating layers of medium gray inorganic silt and darker silty clay. The thickness of the layers rarely exceeds one-half inch, but occasionally very much thicker varves are encountered. The constituents of varved clays were transported into fresh-water lakes by melt water at the close of the ice age. They are likely to combine the undesirable properties of both silts and soft clays.

Bentonite is a clay with a high content of montmorillonite, Article 4. Most bentonites were formed by chemical alteration of volcanic ash. In contact with water dried bentonite swells more than other dried clays, and saturated bentonite shrinks more on drying. Bentonite deposits occur in practically every state west of the Mississippi; in Tennessee, Kentucky, and Alabama; and to a minor extent in several other states. They are also common in Mexico.

Each term used in the field classification of soils includes a rather great variety of different materials. Furthermore, the choice of terms relating to stiffness and density depends to a considerable extent on the person who examines the soil. Because of these facts, the field classification of soils is always more or less uncertain and inaccurate. More specific information can be obtained only by physical tests that furnish numerical values representative of the properties of the soil.

The methods of soil exploration, including boring and sampling, and the procedures for determining average numerical values for the soil properties are a part of the design and construction program. They are discussed in Chapter VII, Part C.

ART. 3. SIZE AND SHAPE OF SOIL PARTICLES

The size of the particles that constitute soils may vary from that of boulders to that of large molecules.

Grains larger than 0.06 mm can be inspected with the naked eye or by means of a hand lens. They constitute the *very coarse* and *coarse* fractions of the soils.

Grains ranging in size from 0.06 mm to 2μ ($1\mu = 1$ micron $= 0.001$ mm) can be examined only under the microscope. They represent the *fine fraction.*

Grains smaller than 2μ constitute the *very fine fraction.* Grains having a size between 2μ and about 0.1μ can be observed under the microscope, but their shape cannot be discerned. The shape of grains smaller than about 1μ can be determined by means of an electron microscope. Their molecular structure can be investigated by means of X-ray analysis.

[The process of separating a soil aggregate into fractions, each consisting of grains within a different size range, is known as *mechanical analysis.* By means of mechanical analysis, it has been found that most natural soils contain grains representative of two or more soil fractions. The general character of mixed-grained soils is determined almost entirely by the character of the smallest soil constituents. In this respect soils are somewhat similar to concrete. The properties of concrete are determined primarily by the cement, whereas the aggregate, which constitutes most of the concrete, is inert. The "aggregate," or the inert portion of a mixed-grained soil, comprises about 80 or 90 per cent of the total dry weight. The decisive or active portion constitutes the remainder.]

Very coarse fractions, for example gravel, consist of rock fragments each composed of one or more minerals. The fragments may be angular, subangular, rounded, or flat. They may be fresh, or they may show signs of considerable weathering. They may be resistant or crumbly.

Coarse fractions, exemplified by sand, are made up of grains composed chiefly of quartz. The individual grains may be angular, subangular, or rounded. Some sands contain a fairly high percentage of mica flakes that make them very elastic or springy.

In the fine and very fine fractions, any one grain usually consists of only one mineral. The particles may be angular, flake-shaped, or, rarely, needle-like. Rounded particles, however, are conspicuously absent. Exceptionally, the fine fraction contains a high percentage of porous fossils, such as diatoms or Radiolaria, that produce abnormal mechanical properties. In general, the percentage of flaky constituents in a given soil increases with decreasing grain size of the soil fraction.

If the size of most of the grains in an aggregate of soil particles is within the limits given for any one of the soil fractions, the aggregate is called a *uniform soil*. Uniform very coarse or coarse soils are common, but uniform very fine or colloidal soils are very seldom encountered. All clays contain fine, very fine, and colloidal constituents, and some clays contain even coarse particles. The finest grain-size fractions of clays consist principally of flake-shaped particles.

The widespread prevalence of flake-shaped particles in the very fine fractions of natural soils is a consequence of the geological processes of soil formation. Most soils originate in the chemical weathering of rocks. The rocks themselves consist partly of chemically very stable and partly of less stable minerals. Chemical weathering transforms the less stable minerals into a friable mass of very small particles of secondary minerals that commonly have a scale-like or flaky crystal form, whereas the stable minerals remain practically unaltered. Thus the process of chemical weathering reduces the rock to an aggregate consisting of fragments of unaltered or almost unaltered minerals embedded in a matrix composed chiefly of discrete scaly particles. During subsequent transportation by running water the aggregate is broken up, and the constituents are subjected to impact and grinding. The purely mechanical process of grinding does not break up the hard equidimensional grains of unaltered minerals into fragments smaller than about 10μ (0.01 mm). On the other hand, the friable flake-shaped particles of secondary minerals, although initially very small, are readily ground and broken into still smaller particles. Hence, the very fine fractions of natural soils consist principally of flake-shaped particles of secondary minerals.

ART. 4. PROPERTIES OF VERY FINE SOIL FRACTIONS

SURFACE ACTIVITY AND ADSORBED LAYERS

[When the coarse fractions of different soils are compared, it is observed that they have similar properties. The fine fractions of most soils also resemble each other in every essential respect. However, the very fine fractions (size less than 2μ) are likely to exhibit a remarkable variety of properties. These facts cannot be explained without a consideration of the forces which have their seat at the surface of the soil particles.]

The surface of every soil particle carries a negative electric charge. The intensity of the charge depends to a large extent on the mineralogical character of the particle. The physical and chemical manifestations of the surface charge constitute the *surface activity* of the mineral. Minerals are said to have high or low surface activity, depending on the intensity of the surface charge.

In nature every soil particle is surrounded by water. Since water molecules are polar, the negative charge on the surface of the soil particle attracts the positive (hydrogen) ends of the water molecules. Hence, in the immediate vicinity of the boundary between solid and water, the water molecules are arranged in a definite pattern. Beyond this zone, to a certain distance from the boundary, the molecular structure of the water is influenced by what may be called molecular chain action. The water located within the zone of influence is known as the *adsorbed layer*. Within the adsorbed layer the physical properties of the water are very different from those of free or normal water at the same temperature. Near the surface of the particle the water has the properties of a solid. At the middle of the layer it resembles a very viscous liquid. As the outer surface is approached, the properties of the water become normal.

In every clay the adsorbed layers contain positively charged particles, known as *ions*, which have migrated from the surrounding liquid. These are furnished by substances, known as *electrolytes*, that dissociate when dissolved in water into positively charged *cations* and negatively charged *anions*. Even water itself is an electrolyte, because a very small fraction of its molecules always dissociates into hydrogen ions H^+ and hydroxyl ions OH^-. Acids break up into cations of hydrogen and such anions as Cl or SO_4. Salts and bases split into metallic cations such as Na, Ca, or Mg, and nonmetallic anions. Since the surface of every soil particle carries a negative charge, all the cations including the H^+ furnished by the water itself are attracted toward the surface of the particles and held near by. These attracted cations enter the adsorbed layers and constitute the *adsorption complex*. The process of replacing cations of one kind by those of another in an adsorption complex is known as *base exchange*.

If one element, such as H, Ca, or Na, prevails over the others in the adsorption complex of a clay, the clay is sometimes given the name of this element, for example, H-clay or Na-clay. The thickness and the physical properties of the adsorbed layer surrounding a given soil particle depend to a large extent on the character of the adsorption complex. In the very fine fraction of ordinary clays, the solid and semisolid portions of the adsorbed layers seem to have an average thickness of about 0.005μ. The properties of the water are not likely to be entirely normal, however, within a distance of about 0.1μ from the surface of the mineral particle. These values are intended merely to suggest the order of magnitude of the dimensions involved. The departures from the average can be very considerable. Even in a given clay the thickness of the adsorbed layer may depend to a large extent on the chemical composition of the adsorption complex.

Because of the phenomena associated with the surface activity, every saturated soil consists not of two but of three different constituents: solid soil particles, adsorbed substances, and free or normal water. The thickness of the adsorbed layers seems to be fairly independent of the grain size. Therefore, the percentage of the total volume occupied by the adsorbed substances increases with decreasing grain size. If the particles are very small and in addition are scale-like in shape, the adsorbed substances constitute a very large portion of the total volume.

The thickness and the physical properties of the adsorbed layers are very different for different minerals. However, in coarse-grained soils such as sands the volume of adsorbed material with respect to the total volume of water in the voids is negligible. Therefore, the properties of such soils depend only on the mechanical properties of the grains themselves. Since these properties are fairly similar for all materials, the properties of coarse-grained soils depend only on the shape and arrangement of the grains.

On the other hand, in very fine-grained soils the adsorbed substances occupy a considerable or even the major part of the voids. Since the physical properties of the adsorbed material depend not only on the chemical and mineralogical composition of the solid particles but also on the nature of the adsorption complex, both the mineralogical character of the grains and the chemical nature of the adsorption complex must be considered.

CLAY MINERALS AND SOIL COLLOIDS

Chemical and mineralogical investigations have shown that the particles which constitute the very fine fraction of clays are commonly crystalline and that they contain chiefly silicon, aluminum, oxygen, and water. The aluminum may be partly replaced by iron or magnesium, and in some instances the silicon may be partly replaced by potassium. According to the chemical combinations in which these constituents occur most of the minerals contained in the very fine soil fractions can be divided into three principal groups: *montmorillonite, illite,* and *kaolinite.* The minerals of all three groups have a laminated crystalline structure, Figure 1, but their surface activities are very different. Least active are the kaolinites. The illites are more active than the kaolinites, and in contrast to the other groups they contain potassium. By far the most active clay minerals are the montmorillonites. [The crystals of this group have the capacity to swell by taking water molecules directly into their space lattice. Furthermore, on account of the exceptionally high surface activity of its colloidal constituents, the physical properties of any given montmorillonite clay may vary between wide limits, depending on the nature of the substances other than water contained in the adsorbed layers. For example, a Ca-montmorillonite has little resemblance to a Na-montmorillonite, although the permanent solid constituents in both clays are the same.]

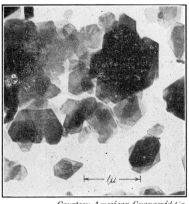

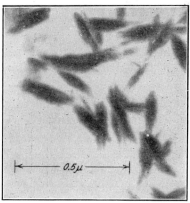

Courtesy American Cyanamid Co.

Courtesy Dr. J. E. Gieseking

(a)

(b)

FIG. 1.   Photographs of clay mineral crystals obtained by means of electron micro-scope. (a) Flake-shaped crystals of kaolinite; (b) needle-shaped crystals of halloysite.

If the very fine fraction of a clay is itself subdivided according to grain size, it is found that within the range between 2μ and 0.2μ some of the grains consist of those minerals which constitute the coarser fractions of the clay. However, in most clays all the grains smaller than 0.2μ consist only of the minerals described in the preceding paragraph. Therefore, these minerals are known as *clay minerals*. They are products of the weathering of the chemically less stable constituents of the parent rocks (see Article 2).

If the particles of any substance are so small that the surface activity has an appreciable influence on the properties of the aggregate, the substance is said to be in a *colloidal state*, and the particles are called *colloidal particles*. The properties that are due exclusively to the influence of surface activity are known as *colloidal properties*. Since the intensity of the surface activity is very different for different substances, the upper limit for the size of colloidal particles is not a constant. It ranges between about 2μ and 0.1μ. At a size of 0.1μ, every solid substance is in the colloidal state. Since the clay minerals are relatively active, the upper limit of the colloidal size of these minerals is about 2μ, and a clay fraction with particles of less than 2μ is likely to exhibit all the characteristics of a colloidal substance. For this reason, 2μ is commonly considered the upper grain-size limit of the very fine soil fraction. The particles smaller than 0.2μ are sometimes referred to as *soil colloids*, because, in contrast to the coarser fractions, the fraction finer than 0.2μ is likely to consist entirely of clay minerals.

Physical Properties of the Very Fine Soil Fractions

If a sample of a very fine soil fraction is agitated and shaken in water, it passes into a state of suspension. The surface of each of the particles is the seat of a negative charge. If the water is pure, no two particles come into contact, because they carry like charges which repel each

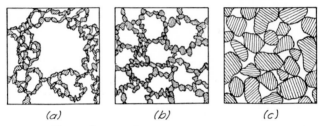

(a)   (b)   (c)

Fig. 2.   Diagram illustrating (a) flocculent structure; (b) honeycomb structure;
(c) single-grain structure.

other. The sample is said to be in a state of *complete dispersion*. As time goes on, the coarser particles settle to the bottom and form a very loose sediment in which the forces of repulsion and gravity are in equilibrium. The finest particles remain in suspension. If a drop of the suspension is examined under the ultramicroscope, it can be seen that the particles travel with a jerky motion, called the *Brownian movement*. Each particle follows a zigzag path, but it does not collide with others.

If a few drops of a suitable electrolyte, such as hydrochloric acid, are added to the suspension, the cations of the electrolyte are adsorbed by the particles, and the negative charges are neutralized. Although the particles continue to move, they now collide, whereupon their adsorbed layers merge and stick together. Thus the particles aggregate into flocks that settle to the bottom of the suspension and form a sediment with a flocculent structure, Figure 2a.

If a flocculated sediment of uniform grain size is gradually buried under superimposed material, its flocculent structure disintegrates first into a honeycombed structure, Figure 2b, and finally into a single-grained structure, Figure 2c. In nature, however, the very fine grain-size fractions are always associated with coarser ones. Since the greatest part of the overburden on mixed-grained sediments is likely to be carried by a skeleton consisting of the coarser soil constituents (see Article 17), the finest soil fraction may permanently retain a honeycombed structure.

If the water content of a soil sample decreases on application of pressure, the soil is said to *consolidate*. If at any stage the pressure is removed while the soil remains in contact with free water, the water content and the volume increase. This phenomenon is known as *swelling*. Each of the various grain-size fractions of a given soil exhibits the property of swelling, but to a different degree. The causes of the swelling are also likely to be different for different fractions. If the pressure is removed from a coarse-grained sand–mica mixture, the mixture swells to a large degree, but the swelling is caused only by elastic restitution of the grains. If the pressure is removed from the very fine fraction of a clay, one part of the swelling is due to elastic restitution, and another part is likely to be due to an increase in the thickness of the adsorbed layers which separate the grains. In clays with a large percentage of montmorillonite, a third though very small part of the swelling is caused by the swelling of the montmorillonite particles themselves. Therefore, swelling as such is not exclusively a colloidal property, but the causes of swelling may be partly of colloidal origin. From a practical point of view, the distinction is irrelevant, because both types of swelling follow similar laws.

The physical properties of a soil containing a large percentage of very fine particles depend on the pressure under which the soil was consolidated. If the consolidation pressure did not exceed about 10 kg per sq cm, the soil is likely to be *plastic*. A soil or soil fraction is called plastic if, within some range of water content, it can be rolled out into thin threads (see Article 8). Plasticity is a colloidal property, because no mineral possesses plasticity unless it is reduced to a powder consisting of particles of colloidal size. The capacity to exhibit Brownian movement and to flocculate in the presence of an electrolyte are also colloidal properties. However, these properties are shared by all substances in a colloidal state, whereas plasticity is an attribute of only a very limited number of colloids. Quartz powder is not plastic at any water content or any degree of fineness, but all the clay minerals are. Since practically all very fine-grained soils contain clay minerals, practically all of them are plastic.

If the consolidation pressure that preceded the removal of load was very great, the soil is hard and brittle. It is said to be in a solid state.

[In both the plastic and the solid states, the very fine soil fraction possesses *cohesion*, or the capacity to resist shearing stresses.] It seems most likely that the cohesion is due not to direct molecular interaction between the soil particles at the points of contact, but to the shearing strength of the adsorbed layers that separate the grains at these points. This hypothesis is corroborated by the fact that the cohesion of a sample of a given very fine soil fraction at a given water content depends to a large extent on the nature of the adsorption complex. If the water content of a very fine-grained saturated soil is reduced by consolidation or surface evaporation, the volume of voids occupied by liquid water decreases whereas the volume occupied by the adsorbed substances remains unchanged. Therefore, the cohesion increases with decreasing water content.

If a sample of a very fine soil fraction is thoroughly kneaded and is then allowed to stand without further disturbance, it acquires cohesive strength, first at a fairly rapid rate and then more and more slowly. If the sample is again kneaded at unaltered water content, its cohesion decreases considerably, but, if it is once more allowed to stand, its cohesion is completely regained. This phenomenon is known as *thixotropy*. The softening and subsequent recovery seem to be due to the destruction and subsequent rehabilitation of the molecular structure of the adsorbed layers.

PRACTICAL ASPECTS OF THE COLLOIDAL SOIL PROPERTIES

The colloidal character of the very fine soil fraction makes the interaction between the solid and the liquid constituents of soils extremely complex. Yet from a practical point of view these complexities can be disregarded. They have been described only to impress on the reader that the physical properties of very fine-grained soils, and even of coarser soils that contain a small amount of very fine-grained binder, are conditioned by a great number of diverse factors other than grain size. The effects of some of these factors, particularly that of time at constant stress, are still incompletely known. Yet, in connection with most practical problems, only the combined effect of all of the factors need be considered. A similar situation prevails in concrete technology. The processes by which Portland cement acquires its strength are also very intricate and still incompletely known. Nevertheless, concrete design is a fairly old and well-established branch of structural engineering. The assumptions on which it is based have been derived from purely mechanical laboratory tests on concrete specimens; certain properties of the cement, such as the increase of its strength with time, are disregarded. Nevertheless, the theories based on these simplifying assumptions are accurate enough for most practical purposes.

Because of the colloidal character of very fine-grained soils, it is possible to change the physical properties of such soils by chemical treatment. This procedure is quite extensively practiced if the soil is to be used as a construction material. It constitutes one of several methods for soil stabilization in connection with highway and airport construction, and occasionally in connection with the construction of earth dams. Most of these methods have grown out of more or less haphazard experimentation in the field. However, further improvements are entirely dependent on the advancement of our knowledge of the colloidal chemistry of the finest soil fractions.

REFERENCE

4.1. E. A. HAUSER, Colloid Chemistry of Clays, *Chem. Rev.*, Vol 37 (1945), pp 287–321. Condensed review of the colloidal properties of clays and some of the practical applications of the results of clay research.

ART. 5. MECHANICAL ANALYSIS OF SOILS

The purpose of mechanical analysis is to determine the size of the grains which constitute a soil and the percentage of the total weight represented by the grains in various size ranges. The most direct method for separating a soil into grain-size fractions is the use of sieves. However, since the openings of the finest mesh readily available are 0.07 mm wide, the use of sieves is restricted to analysis of clean sands. If a soil contains grains smaller than 0.07 mm, it may be separated into two parts by washing with water. As the water becomes turbid, it is drawn off. The coarser portion of the soil remains in the container and can be subjected to a sieve analysis. The soil particles in the turbid liquid, which are too fine to be collected on sieves, can be subjected to wet mechanical analysis or elutriation.

The methods for performing wet mechanical analysis are based on Stokes's law, which determines the velocity at which a spherical particle of given diameter settles in a quiet liquid. In the method commonly used for engineering purposes, 20 to 40 gm of clay soil or 50 to 100 gm of sandy soil are mixed with one liter of water, agitated, and poured into a container. The density of the suspension is measured at various times by means of a hydrometer of special design. At any given time, the size of the largest particles remaining in suspension at the level of the hydrometer can be computed by means of Stokes's law, whereas the weight of the particles finer than that size can be computed from the density of the suspension at the same level. The performance of a test requires several days.

By means of wet mechanical analysis soil fractions can be separated down to a size of about 0.5μ. Still finer fractions can be obtained by means of a centrifuge, but the results of such refined methods are of interest only in connection with scientific research.

Agitation in water transforms many clays into suspensions, not of individual particles, but of flocks. In order to break up the flocks into individual grains, or to disperse the soil, a deflocculating agent must be added to the water. The most common errors in the results of wet mechanical analysis are caused by inadequate dispersion.

The results of wet mechanical analysis are not strictly comparable to those of sieve analysis, because soil grains are never exactly spherical, and the smallest ones are commonly of a flaky shape. In a sieve analysis the width of the flake is measured, whereas the dimension determined by means of elutriation methods is the diameter of a sphere which sinks at the same rate as the flake. This diameter may be very much smaller than the width of the actual flake.

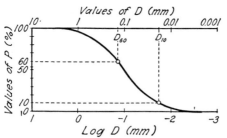

Fig. 3. Semilogarithmic plot of results of mechanical analysis.

The most convenient representation of the results of a mechanical analysis is the semilogarithmic grain-size curve shown in Figure 3. The abscissas of this curve represent the logarithm of the grain size. The ordinates represent the percentage P, by weight, of grains smaller than the size denoted by the abscissa. The more uniform the grain size, the steeper is the slope of the curve; a vertical line represents a perfectly uniform powder. The most important advantage of a semilogarithmic plot is that the grain-size curves of soils having equal uniformity are identical in shape, regardless of the average grain size. In addition, the horizontal distance between two curves of the same shape is equal to the logarithm of the ratio of the average grain sizes of the corresponding soils.

Figure 4 shows several typical grain-size curves. Curve a is a common type. It closely resembles the normal frequency curve that represents one of the fundamental laws of statistics. Since grain size is a statistical phenomenon, attempts have been made to utilize the terms and concepts of statistics to describe the results of mechanical analyses. Such refinements, however, are not warranted in connection with soil mechanics for engineering purposes.

If a sample has the grain-size distribution represented in Figure 4a, the uniformity of the fraction having grains larger than D_{50} (corresponding to $P = 50\%$) is approximately equal to that of the fraction having grains smaller than D_{50}. If the distribution resembles that shown in b, the coarser half of the sample is relatively uniform, whereas the size of the grains in the finer half varies over a wide range. Conversely, the distribution represented in c corresponds to a sample in which the coarser grains are of widely different sizes and the finer ones are more uniform. The curves represented in d and e are said to be composite.

The grain-size curves of imma-ture residual soils are usually sim-ilar to that shown in Figure 4b. With increasing age of the soil, the average grain size decreases because of weathering, and the curves become more nearly straight, Figure 4a. The grain-size curves of mature soils resemble that shown in Figure 4c. Distri-butions represented by b and c are also common among soils of glacial or fluvioglacial origin. Absence of a medium grain size in a sedimentary soil, as exempli-fied by the curve in Figure 4d, appears to be common among sand–gravel mixtures that were deposited by swiftly flowing rivers carrying a large load of sediment. Gravels of this type are said to be poorly graded. [A conspicuous break in the continuity of the grain-size curve may also indicate the simultaneous deposition of the soil by two different agents.] For instance, one fraction might be washed into a glacial lake by a river and another fraction dropped from melting ice floats. Thus a knowledge of the shape of grain-size curves may assist in determining the geological origin of a soil and thereby reduce the risk of error in the interpretation of the data obtained from test borings.

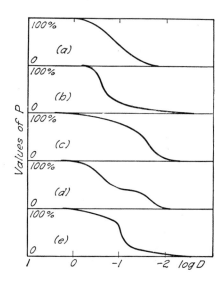

FIG. 4. Typical grain-size curves; (a) normal frequency curve; (b and c) curves for soils having coarser and finer fractions of different uniformity; (d and e) composite curves.

ART. 6. SOIL CLASSIFICATION BASED ON GRAIN-SIZE CHARACTERISTICS

PRACTICAL SIGNIFICANCE OF GRAIN-SIZE CHARACTERISTICS

Ever since the physical properties of soils became a matter of interest, frequent attempts have been made to correlate the grain-size characteristics with the soil constants needed for solving practical problems. The results, however, have been consistently disappointing. Attempts to compute the coefficient of permeability of soils on the basis of the results of mechanical analysis have failed because the permeability depends to a large extent on the shape of the grains, which can be very different for soils with identical grain-size characteristics. Furthermore, it is usually cheaper to perform a permeability test than a mechanical analysis, and the results are more reliable. It has also been claimed that the internal friction of compacted well-graded sands is greater than that of compacted uniform sands. Field experience suggests that this may be

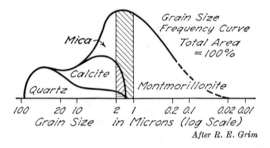

After R. E. Grim

FIG. 5.   Grain size and mineralogical composition of a glacial marine clay.

the case. However, since the angle of internal friction of a sand (see Article 15) depends not only on the grain-size characteristics but also on the shape of the grains and the roughness of their surface, the internal friction of two compacted sands with identical grain-size characteristics can be very different. As a matter of fact, no well-defined relation between grain-size characteristics and the angle of internal friction has yet been observed. Attempts to correlate the grain-size characteristics of fine-grained soils such as silt or clay with the internal friction have been even less successful. The reason is illustrated by Figure 5.

In Figure 5 the heavy uppermost curve represents what is known as the *grain-size frequency curve* for a glacial clay from southeastern Canada. On the horizontal axis are plotted the logarithms of the grain size. The area of the strip located above an arbitrary grain-size range, for instance 2μ to 1μ, represents the quantity of soil particles within this range, in per cent of the total weight of the dried clay. According to the diagram the macroscopic fraction (>0.06 mm), like that of most other clays, consists chiefly of quartz. The microscopic fraction (0.06 to 0.002 mm) consists partly of quartz and calcite and partly of mica flakes. The mica content of this fraction is very different for different clays, and it has a decisive influence on the compressibility and other properties of the clay. The colloidal fraction (< 0.002 mm) consists almost exclusively of montmorillonite, whereas that of other clays may consist chiefly of clay minerals of the kaolin or illite groups. The physical properties of the clay depend to a large extent on the type of clay mineral that dominates the colloidal fraction. They also depend to a large extent on the substances that are present in the adsorbed layers, Article 4. Hence, two clays with identical grain-size curves can be extremely different in every other respect.

Because of these conditions, well-defined statistical relations between grain-size characteristics and significant soil properties such as the angle of internal friction have been encountered only within relatively small regions where all the soils of the same category, such as all the clays or all the sands, have a similar geological origin. In such regions the grain-size characteristics can be used as a basis for judging the significant properties of the soils. This is commonly and successfully done. However, none of the procedures that grow out of experience in such regions can safely be used outside the boundaries of the region where they originated.

Abbreviated Representation of Grain-Size Characteristics

In order to represent the essential results of the mechanical analysis of a great number of soils, it may be convenient to express the grain-size characteristics of each soil either by numerical values indicative of some characteristic grain size and of the degree of uniformity or else by names or symbols that indicate the dominant soil fraction. The most common procedure based on numerical values is known as Allen Hazen's method. On the basis of a great number of tests with filter sands, Hazen found that the permeability of these sands in a loose state depends on two quantities that he called the effective size and the uniformity coefficient. The *effective size* is the diameter D_{10} which corresponds to $P = 10$ per cent on the grain-size diagram. In other words, 10 per cent of the particles are finer and 90 per cent coarser than the effective size. The *uniformity coefficient* U is equal to D_{60}/D_{10}, wherein D_{60} is the grain size corresponding to $P = 60$ per cent.

Hazen's findings led other investigators to the more or less arbitrary assumption that the quantities D_{10} and U are also suitable for expressing the grain-size characteristics of mixed-grained natural soils. With increasing knowledge concerning fine-grained soils, it has become evident that the character of such soils depends chiefly on the finest 20 per cent and that it might be preferable to select D_{20} and D_{70} as the significant quantities. However, the advantage is not sufficiently important to justify a departure from well-established procedure. The use of symbols to indicate the grain-size characteristics of a soil is described at the end of the article.

Methods of Classification

In connection with soil classifications based on grain-size characteristics, it is customary to assign the names of soils, such as "silt" or "clay," to different grain-size fractions. The most widely accepted conventions of this type are shown in graphical form in Figure 6. From

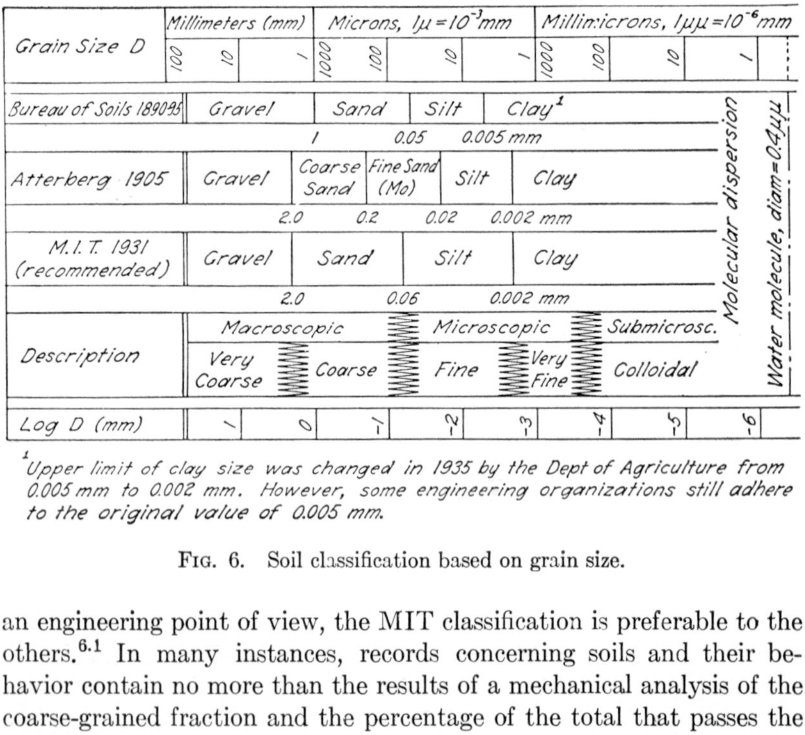

[1] Upper limit of clay size was changed in 1935 by the Dept of Agriculture from 0.005 mm to 0.002 mm. However, some engineering organizations still adhere to the original value of 0.005 mm.

Fig. 6.   Soil classification based on grain size.

an engineering point of view, the MIT classification is preferable to the others.[6.1] In many instances, records concerning soils and their behavior contain no more than the results of a mechanical analysis of the coarse-grained fraction and the percentage of the total that passes the 200-mesh sieve. The latter includes all the soil particles smaller than 0.074 mm. A grain size of 0.074 mm is slightly greater than the value 0.06 mm which, in the MIT classification, represents the boundary between fine sand and coarse silt.

However, any system of classification based on grain size alone is likely to be misleading, because the physical properties of the finest soil fractions depend on many factors other than grain size (see Article 4).

For example, according to any one of the commonly used conventions represented in Figure 6, a soil consisting of quartz grains of colloidal size should be called a clay, whereas in reality it does not possess even a remote resemblance to clay. Hence, if the words "silt" or "clay" are used to express grain size, they should be combined with the word "size," as in the expression "clay-size particle." Since the grain-size classifications are not yet standardized, the descriptive adjectives must be supplemented by numerical values that indicate the grain-size range represented by the adjectives.

With few exceptions natural soils consist of a mixture of two or more different grain-size fractions. Hence, on the basis of its grain-size composition a natural soil can be designated by the names of its principal components, such as "silty clay," or "sandy silt." Or it may be assigned some symbol that identifies it with one of several standard mixtures of grain-size fractions.

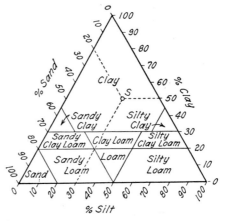

The designation of soils by the names of their principal constituents is facilitated by the use of diagrams such as that adopted by the Public Roads Administration, Figure 7. In this diagram, each of the three coordinate axes pertains to one of the grain-size fractions, designated as sand, silt, or clay. The chart is divided into regions

Fig. 7.   Soil classification chart developed by Public Roads Administration.

to which the names of soil types are assigned. The three co-ordinates of a point represent the percentages of the three fractions present in a given soil and determine the type to which the soil belongs. For example, a mixed-grained soil composed of 20 per cent sand, 30 per cent silt, and 50 per cent clay, represented by point S, is classified as a clay.[6.2]

The identification of a given soil by comparison with standard mixtures can be accomplished rapidly by means of master plots on transparent paper. In these plots each of various standard mixtures of grain-size fractions is represented by a grain-size curve that bears an identifying symbol. To classify a real soil, the transparent master plot is placed over a sheet on which the grain-size curve for the soil has been drawn. The soil is given the symbol of the standard curve that most nearly resembles that of the real soil.[6.2]

REFERENCES

6.1. R. Glossop and A. W. Skempton, Particle-size in Silts and Sands, *J. Inst. Civil Engrs. (London)*, paper 5492, Dec. 1945, pp 81–105. Discussion of the different grain-size classifications from an engineering point of view.

6.2. A. Casagrande, Classification and Identification of Soils, *Proc. ASCE*, June 1947, pp 783–810. Discussion of grain-size classifications and of methods for representing the results of mechanical analysis.

ART. 7. SOIL AGGREGATE

Introduction

The term *aggregate* refers to the soil itself, in contrast to its constituent parts. [Qualitatively, soil aggregates may differ in texture, structure, and consistency.] Quantitatively, they may differ in porosity, relative density, water and gas content, and also in consistency. The qualitative information is obtained in the field by visual inspection. It constitutes the basis for preparing the boring logs or other records which describe the succession of strata in the underground. The quantitative information is obtained by means of laboratory and field tests. Without such information the description of any soil is inadequate.

Texture, Structure, and Consistency

The term *texture* refers to the degree of fineness and uniformity of a soil. It is described by such expressions as *floury*, *smooth*, *gritty*, or *sharp*, depending on the sensation produced by rubbing the soil between the fingers.

The term *structure* refers to the pattern in which the soil particles are arranged in the aggregate. If the particles of a stable aggregate do not stick to each other, they are arranged in a *single-grained structure* in which each grain touches several of its neighbors, Figure 2c. Depending on the arrangement of the grains, a single-grained structure may be *loose* or *dense*.

Fine-grained soils may be stable even if the grains touch each other at very few points, provided the adhesion between the grains is of the same order of magnitude as the weight of the grains. The corresponding structure is called *honeycombed*, Figure 2b.

The flocculent structure, Figure 2a, referred to in Article 4 is rarely found in natural soils, because very fine-grained natural soils almost invariably contain coarser particles. The coarser grains are likely to form a skeleton with its interstices partly filled by a relatively loose aggregation of the finest soil constituents. This arrangement of the particles is called a *skeleton structure*. It is probably responsible for the remarkable instability of many slightly cohesive soils with a grain size between about 0.05 and 0.005 mm (Article 17). In soft clays the inherent instability of the skeleton structure is masked by cohesion.

A few rather exceptional soils, including some marls, consist of relatively large composite grains. These grains constitute an aggregate with a single-grained or a honeycombed structure. However, the grains themselves are clusters of densely packed silt or clay particles. Soils that consist of such clusters are said to have a *cluster structure*. The cluster structure differs from the flocculent structure, Figure 2a, in that the individual clusters do not have a honeycombed but a dense single-grained structure.

Every sediment contains at least a small percentage of scale-like or disk-shaped particles. While these particles settle out of a suspension, their flat sides tend to maintain a horizontal position. Therefore, in the sediment, many of these particles are oriented more or less parallel to horizontal planes. Subsequent increase of the overburden pressure further accentuates this orientation. A sediment containing oriented particles is said to possess *transverse isotropy*.

Since a visual inspection of the structure of fine- or very fine-grained soils is not practicable, the structure of such soils must be judged on the basis of their porosity and various other properties.

Stiff clays may contain tubular root holes extending to a depth of tens of feet below the surface, or they may be divided by hair cracks into prismatic or irregular fragments that fall apart as soon as the confining pressure is removed. Such hair cracks are known as *joints*. Striations produced by movements along the walls of the joints are known as *slickensides*. The origin, nature, and practical implications of such defects of soil strata are discussed in Part C, Article 43. In Part A only intact soils and soil strata are considered.

The term *consistency* refers to the degree of adhesion between the soil particles and to the resistance offered against forces that tend to deform or rupture the soil aggregate. The consistency is described by such terms as *hard*, *stiff*, *brittle*, *friable*, *sticky*, *plastic*, and *soft*. The more nearly a soil approaches the characteristics of a clay, the greater is the variety of states of consistency in which it may be found. The degree of plasticity is sometimes expressed by the terms *fat* and *lean*. A lean clay is one that is only slightly plastic because it contains a large proportion of silt or sand. Further information concerning the consistency of clays is given in Article 8.

Porosity, Water Content, and Unit Weight

The *porosity n* is the ratio of the volume of voids to the total volume of the soil aggregate. The term *volume of voids* refers to that portion of the volume of the soil not occupied by mineral grains. If the porosity is expressed as a percentage, it is referred to as the *percentage of voids*.

The *void ratio e* is the ratio of the volume of voids to the volume of the solid substance. If

$$V = \text{total volume}$$

$$V_v = \text{total volume of voids}$$

then

$$n = \frac{V_v}{V} \tag{7.1a}$$

and

$$e = \frac{V_v}{V - V_v} \tag{7.1b}$$

The relation between void ratio and porosity is expressed by the equations,

$$e = \frac{n}{1 - n} \tag{7.2a}$$

and

$$n = \frac{e}{1 + e} \tag{7.2b}$$

The porosity of a stable mass of equal cohesionless spheres depends on the manner in which the spheres are arranged. In the densest possible arrangement, n is equal to 26 per cent, and in the loosest state to 47 per cent. Natural sands are found with porosities varying from about 25 to 50 per cent. The porosity of a natural sand deposit depends on the shape of the grains, the uniformity of grain size, and the conditions of sedimentation.

The effect of the shape of the grains on the porosity of the aggregate can be demonstrated by mixing various percentages of mica with a uniform angular sand. If the percentage of mica, by weight, is equal successively to 0, 5, 10, 20, and 40, the porosities of the resultant mixtures when loosely dumped into a vessel are, respectively, about 47, 60, 70, 77, and 84 per cent. The porosity of soft natural clays, which contain an appreciable percentage of flat particles, usually ranges between 30 and 60 per cent. It can even be as great as 90 per cent.

Because of the great influence of the shape of the grains and of the degree of uniformity on the porosity, the porosity itself does not indicate whether a soil is loose or dense. This information can be obtained only by comparing the porosity of the given soil with that of the same soil in its loosest and densest possible states. The looseness or denseness of sandy soils can be expressed numerically by the *relative density* D_r, defined by the equation,

$$D_r = \frac{e_0 - e}{e_0 - e_{\min}} \qquad (7.3)$$

in which e_0 = void ratio of the soil in its loosest state

          $e_{\min}$ = void ratio in the densest state which can be obtained in the laboratory

          e = void ratio of the soil in the field

To bring a medium or coarse sand into its loosest state, corresponding to the void ratio e_0, the sand is first dried and then poured from a small height into a vessel. Very fine sands and rock flour are brought into the loosest state by mixing a sample with enough water to transform it into a thick suspension that is then allowed to settle. The value of e_0 is equal to the final void ratio of the sediment.

The relative density of sand has a well-defined meaning because its value is practically independent of the static pressure to which the sand is subjected. It depends primarily on the procedure used in placing and compacting the sand. On the other hand, the degree of density of clays and other cohesive soils depends chiefly on the loads that these soils have carried and, in some instances, on the rate at which the loads were applied. The degree of density of these soils is most clearly reflected by the relative consistency C_r, Article 8, which constitutes an analogue to the relative density D_r of soils with little or no cohesion.

The *water content w* of a soil is defined as the ratio of the weight of water to the dry weight of the aggregate. It is usually expressed as a percentage. In sands located above the water table, part of the voids may be occupied by air. If e_w represents the volume occupied by water per unit volume of solid matter, the ratio,

$$S_r(\%) = \frac{100e_w}{e} \qquad (7.4)$$

represents the *degree of saturation*. The degree of saturation of sands is commonly expressed by such words as dry or moist. Table 1 gives a list of such descriptive terms and of the corresponding degrees of saturation. The nomenclature represented in Table 1 applies only to sands or very sandy soils. A clay in the state of desiccation represented by $S_r = 90\%$ might be so hard that it would be called dry instead of wet.

Coarse sands located above the water table are usually humid. Fine or silty sands are moist, wet, or saturated. Clays are almost always completely or nearly saturated, except in the layer of surface soil that is subject to seasonal variations of temperature and moisture. If a clay contains gas, the gas is present in bubbles scattered throughout the material. The bubbles may be composed of air that entered the deposit

TABLE 1

DEGREE OF SATURATION OF SAND IN VARIOUS STATES

Condition of Sand	Degree of Saturation (%)
Dry	0
Humid	1–25
Damp	25–50
Moist	50–75
Wet	75–99
Saturated	100

during sedimentation, or of gas produced at a later date by chemical processes such as the decomposition of organic material. The gas may be under pressure great enough to cause the clay to swell energetically at constant water content if the confining pressure is decreased. The

TABLE 2

UNIT WEIGHT OF MOST IMPORTANT SOIL CONSTITUENTS

grams per cubic centimeter

Gypsum	2.32	Dolomite	2.87
Montmorillonite*	2.4	Aragonite	2.94
Orthoclase	2.56	Biotite	3.0–3.1
Kaolinite	2.6	Augite	3.2–3.4
Illite*	2.6	Hornblende	3.2–3.5
Chlorite	2.6–3.0	Limonite	3.8
Quartz	2.66	Hematite, hydrous	4.3±
Talc	2.7	Magnetite	5.17
Calcite	2.72	Hematite	5.2
Muscovite	2.8–2.9		

From E. S. LARSEN AND H. BERMAN, *The Microscopic Determination of the Non-opaque Minerals*, second edition, U. S. Department of the Interior, *Bull.* 848, Washington, 1934.

* Theoretical values computed on the basis of the atomic weights of the constituents of the space lattice (according to R. E. Grim).

determination of the gas content of a clay is extremely difficult. If it can be accomplished at all, it requires special equipment and is not a routine test.

The *unit weight* of the soil aggregate is defined as the weight of the aggregate (soil plus water) per unit of volume. It depends on the unit weight of the solid constituents, the porosity of the aggregate, and the degree of saturation. It may be computed as follows: Let

$$\gamma_s = \text{average unit weight of solid constituents}$$
$$\gamma_w = \text{unit weight of water}$$
$$n = \text{porosity (expressed as a ratio)}$$

The unit weight of dry soil $(S_r = 0\%)$ is

$$\gamma_d = (1 - n)\gamma_s \qquad (7.5)$$

and of saturated soil $(S_r = 100\%)$ is

$$\gamma = (1 - n)\gamma_s + n\gamma_w = \gamma_s - n(\gamma_s - \gamma_w) \qquad (7.6)$$

TABLE 3

POROSITY, VOID RATIO, AND UNIT WEIGHT OF
TYPICAL SOILS IN NATURAL STATE

Description	Poros-ity n (%)	Void Ratio e	Water Content w (%)	Unit Weight			
				grams/cm³		lb/ft³	
				γ_d	γ	γ_d	γ
1. Uniform sand, loose	46	0.85	32	1.43	1.89	90	118
2. Uniform sand, dense	34	0.51	19	1.75	2.09	109	130
3. Mixed-grained sand, loose	40	0.67	25	1.59	1.99	99	124
4. Mixed-grained sand, dense	30	0.43	16	1.86	2.16	116	135
5. Glacial till, very mixed-grained	20	0.25	9	2.12	2.32	132	145
6. Soft glacial clay	55	1.2	45	....	1.77	...	110
7. Stiff glacial clay	37	0.6	22	....	2.07	...	129
8. Soft slightly organic clay	66	1.9	70	....	1.58	...	98
9. Soft very organic clay	75	3.0	110	....	1.43	...	89
10. Soft bentonite	84	5.2	194	....	1.27	..	80

w = water content when saturated, in per cent of dry weight
γ_d = unit weight in dry state
γ = unit weight in saturated state

[The unit weight of the principal solid constituents of soils is given in Table 2. For sand grains the average unit weight is usually about 2.65 gm per cu cm. For clay particles the unit weight varies from 2.5 to 2.9 gm per cu cm, with a statistical average of approximately 2.7.]

In Table 3 are given the porosity and the saturated unit weight of typical soils. For sandy soils the weight of dry soil has also been included. The weights have been computed on the assumption that the value of γ_s is 2.65 gm per cu cm for sandy soils and 2.70 gm per cu cm for clays. The tabulated values should be considered only as approximations. Before final computations are made on a given job, the actual unit weight of the soil should always be determined.

PROBLEMS

1. A sample of saturated clay weighed 1526 gm in its natural state, and 1053 gm after drying. Determine the natural water content. If the unit weight of the solid constituents was 2.70 gm per cu cm, what was the void ratio? the porosity? the weight per cubic foot?

Ans. $w = 45.0\%$; $e = 1.22$; $n = 0.55$; $\gamma = 111$ lb per cu ft.

2. A sample of hardpan had a weight of 129.1 gm and a volume of 56.4 cu cm in its natural state. Its dry weight was 121.5 gm. The unit weight of the solid constituents was found to be 2.70 gm per cu cm. Compute the water content, the void ratio, and degree of saturation.

Ans. $w = 6.3\%$; $e = 0.25$; $S_r = 0.67$.

3. The unit weight of a sand backfill was determined by field measurements to be 109 lb per cu ft. The water content at the time of the test was 8.6 per cent, and the unit weight of the solid constituents was 2.60 gm per cu cm. In the laboratory the void ratios in the loosest and densest states were found to be 0.642 and 0.462, respectively. What were the void ratio and the relative density of the fill?

Ans. $e = 0.616$; $D_r = 0.14$.

4. A dry quartz sand weighs 96 lb per cu ft. What is its unit weight when saturated?

Ans. $\gamma = 122$ lb per cu ft.

5. A sample of silty clay was found, by immersion in mercury, to have a volume of 14.88 cu cm. Its weight at the natural water content was 28.81 gm and after oven drying was 24.83 gm. The unit weight of solid constituents was 2.70 gm per cu cm. Calculate the void ratio and the degree of saturation of the sample.

6. Given the values of porosity n for the soils in Table 3, check the values of water content w and unit weight γ (lb per cu ft). For soils 1–5, $\gamma_s = 2.65$ gm per cu cm; for soils 6–10, $\gamma_s = 2.70$ gm per cu cm.

ART. 8. CONSISTENCY AND SENSITIVITY OF CLAYS

CONSISTENCY AND SENSITIVITY OF UNDISTURBED SOILS

The consistency of clays and other cohesive soils is usually described as *soft*, *medium*, *stiff*, or *hard*. The most direct quantitative measure of consistency is the load per unit of area at which unconfined prismatic or cylindrical samples of the soil fail in a simple compression test. This quantity is known as the *unconfined compressive strength* of the soil. Values of the compressive strength corresponding to the various degrees of consistency are given in Table 4.

Clays share with many other colloidal substances the property that **kneading** or working at unaltered water content makes the **material** softer. The process of kneading or working is commonly referred to as *remolding*, and clays that have been subjected to the process are called *remolded clays*. The softening effect is probably due to two different causes: destruction of the orderly arrangement of the molecules in the adsorbed layers, and injury to the structure that the clay acquired during the process of sedimentation. That part of the loss of strength caused by the disturbance of the adsorbed layers is gradually regained, at unaltered water content, after the working has ceased. The remainder, probably caused by permanent alteration of the structure, is irrecoverable unless the water content of the clay is reduced. The ratio between these two parts of the loss of strength is very different for different clays.

TABLE 4

Consistency of Clay in Terms of Unconfined Compressive Strength

Consistency	Unconfined Compressive Strength, q_u (kg per sq cm)
Very soft	Less than 0.25
Soft	0.25–0.5
Medium	0.5 –1.0
Stiff	1.0 –2.0
Very stiff	2.0 –4.0
Extremely stiff*	Over 4.0

* If an extremely stiff clay is also brittle, it is called *hard*.

The term *sensitivity* indicates the effect of remolding on the consistency of a clay, regardless of the physical nature of the causes of the change. The degree of sensitivity is different for different clays, and it may also be different for the same clay at different water contents. If a clay is very sensitive, a slide may turn it into a mass of lubricated chunks capable of flowing on a gently sloping base, whereas a similar slide in a clay with low sensitivity merely produces a conspicuous local deformation. The change in consistency produced by the disturbance of a sensitive clay is always associated with a change of the permeability.

The degree of sensitivity S_t of a clay is expressed by the ratio between the unconfined compressive strength of an undisturbed specimen and the strength of the same specimen at the same water content but in a remolded state. That is,

$$S_t = \frac{\text{unconfined compressive strength undisturbed}}{\text{unconfined compressive strength remolded}} \qquad (8.1)$$

The values of S_t for most clays range between 2 and about 4. For sensitive clays they range from 4 to 8. However, extrasensitive clays are known with values of S_t greater than 8. These high degrees of sensitivity may be due to a well-developed skeleton structure, to a high degree of thixotropy of the finest soil fraction, Articles 4 and 17, or to both. They are encountered chiefly among soft glacial clays that were deposited in brackish or sea water and soft clays derived from the decomposition of volcanic ash.

An indication of the complexity of the structure of a clay can be obtained by comparing the unit weight γ_{di} of an oven-dried specimen of the intact soil with the unit weight γ_{dr} of an oven-dried specimen thoroughly remolded at its natural water content before drying. The greater the difference between the values γ_{di} and γ_{dr}, the more the structure of the undisturbed soil differs from the random structure of the remolded soil.

Consistency of Remolded Soils

After a cohesive soil has been remolded, its consistency can be changed at will by increasing or decreasing the water content. Thus, for instance, if the water content of a clay slurry is gradually reduced by slow desic-

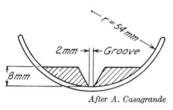

After A. Casagrande

Fig. 8.   Cross section through soil pat for liquid-limit test.

cation, the clay passes from a liquid state through a plastic state, and finally into a solid state. The water contents at which different clays pass from one of these states into another are very different. Therefore, the water contents at these transitions can be used for identification and comparison of different clays. However, the transition from one state to another does not occur abruptly as soon as some critical water content is reached. It occurs gradually over a fairly large range in the value of the water content. For this reason every attempt to establish criteria for the boundaries between the limits of consistency involves some arbitrary elements. The method that has proved most suitable for engineering purposes was taken over from agronomy. It is known as Atterberg's method, and the water contents that correspond to the boundaries between the states of consistency are called the *Atterberg limits*.

The *liquid limit L_w* is the water content in per cent of the dry weight at which two sections of a pat of soil having the dimensions shown in Figure 8 barely touch each other but do not flow together when subjected in a cup to the impact of sharp blows from below. The personal equation has an important influence on the test results. In order to eliminate this factor, a standardized mechanical device is used.

[The *plastic limit* P_w or lower limit of the plastic state is the water content at which the soil begins to crumble when rolled out into thin threads.]

The record of the results of the plastic-limit test should also contain a statement as to whether the threads, immediately before crumbling, were very tough like those of a gumbo, moderately tough like those of an average glacial clay, or weak and spongy like those of an organic or of a micaceous inorganic soil.

The *sticky limit* T_w is the lowest water content at which the soil adheres to metal tools. It is determined by gradually reducing the water content of a clay pat until it becomes possible to clean a nickel-plated spatula by drawing it over the surface of the pat.

The *shrinkage limit* S_w or lower limit of volume change, is the water content below which further loss of water by evaporation does not result in a reduction of volume. As soon as the soil passes below the shrinkage limit, it becomes slightly lighter in color.

The range of water content within which a soil possesses plasticity is known as the *plastic range*, and the numerical difference between the liquid limit and the plastic limit is the *plasticity index* I_w. As the water content w of a cohesive soil approaches the lower limit P_w of the plastic range, the stiffness and degree of compaction of the soil increase. The ratio,

$$C_r = \frac{L_w - w}{L_w - P_w} = \frac{L_w - w}{I_w} \qquad (8.2)$$

is called the *relative consistency* of the soil. It is analogous to the relative density of cohesionless soils (see equation 7.3). If the water content of a natural soil stratum is greater than the liquid limit (relative consistency negative), a process of remolding transforms the soil into a thick viscous slurry. If the natural water content is less than the plastic limit (relative consistency greater than unity), the soil cannot be remolded. The unconfined compressive strength of undisturbed clays with a relative consistency near zero commonly ranges between 0.3 and 1.0 kg per sq cm. If the relative consistency is near unity, the compressive strength generally lies between 1 and 5 kg per sq cm.

In addition to the Atterberg limits, a knowledge of the *dry strength* is useful in the identification and comparison of cohesive soils. The strength of air-dry specimens of clay ranges from about 2 to more than 200 kg per sq cm, and a trained experimenter can distinguish among the degrees of *very low, low, medium, high,* and *very high,* merely by pressing an angular fragment of the soil between his fingers. The strength is called medium if the fragment can be reduced to powder only with great effort. Fragments with very high strength cannot be injured at all, whereas those of very low strength disintegrate completely on gentle pressure. The fragments should be obtained by molding a cylindrical specimen about one inch high and one inch in diameter from a paste at a water content close to the plastic limit. After the cylinder has dried at room temperature, it is broken into smaller pieces, and fragments for the examination are selected from the interior of the specimen.

Soil Classification by Means of Plasticity Chart

In accordance with their general character and outstanding physical properties, the cohesive soils can be divided into eight large groups: inorganic clays of high, medium, or low plasticity; inorganic silty soils of high, medium, or low compressibility; organic clays; and organic silts. This classification is practically identical with the one used by foremen as a basis for their entries into boring logs (see Article 2). If no errors are made, the boring logs inform the designer about the general character of the soil. However, even an experienced foreman or technician cannot always distinguish between the various cohesive soils on the basis of their appearance alone, and the novice is likely to make serious errors. Therefore, various attempts have been made to eliminate the danger of misjudgment. As a result of these attempts, it has been found that the distinction between members of the different groups can be made reliably by means of the *plasticity chart*, Figure 9. [8.1]

In the plasticity chart, the ordinates represent the plasticity index I_w and the abscissas the corresponding liquid limit L_w. The chart is divided into six regions, three above line A and three below. The group to which a given soil belongs is determined by the name of the region that contains the point representing the values of I_w and L_w for the soil. All points representing inorganic clays lie above line A, and all points for inorganic silts lie below it. Therefore, if a soil is known to be inorganic, its group affiliation can be ascertained on the basis of the values of I_w and L_w alone. However, points representing organic clays are usually located within the same region as those representing inorganic silts of high compressibility, and points representing organic silts in the region assigned to inorganic silts of medium compressibility. Usually, the organic soils can be distinguished from the inorganic by their characteristic odor and their dark-gray or black color. In doubtful cases the liquid limit should be determined for an oven-dry specimen as well as a fresh one. If drying decreases the value of the liquid limit by 30 per cent or more, the soil is organic. Finally, if an inorganic and an organic soil are represented in Figure 9 by approximately the same point, the dry strength of the organic soil is considerably greater than that of the inorganic soil.

Experience has shown that the points which represent different samples from the same soil stratum define a straight line that is roughly parallel to line A. As the liquid limit of soils represented by such a line increases, the plasticity and the compressibility of the soils also increase. The dry strength of inorganic soils represented by points on lines

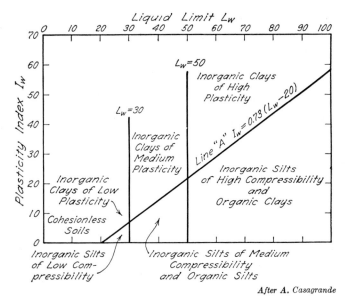

FIG. 9.   Plasticity chart.

located above A increases from medium for samples with a liquid limit below 30 to very high for samples with a liquid limit of 100. On the other hand, if the line representative of inorganic samples from a given stratum is located at a considerable distance below A, the dry strength of samples with a liquid limit less than 50 is very low, and that of samples with a liquid limit close to 100 is only medium. In accordance with these relationships, the dry strength of inorganic soils from different localities but with equal liquid limits increases in a general way with increasing plasticity index. Figure 10 shows the plasticity characteristics of several well-defined types of clay.[8.1]

The samples required for Atterberg-limit tests need not be undisturbed, and the technique of making the tests is simple. Yet, even at the present still incipient state of our knowledge, a great amount of useful information can be derived from the test results. Therefore, the investigation of statistical relations between the Atterberg limits and the other physical properties of cohesive soils constitutes one of the most promising fields for research in soil physics. Every well-established

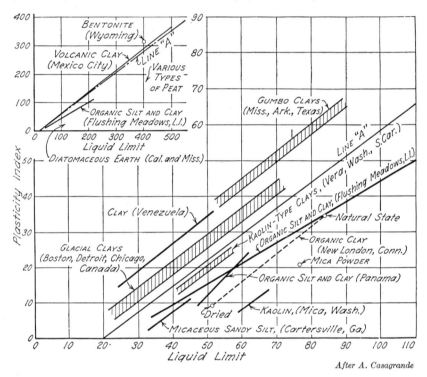

After A. Casagrande

Fig. 10.   Relation between liquid limit and plasticity index for typical soils.

statistical relation of this type broadens the scope of conclusions that can be drawn from the results of limit tests. Two useful relations of this kind are shown in Figures 23 and 29.

REFERENCE

8.1. See Reference 6.2 Detailed discussion of the plasticity characteristics of clays.

ART. 9.   MINIMUM REQUIREMENTS FOR ADEQUATE SOIL DESCRIPTION

In Article 6 suitable procedures were described for dividing coarse-grained soils into several large groups on the basis of their grain-size characteristics, and in Article 8 directions were presented for dividing fine-grained soils into eight large groups on the basis of their plasticity. If the engineer knows the group to which a given soil belongs, he also knows in a general way the more outstanding physical characteristics of the soil. However, each group includes soils with a great variety of properties, and, furthermore, every soil can occur in the field in very different states. In order to distinguish between the individual members of each group and the different states of each member, two different procedures can be used. Either the principal groups can be further subdivided, or else the group name can be supplemented by numerical values representing the pertinent index properties.

The first of these two procedures is suitable for classifying the soils within geographically limited districts, because within such districts the number of different types and states of soil is likely to be fairly limited. As a consequence, the method is used extensively and to advantage by local construction organizations such as state highway departments. However, attempts to use a similar procedure for establishing a universal system of soil classification have little prospects for success, because the required terminology would inevitably be so complex that it would lead to ultimate confusion.

The second procedure, on the other hand, can be used profitably under any circumstances, provided the engineer chooses those index properties which are indicative of the essential physical characteristics of the soil. The properties required for adequate description of the various types of soil are summarized in Table 5. The soils listed in this table have been described in Article 2, which contains all the information required for at least a tentative classification of the soil. After the type has been recognized, the engineer turns to Table 5 and performs all the soil tests prescribed for this type. The test results represent the criteria for distinguishing between different soils of the same type.

With the exception of till, hardpan, and peat, all the soils listed in Table 5 consist either exclusively of coarse grains such as sand and gravel, or exclusively of fine grains having the size of silt or clay particles. Soils that consist of a mixture of these ingredients are regarded as composite. To describe a composite soil, it is first necessary to determine the natural void ratio e, the natural water content w, and the grain-size distribution. The soil is then divided into two parts, one of which contains all the grains larger than about 0.1 mm (width of the openings in the 150-mesh sieve), and the other of which contains the remainder. The coarse fraction is submitted to the classification tests prescribed for sand and gravel, and the remainder to those for silts and clays.

If the soils encountered on a given job are submitted to tests other than those listed in Table 5, the significant results of these tests should be included in the record. Since soil strata are seldom homogeneous, even an apparently homogeneous soil stratum cannot be considered ade-

TABLE 5

DATA REQUIRED FOR SOIL IDENTIFICATION

Column groups: **General Information** = Color – Dry strength. **Results of Classification Tests — Intact Samples[1]** = Natural void ratio – Sensitivity. **Results of Classification Tests — Disturbed Samples** = Max. void ratio – Carbonate content.

Type of Soil	Color	Odor[2]	Texture[3]	Dilatancy[4]	Grain properties[5]	Dry strength[6]	Natural void ratio $\bar{e}$[7]	Natural water content w	Unit weight, natural state	Unit weight, oven-dried γ_{di}	Unconf. compressive strength q_u	Sensitivity S_t[8]	Max. void ratio e_{max}[9]	Min. void ratio e_{min}[10]	Liquid limit L_w[11]	Plastic limit P_w[12]	Unit weight, oven-dried γ_{dr}	Mechanical analysis[13]	Carbonate content[14]
Hardpan[15]	x		x		x				x										
Sand, gravel	x				x		x						x	x				x	
Inorganic silt	x		x	x		x		x	x	x	x	x			x	x	x	x	x
Organic silt	x	x	x	x		x		x	x	x	x	x			x	x	x	x	x
Clay	x		x			x		x	x	x	x	x			x	x	x		x
Organic clay	x	x	x			x		x	x	x	x	x			x	x	x		x
Peat	x	x	x		x			x	x										
Till	x				x		x	x	x				x	x				x	
Tuff, fine-grained	x		x			x		x	x	x	x				x	x	x	x	
Loess[16]	x		x	x		x	x	x	x	x	x		x	x	x	x	x	x	x
Modified loess	x		x	x		x	x	x	x	x	x		x	x	x	x	x	x	x
Adobe	x		x	x		x	x	x	x	x	x		x	x	x	x	x	x	x
Marl	x		x	x		x		x	x	x	x	x			x	x	x	x	x
Lake marl	x		x	x		x		x	x	x	x	x			x	x	x	x	x
Gumbo	x		x			x		x	x	x	x	x			x	x	x	x	x

[1] If no undisturbed or tube samples were obtained, use the spoon samples, Article 44.

[2] If the odor is faint, heat the sample slightly. This intensifies the odor.

[3] Describe appearance of fresh fracture of intact sample (granular, dull, smooth, glossy). Then rub small quantity of soil between the fingers, and describe sensation (floury, smooth, gritty, sharp). If large specimens break up readily into smaller fragments describe appearance of walls of cracks (dull, slickensided) and average spacing of cracks.

[4] Perform shaking test, page 5. Describe results (conspicuous, weak, none) depending on intensity of phenomena observed.

[5] Describe shape (angular, subangular, subrounded, rounded, well rounded) and mineralogical characteristics of macroscopic soil particles only. Mineralogical characteristics include types of rocks and minerals represented among the grains so far as they can be discerned by inspection under the hand lens. Describe rock fragments (fresh, slightly weathered, or thoroughly decomposed; hard or friable). If a sand contains mica flakes, indicate mica content (slightly, moderately, or very micaceous). In connection with peat, the term grain properties refers to the type and state of preservation of the predominant visible remnants of plants such as fibers, twigs, or leaves.

[6] Crush dry fragment between fingers and indicate hardness (very low, low, medium, high, very high).

[7] If no undisturbed samples were obtained, substitute results of standard penetration test (Article 44) or equivalent.

[8] Applies only to clay and fine silt at a water content above the plastic limit.

[9] Prepare sample as described on page 27.

[10] Determine by means of Proctor method, page 375.

[11] If soil may be organic, determine L_w first in fresh state and then after drying in oven at 105°C.

[12] In addition to numerical value of P_w, state whether threads were tough, firm, medium, or weak.

[13] Present results either in form of semilogarithmic graph, or else by numerical values of D_{10} and $U = D_{60}/D_{10}$ (Article 6) accompanied by adjectives indicating the type of grain-size grading (see Figure 4).

quately described unless the index properties of several samples from the stratum have been determined. The record should also contain a brief statement of whatever can be learned about the geological history of the stratum.

Today most large construction organizations, such as the Corps of Engineers of the United States Army, the United States Bureau of Reclamation, and many state highway departments, maintain soil laboratories in which the classification tests are made as a matter of routine. However, the results of these tests are of such practical importance that they should also be made by every engineer who deals with soils. The performance of the tests increases the engineer's familiarity with the various properties of the soils with which he deals, and the test results greatly increase the value of his field records.

After an engineer has personally tested several dozen samples of soil from one locality, he is likely to discover that he can estimate the index properties of most of the soils from that locality without any tests. He will also acquire the ability to discriminate between different soils or different states of the same soil which previously he had considered identical.

Every engineer should develop the habit of expressing his opinion on the plasticity and grain-size characteristics of the soils he encounters by numerical values rather than by adjectives. The grading of a sand should be expressed by the estimated value of the uniformity coefficient, $U = D_{60}/D_{10}$, Article 6, and not by the words "well graded" or "poorly graded." The degree of plasticity should be indicated by the estimated value of the plasticity index I_w, Article 8, and not by the words "trace of plasticity" or "highly plastic." This habit is so important that it should be encouraged from the beginning by the instructor in the classroom. The use of the numerical system prevents misunderstandings and is an incentive to check from time to time the degree of accuracy of the estimates. Without occasional check tests the progressive deterioration of the ability to estimate may pass unnoticed.

---

[14] Calcium carbonate content can be detected by moistening the dry material with HCl. Describe result of test (strong, weak, or no effervescence).

[15] Add to data on texture a description of general appearance, structure, and degree of cohesiveness of chunks in fresh state and after soaking in water.

[16] Add to data on texture a description of the macroscopic features of the loess, such as diameter and spacing of root holes.

Chapter II

HYDRAULIC AND MECHANICAL PROPERTIES OF SOILS

ART. 10. SIGNIFICANCE OF HYDRAULIC AND MECHANICAL PROPERTIES OF SOILS

In the preceding chapter, we have dealt with the index properties of soils. Since these properties reflect the general character of a given soil, they serve to indicate the extent to which soils from different localities may or may not be similar. In addition, they constitute the basis for recording construction experience and for utilizing this experience on subsequent jobs.

It has been emphasized that foundation and earthwork engineering is based chiefly on experience. However, it must also be emphasized that civil engineering in general did not emerge from a state of relative stagnation until the accumulated stock of experience became fertilized by applied science. The function of science was to disclose the relations between events and their causes.

In order to establish these relations in the realm of foundation and earthwork engineering, it has been necessary to investigate the physical properties of the different types of soils, just as it was necessary in structural engineering to investigate the properties of steel and concrete. A given steel or concrete is adequately described for most practical purposes if its strength and modulus of elasticity are known. On the other hand, practical problems involving soils may require the consideration of a variety of soil properties. Foremost among these are the permeability, the compressibility, the resistance against flow and shear, and the stress–deformation relationships. In the following articles, these properties are discussed in detail.

ART. 11. PERMEABILITY OF SOILS

INTRODUCTION

A material is said to be permeable if it contains continuous voids. Since such voids are contained in all soils including the stiffest clays, and in all nonmetallic construction materials including sound granite and neat cement, all these materials are permeable. Furthermore, the flow

40

of water through all of them obeys approximately the same laws. Hence the difference between the flow of water through clean sand and through sound granite is merely one of degree.

The permeability of soils has a decisive effect on the cost and the difficulty of many construction operations, such as the excavation of open cuts in water-bearing sand, or on the rate at which a soft clay stratum consolidates under the influence of the weight of a superimposed fill. Even the permeability of dense concrete or rock may have important practical implications, because water exerts a pressure on the porous material through which it percolates. This pressure, which is known as *seepage pressure*, can be very high. The erroneous but widespread conception that stiff clay and dense concrete are impermeable is due to the fact that the entire quantity of water that percolates through such materials toward an exposed surface is likely to evaporate, even in a very humid atmosphere. As a consequence, the surface appears to be dry. However, since the mechanical effects of seepage are entirely independent of the rate of percolation, the absence of visible discharge does not indicate the absence of seepage pressures. Striking manifestations of this fact may be observed while an excavation is being made in very fine rock flour. The permeability of this material is very low. Yet, a slight change in the pressure conditions in the pore water may suffice to transform a large quantity of the material into a semiliquid.

DEFINITIONS AND DARCY'S LAW

As water percolates through a permeable material, the individual water particles move along paths which deviate erratically but only slightly from smooth curves known as *flow lines*. If adjacent flow lines are straight and parallel, the flow is said to be *linear*.

The hydraulic principles involved in linear flow are illustrated by Figure 11. In this figure, the points a and b represent the extremities of a flow line. At each extremity a standpipe, known as a piezometric tube, has been installed to indicate the level to which the water rises at these points. The water level in the tube at b is designated as the *piezometric level* at b, and the vertical distance from this level to point b is the *piezometric head* at b. The vertical distance between a and b represents the *position head* ΔH. If the water in the hydraulic system stands at the same elevation in the piezometric tubes at a and b, the system is in a state of rest, regardless of the magnitude of the position head. Flow can occur only if the piezometric levels at a and b differ by a distance h known as the *hydraulic head* at a with respect to b. The distance h is also referred to as the *difference in piezometric level* between a and b. It should be observed that the difference in piezometric level is equal to the difference in the piezometric heads at a and b only if the position head ΔH is zero.

In Figure 11, a_1 and b_1 represent any two points at the same elevation in the piezometric tubes rising from a and b respectively. Since the unit weight of the water is γ_w (grams per cubic centimeter), the hydrostatic pressure at a_1 exceeds that at b_1 by the amount $\gamma_w h$. The difference $\gamma_w h$ between the hydrostatic pressure at two points located at the same

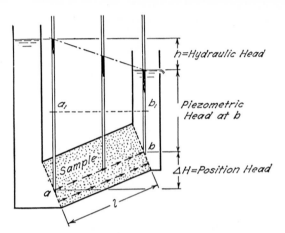

Fig. 11. Diagram illustrating meaning of hydraulic head and piezometric head associated with linear flow of water through soil sample.

elevation is referred to as *excess hydrostatic pressure*. It is this pressure that drives the water through the soil between a and b. The ratio,

$$i_p = \gamma_w \frac{h}{l} = \frac{u}{l} \tag{11.1}$$

in which u is the excess hydrostatic pressure, represents the pressure gradient (grams per cubic centimeter) from a to b. The ratio,

$$i = \frac{i_p}{\gamma_w} = \frac{1}{\gamma_w}\frac{u}{l} = \frac{h}{l} \tag{11.2}$$

is known as the *hydraulic gradient*. It is a pure number.

The *discharge velocity* v is defined as the quantity of water that percolates in a unit time across a unit area of a section oriented at right angles to the flow lines. In a statistically isotropic porous material the porosity of a plane section is equal to the volume porosity n. Hence, the average velocity v_s at which the water percolates through the voids of the material is equal to the discharge velocity divided by the porosity. The value v_s represents the *seepage velocity*. If the term velocity is used without qualification in connection with permeability, it always indicates the discharge and not the seepage velocity.

If water percolates through fine saturated sand or other fine-grained completely saturated soils without affecting the structure of the soil, the discharge velocity is almost exactly determined by the equation,

$$v = \frac{K}{\eta} i_p \qquad (11.3)$$

in which η (gram-seconds per square centimeter) is the viscosity of the water, and K is an empirical constant referred to as the *permeability*. The viscosity of water decreases with increasing temperature, as shown in Figure 12. The value K (square centimeters) is a constant for any permeable material with given porosity characteristics, and it is independent of the physical properties of the percolating liquid. From equations 11.2 and 11.3 we obtain for the discharge velocity the expression,

$$v = \frac{K}{\eta} \gamma_w i \qquad (11.4)$$

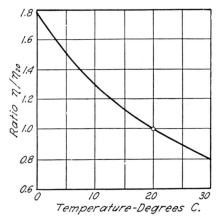

FIG. 12.　Relation between temperature and viscosity of water.

Seepage problems encountered in civil engineering deal almost exclusively with the flow of ground water at moderate depths below the surface and with leakage out of reservoirs. The temperature of the percolating water varies so little that the unit weight γ_w is practically constant, and, in addition, the viscosity η varies within fairly narrow limits. Therefore, it is customary to substitute in equation 11.4

$$k = K \frac{\gamma_w}{\eta} \qquad (11.5)$$

whence

$$v = ki \qquad (11.6)$$

In civil engineering, the value k is commonly called the *coefficient of permeability*. In some other fields it is known as the *transmission constant*, although this term is rather inappropriate because, according to equation 11.5, k is not a constant. Equation 11.6 is commonly known as *Darcy's law*.

It should be emphasized that the permeability characteristics of a porous material are expressed by K (square centimeters) and not by k (centimeters per second). The coefficient K is independent of the properties of the liquid, whereas k depends not only on the properties of the porous material, but also on the properties of the liquid. The use of k in this book, or in civil engineering in general, is justified only by convenience.

The channels through which the water particles travel in a mass of soil have a variable and irregular cross section. As a consequence, the real velocity of flow is extremely variable. However, the average rate of flow through such channels is governed by the same laws that determine the rate of flow through straight capillary tubes having a uniform cross section. If the cross section of the tube is circular, the velocity of flow increases, according to Poiseuille's law, with the square of the diameter of the tube. Since the average diameter of the voids in soil at a given porosity increases practically in proportion to the grain size D, it is possible to express k on the basis of Poiseuille's law as

$$k = \text{constant} \times D^2$$

From his experiments with loose filter sands of high uniformity (uniformity coefficient not greater than about 2), Allen Hazen obtained the empirical equation,

$$k(\text{cm/sec}) = C_1 D_{10}{}^2 \tag{11.7}$$

in which D_{10} is the effective size in centimeters (see Article 6), and C_1 (1/cm sec) varies from about 100 to 150. It should be noted that equation 11.7 is applicable only to fairly uniform sands in a loose state.

Relation between Void Ratio and Permeability

When a soil is compressed or vibrated, the volume occupied by its solid constituents remains practically unchanged, but the volume of the voids decreases. As a consequence, the permeability of the soil also decreases. The influence of the void ratio on the permeability is illustrated by Figure 13. In this figure the abscissas represent the void ratio. The ordinates represent the ratio $k/k_{0.85}$ between the coefficient of permeability k of the soil at any given void ratio e and that of the same soil at a void ratio of 0.85. The plain curve shows the relation between e and $k/k_{0.85}$ for fine or medium clean sands with bulky grains. This relation can be expressed fairly accurately by various simple equations, such as

A. Casagrande's unpublished equation,

$$k = 1.4k_{0.85}e^2$$ (11.8)

In connection with foundation problems, clean sands are seldom encountered. If a sand contains a high percentage of scale-like particles such as mica flakes, the relation between e and $k/k_{0.85}$ resembles that indicated by the dash curve below the plain curve in Figure 13. Fine-grained soils always contain flaky constituents, but, since the proportion is different for different soils, the corresponding $e-k/k_{0.85}$ curves are different.

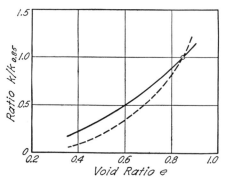

In a soil that contains air bubbles, the size of the bubbles decreases with increasing water pressure. As a consequence, the coefficient of permeability of such a soil increases with increasing hydraulic head. In clays with root holes or open cracks, percolation is almost inevitably associated with internal scour. The detached particles gradually clog the narrowest parts of the water passages whereupon the coefficient of permeability decreases to a small fraction of its initial value. Hence, Darcy's law is not valid unless the volume and shape of the water passages are independent of pressure and time.

FIG. 13. Relation between void ratio and permeability of mixed-grained sand (full line) and soil with flaky constituents (dash line).

PERMEABILITY TESTS

The principal types of apparatus for determining the coefficient of permeability of soil samples are illustrated in Figure 14. The constant-head permeameter (a and b) is suitable for very permeable soils, and the falling-head permeameter (c) for less permeable ones. In order to perform a test with any of these types of apparatus, a hydraulic gradient is established within the sample, and water flows through the soil.

In the constant-head permeameter, Figure 14a, the hydraulic head h is kept constant, and the discharge is measured. In the falling-head permeameter, Figure 14c, the water flows out of a narrow tube P with cross-sectional area A_1, through the sample which has a cross-sectional area A_2, into a stationary vessel V. The coefficient of permeability k is computed on the basis of the observed rate at which the water level descends in the tube P, while the water level in the vessel V remains unchanged.

The most important sources of experimental error in a permeability test are the formation of a filter skin of fine material on the surface of the sample and the segregation of air in the form of bubbles within the soil. Both of these phenomena reduce the average permeability of the specimen. The error due to the formation of a filter skin can be eliminated by measuring the loss of head between two points located in the interior of the sample, as shown in Figure 14b.

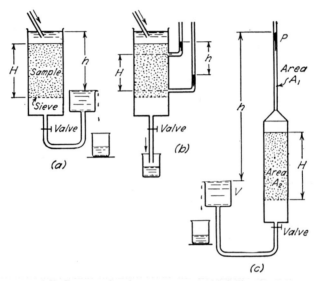

FIG. 14.   (*a* and *b*) Constant-head permeameters; (*c*) falling-head permeameter.

The value of the coefficient of permeability determined by means of a permeability test depends on the temperature at which the test is performed, because k, equation 11.5, is a function of the unit weight of the water γ_w and of the viscosity η. Both of these quantities vary with temperature. However, since the variation of γ_w is negligible in comparison with that of η, we may compute the value of k for any temperature T by means of the equation,

$$k = \frac{\eta_1}{\eta} k_1 \qquad (11.9)$$

In this expression, derived from equation 11.5, k_1 is the coefficient of permeability corresponding to the test temperature, and η_1 is the corresponding viscosity. It is customary to express values of k at a standard temperature of 20°C. In Figure 12, the ordinates represent the ratio between the values of η corresponding to the temperatures given by the abscissas, and the value η_{20} corresponding to $T = 20°C$.

Equation 11.9 was derived on the assumption that the coefficient of viscosity of the water is independent of the porosity and that it changes with temperature in accordance with the law represented by the curve in Figure 12. In clays temperature seems to have a greater influence on viscosity than it has in coarser soils. Furthermore, the average viscosity of the pore water of clay appears to increase with decreasing pore space. At a given porosity, the average viscosity seems to increase temporarily after remolding, even if the temperature is held constant. These facts exclude equation 11.9 from application to clays and other very fine-grained soils, but they do not invalidate Darcy's law, equation 11.6.

If a clay is remolded at unaltered water content, its coefficient of permeability is likely to decrease from the original value k to a smaller value k_r. For most inorganic clays, the ratio k/k_r is not greater than about two. However, for organic clays and for marls with a cluster structure, it may be as great as 30.

For coarse-grained soils with approximately equidimensional grains, such as quartz sand, the relation between the void ratio e and the coefficient of permeability k can be expressed with satisfactory accuracy by a single equation, such as equation 11.8, or by a single curve, such as the plain curve in Figure 13. Hence, it is sufficient to determine the value of k corresponding to one arbitrary value of e. The values of k for other values of e can be derived from the test result by means of equation 11.8 or Figure 13. On the other hand, the value of k for micaceous sands and for practically all the fine-grained soils encountered in the field depends to a large extent on the percentage of flaky constituents and on various other factors that are independent of the void ratio. For this reason, it has already been mentioned that the dash curve in Figure 13 serves merely to illustrate the general character of the relation for such soils and cannot be used as a basis for computation. Hence if a soil is micaceous or if it contains fine or very fine constituents, it is necessary to establish the relation between void ratio and permeability by performing permeability tests on at least three specimens with widely different void ratios.

Table 6 contains information regarding the range of the coefficient of permeability for various soils and the most appropriate methods for performing the permeability tests on these soils.

PERMEABILITY OF STRATIFIED MASSES OF SOIL

Natural transported soils commonly consist of layers which have different permeability. In order to determine the average coefficient of

TABLE 6

PERMEABILITY AND DRAINAGE CHARACTERISTICS OF SOILS

Coefficient of Permeability k in cm per sec (log scale)

10^2	10^1	1.0	10^{-1}	10^{-2}	10^{-3}	10^{-4}	10^{-5}	10^{-6}	10^{-7}	10^{-8}	10^{-9}

Drainage: Good | Poor | Practically Impervious

Soil types: Clean gravel — Clean sands, clean sand and gravel mixtures — Very fine sands, organic and inorganic silts, mixtures of sand silt and clay, glacial till, stratified clay deposits, etc. — "Impervious" soils, e.g., homogeneous clays below zone of weathering

"Impervious" soils modified by effects of vegetation and weathering

Direct determination of k: Direct testing of soil in its original position—pumping tests. Reliable if properly conducted. Considerable experience required

Constant-head permeameter. Little experience required

Falling-head permeameter. Reliable. Little experience required

Falling-head permeameter. Unreliable. Much experience required

Falling-head permeameter. Fairly reliable. Considerable experience necessary

Indirect determination of k: Computation from grain-size distribution. Applicable only to clean cohesionless sands and gravels

Computation based on results of consolidation tests. Reliable. Considerable experience required

After A. Casagrande and R. E. Fadum

permeability of such deposits, representative samples are secured from each of the layers and are tested. Once the values of k are known for the individual strata, the averages can be computed by using the following method. Let

$k_1, k_2 \cdots k_n$ = coefficients of permeability of the individual strata
$H_1, H_2 \cdots H_n$ = thicknesses of corresponding strata
$H = H_1 + H_2 + \cdots H_n$ = total thickness
k_I = average coefficient of permeability parallel to bedding planes (usually horizontal)
k_{II} = average coefficient of permeability perpendicular to bedding planes (usually vertical)

If the flow is parallel to the bedding planes, the average discharge velocity v is

$$v = k_I i = \frac{1}{H}[v_1 H_1 + v_2 H_2 + \cdots v_n H_n] = \frac{1}{H}[k_1 i H_1 + k_2 i H_2 + \cdots k_n i H_n]$$

whence

$$k_I = \frac{1}{H}[k_1 H_1 + k_2 H_2 + \cdots k_n H_n] \qquad (11.10)$$

For flow at right angles to the bedding planes, the hydraulic gradient across the individual layers is denoted by $i_1, i_2 \cdots i_n$. The hydraulic gradient across the series of layers is h/H, where h equals the total loss in head. The principle of continuity of flow requires that the velocity be the same in each layer. Therefore

$$v = \frac{h}{H} k_{II} = k_1 i_1 = k_2 i_2 = \cdots k_n i_n$$

Also,

$$h = H_1 i_1 + H_2 i_2 + \cdots H_n i_n$$

Combining these equations, we obtain

$$k_{II} = \frac{H}{\dfrac{H_1}{k_1} + \dfrac{H_2}{k_2} + \cdots \dfrac{H_n}{k_n}} \qquad (11.11)$$

It can be demonstrated theoretically that for every stratified mass k_{II} must be less than k_I.

SCOUR AND SCOUR PREVENTION AT BOUNDARIES

The engineer is often compelled to divert percolating water out of the soil into wells or ditches, or toward conduits located beneath foundations.

This procedure is known as *drainage* (see Article 21). Wells usually consist of perforated pipes, and conduits of perforated pipes or pipe lines with open joints. The space between the natural soil and the pipes is filled with a coarse-grained material known as a *filler*. If the voids of the filler are very much larger than the finest grains of the adjoining natural soil, the finest soil particles are likely to be washed into the interstices of the filler where they accumulate and gradually obstruct the flow. On the other hand, if the voids in the filler are almost as small as those in the natural soil, the filler may be washed into the conduits and carried away.

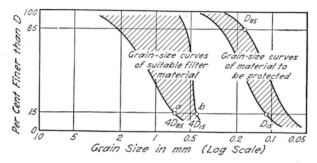

FIG. 15. Diagram illustrating specification for grain size of material suitable for filter. Right-hand shaded area encloses all grain-size curves for material to be protected; left-hand area indicates range within which curves for filter material must lie.

WORK FROM   RIGHT HAND CURVES to LEFT HAND CURVES.

Both conditions are equally undesirable. If they are to be prevented, the filler must consist of a material with a grain size that meets certain requirements. Such a material is known as a *filter*.

Experiments have shown that a material satisfies the essential requirements for a filter if its 15 per cent size D_{15} is at least four times as large as that of the coarsest layer of soil in contact with the filter and not more than four times as large as the 85 per cent size D_{85} of the finest adjoining layer of soil. These requirements are represented graphically in Figure 15. In this figure the shaded area on the right side includes the grain-size curves of all the soils in contact with the filter. In accordance with the preceding specifications, any material satisfies the conditions for a filter if its grain-size curve intersects the horizontal 15 per cent line between the points *a* and *b*. If the filter extends across a boundary between coarse and fine soils, different materials should be used for covering the areas on either side of the boundary.

Since it is desirable to reduce the loss of head due to percolation through the filter to the smallest value compatible with the grain-size requirements, large filters are usually made up of several layers. Each of these layers satisfies the conditions illustrated by Figure 15 with respect to the preceding layer. Such composite filters are said to be *graded*.

The emergence of water from the ground at the boundary between a coarse and a fine soil may cause scour of the finer material, provided the velocity of the discharging water is great enough. Scour usually begins with the formation of small springs at different points along the boundary, from which channels are eroded in a backward direction toward the area where the water enters the soil. Hence, the process is known as *backward erosion*. It is one of the most dangerous menaces to dams, and it has been responsible for some of the most catastrophic dam failures, Article 59. Since the erosion cannot occur unless a large amount of soil is gradually washed out of the ground, it can be prevented effectively by constructing a filter over the area where springs may develop.

PROBLEMS

1. A sample of coarse sand, 15 cm high and 5.5 cm in diameter, was tested in a constant-head permeameter. Water percolated through the soil under a hydrostatic head of 40 cm for a period of 6.0 sec. The discharge water was collected and found to weigh 400 gm. What was the coefficient of permeability at the void ratio and temperature of the test?

   Ans. $k = 1.05$ cm per sec.

2. A bed of sand consists of three horizontal layers of equal thickness. The value of k for the upper and lower layers is 1×10^{-4} cm per sec, and of the middle layer is 1×10^{-2} cm per sec. What is the ratio of the average permeability of the bed in the horizontal direction to that in the vertical direction?

   Ans. 23 to 1.

3. A sample of mixed-grained sand with rounded particles has a void ratio of 0.62 and a coefficient of permeability of 2.5×10^{-2} cm per sec. Estimate the value of k for the same material at a void ratio of 0.73.

ART. 12. EFFECTIVE AND NEUTRAL STRESSES AND CRITICAL HYDRAULIC GRADIENT

Effective and Neutral Stresses

Figure 16*a* shows a cross section through a thin layer of soil that covers the bottom of a container. If a load p per unit of area is applied to the surface of the sample, for example by covering it with lead shot, the void ratio of the soil decreases from e_0 to e_1. The pressure p also produces a change in all of the other mechanical properties of the soil such as its shearing resistance. For this reason, it is known as an *effective pressure*. It is given the symbol $\bar{p}$.

If, instead, the vessel is filled with water to such a height h_w that $h_w = p/\gamma_w$, the normal stress on a horizontal section through the sample is also increased by p. Nevertheless, the increase in pressure due to the weight of the water does not have a measurable influence on the void ratio or on any other mechanical property of the soil such as the shearing resistance. Therefore, the pressure produced by the water load is called a *neutral pressure*. It is said to be zero if it is equal to atmospheric pressure. Hence, the neutral pressure is equal to the piezometric head h_w times the unit weight of water γ_w, or

$$u_w = \gamma_w h_w \qquad (12.1)$$

Neutral pressures are transmitted to the base of the soil stratum through the pore water, whereas effective pressures are transmitted through the points of contact between the soil grains. In accordance with this concept, the total normal stress p at any point on a section through a saturated soil can be resolved into two parts, a neutral stress $u_w = \gamma_w h_w$, and an effective stress $\bar{p}$. Therefore

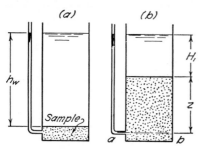

$$p = \bar{p} + u_w \qquad (12.2)$$

This is one of the most important equations in soil mechanics.

FIG. 16.   Apparatus for demonstrating difference between effective and neutral stresses.

The lower part of the container shown in Figure 16b is filled with saturated soil having a unit weight γ. Water stands to a height H_1 above the surface of the soil. After equilibrium is established, the piezometric head h_w at depth z is $H_1 + z$, the neutral stress is

$$u_w = (H_1 + z)\gamma_w \qquad (12.3)$$

and the total normal stress is

$$p = H_1\gamma_w + z\gamma \qquad (12.4)$$

Hence the effective stress at depth z is

$$\bar{p} = p - u_w = H_1\gamma_w + z\gamma - (H_1 + z)\gamma_w = z(\gamma - \gamma_w) = z\gamma' \quad (12.5)$$

in which

$$\gamma' = \gamma - \gamma_w \qquad (12.6)$$

The quantity γ' is called the *submerged unit weight* of the soil. It is equal to the difference between the unit weight γ of the saturated soil and the unit weight of water γ_w.

CRITICAL HYDRAULIC GRADIENT

In the derivation of equation 12.5, the water in the voids of the soil is assumed to be in a state of rest. If, instead, water is flowing through the voids, equation 12.5 must be replaced by an expression that contains the hydraulic gradient i. This can be demonstrated by means of the apparatus shown in Figure 17a. The cylindrical vessel A contains a layer of dense sand resting on a screen. The thickness of the layer is H, and the rim of the vessel is located at a distance H_1 above the top of the sand.

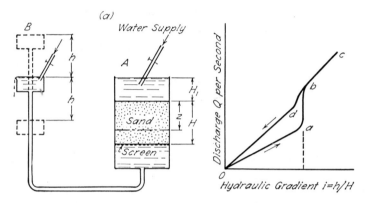

FIG. 17.   (a) Apparatus for illustrating hydraulic conditions associated with boiling of sand; (b) relation between upward hydraulic gradient and discharge through sand in apparatus shown in (a).

The space below the screen communicates through a tube with vessel B. The water level is maintained at the elevation of the upper rim of each vessel. Hence, whatever the position of the water level in B, the total normal stress p on a horizontal section at depth z below the surface of the sand is always equal to p, equation 12.4. The corresponding effective normal stress $\bar{p}$ is equal to

$$\bar{p} = p - u_w$$

Hence, if the neutral stress in the water decreases or increases by Δu_w, the effective stress increases or decreases by the same amount, or

$$\Delta \bar{p} = -\Delta u_w \tag{12.7}$$

As long as the water level in both vessels is at the same elevation, the effective pressure at depth z is equal to $\bar{p} = z\gamma'$, equation 12.5. If the vessel B is lowered through a distance h, water percolates through the sand in a downward direction under a hydraulic gradient $i = h/H$. The neutral stress at depth H is reduced by $h\gamma_w = iH\gamma_w$, and that at any other depth z is proportionately reduced by the amount $\Delta u_w = iz\gamma_w$. The effective stress is increased by the same amount.

On the other hand, if the vessel B is lifted through a distance h, the neutral stress at depth z increases by $\Delta u_w = iz\gamma_w$, and the effective stress decreases to

$$\bar{p} = z\gamma' - iz\gamma_w \tag{12.8}$$

The increase Δu_w of the neutral stress is caused exclusively by the transition of the pore water from a stationary state into a state of flow. The corresponding change Δu_w of the effective pressure in the sand is referred to as the *seepage pressure*. It is produced by the friction between the percolating water and the walls of the voids and can be described as a "drag." If the water percolates in a downward direction, the current drags the soil particles down and thereby increases the effective pressure in the sand. On the other hand, if the water flows in an upward direction, the friction between the water and the walls tends to lift the soil grains. As soon as the hydraulic gradient i in equation 12.8 becomes equal to

$$i_c = \frac{\gamma'}{\gamma_w} \tag{12.9}$$

the effective stress becomes equal to zero at any depth in the layer of sand. In other words, the average seepage pressure becomes equal to the submerged weight of the sand. The value i_c represents the *critical hydraulic gradient*.

Figure 17b illustrates the mechanical effect of the upward flow of water on the properties of the sand. In this diagram, the abscissas represent the hydraulic gradient, and the ordinates the corresponding discharge Q per unit of time. The curve $Oabc$ represents the relation between discharge and hydraulic gradient as the hydraulic gradient is steadily increased. As long as i is less than i_c, the discharge increases in accordance with Darcy's law, equation 11.6, in direct proportion to i, and the value of k remains constant. This fact indicates that the mutual position of the sand grains remains practically unaltered. However, at the instant when i becomes equal to i_c, the discharge increases suddenly, involving a corresponding increase of the coefficient of permeability. If a weight previously rested on the surface of the sand, it now sinks down as if the sand were a liquid. During a further increase of i the discharge again increases in direct proportion to i, and the coefficient of permeability retains the value that it acquired immediately after the hydraulic gradient exceeded the critical value. The decrease of discharge due to lowering the hydraulic gradient from a value greater than i_c is indicated by the line $cbdO$. As soon as i becomes roughly equal to i_c, the permeability decreases and then remains constant throughout any further decrease of i. Since the line bdO is located above the line Oab, the corresponding coefficient of permeability is greater than the original value. This fact suggests that the event represented by the step ab in the line Oab causes a permanent decrease of the density of the sand.

The process represented by the step ab is accompanied by a violent and visible agitation of the sand particles. Hence, it is commonly referred to as a *boiling* of the sand. Sand starts to boil in any open excavation if the ground water rises toward the bottom of the excavation at a hydraulic gradient greater than the critical value i_c. It has often been claimed that the boiling occurs only in certain types of sand known as quicksands. Therefore, it may be well to emphasize that it takes place in every sand and even in gravel, as soon as the hydraulic gradient becomes equal to i_c. The term quicksand should be reserved for the members of a small group of very fine and very loose sands capable of becoming "quick" even if the hydraulic gradient of the seepage water is less than the critical value, and even if there is no perceptible external provocation. The little that is known about the characteristics of real quicksands is discussed in Article 17.

The boiling of ordinary sand can be prevented by constructing a loaded filter above the area in which the seepage emerges from the ground. A properly designed filter has almost no effect on the neutral stress in the soil. Hence, its entire weight serves to increase the effective pressure and to keep the sand particles in their original positions.

REFERENCE

12.1. G. E. BERTRAM, *An Experimental Investigation of Protective Filters*, Harvard University, Graduate School of Engineering, Soil Mechanics Series 7, Jan. 1940.

PROBLEMS

1. A sand is composed of solid constituents having a unit weight of 2.60 gm per cu cm. The void ratio is 0.572. Compute the unit weight of the sand when dry and when saturated, and compare with the effective unit weight when submerged.

Ans. $\gamma_d = 103.2$; $\gamma = 125.9$; $\gamma' = 63.5$ lb per cu ft.

2. The water table in a deep deposit of very fine sand is 4 ft below the ground surface. Above the water table, the sand is saturated by capillary water. The unit weight of the saturated sand is 127 lb per cu ft. What is the effective vertical pressure on a horizontal plane at a depth of 12 ft below the ground surface?

Ans. 1025 lb per sq ft.

3. A submerged stratum of clay has a thickness of 50 ft. The average water content of samples taken from the stratum is 54 per cent, and the unit weight of the solid constituents is 2.78 gm per cu cm. What is the effective vertical pressure, due to the weight of the clay, at the base of the stratum?

4. The unit weight of the particles of a sand is 2.66 gm per cu cm, the porosity in the loose state is 45 per cent, and in the dense state is 37 per cent. What is the critical hydraulic gradient for these two states?

   Ans.   0.91;   1.05.

5. A large open excavation was made in a stratum of stiff clay with a saturated unit weight of 110 lb per cu ft. When the depth of the excavation reached 25 ft, the bottom rose, gradually cracked, and was flooded from below by a mixture of sand and water. Subsequent borings showed that the clay was underlain by a bed of sand with its surface at a depth of 37 ft. Compute the elevation to which the water would have risen from the sand into a drill hole before the excavation was started.

   Ans.   21.2 ft above top of sand.

ART. 13. COMPRESSIBILITY OF CONFINED LAYERS OF SOIL

INTRODUCTION

If a stratum of soft clay is located directly beneath the footings of a building, the footings are likely to settle excessively and perhaps even to break into the soil. However, since unfavorable soil conditions of this kind are readily recognized, designers generally foresee the possible dangers and avoid difficulty by establishing the footings on piers or piles that pass through the soft stratum to a firm layer below.

On the other hand, if a thin layer of soft clay is buried beneath a thick layer of sand, the consequences of the presence of the clay layer are not so obvious. Many engineers believe that the settlement of a footing depends merely on the nature of the soil located immediately below the footing. Hence, if the soft clay is located more than 10 or 15 ft below the base of the footings, its presence is commonly ignored. Yet, because of the gradual consolidation of the clay under the weight of the building, the building is likely to settle excessively and unequally, Article 54.

On account of the relative frequency of unexpected settlements of this kind, the compressibility of confined clay strata has received increasing attention during the last 20 years, and methods have been developed for computing or estimating the amount and the distribution of the settlement. If the computed settlements are found to exceed a tolerable amount, the foundation is redesigned.

Adhesion and friction at the boundaries of confined clay strata prevent the strata from stretching in horizontal directions. Hence, the information required for computing the settlement due to the compression of confined clay strata can be derived from compression tests on laterally confined specimens.

METHOD OF TESTING

A confined compression test is made by placing the sample in a ring as shown in Figure 18. The load is applied to the top of the sample through a rigid slab, and the compression is measured by means of a dial indicator. If the soil is saturated, the sample is placed between two porous disks that permit the escape of water during compression.

The results of the test are presented graphically. The void ratio e is plotted to a natural scale in the vertical direction. If the intensity of pressure p is plotted to a natural scale in the horizontal direction, the resulting curve is designated as an e–p curve. If the pressure is plotted to a logarithmic scale, the result is called an e–log p curve. Since each method of plotting has advantages, diagrams of both types will be used and shown.

A distinction must be made between soils in their natural state and soils in which the original structure has been destroyed by remolding (see Article 8). The constituents of remolded soils are brought into their final positions by a process of kneading that involves slippage along the points of contact, whereas those of a sedimentary deposit are laid down grain by grain. These two processes may lead to very different structural patterns (see Article 17). Furthermore, in the ground, the constituents of most natural soils have not changed their relative positions for hundreds or even thousands of years, whereas those of a remolded soil or of a mineral powder obtained by a process of crushing or grinding reached their final positions only a few hours or days before the test. A point contact of long duration may create molecular intergranular bonds which are wholly absent in a remolded soil. Therefore, the relations between void ratio and pressure for remolded and undisturbed soils are likely to be different. They are discussed under separate subheadings.

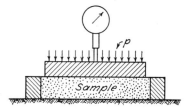

Fig. 18.   Apparatus for performing laterally confined compression test on soil sample.

Compressibility of Crushed Minerals and Remolded Soils

Typical e–p curves for various crushed minerals and remolded soils are shown in Figure 19a, and the corresponding e–log p curves in Figure 19b. The effect of the shape of the grains on the compressibility of the grain aggregate is demonstrated by curves a, b, and d, in Figure 19a. Curve a corresponds to a mixture of 80 per cent sand and 20 per cent mica; curve b to 90 per cent sand and 10 per cent mica; and curve d to 100 per cent sand. Each sample was initially compacted by rodding and vibrating. These curves demonstrate that the compressibility increases greatly with increasing percentages of scale-shaped particles. Furthermore, Figure 19a shows that the average slope of the curve d for dense sand is considerably flatter than that of curve c for the same sand in a loose state and that the void ratio of a loose sand, even under very great pressure, is greater than that of the same sand in a dense state subjected to no pressure.

Figure 19a also shows that the curve e corresponding to a remolded sample of a soft clay is very similar to that for a mixture of 90 per cent sand and 10 per cent mica, but that the void ratio of the clay at any given pressure is much smaller than the corresponding void ratio of the sand–mica mixture.

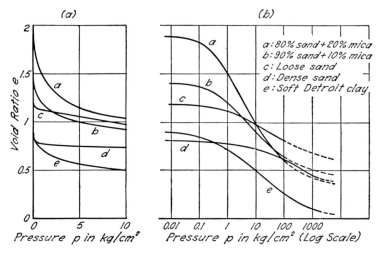

Fig. 19.   (a) Typical e–p curves, and (b) corresponding e–log p curves representing results of compression tests on laterally confined laboratory soil aggregates.

All of the e–log p curves shown in Figure 19b have certain characteristics in common. Each curve starts with a horizontal tangent and probably ends with a tangent that is nearly horizontal. The middle sloping part of each curve is fairly straight. For sands the middle part is straight from a pressure of about 10 to about 100 kg per sq cm. At this pressure the grains begin to crush, and the slope increases. The slope then remains fairly constant up to about 1000 kg per sq cm, whereupon it begins to decrease. The slope of the middle part of the curves for soft remolded clays decreases so slightly throughout the range from about 1 to 2000 kg per sq cm that the curve can be regarded as straight within this entire range. The middle sections of the curves for sand–mica mixtures are practically straight within the range from 1 to 10 kg per sq cm. The slope then decreases as the curves approach a nearly horizontal tangent.

Two other phenomena are of special interest in connection with the compressibility of soils in general. They are the time rate at which the compression takes place and the volume change caused by temporary removal of load.

The time effects associated with the compression of sand are illustrated by Figure 20. In this figure, the curve K_l represents the decrease of the void ratio of a loose sand due to a pressure that increases at a constant

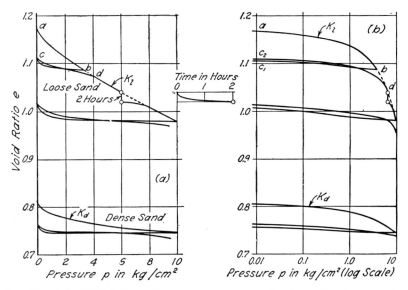

Fig. 20.   (*a* and *b*) Relation between *e* and *p* corresponding to results of compression tests on laterally confined sand.

and fairly rapid rate. If the process of loading is interrupted, the void ratio decreases at constant load, as indicated by the vertical step in the *e–p* curve, and by the corresponding *e–time* curve. If, after an intermission, the process of loading is resumed at the original rate, curve K_l merges smoothly into the curve that would have been obtained by loading the sand at a constant rate without intermission. The decrease of the void ratio at constant load is due to a lag in the adjustment of the position of the grains to the increasing pressure.

Similar time effects due to the same cause are also observed when a sample of saturated remolded clay is tested. However, they are combined with the much more important lag due to the low permeability of the clay. Because of the time lag, an *e–p* curve has no definite physical meaning unless every point corresponds to a stage at which the void ratio has become practically constant at a constant load.

Figure 20 also shows the change in void ratio due to temporary removal of the load. The removal of the load is represented by the *decompression curve bc*, and the subsequent reapplication of load by the *recompression curve cd*. For clays *bc* represents the *swelling curve*. The area between the decompression and recompression curves is a *hysteresis loop*. Hysteresis loops for different soils differ only in slope and in width. In arithmetic plots they are concave upward, whereas in semilogarithmic

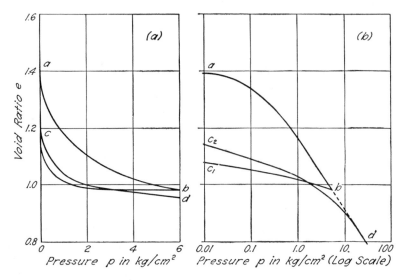

Fig. 21.   Relation between e and p for laterally confined dense sample consisting of 90 per cent sand and 10 per cent mica.

plots they are concave downward. Figure 21 shows a hysteresis loop for a dense mixture consisting of 90 per cent sand and 10 per cent mica. Hysteresis loops for remolded clays are very similar.

UNDISTURBED SAND

In nature all sands are more or less stratified. The compressibility of a stratified deposit in the direction of the bedding planes is somewhat smaller than that in the direction at right angles to them. In addition, most natural sands contain at least traces of cementing material, and above the water table they also contain some soil moisture. Both ingredients produce cohesion. Furthermore, some sands in the natural state have a relative density greater than that which can be obtained by any artificial means other than vibrations. Other sands in a natural state have a much more unstable structure than that of the loosest sand specimens which can be prepared in the laboratory. These facts suggest that the structure of sands in their natural state may be slightly different from that of the same sands in samples made in the laboratory. However, if the void ratios of the sands are the same in both states, the compressibilities are also likely to be approximately equal.

In connection with practical problems, the compressibility of confined strata of sand can usually be disregarded. As a consequence the compressibility of sand has not been extensively investigated.

Undisturbed Normally Loaded Clays

The following discussion is limited to clays that have never been subjected to a pressure greater than that which corresponds to the present overburden. Such clays are referred to as *normally loaded*. Experience indicates that the natural water content w of normally loaded clays is commonly close to the liquid limit L_w. If w is considerably lower than L_w, the sensitivity, Article 8, of the clay is likely to be exceptionally low. On the other hand, if w is considerably greater than L_w, the clay is likely to have a high sensitivity. In any event, normally loaded clays are always soft to a considerable depth below the surface.

In order to obtain information about the compressibility of a confined stratum of normally loaded clay located at depth D below the surface, we may test an undisturbed sample taken at that depth from a test shaft or boring. In Figure 22a the co-ordinates of point a represent the natural void ratio e_0 of the sample and the effective overburden pressure p_0 on the soil at depth D. The pressure p_0 is equal to the sum of the submerged weight of the soil located between depth D and the water table and the full weight of the soil and soil moisture located above the water level. It is expressed in weight per unit of area.

During the process of sampling, the overburden pressure on the clay that constitutes the sample is reduced to a very small value, although the water content remains almost unchanged. In Figure 22a this process is represented by the dash line ae_0. If the pressure on the sample is again increased by loading the sample in the consolidation device, the void ratio of ordinary clays with medium or low sensitivity decreases with increasing load as indicated by the line K_u. The curved portion of K_u represents a recompression curve such as curve c_2d in Figure 21b. It merges into a straight line which, if continued downward, intersects the horizontal axis $e = 0$ at a point f. The upward continuation of the straight part of K_u corresponds to the tangent db to the curve c_2d in Figure 21b. It intersects the horizontal line through a, Figure 22a, at point b. Experience shows that for normally loaded clays point b is always located on the left side of point a.

If we transform the clay sample into a thick paste by mixing it with water and then gradually consolidate the paste under an increasing pressure, we obtain the e–log p line K_r, Figure 22a. Below point c this line is almost straight. Although its slope is somewhat smaller than that of the straight part of K_u, its downward continuation intersects the horizontal axis near point f.

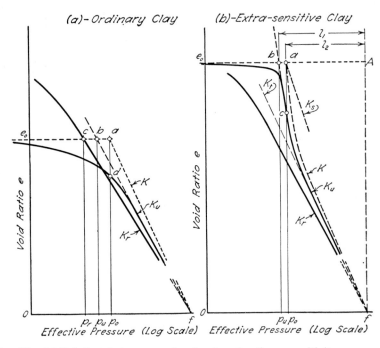

Fig. 22.   (a) Relations between e and p for clay of ordinary sensitivity corresponding to (K_r) remolded and (K_u) undisturbed states in the laboratory and (K) natural state in the field; (b) similar relations for extrasensitive clay.

The consolidation line K that represents the relation between e and log p in the field must pass through a. Yet, neither of the two laboratory lines K_u and K_r passes through this point. Hence, it is obvious that the line K can be determined only by some process of extrapolation from the results of the laboratory tests. If the two lines K_u and K_r are straight and intersect the horizontal axis near the same point f, it seems reasonable to assume that the e–log p curve for the soil in the field is also a straight line that passes through a and if continued downward, also intersects the horizontal axis at point f. The line so obtained is referred to as the *field consolidation line*. If no undisturbed samples are available, point f can be determined with sufficient accuracy from the e–log p curve for a remolded sample, K_r in Figure 22a, provided the load on the sample is increased to at least 20 kg per sq cm.

The value of the ratio p_u/p_0 between the pressures represented by the abscissas of b and a, Figure 22a, indicates the degree to which the structure of the sample has been disturbed. It ranges from about 0.3 to 0.7, with an average value of 0.5. A considerable scattering from the average value is characteristic even for samples taken with the same tool from the same boring. Hence, it seems that the value p_u/p_0 depends to a considerable extent on accidental factors, such as variations in the sensitivity of the clay and whether the test specimen was taken from the soil in the lower, middle, or upper part of the sampling spoon.

For undisturbed samples of ordinary clays, the e–log p curve K_u, Figure 22a, is roughly parabolic. However, the corresponding curve for extrasensitive clays has the shape indicated by K_u in Figure 22b. It remains nearly horizontal until the pressure on the sample becomes almost equal to the overburden pressure p_0, whereupon it turns downward quite abruptly. As the intensity of pressure is increased, the slope of the curve again decreases appreciably until finally the curve passes into an inclined straight line K_t. The shape of this e–log p curve suggests that the structure of the corresponding clay is abnormally sensitive to a relatively rapid increase of the load on the clay. If the pressure on such a clay increases extremely slowly, the corresponding decrease of the void ratio is probably much smaller, as indicated by the dash curve K_s. Otherwise, the water content of thick normally loaded strata of clays of this type would decrease rapidly with increasing depth, but no such phenomenon has ever been observed. However, a relatively rapid increase of the load on the clay due to the construction of a building or a fill may produce a greater compression. The extreme possibility is indicated by the steeply descending dash curve K. Since the real shape of the field consolidation line is not yet known, it is advisable to assume that it has a steep initial tangent like curve K.

The approximate shape of curve K for an extrasensitive clay can be determined by the following procedure. The point b on the ine ae_0 is located by extending in an upward direction the tangent to curve K_u at the point of inflection c. Point f, on the horizontal axis $e = 0$, is located by extending downward the straight part of K_u. Finally, a vertical line is traced through f which intersects the horizontal line ae_0 at A. The curve K is constructed such that for any value of e the ratio between the horizontal distance from K to fA and the distance from K_u to fA is equal to

$$\frac{l_2}{l_1} = \frac{aA}{bA}$$

The curve K_u can be obtained only by testing an undisturbed sample. If the sample is badly disturbed, or remolded and mixed with enough water to transform the clay into a thick paste, the e–log p curve K_r for the remolded material resembles in every respect the e–log p curve K_r, Figure 22a, for ordinary clays. It is practically straight over a wide range of pressure, and its slope is slightly less than that of the tangent K_t to the lower part of the curve K_u in Figure 22b. In other words, the disturbance of the structure of the clay obliterates the properties which cause the sharp bend in the curve K_u below point b in Figure 22b. Therefore, the information required for constructing the field consolidation line for extrasensitive clays can be obtained only from consolidation tests on undisturbed samples.

The field consolidation lines K in Figures 22a and b represent the basis for the computation of the settlement of structures located above confined strata of normally loaded clay. The weight of a fill or of a structure increases the pressure on the clay from the overburden pressure p_0 to the value $p_0 + \Delta p$. The corresponding void ratio decreases from e_0 to e. Hence, for the range in pressure from p_0 to $p_0 + \Delta p$, we may write

$$e_0 - e = \Delta e = a_v \Delta p$$

The value,

$$a_v(\text{cm}^2/\text{gm}) = \frac{e_0 - e}{\Delta p(\text{gm}/\text{cm}^2)} \tag{13.1}$$

represents the *coefficient of compressibility* for the range p_0 to $p_0 + \Delta p$. For a given difference in pressure, the value of the coefficient of compressibility decreases as the pressure increases. The decrease in porosity Δn per unit of the original volume of the soil, corresponding to a decrease in void ratio Δe, may be obtained by means of equation 7.2. The resulting expression is

$$\Delta n = \frac{\Delta e}{1 + e_0}$$

in which e_0 is the initial void ratio. Therefore

$$\Delta n = \frac{a_v}{1 + e_0} \Delta p = m_v \Delta p \tag{13.2}$$

in which

$$m_v(\text{cm}^2/\text{gm}) = \frac{a_v(\text{cm}^2/\text{gm})}{1 + e_0} \tag{13.3}$$

is known as the *coefficient of volume compressibility*. It represents the compression of the clay, per unit of original thickness, due to a unit increase of the pressure. If H is the thickness of a bed of clay under a pressure p, an increase of the pressure from p to $p + \Delta p$ reduces the thickness of the stratum by

$$S = H \cdot \Delta p \cdot m_v \tag{13.4}$$

The field consolidation line K for ordinary clays appears in a semilogarithmic diagram as a straight line, as shown in Figure 22a. This line can be represented by the equation,

$$e = e_0 - C_c \log_{10} \frac{p_0 + \Delta p}{p_0} \tag{13.5}$$

in which C_c (dimensionless) is the *compression index*. It is equal to the tangent of the slope angle of the straight part of line K. In contrast to a_v and m_v, which decrease rapidly with increasing values of the pressure p_0, the value C_c is a constant, and equation 13.5 which contains this constant is valid within a fairly large range of pressure.

In a semilogarithmic plot, the decompression curve, such as bc_1 in Figure 21b, is also fairly straight over a wide range of pressure. If the pressure is reduced from p to $p - \Delta p$, the corresponding decompression curve can be expressed by the equation,

$$e = e_1 + C_s \log_{10} \frac{p_0 + \Delta p}{p_0} \tag{13.5a}$$

in which C_s (dimensionless) is the *swelling index*. It is a measure of the volume increase due to the removal of pressure.

By combining equation 13.5 with equations 13.1 and 13.3, we obtain

$$a_v = \frac{C_c}{\Delta p} \log_{10} \frac{p_0 + \Delta p}{p_0} \tag{13.6}$$

and

$$m_v = \frac{C_c}{\Delta p (1 + e_0)} \log_{10} \frac{p_0 + \Delta p}{p_0} \tag{13.7}$$

Substituting the value of m_v into equation 13.4, we find that the compression S of a confined stratum of normally loaded ordinary clay is

$$S = H \frac{C_c}{1 + e_0} \log_{10} \frac{p_0 + \Delta p}{p_0} \tag{13.8}$$

If a clay is remolded, its e–log p curve changes from K, Figure 22, to K_r. Since the line K_r is straight over a large range of pressure, it can be represented by the equation,

$$e = e_0 - C_c' \log_{10} \frac{p_0 + \Delta p}{p_0} \tag{13.9}$$

which is an analogue to equation 13.5. The symbol C_c', which represents the compression index for the clay in a remolded state, is equal to the tangent of the slope angle of the straight part of the line K_r. The values of C_c' for different clays increase consistently with increasing liquid limit as shown in Figure 23. The abscissas of the points shown in the diagram represent the liquid limit L_w, and the ordinates the corresponding values of C_c' for different clays. The samples were selected at random.

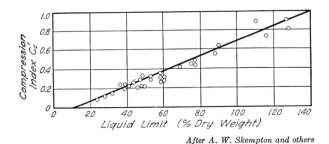

After A. W. Skempton and others

Fig. 23.   Relation between liquid limit and compression index for remolded clays.

They came from different parts of the world, and the assortment includes both ordinary and extrasensitive clays. All the points are located close to a straight line with the equation,

$$C_c' = 0.007\,(L_w - 10\%) \tag{13.10}$$

in which L_w is the liquid limit in per cent of the dry weight of the clay. The scattering of the real values of C_c' from those determined by equation 13.10 is about ± 30 per cent.

For an ordinary clay of medium or low sensitivity, both the e–log p lines K_r and K are straight over a wide range of pressure, and the value of C_c corresponding to the field consolidation line K appears to be roughly equal to 1.30 C_c', equation 13.10. That is,

$$C_c \sim 1.30 C_c' = 0.009(L_w - 10\%) \tag{13.11}$$

If the value of C_c for a given layer of clay is known, the compression of the layer due to a surcharge Δp can be computed by means of equation 13.8. For normally loaded clays with low or moderate sensitivity the value of C_c can be estimated roughly by means of equation 13.11. Hence, the order of magnitude of the settlement of a structure located above a stratum of such clay can be determined without making any tests other than liquid-limit tests.

On the other hand, if a clay is extrasensitive, its field consolidation curve K, Figure 22b, is not straight, and the slope of the upper part of the line may be several times that of K_r. For such clays, the approximate method of computation based on equation 13.11 furnishes merely a lower limiting value for the compression of the clay. The real compression may be several times greater. Fortunately clays of this type are rather rare. They include the clays of Mexico City which are of volcanic origin, certain types of marine clays in southeastern Canada and in the Scandinavian countries, and various highly organic clays. If a clay has a liquid limit greater than 100 per cent, if its natural water content at a depth of more than 20 or 30 ft below the surface is greater than the liquid limit, or if it contains a high percentage of organic material, it is likely to have the consolidation characteristics illustrated in Figure 22b. The sensitivity S_t, equation 8.1, of these clays is greater than about 4, whereas that of ordinary clays is less. If the sensitivity of a clay is greater than 8, it is fairly certain that the clay will have the consolidation characteristics illustrated by Figure 22b.

UNDISTURBED PRECOMPRESSED CLAYS

A clay is said to be precompressed if it has ever been subjected to a pressure in excess of its present overburden pressure. The temporary excess pressure may have been caused by the weight of soil strata that

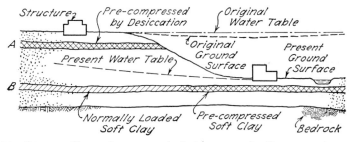

FIG. 24.   Diagram illustrating two geological processes leading to precompression of clays.

were later eroded, by the weight of ice that later melted, or by desiccation due to temporary exposure. If the excess pressure Δp_0 was smaller than about 4 kg per sq cm, the clay may still be soft. If Δp_0 was much greater, however, the clay is stiff.

Two of the processes which lead to the precompression of clays are illustrated in Figure 24. All of the strata located above bedrock were deposited in a lake at a time when the water level was located above the level of the present high ground. When parts of the strata were removed by erosion, the water content of the clay in the right-hand portion of stratum B increased slightly, whereas that of the left-hand portion decreased considerably because of the lowering of the water table. Nevertheless, with respect to the present overburden, the clay on the right-hand side is a precompressed soft clay, and that on the left-hand side is a normally loaded soft clay.

While the water table descended from its original to its final position below the floor of the eroded valley, the sand strata above and below the upper clay layer A became drained. As a consequence, the layer A gradually dried out. In Article 21 it is shown that such a process of desiccation constitutes the mechanical equivalent of consolidation under load. Therefore, layer A is said to be *precompressed by desiccation.*

If a bed of clay is formed by sedimentation in an open body of water subject to seasonal or cyclic variations in water level, the highest portions of the surface of the sediment may emerge from time to time. Beneath these areas dry crusts are formed by desiccation. After the surface is flooded again, the crusts are buried under freshly deposited sediments, but their water content remains abnormally low. Hence, they constitute layers or lenses of precompressed clay located between layers of normally loaded clay.

If a layer of stiff clay is located above a layer of soft clay of the same type, it is certain that the upper layer has been precompressed by desiccation. Furthermore, if the upper layer was exposed to the atmosphere for a long time, it is also likely to be discolored by oxidation. For example, in the Chicago area a thick layer of soft normally loaded clay of grayish color is covered by a layer of stiff precompressed yellow and gray clay between 2 and 6 ft thick. Precompressed layers of glacial clay located between normally loaded layers of soft clay of the same type have been encountered in southern Sweden.

The influence of precompression on the relation between void ratio and pressure is shown in Figure 25. Both diagrams are plotted to a natural scale. Figure 25a represents the relation between e and p for the normally loaded part of the clay stratum B in Figure 24, and Figure 25b shows the corresponding relation for the precompressed part of the same stratum. In both diagrams point a' represents the state of the clay before erosion started. At that time the water table was located above stratum A, and the effective overburden pressure for the entire stratum B was equal to p_0' per unit of area. Since erosion was associated with a lowering of the water table at almost constant total overburden pressure, the effective overburden pressure on the left-hand part of stratum B increased from p_0' to p_0, and the point that represents the state of the clay, Figure 25a, moved from a' to a.

In the right-hand part of stratum B the lowering of the water table took place simultaneously with the removal of most of the overburden.

Hence, the effective pressure on the right-hand part of the stratum decreased from p_0' to p_0, and the clay passed from state a', Figure 25b, into state b. The transition was associated with a slight increase of the void ratio.

An increase of Δp of the effective pressure on the normally loaded part of stratum B, caused by such an operation as the construction of a large heavy building on the high ground, reduces the void ratio of the clay located beneath the building by Δe_n, Figure 25a, and the clay passes from

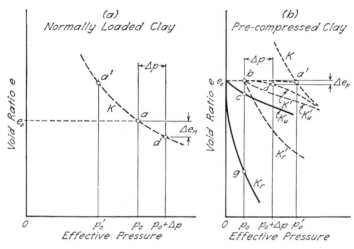

FIG. 25.   (a) Field relation between e and p for normally loaded clay; (b) relations between e and p for similar clay in a precompressed state.

state a into state d. An increase of the effective pressure on the precompressed right-hand part of stratum B by the same amount Δp reduces the void ratio of the clay by Δe_p, Figure 25b, and the clay passes from state b into state d.

If disturbed samples were taken from both parts of stratum B, they would probably create the impression that the precompressed clay is softer than the normally loaded clay, because the water content of the precompressed part of the stratum at the time of sampling would be appreciably greater than that of the normally loaded part. Nevertheless, if Δp is smaller than about one half of $p_0' - p_0$, the compression Δe_p of the precompressed stratum will be much smaller than the compression Δe_n of the normally loaded stratum. This is due to the fact that the point which represents the state of the normally loaded clay in the ground advances from a to d, Figure 25a, on a curve representing the decrease of void ratio due to a steadily increasing pressure, whereas the corresponding point for the precompressed clay moves on a recompression curve from b to d, Figure 25b. As shown in Figures 20 and 21, the slope of a recompression curve is very much smaller than that of a direct compression curve.

Some conception of the amount of compression that the precompressed part of stratum B would experience under the weight of the building can be obtained from the results of consolidation tests on representative samples of this part. However, because of the precompression, the e–p curve for the soil in the field is likely to differ to a considerable extent from that obtained by means of laboratory tests. The magnitude of the difference depends on the degree of disturbance of the samples.

If the sample is badly disturbed, the laboratory relation between e and p resembles the steep curve K_r in Figure 25b. By adding the distance bg to the ordinates of this curve we obtain the curve $K_r{}'$ which passes through point b representing the state of the clay in the ground. However, experience shows that the curve $K_r{}'$ has no resemblance to the field consolidation line bd.

If the consolidation test is made on an undisturbed sample carefully carved out of the ground in a shaft, the curve K_u is obtained. By adding the distance cb to the ordinates of this curve we obtain the curve $K_u{}'$ which passes through b. Although the slope of $K_u{}'$ is much smaller than that of $K_r{}'$, it has been found that, if Δp is smaller than about one half of $p_0{}' - p_0$, the compression of the clay computed on the basis of $K_u{}'$ is still two to five times greater than the actual compression of the clay in the field. Hence, extrapolation from test results to field conditions is very uncertain, irrespective of the care with which sampling operations are carried out.

Computation of the relation between e and p for a clay with a given liquid limit on the basis of equation 13.11 leads to a curve through b which is steeper than $K_r{}'$. The ordinates of this curve with reference to a horizontal line through b are equal to at least twice the ordinates of $K_u{}'$, which in turn are two to five times greater than those of the field e–p curve K'. Hence, the use of equation 13.11 for estimating the compressibility of a precompressed clay leads to values between four and ten or more times greater than the correct ones. Since the same equation furnishes reasonably accurate values when applied to normally loaded clays, it is obvious that the load history of a clay is of outstanding practical importance.

Under the conditions illustrated by Figure 24, the maximum consolidation pressure $p_0{}'$ can be estimated rather accurately on the basis of geological evidence. The geology and physiography of the site leave no doubt that the original ground surface was located at or above the level of the present high ground and that the water table was fairly close to the original ground surface. However, if the geological evidence is not unmistakable, or if the precompression was caused by the weight of an ice sheet which melted without leaving any evidence of its thickness, a geological estimate of the maximum consolidation pressure is very uncertain. In such instances, the only remaining procedure for gaining at least a general conception of the value of $p_0{'}$ is to make an estimate based on the results of laboratory tests.

Several methods have been proposed for determining the value of the maximum consolidation pressure from the results of laboratory tests. The one most commonly used is illustrated by Figure 26. This figure shows the e–log p curve for an undisturbed clay sample. Through point c, at which the radius of curvature is a minimum, a horizontal line is drawn. The bisector of the angle α between this line and the tangent to K_u at c intersects the upward continuation of the straight lower part of K_u at point d. The abscissa of d is assumed to be equal to $p_0{'}$.

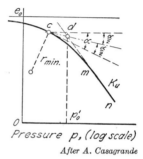

After A. Casagrande

Fig. 26. Diagram illustrating commonly used graphical construction for estimating value of maximum consolidation pressure.

The method illustrated by Figure 26 is based on the observed effect of cyclic loading on the void ratio of undisturbed clay samples. However, in nature, the application of the pressure $p_0{'}$ requires several centuries, rather than a few hours or days. The effect of the rate of loading on the corresponding compression can be very important. Therefore, it is not surprising that the results obtained by means of the graphical procedure, Figure 26, are as a rule rather unsatisfactory. If a sample of a normally loaded clay is tested, the value $p_0{'}$ obtained by the graphical procedure should be equal to the present overburden pressure. Yet, it is generally very much smaller, and the difference between the real and the calculated values for samples from any one drill hole commonly increases in a general way with increasing depth. For heavily precompressed clay the agreement between the two values appears to be better, but conclusive evidence is not yet available. In any event, the results of the investigations as a rule leave a wide margin for interpretation.

However, it is commonly possible to decide without recourse to the graphical method illustrated by Figure 26 whether or not a clay is heavily precompressed, and this information is usually all that is required for practical purposes. If a clay is normally loaded, the points b, Figure 22a, are invariably located to the left of the points a. Hence, if several undisturbed samples from a clay stratum have been tested, and if all of the points *b* obtained from the test results are so located, the value of p_0' is certainly not much greater than the present overburden pressure, and the effect of the precompression on the settlement can be disregarded. On the other hand, if the precompression pressure was considerably greater than the present overburden pressure, at least some of the points *b* are located to the right of *a*. In this event the settlement of the structure to be erected above the clay will be small compared to that predicted on the basis of the test results, because the relation between the laboratory and the field consolidation curves for such a clay resembles that between the curves K_u' and K' in Figure 25*b*.

If part of a normally loaded clay stratum has been precompressed by desiccation, the water content of the precompressed layers is relatively low. Hence, the location and thickness of these layers can be inferred from the water-content profile. In the settlement computation, the precompressed layers can be considered incompressible.

SUMMARY OF METHODS FOR EVALUATING THE COMPRESSIBILITY OF NATURAL SOIL STRATA

If the soil beneath a structure contains layers of sand or stiff clay alternating with layers of soft clay, the compressibility of the sand and stiff-clay strata can be disregarded.

The compressibility of layers of clay depends primarily on two factors: the liquid limit of the clay, and the magnitude of the greatest pressure that has acted on the clay since its deposition. If this pressure has never exceeded the present effective overburden pressure, the layer is said to be normally loaded. Otherwise, it is said to be precompressed.

The compressibility of a normally loaded layer of clay with a known liquid limit can be estimated roughly by means of the empirical equation 13.11, provided the clay has no unusual properties. However, if the clay has a liquid limit above 100, if its natural water content at a depth of 20 or 30 ft is greater than the liquid limit, or if it contains a high percentage of organic material, the compressibility of the layer may be several times as great as that computed by means of equation 13.11. Hence, if a building is to be constructed above a layer of such an exceptional clay, it is advisable to determine the compressibility of the clay by means of consolidation tests on undisturbed samples.

The compressibility of a precompressed clay depends not only on the liquid limit of the clay but also on the ratio $\Delta p/(p_0' - p_0)$, in which Δp is the pressure added by the structure to the present overburden pressure p_0, and p_0' is the maximum pressure that has ever acted on the clay. If this ratio is less than 50 per cent, the compressibility of the clay is likely to be from 10 to 25 per cent that of a similar clay in a normally loaded state. With increasing values of the ratio the effect of the pre-compression on the compressibility of the clay decreases. For values greater than 100 per cent the influence of the precompression on the settlement of the structure can be disregarded.

The precompression of a clay can be due to the weight of soil strata that were removed by erosion, to the weight of ice that melted away, or to desiccation. If the precompression is due to a load that has been removed, the excess pressure that acted on the soil was the same at every point along a vertical line below the ground surface. However, if it was due to desiccation, the excess pressure probably decreased in a downward direction from the former surface of evaporation, and the total depth of the precompressed layer may not exceed a few feet.

The compressibility of heavily precompressed beds of clay is usually irrelevant, unless the engineer is required to construct above a thick bed of stiff clay an unusually large and heavy structure that would be dam-aged even by moderate differential settlement. If the problem warrants a settlement computation, consolidation tests must be made on undis-turbed samples, preferably taken from test shafts. The sources and the importance of the errors involved in settlement computations based on the results of tests on such samples have been discussed on page 70.

REFERENCES

13.1. P. C. RUTLEDGE, Relation of Undisturbed Sampling to Laboratory Testing, *Trans. ASCE.*, Vol 109 (1944), p 1155. With discussions. Review of present methods for interpreting the results of consolidation tests.

13.2. A. W. SKEMPTON, Notes on the Compressibility of Clays, *Quart. J. Geol. Soc. London*, Vol C (1944), pp 119–135. Deals with statistical relations between the Atterberg limits and consolidation characteristics of clays.

PROBLEMS

1. A stratum of clay with an average liquid limit of 45 per cent is 25 ft thick. Its surface is located at a depth of 35 ft below the present ground surface. The natural water content of the clay is 40 per cent, and the unit weight of the solid clay particles is 2.78 gm per cu cm. Between the ground surface and the clay, the subsoil consists of fine sand. The water table is located at a depth of 15 ft below the ground surface. The average submerged unit weight of the sand is 65 lb per cu ft, and the unit weight of the moist sand located above the water table is 110 lb per cu ft. From geological evidence, it is known that the clay is normally loaded. The weight of the building that will be constructed on the sand above the clay increases the present overburden pressure on the clay by 1.2 tons per sq ft. Estimate the average settlement of the building.

Ans. 10 in.

2. The clay stratum *B* shown in Figure 24 has a thickness of 25 ft. Its surface is located at a depth of 30 ft below the average water level in the river and 35 ft below

the present valley floor. The surface of the high ground adjoining the valley is located 150 ft above the present valley floor, and the original water table was 5 ft above this surface. The clay is covered with sand having the same unit weight as that in the preceding problem. Compute the maximum consolidation pressure for the right-hand part of the stratum.

Ans.   4.76 tons per sq ft in excess of the present overburden pressure.

3. The building shown on the valley floor in Figure 24 increases the average pressure on the clay stratum by 1.2 tons per sq ft. The average liquid limit of the clay is 45 per cent. The other data concerning the thickness of the stratum and the location of the site are the same as those in problem 2. The average natural water content of the clay is 35 per cent, and the unit weight of the solid clay particles is 2.78 gm per cu cm. Estimate the upper and lower limits for the settlement of the building.

Ans.   Not more than 25 per cent of 11.6 in., or 2.9 in., and probably not less than 10 per cent of 11.6 in., or 1.2 in.

ART. 14. CONSOLIDATION OF CLAY LAYERS

In the preceding article, it was mentioned that the compression of clay due to an increase in load proceeds very slowly. The source of a small part of the delay is the gradual adjustment of the position of the grains to the

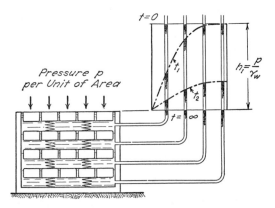

Fig. 27.   Device for demonstrating mechanics of process of consolidation.

increase in pressure. This source is common to both sand and clay. However, in clays, the major part of the delay is due to the fact that clays possess very low permeability. As a consequence, a long time is required to drain out the excess water. The gradual decrease of the water content at constant load is known as *consolidation*.

The mechanics of the delaying effect of low permeability on the compression of an elastic layer under constant load can be demonstrated by means of the device shown in Figure 27. It consists of a cylindrical vessel that contains a series of pistons separated by springs. The space between the pistons is filled with water, and the pistons are perforated. When a pressure p per unit of area is applied to the surface of the uppermost piston, the height of the springs is at the first instant unchanged, because sufficient time has not yet elapsed for the escape of any water from between the pistons. Since the springs cannot carry load until their height decreases, the load p per unit of area must at first be carried entirely by an excess hydrostatic pressure $h_1 \gamma_w = p$ in the water. At this stage, the water in each of the piezometric tubes stands at the height h_1.

After a short time t_1 has elapsed, some water will have escaped from the upper compartment, but the lowest compartment will still be practically full. The decrease in volume of the upper compartment is accompanied by a compression of the upper set of springs. Therefore, the upper springs begin to carry a portion of the pressure p, whereupon the water pressure in the upper compartments decreases. In the lower compartments conditions are still unaltered. At this stage the water levels in the piezometric tubes are located on a curve t_1 that merges into a horizontal line at elevation h_1. The corresponding compression, or decrease in thickness of the set of pistons, is S_1. Any curve, such as t_1, which connects the water levels in the piezometric tubes at a given instant, is known as an *isochrone*. At a later stage the water levels in the tubes are located on the curve t_2. Finally, after a very long time the excess hydrostatic pressure becomes very small, and the corresponding final compression is $S = S_\infty$. For a clay the final compression is determined by the initial thickness of the layer and by equation 13.4. The ratio,

$$U(\%) = \frac{S}{S_\infty} \tag{14.1}$$

represents the *degree of consolidation* at the time t.

The rate of consolidation of the system of pistons and springs can be computed on the basis of the principles of hydraulics. The relation between the degree of consolidation of such a system and the elapsed time is indicated by the solid curves in Figures 28a and 28b.

The rate of consolidation of a clay sample may be investigated in the laboratory by means of the confined compression test described in Article 13. Up to a degree of consolidation of about 80 per cent, the shape of the experimental time–consolidation curves is very similar to that of the curves for spring-piston systems. However, instead of approaching horizontal asymptotes, the curves for clay continue on a gentle slope, as indicated in Figure 28 by dash lines. The progressive consolidation represented by the vertical distance between the full and the dash curves is known as the *secondary time effect*. It seems to be due to the gradual adjustment of the soil structure to stress, combined with the resistance offered by the viscosity of the adsorbed layers to a slippage between grains. In the system of pistons and springs to which the full curves correspond, the lag in compression is due only to the resistance against rapid escape of the excess water.

The results of consolidation tests performed on clay samples have disclosed several simple relationships. For a given clay the time required to reach a given degree of consolidation increases in proportion to the square of the thickness of the layer. For equally thick layers of different clays the time required to reach a given degree of consolidation in-

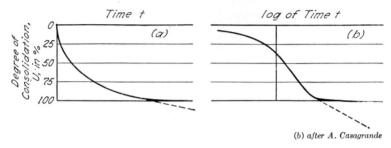

(b) *after A. Casagrande*

Fig. 28.   Time–consolidation curves.   Solid lines represent relation for mechanical device illustrated in Figure 27.   Dash lines represent relation for clay sample with similar consolidation characteristics.

creases in direct proportion to m_v/k, where m_v is the coefficient of volume compressibility, equation 13.3, and k is the coefficient of permeability. The ratio,

$$c_v(\text{cm}^2/\text{sec}) = \frac{k}{m_v}\frac{1}{\gamma_w} \tag{14.2}$$

is known as the *coefficient of consolidation*. With decreasing void ratio, both k and m_v decrease rapidly, but the ratio k/m_v is fairly constant over a considerable range of pressure. The values of c_v for different clays decrease in a general way with the liquid limit, as shown by the diagram, Figure 29. In this figure, the abscissas represent values of the liquid limit, and the ordinates the corresponding values of the coefficient of consolidation of undisturbed samples of clays under normal pressures between 1 and 4 kg per sq cm. The figure shows that the coefficient of consolidation for clays with a given liquid limit varies within a wide range.

Recent experimental investigations indicate that the value of the coefficient of consolidation, equation 14.2, increases at a given initial void ratio e_0 with increasing magnitude of the load increment that produces the consolidation. Hence, in the consolidation tests that serve as a basis for estimating the rate of consolidation of a clay stratum under the weight of a superimposed structure, the increment of load applied to the sample after a pressure equal to the overburden pressure has been reached should be of the same order of magnitude as the load per unit of area on the base of the structure. Since this is common practice, no

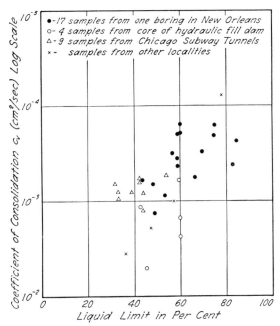

Fig. 29.   Relation between liquid limit and coefficient of consolidation for undisturbed samples of clay.

conspicuous discrepancies between estimated and observed rates of settlement have so far been noticed. The values of c_v given in Figure 29 were obtained by means of standard tests.

If the pressure in a natural clay stratum is relieved, for instance by the excavation of a shaft or tunnel, the corresponding volume expansion of the clay commonly does not begin for a week or more after the excavation is completed. In a few instances it has even been observed that the consolidation of such strata under the influence of superimposed loads did not start for a few weeks after the load was applied. These delays in the reaction of clay to a change in stress, like the secondary time effect and the influence on c_v of the magnitude of the load increment, cannot be explained by means of the simple mechanical concept on which the theory of consolidation is based. Their characteristics and conditions for occurrence can be investigated only by observation.

In spite of the radical simplifications involved, the theory of consolidation serves a useful purpose, because it permits at least a rough estimate of the rate of settlement due to consolidation, on the basis of the results of laboratory tests.Therefore, the theory is presented briefly in Part B, Article 41.

PROBLEMS

1. The results of a consolidation test on a sample of clay having a thickness of 0.75 in. indicate that half the ultimate compression occurs in the first 5 min. Under similar drainage conditions, how long will be required for a building on a 12-ft layer of the same clay to experience half its final settlement? (Neglect the secondary time effect.)

   Ans. $t = 128$ days.

2. The void ratio of clay A decreased from 0.572 to 0.505 under a change in pressure from 1.2 to 1.8 kg per sq cm. The void ratio of clay B decreased from 0.612 to 0.597 under the same increment of pressure. The thickness of sample A was 1.5 times that of B. Nevertheless, the time required for 50 per cent consolidation was three times longer for sample B than for sample A. What is the ratio of the coefficient of permeability of A to that of B?

   Ans.   31 to 1.

3. The subsoil of a building consists of a thick deposit of sand that contains, at about mid-thickness, one layer of soft clay 10 ft thick. A laboratory sample of the clay, drained at both top and bottom, reaches 80 per cent consolidation in 1 hr. The sample is 1 in. thick. How much time will elapse before the degree of consolidation of the clay stratum becomes equal to 80 per cent?   *600 days*

ART. 15.   SHEARING RESISTANCE OF SOILS

INTRODUCTION

If the shearing stress in a body of soil exceeds a certain critical value, the soil fails. Depending on the conditions of soil support and loading, the failure may cause a slide, the collapse of a retaining wall, or the sinking of a footing into the ground. Since it is important to avoid such accidents, the factors that determine the shearing resistance of soils have received considerable attention for more than a century.

METHODS OF INVESTIGATION

The simplest, oldest, and most common method for investigating the shearing resistance of soils is known as the *direct-shear test* or, more briefly, as the shear test. It is performed by means of the *box-shear* or *direct-shear* apparatus illustrated by Figure 30. The apparatus consists of a lower frame that is stationary and an upper one that can be moved in a horizontal direction. The sample is located between two porous stones which serve as drains during the consolidation of saturated samples. The surfaces of contact between the sample and the porous stones are grooved, as shown in the figure, to prevent slippage between sample and stones during the process of shearing.

Before the sample is subjected to shear, a vertical load p per unit of area is applied to the upper stone. Both the application of the load and the subsequent application of a shearing force produce a change in the void ratio of the sample. If the voids of the sample are filled with air, this change takes place almost instantaneously. On the other hand, if the sample is saturated, the resistance against the flow of water through the voids of the soil retards the change. The water content of the soil at the instant of failure depends on the degree of consolidation of the sample under the vertical load before the shearing force is applied, on the permeability of the soil, on the rate at which the shear is increased, and on the drainage conditions. The tests for investigating the influence of these factors on the relation between the vertical load and the shearing resistance are known as slow tests, consolidated-quick tests, and quick tests. In a *slow test* both the load

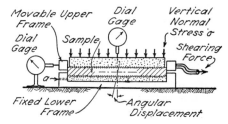

FIG. 30.   Direct-shear apparatus.

and, subsequently, the shearing force are applied so slowly that the water content of even a fully saturated soil with low permeability can adapt itself almost completely to the change in stress. In a *consolidated-quick test* complete consolidation under the vertical load is followed by shear at constant water content. In a *quick test* the water content of the sample remains practically unchanged during the application of both the vertical load and the shearing force.

With box-shear apparatus, Figure 30, quick and consolidated-quick tests can be made only on clay samples, because the other soils are so permeable that even a very rapid increase of the stresses in the sample may cause at least a perceptible change of the water content. Slow tests can be made on any soil. The consolidation of the sample under the vertical load is observed by means of a dial gage that registers the vertical movement of the upper porous stone, as shown in Figure 30. During the shear test the same dial indicates whether the shearing force causes an increase or a decrease of the volume of the sample.

The shearing force is applied by pulling the upper frame of the shear box, and the corresponding displacement between the upper and lower frames is measured. During a test made by means of the common type of box-shear apparatus, the shearing force is applied by increments. If provision is made to increase the force continuously at a suitable rate, the apparatus is said to have *stress control.* On the other hand, if the displacement is increased in a specified manner and the pull required to produce the increase is measured, the apparatus is said to have *strain control.*

As the displacement of the upper frame increases, the force required to increase the displacement increases and approaches a maximum which is referred to as the *peak value.* Then it commonly decreases and approaches an *ultimate value,* as shown by the upper curve in Figure 31*b.* Reliable information on the relation between shear stress and strain beyond the state corresponding to the peak value can be obtained only by means of shear apparatus equipped with strain control.

In practice the box-shear apparatus has several inherent disadvantages. Foremost among these are the change in area of the surface of sliding as the test progresses, the unequal distribution of the shearing stresses over the potential surface of sliding, and the rapidity with which the water content of saturated samples of many types of soil changes as a result of a change in stress.

While the horizontal displacement of the upper frame increases, the area of contact between the upper and the lower half of the sample decreases. Therefore, even with strain-controlled apparatus, reliable information concerning the ultimate shearing resistance of the sample cannot be obtained. Furthermore, the shear failure does not take place simultaneously at every point of the potential surface of sliding. It starts at the two edges and proceeds toward the center. Therefore the peak value of the shearing resistance indicated by the test results is lower than the real peak value. These two shortcomings of the box-shear apparatus have been eliminated by constructing ring-shear apparatus in which the sample has the shape of a ring.[15.1]

However, neither the box- nor the ring-shear apparatus permits reliable performance of quick and consolidated-quick shear tests on soils other than clays. In order to make such tests without the risk of excessive error, triaxial compression apparatus (Article 16) must be used.

The following discussions of the relation between pressure and shearing resistance for soils are based chiefly on the results of ring-shear and triaxial-compression tests. However, for the sake of simplicity, the data are presented as if they had been obtained by means of an ideal box-shear apparatus that possesses all the desirable features of the more elaborate devices without their shortcomings. Hence, when the results of consolidated-quick tests on saturated sand are described, the reader should remember that in practice the data can be obtained only by means of triaxial-compression tests.

SHEARING RESISTANCE OF DRY SAND

In Figure 31b the ordinates represent the shearing stress on the potential surface of sliding in a box-shear sample, and the abscissas the displacement of the upper frame of the apparatus, Figure 30, with reference to the lower one. If the sample consists of loose sand, the shearing stress increases with increasing displacement until failure ensues (curve K_l). The test is repeated with different pressures p. By

plotting the shearing stresses s corresponding to the state of failure in the different tests against the pressure p, a straight line C_l, Figure 31a, is obtained. This line may be represented by the equation,

$$s = p \tan \phi \qquad (15.1)$$

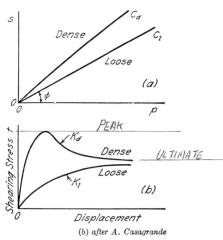

(a)

(b)

(b) *after A. Casagrande*

FIG. 31. (a) Results of direct-shear tests on sand; (b) stress–strain curves obtained from direct-shear tests on sand.

The angle ϕ is called the *angle of internal friction*, and tan ϕ is the *coefficient of internal friction*.

If the sand is dense, the shear failure of the sample is preceded by a decrease of the shearing stress from a peak value to an ultimate value lower than the peak value, as shown by the curve K_d in Figure 31b. The shape of the curve K_d suggests that an increase of the strain beyond that corresponding to the peak value is associated with a progressive disintegration of the structure of the sand. Line C_d in Figure 31a represents the relation between pressure and the corresponding peak value of the shearing resistance of dense sand. In contrast to line C_l, which is straight, line C_d is slightly curved. However, for practical purposes the curvature can be disregarded. The average slope angle of the line C_d represents the angle of internal friction for dense sand.

For a given sand the angle ϕ increases with increasing relative density. For loose sand it is roughly equal to the *angle of repose*, defined as the angle between the horizontal and the slope of a heap produced by pouring dust-dry sand from a small elevation. Hence, the value of ϕ for the loose state can be determined without performing a shear test. Representative values of ϕ are given in Table 7.

The individual grains of some sands are interconnected by minute patches of cementing material such as calcium carbonate. The relation between the normal stress p and the shearing resistance s for such sands in either a dry or moist state can be expressed approximately by the equation,

$$s = c + p \tan \phi \tag{15.2}$$

The value c is called the *cohesion* of the sand. It depends only on the strength of the bond between the sand particles and is, therefore, a constant for the sand. Uncemented sands in a moist state also have a certain amount of cohesion, but, since this cohesion disappears upon immersion, it is referred to as *apparent cohesion*. The angle of internal

TABLE 7

REPRESENTATIVE VALUES OF ϕ FOR DRY SAND
Degrees

	Round Grains, Uniform	Angular Grains, Well Graded
Loose	28.5°	34°
Dense*	35°	46°

* Average of peak values at normal stresses between 0 and 3 kg per sq cm. With increasing normal stress, the value of ϕ is likely to decrease slightly, as shown in Figure 31a.

friction ϕ (equation 15.2) of a cemented sand or of a moist sand is approximately equal to that of the same sand, at the same void ratio, in a cohesionless state.

SHEARING RESISTANCE OF SATURATED SAND

The change in stress caused by pulling the upper frame of the shear box produces a change in the void ratio of the sand. Experience shows that the change in void ratio due to shear depends on both the vertical load and the relative density of the sand. At very low pressures the void ratio at failure is larger and at very high pressures it is smaller than the initial void ratio, whatever the relative density of the sand may be. At intermediate values of pressure the shearing force causes a decrease in the void ratio of loose sand and an increase in the void ratio of dense sand. In saturated sand a decrease of the void ratio is associated with an expulsion of pore water, and an increase with an absorption of water. The expansion of a soil due to shear at a constant value of the pressure is called *dilatancy*.

If the equilibrium of a large body of saturated fine sand in an embankment is disturbed, for instance by the rapid drawdown of the surface of an adjoining body of water, the change in water content of the fill lags behind the change in stress, because time is required for the water to flow from the interior to the surface of the embankment. For given dimensions of the body of sand and a given rate of change in stress, the lag in the adjustment of the water content increases with decreasing permeability of the sand.

If the lag is negligible, the conditions for the failure of the sand in the fill are identical with those associated with a slow-shear test on a saturated sample. On the other hand, if failure occurs before the water content of the fill is appreciably altered, the failure conditions correspond to

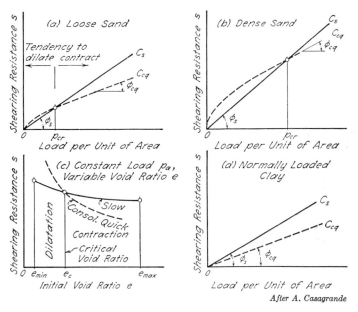

FIG. 32.   (*a* and *b*) Results of slow and consolidated-quick shear tests on saturated samples of loose and dense sand, respectively; (*c*) relation between shearing resistance *s* and initial void ratio *e* for saturated samples of sand after complete consolidation under given pressure p_a; (*d*) results of slow and consolidated-quick shear tests on normally loaded clay.

those that prevail during a consolidated-quick test. Hence the stress conditions for the failure of saturated sand fills are likely to be intermediate between those which determine the resistance of saturated samples against slow shear and those which determine the resistance against consolidated-quick shear.

The results of slow-shear tests on saturated samples are identical with those on the same sand at equal relative density in a dry state, except that the angle ϕ is likely to be 1° or 2° smaller for the saturated sand. The value of ϕ obtained from slow-shear tests on saturated samples is designated by the symbol ϕ_s (see Figures 32a and b).

[When a consolidated-quick-shear test is made, the shearing force is increased at such a rate that the sample fails before the water content has started to adapt itself to the change in stress. The effect of this condition on the shearing resistance depends on whether the increase of the shearing resistance involves a tendency toward a decrease or an increase of the void ratio. A tendency of the void ratio to decrease is associated with an excess hydrostatic pressure in the pore water. Since such a pressure carries part of the vertical load on the sample, the effective vertical pressure on the surface of sliding is smaller than the total vertical pressure, and the sample fails at a smaller shearing stress than does a similar sample submitted to a slow test. A tendency of the sample to expand (dilatancy) has the opposite effect.]

In Figure 32a the full line C_s represents the results of slow-shear tests on saturated samples of loose sand and the dash curve C_{cq} those of consolidated-quick tests on similar samples. At very low pressure the shearing stresses tend to produce dilatancy, whereas at high pressures they tend to cause a contraction. Therefore the line C_{cq} intersects the line C_s. At a pressure p_{cr} the rate of shear has no influence on the shearing resistance.

Figure 32b represents the results of similar tests on saturated samples of dense sand. The value of p_{cr} is very much greater for dense sand than for loose sand, but the general features of the two diagrams, Figures 32a and b, are identical. In both diagrams the slope of the dash curve C_{cq} decreases rapidly, and the curves approach straight lines with a slope angle ϕ_{cq}. The value ϕ_{cq} is referred to as the *consolidated-quick value* of the *angle of shearing resistance*. The few test data now available suggest that the average value of ϕ_{cq} is roughly equal to $2\phi_s/3$, and there is no reason to assume that it can be smaller than $\phi_s/2$. A shock can temporarily transform a mass of saturated sand with an inclined surface into a semiliquid material that flows out as if its angle of internal friction were almost equal to zero. However, failures of this type have no relation to the phenomena discussed in this article, because they are preceded by a sudden increase of the pore-water pressure under unaltered conditions of loading. No such increase has ever been observed during a shear or triaxial-compression test. The conditions which lead to failures of this type are discussed in Article 17.

In Figure 32c the abscissas represent the void ratio of saturated samples after complete consolidation under a given vertical pressure p_a. The ordinates represent the shearing resistance of the samples. The plain curve indicates the results of slow tests, and the dash curve those of consolidated-quick tests performed at the same pressure p_a. For dense sands having low initial void ratios the consolidated-quick-shear values are greater than the corresponding slow-shear values. For loose sands having high initial void ratios they are smaller. At a void ratio e_c the slow- and consolidated-quick-shear values are equal. The value e_c is known as the *critical void ratio* for the pressure p_a. At the critical void ratio, the rate of application of the shearing stress has no effect on the shearing resistance. At low values of p_a this condition is satisfied even by loose sand, Figure 32a, whereas at high values of p_a the relative density must be great, Figure 32b. Hence, it is obvious that the critical void ratio decreases with increasing values of p_a.

In all the saturated specimens to which Figures 32a to c refer, the initial pore-water pressure u_w was negligible. In other words, the initial normal pressure p on the potential surface of sliding was an effective pressure. If a mass of sand is at a considerable depth below the water table, the initial pore-water pressure u_w cannot be disregarded. Under these circumstances, the value of p in equation 15.1 must be replaced by $p - u_w$, whence

$$s = (p - u_w) \tan \phi \tag{15.3}$$

wherein p is the total normal pressure on the surface of sliding. The relations represented by Figures 32a and b remain unchanged, provided the abscissas are made equal to $p - u_w$.

The pore-water pressure u_w in equation 15.3 can also be produced by the rapid application of a surcharge. The effect of such an event on the shearing resistance can be investigated by means of a quick-shear test involving a sudden increase of the pressure on the sample from p to $p + \Delta p$, followed by rapid shear. The increase of the load by Δp at constant water content of the sample increases the pore-water pressure prior to the application of the shearing force from zero to $u_w = \Delta p$. According to the relation expressed by equation 15.3, the result of such a test is the same as if the load on the sample had remained unchanged.

As an example of the practical significance of these relations, the conditions for the stability of slopes on saturated fine sand with respect to sliding will be considered. The shearing resistance of saturated sand depends not only on the angle of internal friction and on the weight of the sand located above the potential surface of sliding, but also on the relative density of the sand and the rate at which the shearing stresses increase.

The most common cause of an increase of shearing stresses in saturated sand is the drawdown of the level of a body of water adjacent to one or both slopes of sand fills. On account of the relations represented in Figure 32, the stability of the slopes after drawdown depends on the density of the sand and the rate of drawdown. If the drawdown occurs slowly, the void ratio of the sand adapts itself to the changes in stress, and the shearing resistance of the sand is determined by the values of ϕ given in Table 7, page 82, reduced slightly because of the state of partial saturation after drawdown. On the other hand, if the drawdown occurs rapidly, the water content of the sand remains practically unaltered. As a consequence, the shearing resistance of the sand is determined by the consolidated-quick values represented by the dash curve in Figure 32c. If the void ratio of the fill is above the critical value, the consolidated-quick shearing resistance is lower than the corresponding slow-shear value. Otherwise it is higher. Hence, it is advisable to compact sand fills subject to temporary or permanent saturation as thoroughly as conditions permit.

SHEARING RESISTANCE OF SILT AND SILTY SAND

The relations between the normal pressure and shearing resistance of silt and silty sand are similar to those shown for clean sand in Figures 32a to c. The values of ϕ_s obtained from slow-shear tests range from about 27° to 30° for the loose state, and 30° to 35° for the dense state. These values are almost as great as those for sand.

Because of the relatively low permeability of silt and silty sand, saturated soils of these categories are likely to fail in the field under conditions similar to those under which consolidated-quick tests are made. The results of consolidated-quick tests on sand are represented by the dash lines in Figures 32a to c. The curvature of the corresponding lines for silt and silty sand is likely to be less marked, because the dilatancy of silt is commonly less pronounced than that of sand with bulky grains. The relation between pressure and the peak value of the resistance against consolidated-quick shear can be expressed approximately by the equation,

$$s = p \tan \phi_{cq} \qquad (15.4)$$

wherein p is the pressure on the surface of sliding prior to the application of the shearing force, and ϕ_{cq} is the slope angle of the straight part of the dash lines (Figures 32a and b) that represent the results of consolidated-quick tests. Since the initial tangent to these lines rises at an angle greater than ϕ_{cq}, the real values of s are greater than those given by the equation. If, prior to the application of the shearing force, the pore-water pressure in the soil adjoining the surface of sliding is equal to u_w, equation 15.4 must be replaced by

$$s = (p - u_w) \tan \phi_{cq} \qquad (15.5)$$

The value of ϕ_{cq} may be as low as 17°, and values between 20° and 22° are common. More specific data are not yet available.

SHEARING RESISTANCE OF REMOLDED CLAY

If the initial water content of a remolded clay is close to the liquid limit, the resistance of the clay to both slow and consolidated-quick shear increases in direct proportion to the pressure on the surface of sliding, as shown in Figure 32*d*. Since the dash line C_{cq} representing the results of consolidated-quick-shear tests is located entirely below the slow-test line C_s, we may conclude that the dilatancy of normally loaded remolded clays is negligible even at very low pressures. Both the lines C_s and C_{cq} are straight. Therefore the relation between pressure and shearing resistance can be expressed accurately by the equations:

Slow tests: $\qquad\qquad\qquad s = p \tan \phi_s$ $\qquad\qquad\qquad$ (15.6)

Consolidated-quick tests: $\quad s = p \tan \phi_{cq}$ $\qquad\qquad\qquad$ (15.7)

The values of ϕ_s and ϕ_{cq} range between the following limits:

$$\phi_s = 28° \text{ to } 30° \text{ (exceptionally as low as } 20°)$$

$$\phi_{cq} = 14° \text{ to } 20° \text{ (exceptionally as low as } 12°)$$

In Figure 33 the straight line Ob is a duplicate of the line C_s in Figure 32*d*. It represents the relation between pressure and shearing resistance for a normally loaded clay subjected to a slow test. It rises at
the angle ϕ_s to the horizontal.
The line bd represents the results of slow tests on samples
that have been precompressed
under a pressure p' and then
allowed to swell under a smaller
pressure p. The shearing resistance of a sample from which
the load has been completely
removed is represented by the
ordinate c of point d. The value
c is commonly referred to as the
cohesion of the clay. However,
in contrast to the cohesion c of
a cemented sand, equation 15.2, the cohesion of a clay is not a constant
for the soil. It increases with increasing precompression pressure p'.

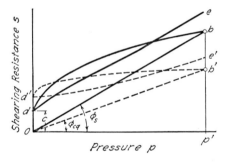

FIG. 33.   Results of shear tests on precompressed, remolded clay. Full lines correspond to slow tests, dash lines to consolidated-quick tests.

The line de in Figure 33 represents the relation between the slow-shear values and the normal pressure on a clay which was first consolidated under the pressure p', then allowed to swell under no pressure, and finally consolidated and subjected to a slow test under a pressure p

smaller than p'. This line rises from d at an angle somewhat smaller than ϕ_s, but as p increases it approaches the upward continuation of Ob.

The location of the line bd with reference to Ob in Figure 33 indicates that part of the shearing resistance produced by consolidation under a pressure p' survives the removal of the pressure. This seems to be due to the cementing properties of the adsorbed water. The consolidation of the clay involves an expulsion of normal and almost normal water, but the amount of adsorbed water remains almost unchanged. Hence, the precompression does not alter the amount of cementing material per unit of volume of solid. However, as the void ratio decreases, the contact between the grains becomes more intimate, and the strength of the cemented aggregate increases rapidly. Although precompression of a sand also produces a permanent decrease of the water content of the sand, the quantity of adsorbed water contained in the sand is negligible, and, as a consequence, the effect of the precompression on the shearing resistance is negligible. If the series of tests represented by Figure 33 is repeated on sand, it will be found that the lines bd and de are practically identical with Ob.

Because of the effect of precompression on the shearing resistance of clays, diagrams showing the relation between void ratio and shearing resistance are very similar to e–p diagrams. In both diagrams the effect of the removal and reapplication of a pressure is represented by a hysteresis loop.

The dash lines in Figure 33 represent the consolidated-quick-test values of the shearing resistance of normally loaded and precompressed samples of the same clay. It should be noted that the slope of the right-hand part of $b'd'$ is very small. This is closely associated with the fact that the slope of the decompression curve bc in Figure 21a is also very small. It indicates that a considerable part of the load p' can be removed without seriously impairing the consolidated-quick shearing resistance of the clay.

If the load on a sample in any one of the states represented by the dash line $Ob'd'e'$ in Figure 33 is rapidly increased from p to $p + \Delta p$ and the increase is followed immediately by rapid shear, the test constitutes a quick test. The results of such tests show that the shearing resistance is equal to the consolidated-quick value corresponding to p, irrespective of the value of Δp. The reason has been explained in the discussion of the shearing resistance of saturated sand.

In the preceding discussions, we have been concerned solely with the peak value of the shearing resistance. However, the shear failure of both normally loaded and precompressed clays is followed by a decrease of the shearing resistance toward an ultimate value as shown in Figure 31b by curve K_d for dense sand. The ratio between the peak value and the ultimate value in slow tests ranges from about 2.5 for highly plastic clays to about 1.4 for silty clays. Because of thixotropic effects, the ratio is somewhat greater for tests in which the shearing stress is increased at a very slow rate. The lowest ultimate value which has thus far been reported for ϕ_s is about 7°. It was obtained on a highly plastic clay ($L_w = 126\%$, $I_w = 90\%$). For a given clay the value of the ratio between the peak and ultimate values for consolidated-quick shear seems to be considerably larger than that for slow shear, but insufficient data have been accumulated to establish numerical values.

As soon as the shearing stress in a clay becomes greater than about one-half the peak value, the clay is likely to "creep" at constant shearing stress. In other words, the time–displacement curves, Figure 34, approach inclined and not horizontal tangents. The slope of these tangents and the corresponding rate of creep increase with increasing values of the constant shearing stress.

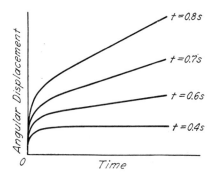

FIG. 34.   Time–displacement curves for clay samples subject to shearing stresses of different intensities.

SHEARING RESISTANCE OF CLAY FILLS

In engineering practice, remolded clays are used as construction materials for dams and embankments. During construction the water content of the clay remains practically unchanged. Therefore, the shearing resistance of such clays immediately after construction corresponds to that determined by means of quick-shear tests, made on samples at the water content that the clay will have in the finished dam immediately after construction. If the clay is saturated, the quick-shear values are independent of the normal pressure on the clay, as mentioned before. On the other hand, if it contains air, the shearing resistance s increases with increasing normal stress p. The relation between these two values can be expressed approximately by the equation,

$$s = c + p \tan \phi_a \qquad (15.8)$$

The cohesion c depends on the initial consistency of the clay, and ϕ_a on the compressibility and air content. For a completely saturated clay $\phi_a = 0$, and for a fairly dry clay ϕ_a is about 30°.

In practice, the evaluation of c and ϕ_a by means of quick-shear tests involves several uncertainties, due largely to the influence of progressive failure in the field. This phenomenon and its implications are discussed under the following two subheadings.

SHEARING RESISTANCE OF NATURAL CLAY STRATA

The relations between pressure and shearing resistance of undisturbed samples from natural clay strata are very similar to the corresponding relations for precompressed samples of the same clay in a remolded state. However, at a given precompression pressure and a given load the ratio between the peak value and the ultimate value of the shearing resistance is commonly higher for undisturbed samples than for remolded samples of the same clay.

A shear failure in a natural clay stratum may be caused either by excavation or by the local application of a load such as the weight of a structure or a fill. In order to compute the factor of safety of a slope on clay with respect to sliding, or that of a superimposed load with respect to a base failure, it is necessary to determine the resistance against shear along the potential surface of sliding.

Before construction the clay is completely consolidated under the effective weight of the soil located above the potential surface of sliding. During construction the water content of the clay remains almost unchanged because of the low permeability of the soil. Therefore, it is customary to assume that the shearing resistance of the clay at any point on the surface of sliding is approximately equal to the peak value obtained by means of a consolidated-quick-shear test performed on an undisturbed sample, taken at that point and tested after preceding consolidation under a vertical pressure equal to the original effective overburden pressure.

However, during the process of consolidation in the laboratory, the water content of the clay decreases below the natural water content (see Figure 22a). As a consequence, the shearing resistance increases. To eliminate this error, the laboratory values of the consolidated-quick shearing resistance are plotted against the void ratio. By means of the diagram thus obtained, the shearing resistance corresponding to the natural water content is estimated by extrapolation.

After the peak shearing resistance has been determined for an adequate number of representative samples, the total resistance against sliding along the surface under investigation can be computed. However, by applying this method to the computation of the shearing resistance of clay strata that actually have failed, it has been found that the real average shearing resistance along such surfaces is consistently very much smaller than the value computed on the basis of test results. This conspicuous discrepancy is commonly ascribed to the effects of progressive failure.

The term *progressive failure* indicates the spreading of the failure over the potential surface of sliding from a point or a line toward the boundaries of the surface. While the stresses in the clay near the periphery of this surface approach the peak value, the shearing resistance of the clay at the area where the failure started is already approaching the much smaller ultimate value. As a consequence the total shearing force that acts on a surface of sliding at the instant of complete failure is considerably smaller than the shearing resistance computed on the basis of the peak values.

The failure starts as soon as the shearing stress at one point of the potential surface of sliding becomes equal to the peak value of the shearing resistance of the clay at that point. Hence, theoretically it should be possible to compute the factor of safety with respect to incipient failure by comparing the shearing stresses at different points of the potential surface of sliding with the experimentally determined peak values of the shearing resistance at these points. Since such computations are necessarily based on the assumption that the soil is perfectly elastic, the procedure is referred to as the *elasticity method.* However, the elasticity method cannot be recommended for practical use, because the evaluation of the shearing stresses in natural soil is, at the very best, unreliable, Article 52. The ratio between the value of the shearing resistance along a potential surface of sliding, as computed from the peak values, and the resistance against progressive failure is not yet known. Furthermore, it is doubtful whether this ratio has a constant value.

The factor of safety with respect to ultimate rather than incipient failure can be computed by means of the *plasticity method*. This method is based on the observation that the average shearing stress on surfaces of sliding in natural strata of soft clay is, at the instant of failure, consistently somewhat less than half the average unconfined compressive strength q_u of the clay. The probable physical causes of this relationship are discussed in Article 17. Until and unless conclusive evidence is brought forth that the elasticity method is both practicable and consistently more reliable than the plasticity method, computations for determining the factor of safety of a slope on soft clay with respect to sliding should always be made by means of the plasticity method. The average shearing resistance should be taken as $q_u/2$ for slightly disturbed samples of the clay, or somewhat less than $q_u/2$ for undisturbed samples.

SUMMARY OF METHODS FOR EVALUATING THE SHEARING RESISTANCE OF
SOILS IN THE FIELD

The results of shear tests on saturated soils depend to a large extent on
the rate at which the shearing force is increased, the dimensions of the
specimen, and other details of the testing procedure. Therefore, if the
results of shear tests are presented in a paper or a report, all the essential
features of the testing procedure should be fully described. Otherwise,
the data can be very misleading.

The angle of internal friction ϕ of a perfectly cohesionless sand in a
loose dry state is approximately equal to the angle of repose. Before the
angle of repose is determined, the sand should be dried in an oven;
otherwise, the values obtained are too high. The value ϕ of a given sand
in a thoroughly compacted state under a pressure of less than 2 tons per
sq ft is 5° to 10° higher than its angle of repose. On the basis of these
statements, the value ϕ can be estimated roughly without shear tests.
In practice, more accurate values are seldom required.

The angle of internal friction ϕ_s of a completely submerged sand is
about 1° or 2° less than the value of ϕ for the same sand at the same relative density, but in a perfectly dry state. However, if a submerged sand
is very loose, it may pass on slight provocation into a semiliquid state
(see Article 17). Shear tests on the sand do not disclose the existence of
such a danger, but experience shows that it is very real. Consequently,
sand embankments subject to temporary saturation, or thick strata of
loose sand located beneath the site of proposed foundations, should be
compacted by adequate means.

The shear properties of silty sand and silt are similar to those of very
fine sand. Because of the relatively low permeability of these soils, shear
failures in saturated strata consisting of such soils are likely to take place
under conditions similar to those under which consolidated-quick tests
are made in the laboratory. The values of the corresponding angle of
shearing resistance ϕ_{cq} commonly range between 20° and 22°. Exceptionally these values can be as low as 17°.

Quick-shear tests can be used to determine the shearing resistance of a
clay to be placed in an embankment. For a given fill material, the test
results depend primarily on the initial consistency and the air content.
However, the influence of progressive failure on the average shearing
resistance of the finished clay embankment is not yet known. The
differences between the physical state of the laboratory samples and that
of the clay in the embankment after construction constitute a further
source of uncertainty, and the test results leave a wide margin for interpretation. Hence, the procedure must still be used with discrimination.

For computing the factor of safety of slopes on natural clay strata with respect to sliding, the plasticity method is recommended. It is based on the observation that the average shearing resistance along surfaces of sliding in soft natural clay strata is roughly equal to one-half the average unconfined compressive strength of fairly undisturbed samples of the clay taken close to these surfaces. The compression tests can be performed quickly, and the technique is simple.

Function of Shear and Triaxial Tests

The preceding summary leads to the conclusion that the legitimate field for the use of shear tests is at present limited to the investigation of the shearing resistance of silty soils intermediate in character between sand and clay. Shear tests on sand are seldom justified, because the lower limit for the angle of internal friction ϕ is equal to the angle of repose which can be determined without shear tests, and the influence of the relative density on the value of ϕ can be estimated. Shear tests on clay will not acquire any practical value unless future observation should demonstrate that the elasticity method for solving stability problems involving soft natural clay strata is both practicable and considerably more reliable than the plasticity method. Unless and until conclusive evidence in favor of the elasticity method is produced, the estimate of the shearing resistance of natural clay strata should be based on the results of unconfined compression tests.

Practical problems involving the shearing resistance of silty soils are relatively uncommon. Laboratory investigations to determine the consolidated-quick values for such soils should be made with triaxial-compression apparatus, because consolidated-quick box-shear tests on any soils other than soft clays are unreliable at best. The performance of triaxial compression tests requires special training and experience. Hence, if a job is important enough to justify shear tests, the samples should be forwarded to a laboratory equipped and qualified for such investigations. If the job is too small to warrant the expenditure for soil testing, the design should be based on the lowest values given in this article or else on local experience.

REFERENCE

15.1. M. J. Hvorslev, Torsion Shear Tests and Their Place in the Determination of the Shearing Resistance of Soils, *Proc. ASTM*, Vol 39, p 999.

ART. 16. TRIAXIAL–COMPRESSION TESTS

Purpose of Tests

In the preceding article it was pointed out that the results of quick- and consolidated-quick-shear tests on soils other than soft clay cannot be relied upon. This is due to the fact that the water content of box-shear or ring-shear samples of such soils cannot be kept sufficiently constant while the stresses in the sample change. The importance of the resulting error increases with increasing permeability of the soil. Consolidated quick-shear tests cannot be made at all on saturated samples of sand. Reliable information on the resistance of soils with medium and high permeability against shear at constant water content can at present be obtained only by means of triaxial compression tests.

For the time being, the principal legitimate field for the practical application of the triaxial testing method is the investigation of the shearing properties of saturated silt and silty soil. The reasons have been stated at the end of the preceding article.

Essential Features of Triaxial Test

The principle of the triaxial test is illustrated by Figure 35. The sample, of cylindrical shape, is enclosed in a watertight cover and placed in a chamber that can be filled with fluid under a pressure p_c. An additional axial pressure q per unit of area can be applied to the top of the sample through a rigid head. Water may enter or leave the sample through a porous stone in the bottom, provided the valve V is left open. The pressure of the water in the sample may be measured by means of a pressure gage connected to the discharge pipe above the valve V. An extensometer is provided to measure the strain of the sample in the vertical direction.

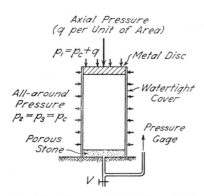

Fig. 35. Diagram illustrating principal features of triaxial-test apparatus.

In the performance of a slow or a consolidated-quick test, the first step is to permit the complete consolidation of the sample under the all-around pressure p_c. During consolidation valve V must be open. Since the fluid pressure acts on the top of the sample as well as on the sides, there are no shearing stresses in the sample at this stage.

The sample is then subjected to the supplementary axial pressure q per unit of area. The axial pressure is increased until the specimen fails. During the application of this pressure the valve V may be either closed or open. If it is closed, the shearing stresses develop at a constant water content. The results of a test with the valve closed represent the equivalent of a consolidated-quick-shear test made in a shear box, but they are

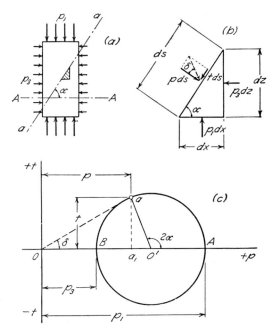

FIG. 36.   (a) Stresses acting on soil sample in triaxial test; (b) stresses acting on prismatic element of sample; (c) Mohr's circle of stress representing state of stress in specimen shown in (a).

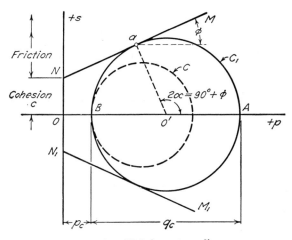

FIG. 37.   Mohr's rupture diagram.

much more reliable because the test arrangement prevents any change in water content during the increase of shearing stress from zero to the state of failure. Therefore, the data obtained from such tests are referred to as consolidated-quick values, regardless of the rate at which the axial load is applied. If the valve V remains open and the axial pressure is applied very slowly, so that the water within the sample has time to adjust itself to the change in stress, the test corresponds to a slow-shear test made with box-shear apparatus. Hence, the values obtained in this manner are referred to as slow-test values.

In quick tests the valve V remains closed from start to finish. As a consequence, failure occurs at the initial water content, irrespective of the rate of loading.

In any case, the sample fails along inclined shear planes. However, the normal and shearing stresses on the failure surface cannot be measured directly. The readings merely furnish the values of the total principal stresses that existed in the specimen at the instant of failure. The major principal stress p_1 is equal to the all-around pressure p_c plus the additional vertical pressure q_c which caused the failure. The other two principal stresses $p_2 = p_3$ are equal to the all-around pressure p_c. The stress conditions on the surface of failure can be determined by computation or, more expediently, by an equivalent graphical construction known as Mohr's diagram.

Mohr's Diagram

Figure 36a shows a section through a triaxial test specimen at an intermediate stage of the test. The vertical stress $p_1 = p_c + q$ is the major principal stress, and the horizontal plane section $A–A$ on which it acts represents one principal plane. The direction of an arbitrarily inclined plane section $a–a$ through the specimen is designated by the angle α between the inclined section and the principal plane $A–A$. The normal stress on plane $a–a$ is denoted by p, and the shearing stress by t.

The shaded area in Figure 36a represents a prismatic element of the material bounded by planes parallel to the principal planes and to the inclined plane $a–a$. An enlarged view of the element is shown in Figure 36b. The equilibrium of this element requires that

$$p_3 \, ds \sin \alpha - p \, ds \sin \alpha + t \, ds \cos \alpha = 0$$

and

$$p_1 \, ds \cos \alpha - p \, ds \cos \alpha - t \, ds \sin \alpha = 0$$

whence

$$p = \tfrac{1}{2}(p_1 + p_3) + \tfrac{1}{2}(p_1 - p_3) \cos 2\alpha \qquad (16.1)$$

and

$$\text{SHEAR STRESS} \quad t = \tfrac{1}{2}(p_1 - p_3)\sin 2\alpha \tag{16.2}$$

The shear stress t given by equation 16.2 is considered positive if the corresponding resultant stress on the inclined plane deviates in a clockwise sense from the normal to the section. Since the shearing stress is positive, the corresponding angle of inclination δ of the resultant stress is also considered positive. Hence, if α is less than $90°$, δ is positive.

A graphical solution of equations 16.1 and 16.2 is represented by Figure 36c. This figure shows a rectangular co-ordinate system in which the horizontal distance from the origin of co-ordinates represents the normal stress on a given plane section, and the vertical distance represents the shearing stress. Since the shearing stresses on principal planes are equal to zero, the horizontal axis is reserved for principal stresses. The principal stress p_1 is represented by the distance OA on the horizontal axis, and the principal stress p_3 by OB. A circle with center O' is constructed with the distance BA as a diameter. If the radial line $O'a$ is laid off so that the angle $AO'a$ is equal to 2α, the horizontal and vertical co-ordinates of point a are equal, respectively, to the normal stress p and the shearing stress t in equations 16.1 and 16.2. This is readily apparent from the facts that the distance OO' in Figure 36c is equal to $\tfrac{1}{2}(p_1 + p_3)$ and that the radius of the circle is equal to $\tfrac{1}{2}(p_1 - p_3)$. The circle, which is the locus of all points defined by equations 16.1 and 16.2, is known as *Mohr's circle of stress*.

Equations 16.1 and 16.2 and the graphical procedure illustrated by Figure 36 are strictly valid for any section through any material. However, in order to use them for calculating the position of the failure plane and the stresses on this plane, it is necessary to make some assumptions regarding the relation between normal stress and shearing resistance on the failure surface. Hence, the results of the following investigations are valid only if the mechanical properties of the material are in accordance with the assumptions stipulated in the following paragraph.

It is assumed that the shearing resistance s of the soil subject to the triaxial-compression test is determined by the equation,

$$s = c + p\tan\phi \tag{16.3}$$

in which p is the normal stress on the surface of sliding, c is a constant called the cohesion, and ϕ is the angle of internal friction. Equation 16.3 is known as *Coulomb's equation*. Furthermore, it is assumed that the values of c and ϕ are entirely independent of the states of stress which preceded the failure. According to Article 15, this condition is approximately satisfied for cemented sand and gravel, moist sand, and, to a lesser degree, clay with a high air or gas content. On the other hand, it is not satisfied at all for completely saturated clay soils. Hence, the errors associated with the interpretation of triaxial tests on the basis of equation 16.3 are very different for different soils. In the following discussion, it is assumed that the conditions for the validity of equation 16.3 are strictly satisfied. The nature and importance of the errors due to this assumption are discussed at the end of the article.

In Figure 37 equation 16.3 is represented by the straight line NM, known as the *line of rupture*. If a circle of stress, such as C, does not touch the line NM, there is no section through the specimen for which the failure condition, equation 16.3, is satisfied. If a circle intersects the line NM, it represents an impossible state of stress, because, on every section determined by a point of the circle above NM, the shearing stress is greater than s, equation 16.3. Therefore, no circle can represent the state of stress at failure unless it just touches the line NM. Any circle which satisfies this condition is called a *circle of rupture*, and the diagram in which the circles of rupture are plotted is known as *Mohr's rupture diagram*.

The geometrical relations represented in Figure 36 demonstrate that the angle $AO'a$ in Figure 37 is equal to twice the angle α between the shear plane and the principal plane A–A in Figure 36a. Hence, according to Figure 37,

$$\alpha = 45° + \frac{\phi}{2} \tag{16.4}$$

From Figure 37, we also obtain by geometry the relation,

$$p_c + q_c = p_c N_\phi + 2c\sqrt{N_\phi} \tag{16.5}$$

in which the expression,

$$N_\phi = \tan^2\left(45° + \frac{\phi}{2}\right) \tag{16.6}$$

is called the *flow value*. The quantity,

$$q_c = p_c(N_\phi - 1) + 2c\sqrt{N_\phi} \tag{16.7}$$

is called the *confined compressive strength* of the soil. It is a function of the *confining pressure* p_c.

For sand and for normally loaded clays, $c = 0$, and

$$q_c = p_c(N_\phi - 1) \tag{16.8}$$

Substituting into this equation the numerical values of ϕ_s and ϕ_{cq} for remolded clay (see page 87), we obtain for the confined compressive strength the values given in Table 8.

If the sides of a test specimen are not acted on by a horizontal pressure, the load required to cause failure of the specimen is equal to the unconfined compressive strength q_u per unit of area, Article 8. It is obvious that an unconfined compression test can be performed only on a cohesive soil. According to equation 16.5, the unconfined compressive strength is equal to

$$q_u = 2c\sqrt{N_\phi}$$

For some soils, such as very dense sand or sandy clay, the line of rupture NM, Figure 37, has a slight downward curvature. By theory it can be shown that the curvature of the line of rupture does not invalidate

TABLE 8

CONFINED COMPRESSIVE STRENGTH OF REMOLDED CLAYS

Type of Test	Usual Range of Values	Least Value, Exceptional
Slow	$1.77p_c$–$2.00p_c$	$1.05p_c$
Consolidated-quick	$0.64p_c$–$1.05p_c$	$0.48p_c$

p_c indicates confining pressure.

the fundamental principles of the graphical procedure. A specimen fails as soon as the circle of stress touches the line of rupture. The co-ordinates of the point of contact between the line of rupture and the curve represent the two components of the stress on the surface of sliding in one test specimen. The normal stress on the plane of shear is equal to the abscissa of the point of tangency, and the slope angle of the tangent to the envelope at this point represents the corresponding angle of internal friction. By substituting this value into equation 16.4 the slope angle α of the shear plane is obtained.

In order to determine the line of rupture for a given soil, triaxial compression tests are made on several specimens at different confining pressures. Each test furnishes the data for plotting one circle of rupture. The line of rupture is obtained by drawing the envelope of all the circles.

Whatever the shape of the line of rupture may be, the use of triaxial tests to investigate the relations between normal stress and shearing resistance for soils is based on the assumptions previously stated. Since these assumptions are more or less at variance with the mechanical properties of real soils, the information obtained from Mohr's diagram may also be at variance with reality. A critical study of the errors associated with the procedure leads to the following conclusions: If the circles represent the results of tests on dry sand or silt or of slow tests on saturated samples of such soils, the envelope of the circles represents almost exactly the relation between normal pressure and shearing resistance. On the other hand, if they represent the results of consolidated-quick tests on any soil or of slow tests on saturated clay, the shearing resistance of the soil at any normal pressure is somewhat smaller than the corresponding ordinate of the envelope. If such a discrepancy exists, the plane determined by the point of contact between any circle and the envelope does not correspond even approximately to the surface along which the specimen actually fails during the test represented by the circle.

PROBLEMS

1. A sample of dense dry sand is subjected to a triaxial test. The angle of internal friction is believed to be about 37°. If the minor principal stress is 2 kg per sq cm, at what value of the major principal stress is the sample likely to fail?

  Ans. 8.0 kg per sq cm.

2. Solve problem 1 on the assumption that the sand has a slight cohesion, equal to 0.10 kg per sq cm.

  Ans. 8.4 kg per sq cm.

3. The shearing resistance of a soil is determined by the equation, $s = c + p \tan \phi$. Two triaxial tests are performed on the material. In the first test the all-around pressure is 2 kg per sq cm, and failure occurs at an added axial unit stress of 6 kg per sq cm. In the second test the all-around pressure is 3.5 kg per sq cm, and failure occurs at an added stress of 10.5 kg per sq cm. What values of c and ϕ correspond to the test results?

  Ans. 0; 37°.

ART. 17. SHEAR CHARACTERISTICS OF QUICKSAND AND SOFT CLAY

In everyday language, the term *quicksand* indicates a natural mass of saturated sand into which a person or object sinks. The lack of bearing power may be due to the seepage pressure of water percolating through the sand in an upward direction. On the other hand, it may be due to inherent instability of the structure of the sand, unaided by seepage pressure.

Quicksand conditions produced by seepage pressure are frequently encountered at the bottom of excavations in sand below the water table. The mechanical causes of this condition are explained in Article 12, and the means for preventing their occurrence are discussed in Article 47. However, to prevent any misunderstanding, the term quicksand is applied in this book only to those inherently unstable sands that may exhibit quicksand properties even in the absence of seepage pressure.

The sudden decrease of the shearing resistance of a quicksand from its normal value to almost zero without the aid of seepage pressure is referred to as *spontaneous liquefaction*. It is caused by a collapse of the structure of the sand, associated with a sudden but temporary increase of the pore-water pressure. The liquefaction involves the temporary transformation of the sand into a very concentrated suspension. As soon as the flow stops, the sand again passes into the state of a sediment. The structure of the newly formed sediment may or may not be somewhat denser than the original structure. While the sand is temporarily liquefied, its bearing capacity is close to zero. This can be demonstrated by filling a vessel with very loose saturated sand and placing a weight on the surface of the sand. If a glass rod is pushed rapidly into the sand, the weight sinks as if the sand were a liquid. A gentle blow on the side of the vessel produces the same effect.

Many engineers seem to believe that every sand with a void ratio greater than the critical void ratio, Article 15, may turn liquid on sufficient provocation. However, there is no positive evidence that this opinion is justified, and there does not appear to be any reason why the assumed relation should exist. If the void ratio of a sand is above the critical value, the consolidated-quick shearing resistance of the sand is somewhat lower than the slow value, but it has never been observed that it becomes equal to zero. The difference between the two values is due to a slight tendency of the sand to contract prior to failure, whereas spontaneous liquefaction is associated with a collapse of the structure of the sand. Therefore, the prerequisites for these two phenomena are likely to be entirely different. If a very loose sand is under low pressure, its void ratio is likely to be lower than the critical value (see Figure 32a). Nevertheless, it is conceivable that it may be liquefied by a severe shock. On the other hand, it is very doubtful whether a sand with medium density acted on by a high overburden pressure can temporarily pass into a state of suspension, regardless of whether its void ratio is above or below the critical value. There is no evidence that any saturated sand can start to flow unless its relative density is less than 0.4 or 0.5, irrespective of the value of the critical void ratio.

Experience shows that the intensity of the disturbance required to liquefy a loose sand is different for different sands. The most unstable sands so far encountered consist chiefly of rounded grains. The effective size is smaller than 0.1 mm, and the uniformity coefficient less than 5. The porosity of the sand in the field is at least 44 per cent, and it may even be considerably higher than the porosity of the same sand after rapid sedimentation in the laboratory. Fine sands and coarse silts of this type seem to constitute an analogue to the extrasensitive clays with the abnormal e–log p characteristics illustrated by Figure 22b. They rank among the most treacherous materials that can be encountered in the field, and they are the only ones that really deserve the name quicksand.

In contrast to ordinary loose sands, they may pass into the liquid state without being subjected to a sudden and violent shock.

It has been observed that exceptionally unstable sands have also an exceptionally high void ratio after sedimentation in the laboratory. However, by removing either the finest or the coarsest constituents of such a sand, the capacity of the sand to constitute an abnormally porous aggregate can be eliminated. These findings indicate that the degree of sensitivity of the structure of a fine sand depends not only on the manner in which the sand was deposited, but also, to a large extent, on

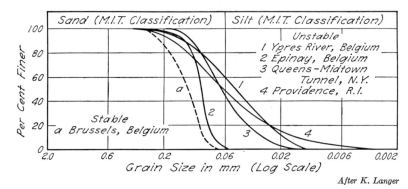

After K. Langer

Fig. 38.   Grain-size curves of exceptionally unstable (full lines) and stable (dash line) sands.

apparently minor details of its grain-size characteristics. As a matter of fact, the difference between the grain-size characteristics of exceptionally unstable and normal sands is surprisingly slight, as shown in Figure 38. In this figure, the plain curves represent the grain-size characteristics of notoriously unstable sands, and the dash line those of a normal one.

The spontaneous liquefaction of a mass of very loose saturated sand indicates that the consolidated-quick value ϕ_{cq} of the angle of internal friction of the sand temporarily becomes equal to zero. Yet, if specimens of the same sand are prepared in the loosest state that can be produced in the laboratory, triaxial compression tests on these specimens show without exception that the consolidated-quick value of the angle of internal friction ϕ_{cq} is equal to at least 20°. This observation demonstrates that there are field conditions for the failure of soils that cannot be reproduced in the laboratory. It further suggests that the absence of a noticeable influence of the overburden pressure on the shearing resistance of soft clay in the field ($\phi_{cq} = 0$; see page 91) may belong in the same category and be due to similar causes. As a matter of fact, the mineralogical composition and grain-size characteristics of clay soils and the process of sedimentation that leads to soft clay strata make it almost inevitable that the coarsest constituents of such strata should be arranged in a pattern resembling that of a very loose sand.

In Article 3 it is shown that most clays consist of a mixture of more or less equidimensional particles that constitute the coarsest fraction, and flaky or, exceptionally, needle-like particles that make up the balance. If a mixture of such grains is deposited by sedimentation, the uppermost layer of the sediment is composed of a honeycombed extremely compressible aggregate of clay particles. This layer contains the coarser grains in a random distribution. If such a sediment is subsequently compressed, the coarse equidimensional grains come in contact with each other like the particles of a sand in the process of sedimentation. Their arrangement is inevitably very unstable, because the clay which occupies the interstices prevents the grains from tipping and rolling into stable positions with reference to each other. After they touch each other, they constitute a more or less self-supporting skeleton, embedded in a clay matrix. As long as the sediment is laterally confined, the skeleton is able to carry all or at least the major part of the overburden pressure, as does a very loose sand or even a true quicksand. However, a slight disturbance, such as a gentle deformation, destroys the equilibrium of the grains composing the skeleton. At that instant all the stresses previously carried by the skeleton are transferred onto the matrix. The shearing strength of the matrix is independent of the overburden pressure and is due exclusively to thixotropic hardening (Article 4). As a consequence, in the field the clay would behave as if its angle of internal friction ϕ_{cq} were equal to zero.

If a specimen of soft clay is taken out of a drill hole and brought into the laboratory, the structure of the soil skeleton is somewhat disturbed, and the pattern of the internal supports is altered. The renewed application of the load equal to the previously acting overburden pressure causes a complete breakdown of the original skeleton structure and is associated with a supplementary consolidation of the clay matrix which again brings the larger grains into contact and equilibrium with each other. This permits the development of frictional resistance between the coarser grains. Therefore, in contrast to the shearing resistance of the clay in the field, that of the clay in the laboratory increases with increasing pressure like that of a soil with a value of ϕ_{cq} between 12° and 20°.

The preceding discussions show that the value of the shearing resistance of soft clay in the field is not necessarily equal to the value obtained by means of shear or of triaxial tests. Field experience points in the same direction. Therefore, the results of consolidated-quick tests of any kind cannot be considered a reliable basis for evaluating the degree of stability of large bodies of clay in the field unless and until the soundness of the procedure has been demonstrated in very different clays by reliable field observations. So far no conclusive evidence of this kind has been produced.

The concept illustrated by Figure 39 could be called the *quicksand concept of clay structure*, because it involves the assumption that the coarse soil particles constitute a pattern similar to that of the sand grains in a true quicksand. In other words, it is assumed that the clay consists of two parts with very different functions and properties. One part, composed of the coarser grains, carries the load by the same

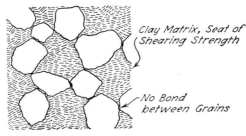

Fig. 39.   Diagram illustrating quicksand concept of clay structure.   The coarse particles are assumed to touch each other without being cemented together, like the grains of a loose sand.

mechanism of pressure transfer from grain to grain as does a very loose sand. The other part consists chiefly of the clay fraction. It occupies the interstices of the load-carrying skeleton. It carries a very small load, but it acquires considerable strength and rigidity by thixotropic hardening. If the skeleton possesses adequate stability to start with, both the water content and the unconfined compressive strength of the clay should be practically independent of depth. As a matter of fact, soft clay strata with such properties are by no means uncommon. Some of them possess the abnormal laboratory consolidation characteristics illustrated by Figure 22b, involving excessive compressibility under the first increments of load greater than the overburden pressure. According to the quicksand concept, the high initial compressibility is due to a high degree of instability of the load-carrying skeleton. The other extreme would be a clay that does not contain any equidimensional grains at all. The compressibility of such a clay would be equal to that of the clay matrix, which is very high. Therefore, the water content of such a clay would decrease rapidly with increasing depth, and the unconfined compressive strength would increase. In intermediate types, part of the overburden pressure would be carried by the skeleton, and the remainder by the clay matrix.

Because of the infinite variety of natural processes that lead to the formation of clay deposits, any type intermediate between clay with quicksand structure and structureless clay should be encountered. This may account for the fact that the strength of some normally loaded clay deposits increases conspicuously with depth, whereas that of others does not increase at all.

The preceding discussion refers only to sedimentary clays. Residual clays, formed *in situ* by the chemical weathering of rocks or the solution of limestone, have no opportunity to acquire the structure illustrated by Figure 39. Hence it is probable, though not yet certain, that the shearing resistance of such clays is governed by laws very different from those that apply to normally consolidated sedimentary clays.

REFERENCES

17.1. K. LANGER, Some Characteristics of Quicksand (in French), *Compt. rend. recherchés effectués durant l'année 1938*, Laboratories du Batiment et des Travaux Publiques, Paris (XV), pp 28–32. Results of investigation of notorious quicksands.

17.2. K. TERZAGHI, Shear Characteristics of Quicksand and Soft Clay, *Proc. Seventh Texas Conf. Soil Mech. Found. Eng.*, Bureau of Engineering Research, University of Texas, Jan. 1947.

ART. 18. STRESS AND STRAIN IN SOILS

PRACTICAL CONSIDERATIONS

The relations between stress and strain in soils determine the settlement of soil-supported foundations. They also determine the change in earth pressure due to small movements of retaining walls or other earth supports.

If the settlement of a foundation is due chiefly to the consolidation of strata of soft soil located between layers of relatively incompressible material, it can be computed or estimated as explained in Article 13. However, this method can be used only on the condition that the horizontal deformation of the compressible layers is negligible in comparison to the vertical deformation. If the subsoil does not contain any layers that interfere with horizontal deformation, local application of load causes a yield of the soil mass in every direction. The stress–strain relations that determine the yield are so complex that it is not possible to make a settlement computation comparable to that for a building located above confined layers of soft clay. As a consequence, estimates of the settlement can be made only on the basis of the results of observations concerning the settlement of other buildings supported by similar soils. However, the chances are slight that a proposed foundation would have the same dimensions as an existing one. Therefore, even an estimate based on experience requires a knowledge of the influence on the settlement of the size of the loaded area, the depth of foundation, and other factors. This influence is governed solely by the general relations between stress and strain for soils.

The stress–strain relations for soils can be grasped most readily by comparing them with those for ideal perfectly elastic solids. After this comparison has been made for soils in the laboratory, the stress–strain relationships for soils in place will be considered.

STRESS AND STRAIN IN IDEAL ELASTIC SOLIDS

Let

p = normal stress in a given direction

ϵ = strain in the direction of p

ϵ_l = strain at right angles to this direction

If a material is perfectly elastic, the ratio,

$$E\,(\mathrm{kg/cm^2}) = \frac{p\,(\mathrm{kg/cm^2})}{\epsilon} \tag{18.1}$$

known as the *modulus of elasticity*, is a constant independent of the state of stress in the material. That is, the relation between stress and strain for an elastic material is linear. Furthermore, the ratio,

$$\mu = \frac{\epsilon_l}{\epsilon} \tag{18.2}$$

known as *Poisson's ratio*, is also a constant independent of the state of stress in the material. Therefore, the stress–strain characteristics of an elastic material are completely defined by the quantities E and μ.

If p_1, p_2, and p_3 represent the three principal stresses, the unit volume change produced by the application of these stresses to an elastic material is

$$\frac{\Delta V}{V} = \frac{1 - 2\mu}{E}\,(p_1 + p_2 + p_3) \tag{18.3}$$

For $\mu = 0.5$, the volume change is zero, and the material is said to be incompressible.

Steel is the only common construction material that has stress–strain characteristics complying almost strictly with those defined by the preceding equations. Poisson's ratio for steel is about 0.3. Hence, the increase of a normal stress in steel produces a slight volume decrease.

STRESS–STRAIN CHARACTERISTICS OF UNCONFINED CLAY SAMPLES

In Figure 40 the abscissas represent the vertical pressure on an unconfined clay specimen, and the ordinates the corresponding vertical strain.

The curve Oc shows the manner in which the strain increases while the pressure is increased at a constant rate. If the load is held constant at some value, the sample continues to get shorter, as indicated by the vertical line ab. The rate of shortening decreases with time and finally becomes equal to zero, provided the shearing stress on the potential surface of failure is smaller than the stress required to produce creep (see Article 15). If at any time during the test a further increase in strain is prevented, the stress in the specimen decreases at a decreasing rate and finally becomes constant. In the diagram, this process would be represented by a short horizontal line (not shown). In either case the resumption of loading at the original rate leads to a curve which joins the main branch Oc without any break.

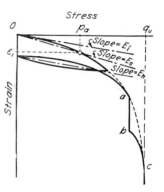

FIG. 40.   Stress–strain diagram for soil.

If the load is removed at the same rate at which it was previously applied, the elastic recovery is smaller than the preceding compression. If the load is again applied, the recompression curve joins the main branch without any break, and the decompression and recompression curves enclose a hysteresis loop. As soon as the pressure becomes equal to the unconfined compressive strength q_u of the material, the specimen fails by shearing or bulging. During the entire test the volume of the specimen remains constant. Hence, Poisson's ratio μ, equation 18.2, remains equal to 0.5 throughout the test.

Since for most soils the stress–strain curve Oc in Figure 40 is curved throughout its entire length, the relation between stress and strain for soils, unlike that of elastic materials, cannot be expressed by a single numerical value E, equation 18.1. In order to compare the stress–strain properties of different soils or those of the same soil under different conditions, one of the following three quantities may be used: the initial tangent modulus E_i, the secant modulus E_s, or the hysteresis modulus E_h. These quantities are equal, respectively, to the slopes (stress per unit of strain) of the dash-dotted lines in Figure 40. The secant modulus E_s represents the average slope of the stress–strain curve for the range in stress between zero and some arbitrary value p_a, usually taken as $q_u/3$.

If an undisturbed clay specimen is first tested and then remolded at unaltered water content and tested again, it may be observed that the values of q_u, E_i, E_s, and E_h are very much smaller for the remolded than for the undisturbed material, but the general character of the stress–strain diagram remains unaltered (see Figure 41). The magnitude of the decrease of strength and stiffness depends on the degree of sensitivity of the clay, Article 8. If the remolded specimens are allowed to age without change in water content, their strength and stiffness increase at a rate that decreases with time, but it is doubtful whether they would ever attain values corresponding to those for the undisturbed specimens.

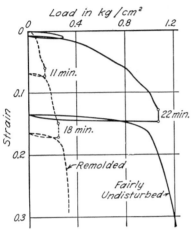

FIG. 41.   Influence of remolding on stress–strain relationship for clay.

STRESS–STRAIN CHARACTERISTICS OF PARTLY CONFINED SOIL SAMPLES

At any depth below the ground surface the vertical pressure due to the weight of the overburden is associated with a lateral pressure. Both pressures combined constitute a state of initial confinement. The intensity of lateral pressure is usually less than that of the vertical pressure. However, for the purposes of a general discussion of the stress–strain properties of partly confined soils, it is sufficiently accurate to assume that the intensity p_c of the initial confining pressure is equal in all directions. The application of a surcharge on part of the ground surface increases the all-around pressure in the soil beneath the loaded area. It also produces an additional unidirectional pressure q that acts at some angle to the vertical direction. In order to get a conception of the influence of the all-around pressure on the deformation produced by a unidirectional excess pressure, a cylindrical specimen of the soil may be subjected to a triaxial compression test in which the all-around pressure p_c is held constant while an excess pressure q is added in the vertical direction.

If the test is made on a specimen of sand and the value of q is plotted against the vertical strain, a diagram is obtained that has all of the characteristics of Figure 40. If the sand is loose, its volume at the end of the test is slightly smaller than the initial volume. If the sand is dense, the increase of q is accompanied by a volume expansion. These facts account for the extraordinary resistance of dense sand to the penetration of piles. In a very loose sand, cylindrical piles can be driven without difficulty to any depth.

The failure stress q_c increases, according to equation 16.8, approximately in direct proportion to the confining pressure p_c. For values of

p_c up to 5 kg per sq cm, it ranges from about 1.8 p_c for loose uniform sand with rounded grains to 5.1p_c for very dense well-graded sand with angular grains. The values of E_i, E_s, and E_h increase with increasing values of p_c (see Figure 42). Since p_c increases with increasing depth below the ground surface, the stress–strain properties of a sand stratum have no resemblance to those of a homogeneous elastic solid.

If a very fine-grained or silty sand is completely saturated, its water content remains practically unchanged during a rapid change in stress, because the permeability of such soils is relatively low. The mechanical consequences of this fact depend primarily on the relative density of the sand. If the void ratio is greater than the critical value that corresponds to the effective overburden pressure, Article 15, the values of q_c, E_i, E_s, and E_h are smaller than those that would correspond to the same change in stress at a very slow rate. Otherwise, the values are larger. For this reason, the resistance against driving a sampling spoon, Article 44, or piles into a very fine dense sand is much greater if the sand is saturated than if it is dry or moist.

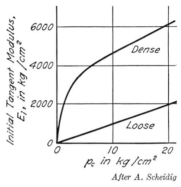

After A. Scheidig

Fig. 42.   Relation between initial tangent modulus and all-around pressure for sand.

The stress–strain characteristics of partly confined normally loaded clays are very similar to those of fine-grained and saturated loose sands. However, at a given confining pressure the values of q_c and of E_i, E_s, and E_h for clay are very much smaller than the corresponding values for sand. If a unidirectional stress is added to an all-around pressure in clay, the relation between this stress and the corresponding strain is very similar to that shown in Figure 40. The initial tangent modulus increases like that of a loose sand in simple proportion to the confining pressure, Figure 42. That is,

$$E_i = Cp_c \qquad (18.4)$$

The value of C depends on the type of clay and on the conditions of drainage. If the clay is first completely consolidated under the pressure p_c, and the unidirectional stress is added without permitting the water content of the specimen to change, the value of C ranges from about 10 for highly colloidal clays to 100 for silty or slightly sandy clays. From slow tests very much smaller values are obtained.

Stress–Strain Characteristics of Soils in Place

The stress–strain relations illustrated by Figure 40 are characteristic for all soils in any state. As a consequence, they determine the general nature of the deformations of any mass of soil due to the application or removal of load or due to excavation. Whenever the engineer has an opportunity to observe the deformation of soils or the displacements due to a change in load on a footing or on a pile, he will recognize the fundamental relations shown in the figure. They have not the remotest resemblance to the corresponding relations for perfectly elastic materials. This fact alone should suffice to discourage indiscriminate reliance on conclusions based on the fundamental assumptions of the theory of elasticity.

Experience indicates that the stress–strain characteristics of sand in place are not significantly different from those of the same materials in the laboratory. However, for clays, the values of the moduli E_i, E_s, and E_h in the field are much greater than the results of laboratory tests on undisturbed samples would lead us to expect. Even the so-called soft clays in place appear to have the stress–strain characteristics of fairly rigid solids, except in those parts of the mass where the structure of the clay has been considerably disturbed by a radical change in stress due to load or excavation. However, this difference does not invalidate the general relations between the changes in stress due to construction operations and the corresponding linear and volumetric changes in strain in the soil.

Application of a surcharge to part of the surface of a clay stratum increases the all-around pressure p_c in the clay beneath the loaded area. However, because of the low permeability of the clay, the increase of the effective part of the additional all-around pressure and the corresponding consolidation take place very slowly. Since an increase in the neutral part of the all-around pressure changes neither the strength nor the stress–strain characteristics of a soil, these properties do not change during the application of the load. As time goes on, the neutral stresses decrease as the clay consolidates, and the properties of the clay experience a corresponding change.

The excavation of a cut or a tunnel reduces the pressure p_c in the adjoining clay and causes the clay to swell. Experience indicates that the swelling commonly does not start until a few days after the pressure has been reduced and that it then proceeds at a slow rate. Since the slope of the right-hand part of the decompression curve of every soil is very gentle (for example curve bc in Figure 21a), the swelling of normally loaded clays is likely to be imperceptible except in those parts of the mass where the confining pressure drops to less than about 30 per cent of its initial value.

ART. 19. EFFECT OF VIBRATIONS ON SOILS

It is a matter of common experience that vibrations due to pile driving, traffic, or the operation of machinery increase the density of a sand and cause its surface to subside. Damage to buildings may be caused by the subsidence and is often the subject of lawsuits against the parties responsible for the vibrations. On the other hand, vibrations are also one of the most economical means for compacting embankments of sand or natural layers of loose sand prior to the construction of foundations, Article 50. Hence, the effect of vibrations on soils may be harmful or beneficial, but it always deserves attention.

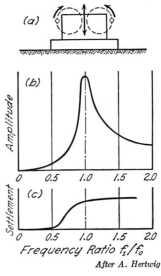

In order to investigate the factors that influence the compacting effect of vibration, the apparatus shown diagramatically in Figure 43a has been used. It consists of a bearing plate 2.5 to 10 sq ft in area and two equal eccentric weights which rotate in opposite directions. The total weight of the vibrator is about 24 tons. The pressure exerted on the ground by the base plate of the apparatus consists of a static pressure equal to the weight of the equipment, plus a pulsating force with a maximum intensity equal to the centrifugal force of the two eccentric weights. The number of downward impulses per unit of time is the *frequency* of the impulse expressed in cycles per second. The greatest vertical distance through which the base moves from its equilibrium position is called the *amplitude* of the vibrations of the base. At a certain frequency the amplitude is a maximum (see Figure 43b). This frequency is approximately equal to the natural frequency f_0 of the vibrator and the vibrating portion of the supporting soil.

FIG. 43. (a) Principle of soil vibrator; relation between frequency and (b) amplitude of vibrations and (c) settlement of vibrator base.

The term *natural frequency* indicates the frequency of the vibrations that ensue if a body with well-defined boundaries is acted on by a single impulse. If the impulse is periodic, the amplitude of the resulting *forced vibrations* increases as the frequency f_1 of the impulse approaches the natural frequency of the body. At a frequency close to the natural frequency, the amplitude is a maximum. This state is called *resonance*. In Figure 43*b* it is represented by a peak.

Table 9 contains values of the natural frequency of the vibrator shown in Figure 43*a*, operating on different soils and soft rocks. The values were obtained by steadily increasing the frequency of the impulse until resonance occurred.

TABLE 9

NATURAL FREQUENCY OF VIBRATOR ON VARIOUS TYPES OF SOIL

Supporting Soil or Rock	Frequency, cycles per second
Loose fill	19.1
Dense artificial cinder fill	21.3
Fairly dense medium sand	24.1
Very dense mixed-grained sand	26.7
Dense pea gravel	28.1
Soft limestone	30.0
Sandstone	34.0

From H. LORENZ, Neue Ergebnisse der dynamischen Baugrunduntersuchung, *Z. Ver. deut. Ing.*, Vol 78, 1934.

The natural frequency depends not only on the properties of the supporting soil but also to a certain extent on the weight and dimensions of the vibrator. However, if the same equipment is used on different soils, the natural frequency increases with increasing density and decreasing compressibility of the soil. By taking advantage of this fact, extensive use has been made of the equipment shown in Figure 43*a* for determining the degree of compaction of artificial fills and for comparing the effectiveness of different methods of compaction.

If a vibrator operates on sand, the sand beneath the bearing plate becomes compacted. At constant frequency of the impulses, the size of the zone of compaction increases at a rate that decreases with time. The ultimate size of the zone depends on the intensity of the periodic impulses exerted by the vibrator and on the initial density of the sand. Beyond the boundaries of this zone the density of the sand remains practically unchanged.

Since the vibrator rests on the surface of the zone of compaction, the process of compaction is associated with a settlement of the vibrator. If the frequency of the impulse is gradually increased, the corresponding settlement of the vibrator increases as shown in Figure 43*c*. As the natural frequency is approached, the settlement increases rapidly and becomes many times greater than the settlement produced by a static load of the same magnitude as the pulsating force. The range of frequencies within which the increase of settlement is greatest is called the *critical range*. It seems to extend from $\frac{1}{2}$ to $1\frac{1}{2}$ times the natural frequency.

If the frequency of a vibrating engine supported on sand is within the critical range for the sand, the resulting settlement is very much greater than that which would be caused by the equivalent static forces. The frequency of vibrations caused by the slight but inevitable eccentricity of the rotating parts of steam turbines happens to be within the critical range for sand (Article 62). Therefore, foundations for steam turbines on strata of loose sand settle excessively unless the sand is artificially compacted before the turbine foundations are constructed. Whatever the subsoil conditions may be, it is advisable to make special provisions to reduce the amplitude of the forced vibrations.

The effect of vibration on clays is far less conspicuous than on sand because the cohesive bond between clay particles interferes with intergranular slippage. Nevertheless, even a soft clay consolidates to a moderate extent when it is continually subjected to intense vibrations having a frequency close to the natural frequency of the clay.

Chapter III

DRAINAGE OF SOILS

ART. 20. WATER TABLE, SOIL MOISTURE, AND CAPILLARY PHENOMENA

Definitions

The terms *water level, water table,* and *phreatic surface* designate the locus of the levels to which water rises in observation wells in free communication with the voids of the soil in situ. The water table can also be defined as the surface at which the neutral stress u_w, Article 12, in the soil is equal to zero.

If the water contained in a soil were subject to no force other than gravity, the soil above the water table would be perfectly dry. In reality, every soil in the field is completely saturated for a certain distance above the water table and is partly saturated above this level. The water that occupies the voids of the soil located above the water table constitutes *soil moisture*.

If the lower part of a mass of dry soil comes into contact with water, the water rises in the voids to a certain height above the free-water surface. The upward flow into the voids of the soil is attributed to the *surface tension* of the water. The seat of the surface tension is located at the boundary between air and water. Within the boundary zone the water is in a state of tension comparable to that in a stretched rubber membrane attached to the walls of the voids of the soil. However, in contrast to the tension in a stretched membrane, the surface tension in the boundary film of water is entirely unaffected by either the contraction or stretching of the film. The concepts regarding the molecular interactions that produce surface tension are still in a controversial state. Nevertheless, the existence of a tensile stress in the surface film was established beyond any doubt more than a century ago, and the intensity of this stress has since been determined by very different methods with consistent results.

Rise of Water in Capillary Tubes

The phenomenon of capillary rise can be demonstrated by immersing the lower end of a very small-diameter glass tube into water. Such a tube is known as a capillary tube. As soon as the lower end of the tube comes into contact with the water, the attraction between the glass and the water molecules combined with the surface tension of the water pulls the water up into the tube to a height h_c above the water level, Figure 44a. The height h_c is known as the *height of capillary rise*. The upper surface of the water assumes the shape of a cup, called the *meniscus*, that joins the walls of the tube at an angle α known as the *contact angle*. The value of α depends on the material that constitutes the wall and on the type of impurities that cover it. For glass tubes with chemically clean or wetted walls α is equal to 0°, and the water rises in such tubes to the greatest height compatible with the diameter of the tube and the surface tension of the water. If the walls are not chemically clean, α is likely to have some value intermediate between 0° and 90°, and the corresponding height of capillary rise is smaller than h_c for $\alpha = 0°$. Finally, if the walls are covered with a thin film of grease, α is greater than 90°, and the meniscus is located below the free-water level. This phenomenon is ascribed to a repulsion between the molecules of the water and the grease.

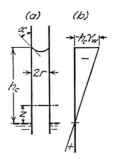

FIG. 44. (*a*) Rise of water in capillary tube; (*b*) state of stress of water in capillary tube.

If T_s denotes the surface tension in grams per centimeter, and γ_w the unit weight of water, equilibrium requires that

$$h_c \pi r^2 \gamma_w = 2\pi r T_s \cos \alpha$$

whence

$$h_c = \frac{2T_s}{r\gamma_w} \cos \alpha \qquad (20.1)$$

The value of T_s decreases slightly with increasing temperature. At room temperature it is about 0.075 gm per cm, and γ_w is equal to 1 gm per cu cm. Therefore,

$$h_c(\text{cm}) = \frac{0.15}{r(\text{cm})} \cos \alpha \qquad (20.2)$$

Above the free-water level the hydrostatic pressure in the water u_w is negative. At an elevation z it is

$$u_w = -z\gamma_w \qquad (20.3)$$

Capillary Rise of Water in Soils

In contrast to capillary tubes, the continuous voids in soils and most other porous materials have a variable width. They communicate with each other in every direction and constitute an intricate network of voids. If such a network is invaded by water from below, the lower part of the network becomes completely saturated. In the upper part, however, the water occupies only the narrowest voids, and the wider ones remain filled with air. In the laboratory, the rise of water into the voids of a dry sand due to surface tension can be demonstrated by the test arrangement shown in Figure 45a. The sand is poured into an upright glass tube with a screen across the bottom. The bottom of the tube is then placed just below a free-water surface, whereupon the water rises into the sand. That part of the sand in which the voids become partly or

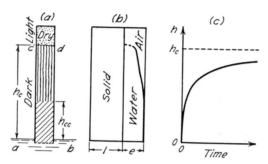

Fig. 45.   Capillary rise of water into dry sand.

completely occupied by liquid assumes a dark color, whereas the remainder is light. To a height h_{cc} above the water level the sand is completely saturated. Between h_{cc} and h_c it is partially saturated, as shown in Figure 45b. The height h_c is called the *height of capillary rise*. Figure 45c shows the time rate at which the upper surface of the moistened zone approaches its equilibrium position at elevation h_c.

As the effective grain size decreases, the size of the voids also decreases, and the height of capillary rise increases. The height h_c (cm) is approximately equal to

$$h_c = \frac{C}{eD_{10}} \qquad (20.4)$$

in which e is the void ratio, D_{10} (centimeters) is Allen Hazen's effective size, Article 6, and C (square centimeters) is an empirical constant that depends on the shape of the grains and on the surface impurities. It ranges between 0.1 and 0.5 sq cm. However, since the decrease in permeability associated with a decrease in effective size reduces the rate of capillary rise, the height to which water will rise within a specified time, such as 24 hr, is a maximum at some intermediate grain size. In Figure 46 the abscissas represent the logarithm of the grain size of a uniform quartz powder in a fairly dense state, and the ordinates represent the height to which the water rises in 24 hr. The height of rise is a maximum for a grain size of about 0.02 mm. For a 48-hr rise the optimum grain size would be slightly smaller.

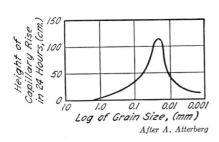

After A. Atterberg

FIG. 46. Relation between grain size of uniform quartz powder and height of capillary rise for 24-hr period.

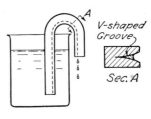

FIG. 47. Capillary flow through V-shaped groove.

CAPILLARY SIPHONING

Capillary forces are able to raise water against the force of gravity not only into capillary tubes or the voids in columns of dry soil, but also into narrow open channels or V-shaped grooves. This fact can be demonstrated by the apparatus shown in Figure 47. If the highest point of the groove is located below the level to which the surface tension can lift the water, the capillary forces will pull the water into the descending part of the groove and will slowly empty the vessel. This process is known as *capillary siphoning*. The same process may also occur in the voids of a soil in the field. For example, water may flow over the crest of an impermeable core in a dam

FIG. 48. Capillary flow over impermeable core in earth fill.

or dike, as shown in Figure 48, in spite of the fact that the elevation of the free-water surface is below that of the crest of the core. Capillary siphoning over the crest of cores was found to cause a loss of 450 gal per min for a length of 12 miles of the canal between Berlin and Stettin in Germany. The impermeable core of the dikes extended one foot above the water table. When the height of the core was increased 16 in., the loss was reduced to 100 gal per min.

DISCONTINUOUS SOIL MOISTURE

Between the heights h_{cc} and h_c, Figure 45a, some of the void space is occupied by continuous channels of air. The remainder is occupied by threads of water. Since these threads are also continuous, the stress in the water up to an elevation h_c is governed by equation 20.3. However, if a sand is only moist, the water particles do not communicate with each other, and equation 20.3 is not applicable.

The water contained in a moist sand is known as *contact moisture* because each drop of water surrounds a point of contact between two soil grains, as shown in Figure 49. The surface tension at the boundary between the water and the air in the adjoining voids pulls the soil grains together with a force P known as the *contact pressure*. The frictional resistance produced by the contact pressure has the same effect as if the sand had a certain amount of cohesion (see Figures 52a and b). As soon as the sand is immersed, the surface tension is eliminated, the contact pressure becomes equal to zero, and the sand disintegrates.

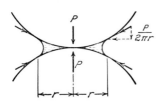

Fig. 49.   Forces produced by contact moisture.

The mechanical effect of the cohesion due to contact moisture depends on the relative density of the sand. If the sand is dense, the cohesion increases its shearing resistance to such an extent that vertical slopes with a height of several feet can stand without lateral support. On the other hand, if a damp sand is loosely deposited, for instance by dumping, the cohesion prevents the soil particles from settling into stable positions and reduces the bearing capacity of the sand almost to zero. The volume of such a sand may exceed that of the same sand in a loose dry state by 20 to 30 per cent. This phenomenon is known as *bulking*. Since the forces that maintain the grains in their unstable positions are extremely small, bulking occurs only within a depth of 1 or 2 ft below the surface of the sand. Watering reduces the porosity of the sand to that of the same sand in a dry or saturated loose state because it eliminates the surface tension of the water.

Common Misconceptions

Since the physical causes of the capillary movement of water through soils are not so obvious as those of percolation under the influence of gravity, several misconceptions have found their way into publications. It has, for instance, been maintained that water cannot rise in a capillary tube higher than in the suction tube of a pump (about 30 ft). The height to which water can be lifted by suction depends on the atmospheric pressure, and it is independent of the diameter of the suction tube. On the other hand, the height to which water can be lifted by capillarity is independent of atmospheric pressure, and it increases with decreasing diameter of the tube. Hence it is evident that the two types of rise have nothing in common. In a vacuum water cannot be lifted in a suction tube to any height, whereas the height of capillary rise is the same as under atmospheric pressure.

It has also been maintained that most of the water contained in fine sand does not participate in the flow of seepage because it is held in the sand by molecular attraction. This opinion is incompatible with the well-established fact that the thickness of the layers of water that are bound to the solid by molecular attraction does not exceed about 0.1μ. Beyond these layers the water is normal and able to flow as freely as in a pipe line. Since the quantity of water located within a distance of 0.1μ from the surface of the grains in a saturated sand is negligible compared to the total, practically the entire water content consists of normal water which participates in seepage flow.

PROBLEMS

1. The effective size of a very fine sand is 0.05 mm, and its void ratio is 0.6. What is the height h_c of capillary rise for this sand?

   Ans.   Between 33 and 165 cm.

2. The unconfined compressive strength of a dense fine moist sand is 0.2 kg per sq cm, and its angle of internal friction is 40°. What is the intensity of the all-around pressure p_c that would be required to produce the same effect on the strength of the sand as the cohesion produced by the contact moisture?

   Ans.   0.056 kg per sq cm.

ART. 21.   PROCESSES OF DRAINAGE

PURPOSE AND TYPES OF DRAINAGE

In engineering practice drainage is used wherever it is desirable to eliminate seepage pressure, to reduce the danger of frost damage, or to increase the shearing resistance of the soil by reducing the neutral stresses (see Articles 12 and 15). It consists of lowering the water table below the base of the mass of soil which requires protection or reinforcement.

In order to lower the water table to a given elevation, it is necessary to establish below this level a system of collectors located in wells, galleries, or ditches. The water flows by gravity out of the soil into the collectors, and it is removed from the collectors by pumping or other appropriate means. Since the hydraulic gradient at the walls of every collector is very high, the finer soil particles are gradually washed out of the ground into the collectors unless the walls are surrounded by filters which consist of wire mesh or of screened sand or gravel. The openings of filter screens should be roughly equal to the 60 per cent grain size D_{60} of the adjoining natural soil. Sand or gravel filters should satisfy the grain-size requirements specified at the end of Article 11.

Drainage wells are commonly lined with steel tubes called *well casings*, which are perforated where they are in contact with water-bearing strata. If the casing has a diameter less than about $2\frac{1}{2}$ in., it is called a *well point*. The water is pumped out of a group of well points through a *header pipe* that interconnects the upper ends of all the casings. If the diameter of a drainage well is 12 in. or more, the water is commonly pumped out through a suction tube with a very much smaller diameter, and the space between the tube and the walls of the hole is filled with coarse sand or gravel. Such wells are known as *filter wells*. The annular filter acts as a substitute for the perforated well casing. Collectors in ditches or galleries usually consist of open-jointed pipe lines embedded in sand or gravel that satisfies the grain-size requirements for a filter.

In sand part of the water that flows out of the voids into the collectors is replaced by air (*drainage by air invasion*). However, very fine-grained soils remain in a saturated state, and the volume of the voids of the soil decreases by an amount equal to that of the expelled water (*drainage by consolidation*).

The drainage of any type of soil can also be accomplished by evaporation from a surface exposed to the atmosphere. This process is called *drainage by desiccation*. Depending on the type of soil, it can take place by air invasion, by consolidation, or by air invasion preceded by consolidation.

Very fine-grained soils can also be drained by passing an electric current through them. This process is known as *drainage by electro-osmosis*. If the uppermost part of a saturated mass of very fine-grained soil is exposed to a temperature below the freezing point, water is drawn out of the lower part and accumulates in the upper part, where it participates in the formation of ice layers. The seepage pressure of the percolating water consolidates the layer of soil located beneath the zone of freezing. Therefore, it may be said that this layer is subject to *drainage by frost action*. On the other hand, the average water content of the soil contained within the zone of freezing increases. The following paragraphs contain a description of the different processes of drainage.

Drainage by Gravity

The smallest value to which the water content of a soil can be reduced by gravity drainage is known as the *water-holding capacity* of the soil. In order to obtain numerical values for comparing the water-holding capacity of different soils, various laboratory procedures are used. In some, known as *gravity methods*, the water drains out of the sample under the influence of gravity alone. In others, known as *suction methods*, the force of gravity is augmented by applying a vacuum at the bottom of the sample or air pressure at the top. In a third type, known as *centrifuge methods*, the gravity forces are replaced by inertia forces of much greater intensity.

If the void ratio of a soil after drainage, the unit weight of the solid soil particles, and the water-holding capacity are known, the degree of

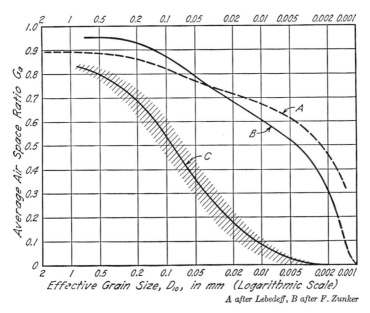

A *after Lebedeff*, B *after F. Zunker*

Fig. 50.   Relation between grain size and degree of aeration after drainage. Curve *A* obtained by suction method; curve *B* by centrifuge method; curve *C* by field measurements.

saturation S_r (per cent), see Article 7, and the air-space ratio G_a of the drained soil can be computed. The *air-space ratio* is defined by the equation,

$$G_a = \frac{\text{air space}}{\text{total void space}} = 1 - \frac{S_r(\%)}{100} \tag{21.1}$$

Curves *A* and *B* in Figure 50 represent the relation between the air-space ratio and the effective grain size for different soil fractions that were drained by using two different methods. The data for plotting curve *A* were obtained by submitting saturated samples to drainage by suction. A vacuum was applied for 2 hr at the bottom of samples 4 in. high. Curve *B* represents the results of tests made by the centrifuge method, in which the samples were subjected for 2 min to a force 18,000 times that of gravity.

In the laboratory the drainage of sand under the influence of gravity continues for years at a decreasing rate, even if the sand is fairly coarse. Figure 51a represents two samples of sand $2\frac{1}{2}$ years after the start of drainage. In both samples the air-space ratio increased quite rapidly

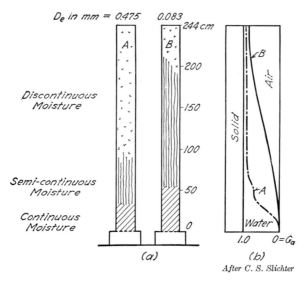

FIG. 51. Soil moisture in two different samples of sand after drainage for $2\frac{1}{2}$ years in laboratory.

with increasing elevation above the water table, as shown in Figure 51b. Furthermore, even at the end of $2\frac{1}{2}$ years, the average air-space ratio of both samples was still increasing.

In the field every process of drainage by gravity is accompanied periodically by an inflow of water from rain or melting snow and ice. The effect of the recharge on the average moisture content of a drained soil in the field depends not only on the amount of recharge and evaporation, but also to a considerable extent on details of stratification. Furthermore, experience indicates that the air-space ratio for a drained soil in the field is practically independent of the elevation above the water table, whereas in drained laboratory specimens it increases consistently in an upward direction, as shown in Figure 51b. Hence, there is no definite relation between the water-holding capacity of a soil after drainage in the laboratory and that of the same soil after drainage in the field. This can be seen by comparing the laboratory curves A and B in

Figure 50 with curve *C*. The shaded area surrounding curve *C* represents the relation between air-space ratio and effective grain size of various soils after gravity drainage in the field under climatic conditions similar to those in the east-central part of the United States. Observations in regions with different climatic conditions may lead to very different curves. Yet no field curves can be expected to have more than the general trend in common with the laboratory curves.

Fortunately, in connection with engineering operations, the quantity of water drained out of the ground is seldom of importance. Of much greater significance are the mechanical effects of the drainage and the time required to produce them.

RATE AND EFFECT OF DRAINAGE BY GRAVITY

As stated before, drainage can be accomplished by pumping from filter wells, by tapping the water-bearing strata with galleries, or by diverting the water into drainage ditches. Whatever the method of drainage may be, the time required for draining the soil is always a factor of outstanding importance.

Theoretical methods for estimating the rate of drainage by air invasion are still rather unsatisfactory. Hence, in order to estimate the time required for draining a sand stratum, the engineer must rely primarily on experience. The drainage of a stratum of clean coarse sand by pumping from filter wells spaced not in excess of 40 ft can usually be accomplished within a few days (very rapid drainage). On the other hand, the same operation in a very fine sand may require several months (slow drainage). The methods available for draining soils and the conditions for their successful application are discussed in Article 47. The settlements associated with lowering the water table are the subject of Article 61.

DESICCATION OF SOILS

If a specimen of soft clay is exposed to the air, water is drawn from the interior of the specimen toward the surface where it evaporates. During this process, the clay becomes stiffer and finally very hard. The state at which evaporation ceases depends on the relative humidity of the surrounding air. According to the laws of physics, water evaporates at every air–water boundary unless the relative humidity of the air is at least equal to a certain value that is a function of the tension in the water. The *relative humidity* h_{ra} is defined as the ratio between the weight of water vapor actually contained in the air at a given temperature and the greatest quantity of vapor that can be contained in the air at the same temperature. In humid climates the relative humidity commonly ranges between 0.15 and 0.95 and exceptionally reaches 0.99. If the relative humidity of the air above a free-water surface is smaller than 1.0, water evaporates until the relative humidity of the superincumbent air is equal to 1.0, or until the water has completely evaporated. If the water is in a state of tension, it ceases to evaporate at a lower value of relative humidity. This lower value h_r is designated as the *relative vapor pressure* of the water. Within a temperature range of 10° to 30° C, and a relative vapor-pressure range of 0.7 to 1.0, the relationship between the neutral stress u_w in the water and the relative vapor pressure h_r of the water can be expressed approximately by the equation,

$$u_w(\text{kg/cm}^2) = -1500(1 - h_r) \qquad (21.2)$$

For example, if $h_r = 0.90$, $u_w = -150$ kg per sq cm. Hence, if the neutral stress in an exposed specimen of clay is equal to -150 kg per sq cm, the water content of the clay does not remain constant unless the relative humidity of the surrounding air is equal to 0.90. If the relative vapor pressure is smaller, the clay continues to lose water by evaporation, whereas, if it is greater, water condenses on the surface of the clay and causes the clay to swell until the tension in the water drops to the value determined by equation 21.2. This fact can be used as a basis for computing the tension in the water contained in fine-grained porous materials such as clays.

If the water evaporates at the ends of a capillary tube having a radius r (centimeters), the curvature of the menisci and the stress u_w in the water increase until u_w equals $-h_c\gamma_w$. Substitution of h_c from equation 20.2 leads to

$$u_{w\max} (\text{gm/cm}^2) = -\frac{0.15\gamma_w \ (\text{gm/cm}^3)}{r(\text{cm})} \cos \alpha \qquad (21.3)$$

Further evaporation causes the water to withdraw into the interior of the tube at a constant neutral stress. A similar process takes place in the pore water of desiccating soils. When a soil dries, the value u_w first increases until it assumes the greatest value compatible with the size of the voids at the surface of the soil. Further evaporation causes air to penetrate the specimen, whereupon the color of the soil changes from dark to light. At the beginning of this second stage, the water content of the specimen is equal to the shrinkage limit, Article 8. However, during this stage, the neutral stress u_w can increase further because the water withdraws into the narrowest corners and grooves. Evaporation does not cease until the relative vapor pressure h_r, equation 21.2, becomes equal to the relative humidity h_{ra}.

The water that remains in the dried soil constitutes the contact moisture mentioned in Article 20. After desiccation at room temperature, the water content of soils ranges from almost zero for clean sand to 6 or 7 per cent for typical clays. The corresponding air-space ratio ranges from 1.0 to about 0.8. At this state a perfectly clean sand is cohesionless, whereas a clay is very hard.

If an oven-dried soil specimen is cooled in contact with the atmosphere, its water content increases. The water taken up by the soil particles from the surrounding atmosphere is called the *hygroscopic moisture*. The amount of hygroscopic moisture varies for a given specimen with the temperature and relative humidity of the air. In a general way it increases with decreasing grain size. For sands it is negligible. For silty soils it is very small, yet sufficient to induce bulking. In clay it may amount to more than 5 per cent of the dry weight.

When an air-dry clay specimen is heated to a temperature somewhat above the boiling point of water, its water content decreases slightly. At this stage some of the physical properties of the clay undergo changes that appear to be permanent. The changes are disclosed by permanent changes in the Atterberg limits. Further increase of the temperature to several hundred degrees centigrade above the boiling point leads to actual fusion between the grains at their points of contact. This process produces a strong and permanent bond between the grains and gives the clay the characteristics of a solid body. The transformation of sand–clay mixtures into brick occurs in a similar manner.

The rate at which water evaporates from the surface of clay specimens under given conditions of exposure decreases with decreasing water content. At the liquid limit the rate of evaporation is approximately equal to that from a free surface. At such a surface the rate of evaporation depends on the temperature, the relative humidity, and the wind velocity. In the United States the area of lowest evaporation from large free-water surfaces is the Great Lakes region, where the rate of evaporation ranges from 15 to 20 in. per year. To the west and south of the Great Lakes region it gradually increases. It amounts to about 70 in. in southwest Texas and southeast New Mexico. In the central parts of the Imperial Valley, Calif., values up to 90 in. per yr have been recorded.

Even if a clay sample coated with paraffin is stored in a humid room, it gradually shrinks away from its shell. This shrinkage indicates the escape of water vapor through invisible but continuous voids in the paraffin. To prevent loss of water by evaporation, it is necessary to keep the samples in metal tubes and to insert metal disks between the ends of the samples and the paraffin seal at the ends of the tubes.

As the water content of a desiccating clay decreases, the rate of evaporation also decreases because the tension in the pore water increases. According to equation 21.2, the increase in tension involves a decrease in the relative vapor pressure. Such a decrease has the same retarding effect on the rate of evaporation at constant relative humidity as an increase of the relative humidity has on the rate of evaporation from a free-water surface.

Below the shrinkage limit the rate of evaporation is further retarded, because the relative humidity of the air in the voids is always higher than in the adjoining open air. As soon as the relative vapor pressure in the pore space becomes equal to the relative humidity of the surrounding air, further evaporation ceases. If the relative humidity then increases, the water content of the clay increases slightly.

EFFECT OF DESICCATION ON STRENGTH OF SOILS

While a soil is drying, tension develops in the pore water. This tension increases with decreasing water content, whereas the total normal stress on a given section through the soil remains practically unaltered. Since the total normal stress is equal to the sum of the neutral and effective stresses, the increasing tension in the pore water involves an equivalent increase of the effective pressure. As desiccation increases the tension in the pore water from zero to $-u_w$, the surface tension simultaneously produces an effective all-around pressure,

$$p_k = -u_w \qquad (21.4)$$

This pressure is known as *capillary pressure*. It increases the shearing resistance of the soil along any section by

$$\Delta s = p_k \tan \phi \qquad (21.5)$$

wherein ϕ represents the angle of internal friction for sand or the consolidated-quick value of the angle of shearing resistance for clays.

At the shrinkage limit air invades the voids of the specimen, and, as a consequence, the soil moisture ceases to be continuous. The tension in the water that remains in the clay produces contact pressures, as illustrated in Figure 49, and the contact pressures in turn produce shearing resistance. However, because of the discontinuity of the pore water, the relation between Δs and u_w is no longer governed by equations 21.3 and 21.5.

Because of capillary pressure even perfectly cohesionless materials such as fine clean sands may temporarily acquire the characteristics of cohesive materials. As a consequence, samples of the material possess a definite compressive strength when unconfined. Since the cohesion of such soils disappears completely after immersion, it is referred to as *apparent cohesion*.

The water content at which the unconfined compressive strength q_u of a desiccating soil sample is a maximum depends chiefly on the grain size. This statement is illustrated by Figure 52, which shows the effect of a decrease of the water content, due to desiccation, on the compressive strength of three different soils.

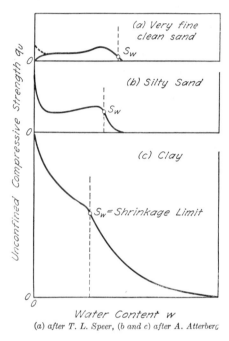

The water content of each soil at the shrinkage limit is denoted by S_w. For values of w smaller than S_w the degree of saturation, equation 7.4, is approximately equal to $100w/S_w$.

For a perfectly clean fine sand moistened with distilled water, Figure 52a, q_u is a maximum for a degree of saturation of about 80 per cent. Further desiccation ultimately reduces q_u to zero. However, if the interstices are filled with tap water, the impurities are precipitated during evaporation and form a very thin but continuous layer that adheres to the grains and interconnects them at their points of contact. Thus, during the last stage of desiccation, the sand acquires a slight cohesion, as indicated in Figure 52a by the dash line.

(a) after T. L. Speer, (b and c) after A. Atterberg

Fig. 52.   Unconfined compressive strength of various soils at water contents above and at various stages of desiccation below the shrinkage limit.

The relation between w and q_u for a fine silty sand is shown in Figure 52b. As the water content approaches the shrinkage limit, the strength increases. At the shrinkage limit, air invades the voids of the specimen, and the strength decreases gradually until the degree of saturation becomes approximately equal to 10 per cent. Thereafter it increases and becomes greater than at the shrinkage limit.

The strength of clays, Figure 52c, below the shrinkage limit increases at an increasing rate as the dry state is approached.

DESICCATION UNDER FIELD CONDITIONS

In nature desiccation takes place whenever the surface of the soil is not permanently flooded. The apparent cohesion of very fine-grained silty sands due to periodic desiccation may be quite large. Since rain water does not expel more than a small part of the air contained in the voids, the cohesion survives even wet spells of long duration. As a consequence, such soils have often been mistaken, particularly in semi-arid and arid regions, for soft rocks. However, if the surface of the soil is flooded, the cohesion gradually disappears, and the soil may start to slide.

The desiccation of a soft clay layer proceeds very slowly from the exposed surface in a downward direction and leads to the formation of a crust that becomes thicker with age. As explained in Article 13, if such a crust is buried beneath clay sediments and is permanently flooded, it constitutes a stiff precompressed layer located between soft normally loaded strata. Thick layers of soft clay can be consolidated by circulating hot dry air through systems of ventilation tunnels, but such a procedure is rarely economical.

In semiarid regions such as western Texas the desiccation of clays in the dry season proceeds to a depth as great as 20 ft. Within this depth the clay is broken up by shrinkage cracks. During the rainy season water enters the cracks, and the clay swells. The swelling causes an important rise of the ground surface. Beneath areas covered by buildings the loss of water due to evaporation is very much smaller than the corresponding loss beneath the adjacent areas. Hence, the water content of the clay located beneath the covered areas increases for many years at a decreasing rate and causes a heave of the central part of the areas with reference to their outer boundaries. The amount of heave is practically independent of the weight of the buildings, but its effect on the buildings is very similar to that of unequal settlement. Under unfavorable climatic and soil conditions, the heave can, in the course of time, become greater than a foot.

If the basement floor of a centrally heated building rests on clay, the pore water of the clay may evaporate through the voids of the concrete, whereupon the clay shrinks away from the concrete and deprives the floor of its support. This undesirable development can be prevented by covering the surface of the clay with a bituminous layer before placing the concrete.

Slaking

When a dried specimen of clay, Figure 53, is rapidly immersed in water, the outer portions of the specimen become saturated, and air is trapped in the inner portions. If the surrounding water were weightless, the tension in the water at the edge of the trapped air would be equal to the maximum capillary tension $-p_k$, and the pressure in the trapped air would equal p_k. If the weight of the surrounding water produces a pressure u_w at mid-height of the specimen, the pressure in the trapped air is $p_k + u_w$. The pressure in the air produces a tension in the solid skeleton that is likely to cause failure in tension along some surface such as ab. This process is known as *slaking*. It is responsible for the breaking up and ultimate sloughing of unprotected clay slopes.

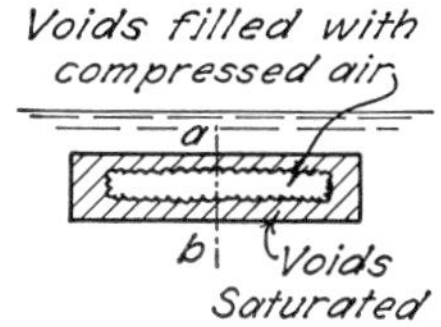

Fig. 53. Diagram illustrating process of slaking of dried clay.

DRAINAGE BY ELECTRO–OSMOSIS

If two electrodes are driven into a saturated soil and an electric current is made to flow from one to the other, the water contained in the soil migrates from the positive electrode (anode) toward the negative one (cathode). If the cathode consists of a well point, the water seeps into it, whence it can be removed by pumping.

The movement of the water is due to the fact (see Article 4) that the surface of the soil particles carries a negative charge. As a consequence, positively charged ions in the water are attracted toward the soil particles, and the film of water adjacent to the soil is positively charged because of the preponderance of positive ions. Although there is no sharp boundary between the positively charged and the neutral water, for present purposes the seat of the electric charges may be regarded as a well-defined layer, Figure 54a, known as the *electric double layer*. The positive ions, which are concentrated in the water near the soil particles, are attracted by the negative electrode and repelled by the positive one. Hence, the positive layer together with the enclosed column of neutral water migrates toward the cathode. The flow of water produced by the electric current is known as an *electro-osmotic phenomenon*.

It should be noted that the velocity of flow is constant over the cross section of the entire column of water surrounded by the double layer, whereas the velocity of gravity flow through a capillary increases from the walls toward the center of the tube as shown in Figure 54b.

The velocity v (centimeters per second) at which water flows by electro-osmosis through a cylindrical tube is given approximately by the equation,

$$v = \frac{1.02 \times 10^{-4} deE}{\eta l} \qquad (21.6)$$

wherein e (coulombs/cm^2) = electric charge per unit of area of the walls of the tube,

E (volts) = difference in electric potential of the two ends of the tube,

d (cm) = thickness of the electric double layer,

η (gm sec/cm^2) = viscosity of the water

l (cm) = length of the tube

For capillaries with a diameter less than about 0.002 mm, the viscosity η increases somewhat with decreasing diameter. Hence, the

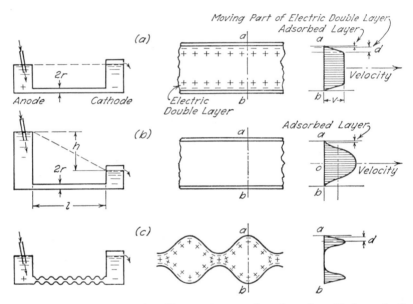

Fig. 54. Diagrams illustrating difference between flow through capillaries and soils produced by a hydraulic head (b) and by an electric current (a and c).

velocity v decreases. However, the few experiments that have been made indicate that the decrease of velocity with decreasing grain size is much more rapid than can be accounted for by the increase of the viscosity. The probable cause of this phenomenon is as follows. In contrast to the width of capillaries in a bundle of capillary tubes, that of the voids in soils varies from point to point. Consequently, the average velocity of the water varies from section to section, Figure 54c. In the narrow channels interconnecting the bulbs the velocity is very high. In the bulbs, however, the water is almost stationary, and the friction along the outer boundaries of the stationary bodies of water retards the movement of the charged film near the walls of the bulbs. The distribution of the velocity within the bulbs probably resembles that shown in the right side of Figure 54c. These conditions invalidate equation 21.6.

The quantities e and d in equation 21.6 depend to a large extent on the chemical composition of the walls of the capillary tube and of the substances other than water contained in the adsorbed layer (see Article 4). Hence, for a given length of tube, the quantity of electricity required to move a unit of water from one end of the tube to the other in a given length of time depends to a large extent on the chemical constitution of the adsorbed layer. Laboratory tests have indicated that these conclusions are also valid for soils.

Electro-osmotic drainage of fine-grained soils is associated with consolidation. Like any other process of consolidation, it starts at the drainage surface (cathode) and proceeds toward the interior of the mass.

Frost Heave and Frost–Heave Prevention

If the water contained in the voids of a saturated clean sand or gravel freezes, the structure of the soil remains unchanged. The process of freezing merely increases the volume of each void by 9 per cent because of the expansion of the water contained in the void. On the other hand, if a saturated fine-grained soil freezes, the process involves the formation of layers of clear ice oriented roughly parallel to the surface exposed to low temperature. The thickness of the individual ice layers may increase to several inches, and the soil subject to freezing assumes the character of a stratified material consisting of alternate layers of soil and clear ice.

Opinions regarding the molecular mechanics of the formation of the ice layers and the intensity of the forces involved are still controversial. Nevertheless, the conditions for the formation of the layers and the means for preventing it are already known.

Ice layers develop only in fine-grained soils. However, the critical grain size marking the boundary between soils that are subject to ice-layer formation and those that are not depends on the uniformity of the soil. In perfectly uniform soils ice layers do not develop unless the grains are smaller than 0.01 mm. Fairly uniform soils must contain at least 10 per cent of grains smaller than 0.02 mm. The formation of ice layers in mixed-grained soils requires, as a rule, that grains with a size less than 0.02 mm constitute at least 3 per cent of the total aggregate. In soils with less than 1 per cent of grains smaller than 0.02 mm ice layers are not formed under any conditions which may be encountered in the field.

The mechanical causes of the flow of water toward a zone of freezing are identical with those compelling the water to flow from a ground-water reservoir through the voids of a soil toward a surface of evaporation. As the ice crystals grow, they act like jacks which push the soil grains apart and thus increase the void space.

Figure 55 represents three cylindrical specimens of a fine saturated silt. Specimen *a* is surrounded by air, whereas the lower ends of specimens *b* and *c* are immersed in water. The temperature of the upper end of each specimen is kept below the freezing point. In *a* the water that enters the ice layers is drawn out of the lower part of the specimen. As a consequence, the lower part consolidates in the same manner as if the water were pulled toward a surface of evaporation at the upper end. The

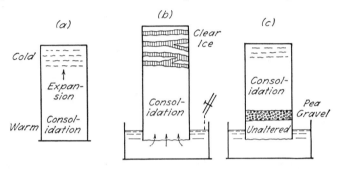

FIG. 55.   Diagram illustrating frost action in soils.   (*a*) Closed system; (*b*) open system; (*c*) method of transforming open into closed system by means of a layer of coarse sand that intercepts capillary flow toward zone of freezing.

growth of the ice layers probably continues until the water content of the lower part is reduced to the shrinkage limit. Since all the water entering the ice layers comes from within the specimen, the sample is referred to as a *closed system*. The volume increase associated with the freezing of a closed system does not exceed the volume increase of the water contained in the system. It ranges between about 3 and 5 per cent of the total volume.

In *b* the water required for the initial growth of the ice layers is also drawn out of the specimen, whereupon the lower part of the sample consolidates. However, as the consolidation progresses, more and more water is drawn from the pool of free water located below the specimen. Finally, both the rate of flow toward the zone of freezing and the water content of the unfrozen zone through which the water percolates become constant. Such a sample constitutes an *open system*. The total thickness of the ice layers contained in such a system can, at least theoretically, increase indefinitely.

The open system represented by sample *b* can be transformed into a closed system by inserting a layer of coarse-grained material between the zone of freezing temperature and the water table, as shown by *c*. Since the water cannot rise by capillarity through the coarse layer, the upper part of the sample represented in c constitutes a closed system. The lower part of the system is subject to drainage by frost action.

In engineering practice open systems are encountered wherever the vertical distance between the water table and the frost line is smaller than the height of capillary rise of the soil. Since the water that migrates out of the ground-water reservoir is continually replenished, the ice layers grow continually during the frost periods, and the ground surface located above the zone of freezing rises. This phenomenon is commonly known as *frost heave*. Even in regions with moderate winter climate, such as New England, frost heaves up to 6 in. are by no means uncommon. Since the thickness of the ice layers reflects very conspicuously the variations of the permeability of the underlying soil, the frost heave is usually nonuniform. As a consequence, highway pavements located above the heaving zone are likely to be broken up. Subsequent thaws transform the soil containing the ice layers into a zone of supersaturated material of a mushy consistency. This condition is likely to be even more detrimental to pavements than the preceding heave.

The tendency of the ice layers to develop and grow increases rapidly with decreasing grain size. On the other hand, the rate at which the water flows in an open system toward the zone of freezing decreases with decreasing grain size. Hence it is reasonable to expect that the worst frost-heave conditions would be encountered in soils having an intermediate grain size. As a matter of fact, experience has shown that the greatest difficulties with frost heave occur in fine silts and sand–silt mixtures, somewhat finer than the soils for which the capillary rise in a 24-hr period is a maximum (see Figure 46). In a body of soil with given grain-size characteristics, constituting a closed system, the intensity of the growth of ice layers increases with increasing compressibility of the soil.

Frost action in humid regions with severe winters constitutes a counterpart to the annual volume changes due to desiccation in semi-arid regions with hot summers, such as central Texas. It not only damages roads but also displaces retaining walls (see Article 46) and lifts shallow foundations. However, by inserting a layer of gravel between the highest water table and the frost line, the body of soil subject to freezing can be transformed from an open into a closed system, and frost heave can usually be kept within tolerable limits.

REFERENCES

21.1. *Physics of the Earth—Part IX, Hydrology*, edited by O. E. Meinzer, McGraw-Hill Book Company, first edition, New York, 1942, pp 331–384. Review of present knowledge concerning soil moisture

21.2. W. E. SIMPSON, Foundation Experiences with Clay in Texas, *Civil Eng.*, Vol 4 (1934), pp 581–584. Description of foundation difficulties due to periodic desiccation of subsoils in Texas.

21.3. D. WOOLTORTON, A Preliminary Investigation into the Subject of Foundations in the "Black Cotton" and "Kyatti" Soils of the Mandalay District, Burma, *Proc. Intern. Conf. Soil Mech.*, Cambridge, Mass. (1936), Vol III, pp 242–256. Description of foundation difficulties in Burma similar to those in Texas.

21.4. J. O. OSTERBERG, A Survey of the Frost-Heaving Problem, *Civil Eng.*, Vol 10 (1940), pp 100–102. Contains a condensed bibliography on the subject.

PROBLEMS

1. The water content of a sample of drained soil is 16.0 per cent, the porosity 42.0 per cent, and the unit weight of the solid soil particles is 2.70 gm per cu cm. Compute the air-space ratio.

    Ans.   0.40.

2. An undisturbed sample of very soft clay is kept without any protection in a humid room. It is noticed that the clay becomes stiffer until its unconfined compressive strength ultimately becomes equal to 10 kg per sq cm. The consolidated-quick value of the angle of shearing resistance of the clay is 20°. Compute the relative humidity of the air.

    Ans.   0.9936.

PART B
THEORETICAL SOIL MECHANICS

Theoretical soil mechanics deals principally with the limiting conditions for the equilibrium of soil masses, Chapter IV; with the deformations produced by external forces, Chapter V; and with the interaction between soil and water, Chapter VI. The soil constants that appear in the final equations are either estimated on the basis of experience or else obtained by taking the average of values furnished by laboratory tests on what are believed to be representative samples. Hence, none of the theories should be regarded as more than a means for making rough estimates. Some of them, such as those which deal with the settlement of footings on unstratified masses of soil, are intended to serve merely as a guide to judgment in the process of establishing semiempirical rules based on construction experience.

Because of the unavoidable uncertainties involved in the fundamental assumptions of the theories and in the numerical values of the soil constants, simplicity is of much greater importance than accuracy. If a theory is simple, one can readily judge the practical consequences of various conceivable deviations from the assumptions and can act accordingly. If a theory is complicated, it serves no practical purpose until the results are condensed into graphs or tables that permit rapid evaluation of the final equations on the basis of several different assumptions. In this book only the simple theories are set forth in detail. All other theories that require consideration are presented only in an abstracted form, because the mathematics that leads to the final conclusions is of interest only to the research worker. Advanced theories that cannot be regarded as essential tools for design are not even mentioned.

CHAPTER IV

PLASTIC EQUILIBRIUM IN SOILS

ART. 22. FUNDAMENTAL ASSUMPTIONS

This chapter deals with the earth pressure against lateral supports such as retaining walls or the bracing in open cuts, with the resistance of the earth against lateral displacement, with the bearing capacity of footings, and with the stability of slopes. Problems of this kind merely require the determination of the factor of safety of the lateral support or the slope with respect to failure. The solution is obtained by comparing the magnitude of two sets of forces: those that tend to produce a failure, and those that tend to prevent it. Such an investigation is called a *stability computation*. In order to make a stability computation, it is necessary to determine the position of the potential surface of sliding and to compute or to estimate the resistance against sliding along this surface.

Not only does the sliding resistance s per unit of area depend on the type of soil, but it may also depend on the normal stress p on the surface of sliding. In Article 15 it was shown that the relation between s and p can be expressed by one of the following approximate equations:

$$s = (p - u_w) \tan \phi, \text{ valid for cohesionless sands} \qquad (15.3)$$

$$s = c + p \tan \phi, \text{ valid for moist or dry cohesive soils} \atop \text{located above the water table} \qquad (15.2)$$

$$s = \tfrac{1}{2}q_u = c, \text{ valid for soft clay} \qquad (22.1)$$

Stiff clays commonly contain a network of hair cracks that make the conditions for their stability dependent to a large extent on the degree and duration of exposure to atmospheric agencies (see Article 43). Therefore, such clays are beyond the scope of theoretical treatment.

Each of the stability problems will be solved first for a dry $(u_w = 0)$ cohesionless sand to which equation 15.3 is applicable and then for a cohesive material to which equation 15.2 applies. After the reader is able to solve problems on the basis of these two equations, he can readily solve similar problems dealing with partly or completely submerged sand or with soft clay.

Pore
water
Pressure

In a partly submerged mass of sand in which the water is at rest, the neutral stress u_w at any depth z below the water table is

$$u_w = \gamma_w z$$

This stress reduces the effective unit weight of that part of the sand below water level from γ to the submerged unit weight γ', equation 12.6. Hence a stability calculation dealing with a partly submerged sand can be made on the assumption that the sand is dry, provided that the unit weight γ of the soil below water level is replaced by γ'. The pressure exerted by a partly submerged mass of sand against a lateral support is equal to the sum of the sand pressure, computed on the basis just mentioned, and the full water pressure. However, if the water percolates through the voids of the soil instead of being stagnant, the procedure outlined in this paragraph is not applicable. The seepage pressure of percolating water is discussed in Chapter VI.

By substituting $\phi = 0$, equation 15.2 can be reduced to equation 22.1 that approximately determines the shearing resistance of soft clay. Hence, the methods for solving stability problems on the basis of equation 15.2 are also applicable to soft clay. Nevertheless, it should be emphasized that the empirical equation 22.1 was derived from short-time observations, limited to a few weeks. Therefore, the results of stability computations do not furnish any information regarding the mechanical effects of gradual changes in the volume or strength of the clay. These time effects can be predicted only in a general way, on the basis of a knowledge of the physical properties of the soil. Some of the effects of time are discussed in Part C.

ART. 23. STATES OF PLASTIC EQUILIBRIUM

Fundamental Concepts

A body of soil is in a *state of plastic equilibrium* if every part of it is on the verge of failure. Rankine (1857) investigated the stress conditions corresponding to those states of plastic equilibrium which can be developed simultaneously throughout a semi-infinite mass of soil acted on by no force other than gravity. States of plastic equilibrium identical with those which Rankine considered are referred to as *Rankine states of plastic equilibrium*. A discussion of the Rankine states in a semi-infinite mass serves primarily as an introduction to the more complicated states of plastic equilibrium encountered in connection with practical problems.

The Rankine states are illustrated by Figure 56. In this figure, *AB* represents the horizontal surface of a semi-infinite mass of cohesionless sand with a unit weight γ, and *E* represents an element of the sand with a depth z and a cross-sectional area equal to unity. Since the element is symmetrical with reference to a vertical plane, the normal stress on the base,

$$p_v = \gamma z \tag{23.1}$$

is a principal stress. As a consequence, the normal stresses p_h on the vertical sides of the element at depth z are also principal stresses.

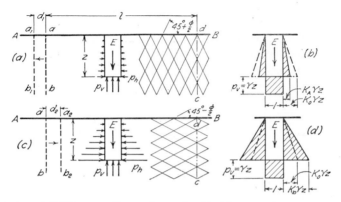

FIG. 56. (*a* and *b*) Diagrams illustrating active Rankine state in semi-infinite mass of sand; (*c* and *d*) corresponding diagrams for passive Rankine state.

According to equations 16.8 and 16.6, the ratio between the major and minor principal stresses in a cohesionless material cannot exceed the value,

$$\frac{p_1}{p_3} = N_\phi = \tan^2 \left(45° + \frac{\phi}{2} \right)$$

Since the vertical principal stress p_v in the mass of sand shown in Figure 56*a* can be either the major or the minor principal stress, the ratio $K = p_h/p_v$ can assume any value between the limits,

$$K_A = \frac{p_h}{p_v} = \frac{1}{N_\phi} = \tan^2 \left(45° - \frac{\phi}{2} \right) \tag{23.2}$$

and

$$K_P = \frac{p_h}{p_v} = N_\phi = \tan^2 \left(45° + \frac{\phi}{2} \right) \tag{23.3}$$

After a mass of sand has been deposited by either a natural or an artificial process, K has a value K_0 intermediate between K_A and K_P, and

$$p_h = K_0 p_v \tag{23.4}$$

wherein K_0 is an empirical constant known as the *coefficient of earth pressure at rest*. Its value depends on the relative density of the sand and the process by which the deposit was formed. If this process did not involve artificial compaction by tamping, the value of K_0 ranges from about 0.40 for loose sand to 0.50 for dense sand. Tamping in layers may increase the value to about 0.8.

In order to change the value of K for a mass of sand from K_0 to some other value, it is necessary to give the entire mass an opportunity either to stretch or to be compressed in a horizontal direction. Since the weight of sand above any horizontal section remains unchanged, the vertical pressure p_v is unaltered. The horizontal pressure $p_h = K p_v$, however, decreases if the mass stretches and increases if it compresses.

As the mass stretches, any two vertical sections such as *ab* and *cd* move apart, and the value of K decreases until it becomes equal to K_A, equation 23.2. The sand is then in what is known as the *active Rankine state*. In this state the intensity of the horizontal pressure at any depth z is equal to

$$p_h = K_A p_v = K_A \gamma z = \gamma z \frac{1}{N_\phi} \qquad (23.5)$$

in which K_A is called the *coefficient of active earth pressure*. The distribution of pressure over the sides and base of an element such as E is shown in Figure 56b. Further stretching of the mass has no effect on p_h, equation 23.5, but sliding occurs along two sets of plane surfaces as indicated on the right-hand side of Figure 56a. According to equation 16.4, such surfaces of sliding intersect the direction of the minor principal stress at the angle $45° + \phi/2$. Since the minor principal stresses in the active Rankine state are horizontal, the shear planes rise at an angle of $45° + \phi/2$ with the horizontal. The pattern formed by the traces of the shear planes on a vertical section parallel to the direction of stretching is known as the *shear pattern*.

A horizontal compression of the entire mass of sand causes *ab* to move toward *cd*, as shown in Figure 56c. As a consequence, the ratio $K = p_h/p_v$ increases. As soon as K becomes equal to K_P, equation 23.3, the sand is said to be in the *passive Rankine state*. At any depth z the horizontal pressure is

$$p_h = K_P p_v = K_P \gamma z = \gamma z N_\phi \qquad (23.6)$$

in which K_P is the *coefficient of passive earth pressure*. Since the minor principal stress in the passive Rankine state is vertical, the surfaces of sliding rise at an angle of $45° - \phi/2$ with the horizontal, as shown in Figure 56c.

The active and the passive Rankine states constitute the two limiting states for the equilibrium of the sand. Every intermediate state, including the state of rest, is referred to as a *state of elastic equilibrium.*

LOCAL STATES OF PLASTIC EQUILIBRIUM

The Rankine states illustrated by Figure 56 were produced by uniformly stretching or compressing every part of a semi-infinite mass of sand. They are known as *general states of plastic equilibrium.* However, in a stratum of real sand, no general state of equilibrium can be produced

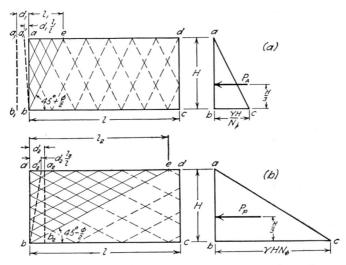

FIG. 57.   (*a*) Diagrams illustrating local active Rankine state in sand contained in rectangular box; (*b*) corresponding diagrams for local passive Rankine state.

except by a geological process such as the horizontal compression by tectonic forces of the entire rock foundation of the sand strata. Local events, such as the yielding of a retaining wall, cannot produce a radical change in the state of stress in the sand except in the immediate vicinity of the source of the disturbance. The rest of the sand remains in a state of elastic equilibrium.

Local states of plastic equilibrium can be produced by very different processes of deformation. The resulting states of stress in the plastic zone and the shape of the zone itself depend to a large extent on the type of deformation and on the degree of roughness of the surface of contact between the soil and its support. These factors constitute the *deformation* and the *boundary conditions.* The practical consequences of these conditions are illustrated by Figures 57 and 58.

Figure $57a$ is a vertical section through a prismatic box having a length l equal to the distance between the vertical sections ab and cd in Figure 56. If sand is deposited in the box by the same process that was responsible for the formation of the semi-infinite mass represented in Figure 56, the states of stress in both masses are identical. They represent states of elastic equilibrium.

When the state of the semi-infinite mass of sand, Figure $56a$, was changed from that of rest to the active Rankine state, the vertical section ab moved through the distance d_1. In order to change the state of the entire mass of sand contained in the box, Figure $57a$, into the active Rankine state, the wall ab must be moved through the same distance. This constitutes the deformation condition. While the wall ab, Figure $57a$, moves out, the height of the mass of sand decreases, and its length increases. These movements involve displacements between the sand and all of the surfaces of the box with which it is in contact. If the contact surfaces are rough, shearing stresses will develop along vertical and horizontal planes.

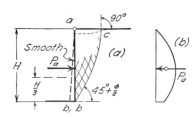

Fig. 58. Failure of sand behind smooth vertical wall when deformation condition for active Rankine state is not satisfied. (a) Section through back of wall; (b) stress against back of wall.

Since in the active Rankine state the shearing stresses on these planes are zero, this state cannot materialize unless the sides and bottom of the box are perfectly smooth. This requirement constitutes the boundary condition for the transition of the sand in the box to the active Rankine state. If this condition is satisfied, the sand passes into an active Rankine state as soon as the wall ab reaches the position a_1b_1. At this stage, the unit stretch of the soil is d_1/l. Any further movement of the wall causes slippage along the two sets of surfaces of sliding indicated by dash lines in Figure $57a$, but the stress conditions remain unchanged.

If the wall ab is perfectly smooth but the bottom of the box is rough, the sand located between the wall ab and the potential surface of sliding be is free to deform in exactly the same manner as it does in a box with a smooth bottom, but the state of stress in the balance of the sand cannot change materially because the friction along the bottom prevents the required deformation. Hence, an outward movement of the wall ab produces an active Rankine state only within the wedge-shaped zone abe. Since the width of the wedge increases from zero at the bottom to l_1 at the top, the unit stretch d_1/l required to establish the active Rankine state in the wedge is attained as soon as the left-hand boundary of the wedge moves from ab to $a_1'b$, Figure 57a. This is the deformation condition for the development of an active Rankine state within the wedge. As soon as the wall ab passes beyond this position, the wedge slides downward and outward along a plane surface of sliding be which rises at an angle of $45° + \phi/2$ with the horizontal.

If the wall ab is pushed toward the sand, and if both the walls and the bottom of the box are perfectly smooth, the entire mass of sand is transformed into the passive Rankine state, Figure 57c, as soon as the wall moves beyond a distance d_2 from its original position. The planes of sliding rise at an angle of $45° - \phi/2$ with the horizontal. If the wall ab

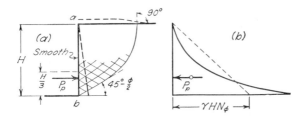

FIG. 59.   Failure of sand behind smooth vertical wall when deformation condition for passive Rankine state is not satisfied.   (*a*) Section through back of wall; (*b*) stress on back of wall.

is perfectly smooth but the bottom of the box is rough, the passive Rankine state develops only within the wedge-shaped zone abe. The transition from the elastic to the plastic state does not occur until ab moves into or beyond the position $a_2'b$.

If the end of the box is free to move outward at the bottom but is restrained at the top, as indicated in Figure 58, the sand fails by shear along some surface of sliding as soon as the tilt becomes perceptible, because the deformations compatible with an elastic state of equilibrium are very small. However, even at the state of failure, the sand between the wall and the surface of sliding does not pass into the active Rankine state because the upper part of the wall cannot move, and, as a consequence, the deformation condition for the active Rankine state within the sliding wedge is not satisfied.

Theoretical and experimental investigations regarding the type of failure caused by a tilt of the lateral support about its upper edge have led to the conclusion that the surface of sliding starts at b, Figure 58a, at an angle of $45° + \phi/2$ with the horizontal and that it becomes steeper until it intersects the ground surface at a right angle. The upper part of the sliding wedge remains in a state of elastic equilibrium until the lower part of the wedge has passed completely into a state of plastic equilibrium. The distribution of pressure against the lateral support is roughly parabolic, Figure 58*b*, instead of triangular, Figure 56*b*.

Similar investigations regarding the effect of pushing the bottom of the support toward the soil, Figure 59*a*, have shown that the surface of sliding rises from *b* at an angle $45° - \phi/2$ with the horizontal and that it also intersects the ground surface at a right angle. The corresponding distribution of pressure is shown in Figure 59*b*.

ART. 24. RANKINE'S EARTH–PRESSURE THEORY

Earth Pressure against Retaining Walls

Retaining walls serve the same function as the vertical sides of the box shown in Figure 57. The soil adjoining the wall is known as the *backfill*. It is always deposited after the wall is built. While the backfill is being placed, the wall yields somewhat under the pressure. The ultimate value of the pressure depends not only on the nature of the soil and the height of the wall but also on the amount of yield. If the position of the wall is fixed, the earth pressure is likely to retain forever a value close to the earth pressure at rest, Article 23. However, as soon as a wall starts to fail, it automatically satisfies the deformation condition for the transition of the adjoining mass of soil from the state of rest into an active state of plastic equilibrium. Hence, if a retaining wall can withstand the active earth pressure, it does not fail.

Although the back of every real retaining wall is rough, approximate values of the earth pressure can be obtained on the assumption that it is smooth. In the following paragraphs, this assumption is made. Methods for obtaining more accurate values will be described in subsequent articles.

Active Earth Pressure of Cohesionless Soil against Smooth Vertical Walls

If the surface of a sand backfill is horizontal, and if the back of the retaining wall is vertical and perfectly smooth, the magnitude and the distribution of pressure against the back of the wall are identical with those of the active pressure against the fictitious plane *ab* in Figure 56*a*. Therefore, the earth pressure can be computed on the basis of the equations already derived. In reality, there are no perfectly smooth surfaces. However, the equations based on this assumption are so simple that they are quite commonly used for evaluating the earth pressure against real retaining walls and other structures acted on by earth pressure. It is shown subsequently that the roughness of the back of a wall commonly reduces the active and increases the passive earth pressure. Hence, as a rule, the error associated with the assumption is on the safe side.

Furthermore, in one case of considerable practical importance, the assumption of a smooth vertical wall is almost strictly correct. This case is illustrated by Figure 60 which represents a cantilever wall. If such a wall yields under the influence of the earth pressure, the sand fails by shear along two planes rising from the heel of the wall at angles of $45° + \phi/2$ with the horizontal. Within the wedge-shaped zone located between these two planes, the sand is in the active Rankine state, and no shearing stresses act along the vertical plane ab through the heel. Hence, the earth pressure against this plane is identical with that against a smooth vertical wall.

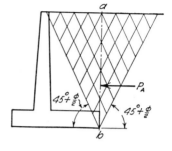

If the sand backfill is perfectly dry, the active pressure against a smooth vertical wall at any depth z is

FIG. 60.   Failure of sand behind cantilever retaining wall; deformation condition for active Rankine state is almost satisified.

$$p_h = \gamma z \frac{1}{N_\phi} \qquad (23.5)$$

It increases in simple proportion to the depth, as indicated by the pressure triangle abc, Figure 57a. The total pressure against the wall is

$$P_A = \int_0^H p_h \, dz = \frac{1}{2} \gamma H^2 \frac{1}{N_\phi} \qquad (24.1)$$

The point of application of P_A is located at a height $H/3$ above b.

If the wall is pushed into the position $a_2'b$ in Figure 57b, the pressure p_h against the wall assumes a value corresponding to the passive Rankine state,

$$p_h = \gamma z N_\phi \qquad (23.6)$$

and the total pressure against the wall becomes equal to

$$P_P = \int_0^H p_h \, dz = \frac{1}{2} \gamma H^2 N_\phi \qquad (24.2)$$

ACTIVE EARTH PRESSURE OF PARTLY SUBMERGED SAND SUPPORTING A UNIFORM SURCHARGE

In Figure 61a the line ab represents the smooth vertical back of a wall with height H. The effective unit weight of the sand when dry is γ_d and when submerged is γ' (see Article 12); the unit weight of water is γ_w. The surface of the horizontal backfill carries a uniformly distributed surcharge q per unit of area. Within the backfill the water table is located at depth H_1 below the crest of the wall. The angle of internal friction of both the dry and submerged sand is assumed to be ϕ.

As the wall yields from position ab into position $a_1'b$, the pressure against its back decreases from the value of the earth pressure at rest to that of the active Rankine pressure. At the end of Article 22, it was shown that the entire effect of the pore-water pressure on the effective stresses in the sand can be taken into account by assigning to the submerged part of the sand the submerged unit weight γ', equation 12.6. Within the

CREST ∿ TOP

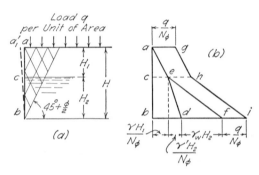

Fig. 61.   Active earth pressure of partly submerged sand supporting a uniform surcharge.   (*a*) Section through back of supporting structure; (*b*) pressure against back of structure.

depth H_1 the pressure on the wall due to the weight of the adjoining sand is represented by the triangle ace in Figure 61*b*. At any depth z' below the water table the effective vertical pressure on a horizontal section through the sand is

$$p_v = H_1\gamma + z'\gamma'$$

For the corresponding horizontal active Rankine pressure we obtain by means of equation 23.5

$$p_h = \frac{p_v}{N_\phi} = (H_1\gamma + z'\gamma')\frac{1}{N_\phi} \tag{24.3}$$

The total effective horizontal pressure below the water level is represented by the area $bced$ in Figure 61*b*. To this pressure must be added the total water pressure,

$$P_w = \tfrac{1}{2}\gamma_w H_2{}^2$$

which acts against the lower part cb of the wall. In Figure 61*b*, the water pressure is represented by the triangle def.

If the fill carries a uniformly distributed surcharge q per unit of area, the effective vertical stress p_v increases at any depth by q, and the corresponding horizontal active Rankine pressure increases by

$$\Delta p_h = \frac{q}{N_\phi} \qquad (24.4)$$

In Figure 61b the pressure produced by the surcharge q is represented by the area *aefihg*.

ACTIVE EARTH PRESSURE OF COHESIVE SOILS AGAINST SMOOTH VERTICAL SURFACES

In Figure 62a the line ab represents the smooth vertical back of a wall in contact with a cohesive soil having a unit weight γ. The shearing

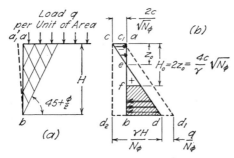

FIG. 62.   Failure of clay behind smooth vertical wall when deformation condition for active earth pressure is satisfied.   (a) Section through back of wall; (b) pressure against back of wall.

resistance of the soil is defined by the equation,

$$s = c + p \tan \phi \qquad (15.2)$$

which, according to Article 22, applies to dry or moist cohesive soil located above the water table. The relation between the extreme values of the principal stresses in such soils is determined by the expression,

$$p_c + q_c = p_c N_\phi + 2c\sqrt{N_\phi} \qquad (16.5)$$

wherein $p_c + q_c$ and p_c are, respectively, the major and minor principal stresses, and

$$N_\phi = \tan^2\left(45° + \frac{\phi}{2}\right) \qquad (16.6)$$

is the flow value. In Article 16 it is also shown that the surfaces of sliding intersect the direction of the minor principal stress at an angle $45° + \phi/2$, regardless of the value of c, equation 15.2.

Since the back of the wall is smooth, the vertical principal stress at depth z below the horizontal surface of the backfill is $p_v = \gamma z$. Before the support ab moves, it is acted on by the earth pressure at rest. In this state the horizontal stress p_h is the minor principal stress. An outward movement of the support into or beyond the position $a_1'b$ reduces p_h to the value corresponding to the active Rankine pressure. Substituting $p_v = p_c + q_c = \gamma z$ and $p_h = p_c$ into equation 16.5, we obtain

$$p_h = \gamma z \frac{1}{N_\phi} - 2c \frac{1}{\sqrt{N_\phi}} \tag{24.5}$$

This stress at any depth z is represented by the horizontal distance between the lines ab and cd in Figure 62b. At depth,

$$z_0 = \frac{2c}{\gamma} \sqrt{N_\phi} \tag{24.6}$$

the stress p_h is equal to zero. At a depth less than z_0, the pressure against the wall is negative, provided that a crack does not open up between the wall and the uppermost part of the soil. The total earth pressure against the wall is

$$P_A = \int_0^H p_h \, dz = \frac{1}{2} \gamma H^2 \frac{1}{N_\phi} - 2c \frac{H}{\sqrt{N_\phi}} \tag{24.7}$$

If the wall has a height,

$$H = H_c = \frac{4c}{\gamma} \sqrt{N_\phi} = 2z_0 \tag{24.8}$$

the total earth pressure P_A is equal to zero. Hence, if the height of a vertical bank is smaller than H_c, the bank should be able to stand without lateral support. However, the pressure against the wall increases from $-2c/\sqrt{N_\phi}$ at the crest to $+2c/\sqrt{N_\phi}$ at depth H_c, whereas on the vertical face of an unsupported bank the normal stress is zero at every point. Because of this difference the greatest depth to which a cut can be excavated without lateral support of its vertical sides is slightly smaller than H_c (see Article 31).

For soft clay, $\phi = 0$ and $N_\phi = \tan^2 \left(45° + \frac{\phi}{2} \right) = 1$. Therefore

$$P_A = \tfrac{1}{2}\gamma H^2 - 2cH \tag{24.9}$$

and

$$H_c = \frac{4c}{\gamma} \tag{24.10}$$

Since the soil does not necessarily adhere to the wall, it is commonly assumed that the active earth pressure of cohesive soils against retaining walls is equal to the pressure represented in Figure 62b by the triangular area bde, equal to area cdd_2 − area $cebd_2$. Therefore,

$$P_A = \frac{1}{2} \gamma H^2 \frac{1}{N_\phi} - 2cH \frac{1}{\sqrt{N_\phi}} + \frac{2c^2}{\gamma} \qquad (24.11)$$

For soft clay, $\phi = 0°$, and

$$P_A = \frac{1}{2} \gamma H^2 - 2cH + \frac{2c^2}{\gamma} \qquad (24.12)$$

PASSIVE EARTH PRESSURE OF COHESIVE SOILS IN CONTACT WITH SMOOTH VERTICAL SURFACES

If the face ab of the wall or block that supports the soil and its uniform surcharge q is pushed toward the backfill as indicated in Figure 63a, the horizontal principal stress p_h increases and becomes greater than p_v. As

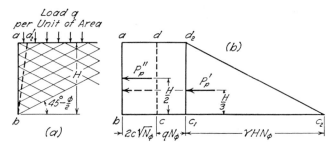

FIG. 63. Failure of clay behind smooth vertical wall when deformation condition for passive earth pressure is satisfied. (a) Section through back of wall; (b) stress on back of wall.

soon as ab arrives at or beyond the position $a_2'b$, which represents the deformation condition for the passive Rankine state, the stress conditions for failure, equation 16.5, are satisfied. Since p_h represents the major principal stress, we may substitute $p_h = p_c + q_c$ and $p_v = p_c = \gamma z + q$ into equation 16.5 and obtain

$$p_h = \gamma z N_\phi + 2c\sqrt{N_\phi} + q N_\phi \qquad (24.13)$$

The stress p_h can be resolved into two parts. One part,

$$p_h' = \gamma z N_\phi$$

increases like a hydrostatic pressure in simple proportion to depth. In

Figure 63b the stresses p_h' are represented by the width of the triangle $c_1c_2d_2$ with the area,

$$P_P' = \tfrac{1}{2}\gamma H^2 N_\phi \qquad (24.14)$$

The point of application of P_P' is located at an elevation $H/3$ above b. The quantity P_P' represents the total passive earth pressure of a cohesionless material with an angle of internal friction ϕ and a unit weight γ.

The second part of p_h is

$$p_h'' = 2c\sqrt{N_\phi} + qN_\phi$$

This part is independent of the depth. It is represented by the width of the rectangle abc_1d_2 in Figure 63b. The total pressure is equal to the area of the rectangle. Hence,

$$P_P'' = H(2c\sqrt{N_\phi} + qN_\phi) \qquad (24.15)$$

The point of application of P_P'' is at mid-height of the surface ab. Since equation 24.15 does not contain the unit weight γ, the value P_P'' can be computed on the assumption that the backfill is weightless. From equations 24.14 and 24.15, we find that the total passive earth pressure is

$$P_P = P_P' + P_P'' = \tfrac{1}{2}\gamma H^2 N_\phi + H(2c\sqrt{N_\phi} + qN_\phi) \qquad (24.16)$$

According to the preceding discussion, P_P can be computed by means of two independent operations. First, P_P' is computed on the assumption that the cohesion and the surcharge are zero ($c = 0$, $q = 0$). The point of application of P_P' is located at the lower third-point of H. Secondly, P_P'' is computed on the assumption that the unit weight of the backfill is zero ($\gamma = 0$). The point of application of P_P'' is at the mid-point of H. In the following articles this simple procedure is used repeatedly for determining the point of application of the passive earth pressure of cohesive soils. The subdivision of P_P into the two parts P_P' and P_P'' is strictly correct only when the back of the wall is vertical and perfectly smooth. For all other conditions, the procedure is approximate.

PROBLEMS

1. A wall with a smooth vertical back 10 ft high retains a mass of dry cohesionless sand that has a horizontal surface. The sand weighs 113 lb per cu ft and has an angle of internal friction of 36°. What is the approximate total pressure against the wall, if the wall is prevented from yielding? if the wall can yield far enough to satisfy the deformation condition for the active Rankine state?

Ans. 2260 to 2830 lb per lin ft;   1470 lb per lin ft.

earth pressure at rest

2. The water level behind the wall described in problem 1 rises to an elevation 4 ft below the crest. The submerged unit weight of the sand is 66 lb per cu ft. If the deformation condition for the active Rankine state is satisfied, what is the total pressure that the earth and water exert against the wall? At what height above the base does the resultant of the earth and water pressures act?

Ans. 2380 lb per lin ft; 2.83 ft.

3. What is the total lateral pressure against the yielding wall in problem 1, if the sand mass supports a uniformly distributed load of 400 lb per sq ft? At what height above the base of the wall is the center of pressure?

Ans. 2510 lb per lin ft; 4.02 ft.

4. The space between two retaining walls with smooth backs is filled with sand weighing 113 lb per cu ft. The foundations of the walls are interconnected by a reinforced-concrete floor, and the crests of the walls by heavy steel tie rods. The walls are 15 ft high and 50 ft apart. The surface of the sand is used for storing pig iron weighing 300 lb per sq ft. If the coefficient of the earth pressure at rest is $K_0 = 0.50$, what is the total pressure against the walls before and after the application of the surcharge?

Ans. 6360 lb per lin ft; 8610 lb per lin ft.

5. The same wall as in problem 1 supports a purely cohesive soil having a cohesion $c = 200$ lb per sq ft and a unit weight of 110 lb per cu ft. The value of ϕ is zero. What is the total active Rankine pressure against the wall? At what distance above the base is the center of pressure? At what depth is the intensity of pressure zero?

Ans. 1500 lb per lin ft; −1.11 ft; 3.64 ft.

6. A vertical bank was formed during the excavation of a plastic clay having a unit weight of 120 lb per cu ft. When the depth of excavation reached 18 ft, the bank failed. On the assumption that $\phi = 0°$, what was the approximate value of the cohesion of the clay?

Ans. 540 lb per sq ft.

7. A smooth vertical wall 20 feet high is pushed against a mass of soil having a horizontal surface and a shearing resistance given by Coulomb's equation in which $c = 400$ lb per sq ft and $\phi = 15°$. The unit weight of the soil is 120 lb per cu ft. Its surface carries a uniform load of 200 lb per sq ft. What is the total passive Rankine pressure? What is the distance from the base of the wall to the center of pressure? Determine the intensity of lateral pressure at the base of the wall.

Ans. 68,400 lb per lin ft; 8.01 ft; 5460 lb per sq ft.

ART. 25. INFLUENCE OF WALL FRICTION ON THE SHAPE OF THE SURFACE OF SLIDING

The back of the wall in Figure 64a is assumed to be rough. Otherwise it is identical with that shown in Figure 57a. The backfill consists of clean sand. If the wall moves outward, the sliding wedge subsides, and the sand moves downward along the back of the wall. The downward movement of the sand with reference to the wall develops frictional forces that cause the resultant active earth pressure to be inclined at an angle δ to the normal to the wall. This angle is known as the *angle of wall friction.* It is considered positive when the resultant reaction is oriented such that its tangential component acts in an upward direction, Figure 64a. Advanced theoretical analyses as well as experiments have shown that the corresponding surface of sliding *bc* consists of a curved lower portion and a straight upper part. Within the section *adc* of the sliding wedge the shear pattern is identical with the active Rankine pattern, Figure 57*a*. Within the area *adb* the shear pattern consists of two sets of curved lines.

If the wall is forced down with reference to the backfill, for instance by the action of a heavy load on its crest, the value of δ becomes negative, and the curvature of the lower part of the surface of sliding is reversed, as shown in Figure 64*b*.

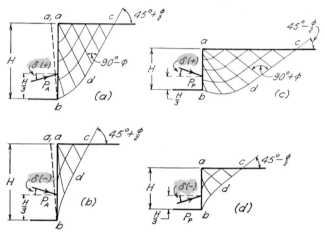

Fig. 64.   Shear patterns associated with failure of sand behind rough vertical wall.

If the wall is pushed toward the fill, the movement is resisted by the passive earth pressure. If the weight of the wall is greater than the friction between the sand and the wall, the sand rises with reference to the wall, and the reaction to the resultant passive earth pressure acts at an angle δ with the normal to the back of the wall. The tangential component of this force tends to prevent the rise of the sand. Under this condition the angle δ, Figure 64*c*, is considered positive. The straight portion of the surface of sliding rises at an angle $45° - \phi/2$ with the horizontal. Within the isosceles triangle *adc* the shear pattern is identical with that shown in Figure 57*b*, and the material is in the passive Rankine state. Within the area *adb* both sets of lines which constitute the shear pattern are curved.

If the weight of the wall is smaller than the friction between the sand and the wall, the angle between the normal to the back of the wall and the reaction to the resultant passive pressure is smaller than δ. Finally, if the wall is acted on by an upward force equal to the sum of the weight of the wall and the friction between the sand and the wall, the resultant passive earth pressure is oriented as shown in Figure 64d, and the angle of wall friction is considered negative. The curvature of the curved portion of the surface of sliding is reversed.

The deformation conditions for the plastic states represented by the shear patterns in Figures 64a and b require a certain minimum lengthening of every horizontal element of the wedge. The deformation conditions for the plastic states represented in Figures 64c and d require a certain minimum shortening of every horizontal element. These requirements are the equivalent of those for producing the active or passive Rankine states in the backfill of a perfectly smooth wall, as illustrated by Figures 57a and b.

ART. 26. COULOMB'S THEORY OF ACTIVE EARTH PRESSURE AGAINST RETAINING WALLS

INTRODUCTION

Since the back of every real retaining wall is more or less rough, the boundary conditions for the validity of Rankine's theory are seldom satisfied, and earth-pressure computations based on this theory usually involve an appreciable error. Most of this error can be avoided by using Coulomb's theory. Coulomb's method can be adapted to any boundary condition, but, in exchange, it involves a simplifying assumption regarding the shape of the surface of sliding. However, the error due to this assumption is commonly small compared to that associated with the use of Rankine's theory. When the boundary conditions for the validity of Rankine's theory are satisfied, the two theories lead to identical results.

Both Coulomb's and Rankine's theories are based on the assumptions that the wall is free to move into or beyond the position a_1b, Figure 64a, and that the water contained in the voids of the soil does not exert any appreciable seepage pressure. It is also quite obviously assumed that the soil constants that appear in the equations have definite values that can be determined.

COULOMB'S THEORY

The surface of sliding in the backfill of a real retaining wall is slightly curved, as shown in Figures 64a and b. In order to simplify the computations, Coulomb assumed it to be plane. The error due to disregarding the curvature is, however, quite small.

The forces that act on the sliding wedge are shown in Figure 65a, in which the straight line bc_1 is arbitrarily assumed to represent the surface of sliding. The wedge abc_1 is in equilibrium under the weight W_1, the reaction to the resultant earth pressure P_1, and the reaction F_1. The reaction F_1 is inclined at the angle ϕ to the normal to bc_1 because the frictional resistance is assumed to be fully developed along the surface of sliding. If the retaining wall rests on a firm foundation, the force P_1 is inclined to the normal to the back of the wall at the angle of wall friction $+\delta$, as indicated by the solid arrow in the figure. On the other hand, if it is likely that the wall may settle more than the backfill, the force P_1 will be inclined at the angle $-\delta$, as shown by the dash arrow. Since the magnitude of W_1 is known and the directions of all three forces are also known, the earth pressure P_1 can be scaled from the polygon of forces, Figure 65b. Inasmuch as bc_1 is not necessarily the real surface of sliding, similar constructions are made to determine the earth pressures P_2, P_3, etc., for other arbitrarily selected surfaces bc_2, bc_3, etc. (not shown). The greatest value of the earth pressure obtained in this manner is equal to the active earth pressure P_A.

Culmann's Graphical Construction

An expedient method was devised by Culmann for performing the graphical constructions described in the preceding paragraph. It is illustrated in Figure 65c. The first step in Culmann's procedure is to trace the line bS which passes through the bottom edge b of the back of the wall and rises at the angle ϕ above the horizontal base of the backfill. This line is known as the *slope line* because it represents the natural slope of the backfill material. The next step is to trace the *earth-pressure line* bL, which is located below the slope line and which intersects it at the angle θ. The angle θ is equal to the angle between the vertical and the direction of the resultant earth pressure P_A, as shown in Figure 65. It depends on the angle of wall friction δ and the inclination α of the back of the wall.

In order to determine the earth pressure P_1 exerted by a wedge located above an arbitrary plane surface of sliding bc_1, it is first necessary to compute the weight W_1 of this wedge. This weight is laid off along bS at any convenient scale of forces. Thus point d_1 is obtained. The line d_1e_1 is then traced parallel to bL. Since the triangle e_1d_1b in Figure 65c is similar to the force polygon, Figure 65b, the distance d_1e_1 is equal to the earth pressure corresponding to the surface of sliding bc_1. To find the active earth pressure P_A, the construction is repeated for different planes bc_2, etc. The points e_1, e_2, etc., are connected by a curve C, known as the *Culmann line*, and a tangent to C is traced parallel to bS. The distance ed represents P_A, and the real surface of sliding passes through point e.

EARTH PRESSURE DUE TO LINE LOAD

Figure 66 is a section through a wall that supports a mass of sand with an inclined surface. Along a line parallel to the crest of the wall, at a distance ac' from the crest, the surface of the backfill carries a load q' per unit of length of the line. The procedure for determining the active

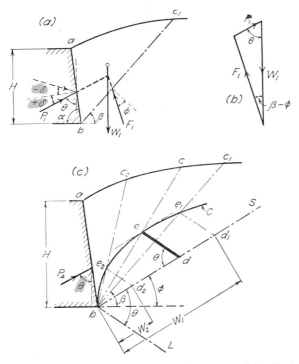

FIG. 65. (*a* and *b*) Diagrams illustrating assumptions upon which Coulomb's theory of active earth pressure is based; (*c*) Culmann's graphical method for determining earth pressure of sand.

earth pressure against the wall is essentially the same as that illustrated in Figure 65c. However, if the right-hand boundary of a wedge intersects the ground surface to the right of c', the distance to be laid off on the slope line bS is proportional to the weight of the sand that constitutes the wedge, plus the line load q' (see Figure 66).

If the ground surface carried no surcharge, the Culmann line C (dash curve) in Figure 66 would correspond to the line C in Figure 65c. If the surface carries a line load q' at some point c', the Culmann line consists of two sections. The section to the left of plane bc' is identical with C, because the wedges bounded by planes to the left of bc' carry no surcharge. On the right side of bc' the Culmann line for the loaded backfill is located above C, as indicated by the solid curve C' in Figure 66, because every wedge bounded by a plane to the right of bc' is acted on by the weight q'. Therefore the complete Culmann line consists of the curve C to the left of bc', and the curve C' to the right. It has a discontinuity at the plane bc' which passes through the point of application of the line load.

If the load is located on the left side of c_2', the value of the active earth pressure exerted by the loaded backfill corresponds to the greatest

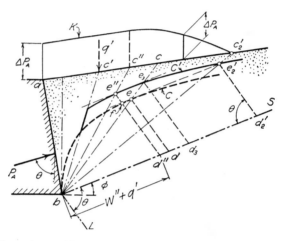

Fig. 66. Culmann's graphical method for determining earth pressure exerted by sand backfill that carries a line load.

distance between the Culmann line C' and the slope line bS measured in a direction parallel to the earth pressure line bL. If the line load acts at any position on the surface of the fill between points a and c'', the greatest distance is $d''e''$. Therefore, the slip occurs along the plane bc'' which passes through e''. The quantity $d''e''-de$ represents that part ΔP_A of the active earth pressure due to the line load q'.

The ordinates of the curve K, Figure 66, with reference to the ground surface represent the values of ΔP_A corresponding to the various positions c' at which q' may be located. Between a and c'', K is straight and parallel to the surface of the backfill because ΔP_A is independent of the position of q' between these two points.

If q' moves to the right beyond c'' to such a position as c, the Culmann line consists of the dash curve C to the left of bc and the solid curve C' to the right. The maximum value P_A of the earth pressure is represented by the line e_3d_3. The failure plane passes through the point e_3

and intersects the ground surface at the line of application of q'. As the line of application of q' moves to the right, the value of ΔP_A decreases steadily as indicated by the ordinates of curve K, Figure 66, until at c_2' it becomes equal to zero.

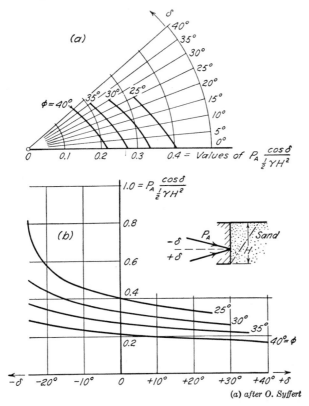

FIG. 67. Two types of charts that furnish coefficients for computation of active earth pressure.

Finally, if the line of action of q' is at c_2', the value of the earth pressure $e_2'd_2'$, determined by means of curve C', is equal to the value ed that represents the active earth pressure when there is no surcharge. If q' moves to the right of c_2', the earth pressure determined by means of C' becomes smaller than ed. Hence, if the line load acts on the right side of c_2', it no longer has any effect on the active earth pressure, and the surface of sliding has the same position bc as it does for a backfill that carries no surcharge. The greater the line load q', the farther c_2' moves to the right. Therefore, the distance within which q' has an influence on the earth pressure depends on the magnitude of q'.

Culmann's method is chiefly used if the wall has an inclined or broken back, and if the backfill has an irregular surface or carries a surcharge. If a vertical wall supports a cohesionless backfill with a horizontal surface, it is more expedient to obtain the value of P_A from charts prepared for this purpose. Figure 67 consists of two different charts of this kind.

PROBLEMS

1. A vertical retaining wall 20 ft high supports a cohesionless fill that weighs 115 lb per cu ft. The upper surface of the fill rises from the crest of the wall at an angle of 20° with the horizontal. The angle of internal friction is 28°, and the angle of wall friction is 20°. By Culmann's method compute the total active earth pressure against the wall.

    Ans.   10,600 lb per lin ft.

2. The stem of a cantilever retaining wall is 36 ft high. It retains a storage pile of cohesionless iron ore. The wall has a cross section symmetrical about its vertical center line. At the top its width is 6 ft, and at the base of the stem is 12 ft. From a point on the back of the wall 4 ft below the crest, the surface of the ore pile rises at an angle of 35° with the horizontal to a maximum height of 65 ft above the base of the stem. The remainder of the pile is level. If ϕ and δ are each equal to 36° and γ is 160 lb per cu ft, what is the total lateral pressure of the ore above the base of the stem? If the entire lateral force against the stem is resisted by steel tie rods 3 in. square, stressed to 27,000 lb per sq in., what spacing of the rods is required?

    Ans.   48,800 lb per lin ft;   5 ft.

3. A vertical wall 18 ft high supports a cohesionless fill weighing 105 lb per cu ft. The surface of the fill is horizontal. The values of ϕ and δ are 31° and 20°, respectively. The fill supports two line loads of 2000 lb per lin ft, parallel to the crest of the wall, at distances of 8 and 13 ft, respectively. Compute the value of the total active earth pressure against the wall. Determine the horizontal distance from the back of the wall to the point at which the surface of sliding intersects the surface of the fill.

    Ans.   6310 lb per lin ft;   13 ft.

4. A retaining wall 15 ft high with a vertical back is just adequate to support a level fill of sand having a unit weight of 115 lb per cu ft and a value of ϕ equal to 32°. The value of δ is 20°. A vertical load of 5000 lb per lin ft is to be added along a line parallel to the crest of the wall. What is the minimum horizontal distance at which the load can be located from the back of the wall without increasing the earth pressure against the wall?

    Ans.   16.2 ft.

5. If the fill in problem 3 carries no surcharge, what is the magnitude of the active earth pressure? Check the graphical computation by means of the charts, Figure 67.

    Ans.   4870 lb per lin ft.

ART. 27. POINT OF APPLICATION OF EARTH PRESSURE

The procedure described in Article 26 makes it possible to determine the magnitude of the total earth pressure provided its direction is known. However, it does not furnish any information regarding the point of application of the pressure. In order to get this information, Coulomb assumed that every point on the back of a wall represents the foot of a potential surface of sliding. For example, the point d on the curved line ab in Figure 68a represents the lower extremity of a potential surface of sliding de. The earth pressure P_A on ad can be computed by means of Culmann's procedure as described in Article 26. If the depth to the foot of the potential surface of sliding is increased from z to $z + dz$, the earth pressure is increased by

$$dP_A = p_A \, dz$$

where p_A is the average intensity of pressure over the increment of depth dz. Therefore,

$$p_A = \frac{dP_A}{dz} \tag{27.1}$$

By means of this equation the distribution of the earth pressure on the back of the wall can be determined. When the distribution is known, the point of application of the resultant pressure can be located by means of a suitable analytical or graphical method. At any point the line of action of the pressure p_A makes an angle δ with the normal to the back of the wall.

In practice, this method is rather cumbersome. Therefore, simplified methods are used that give approximately the same results. For instance, in Figure 68a, the point of application O_1 is located approximately at the point of intersection of the back of the wall and a line OO_1, which is parallel to the surface of sliding bc and which passes through the center of gravity O of the sliding wedge abc.

Figures 68b and c illustrate a simplified method for estimating the position of the point of application of the additional pressure ΔP_A produced by a line load q'. The lines bc, bc'', etc., correspond to the lines bc, bc'', etc., in Figure 66. If q' acts between a and c'', Figure 68b, $b'c'$ is traced parallel to the surface of sliding bc'', and $a'c'$ is traced parallel to bS, the slope line (see Figure 66). The force ΔP_A acts at the upper third-point of $a'b'$. If q' acts between c'' and c_2', $a'c'$ is traced parallel to bS, and ΔP_A acts at the upper third-point of $a'b$, as shown in Figure 68c.

All these procedures are based on Coulomb's assumption that every point on the back of a wall represents the foot of a potential surface of sliding. This assumption is justified in connection with retaining walls, because no retaining wall can fail without yielding in a manner that satisfies the deformation condition for the plastic state. Coulomb, however, did not specify this deformation condition. As a consequence, the theory was commonly used for computing the active earth pressure against lateral supports that did not satisfy the deformation condition, such as the bracing in open cuts (see Article 32). Since it was found that the results of the computations did not agree with reality, many experienced engineers concluded that the theory as such was unreliable. Therefore, it should be emphasized that Coulomb's theory is as satisfactory as any theory in structural engineering, provided the deformation condition for its validity is satisfied.

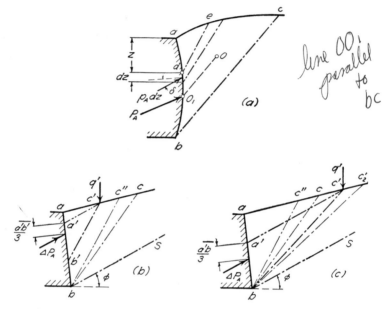

Fig. 68.   Diagrams illustrating simplified procedure for determining point of application of active earth pressure.

PROBLEMS

1. At what distance above the base of the stem of the retaining wall of problem 2, Article 26, does the resultant earth pressure act?

Ans. 10.8 ft.

2. Locate the center of pressure of the added earth pressure due to each of the two line loads in problem 3, Article 26, on the assumption that the influence of each of the two loads can be considered separately.

Ans. 10 ft;   6.75 ft from the bottom of the wall.

ART. 28. PASSIVE EARTH PRESSURE AGAINST ROUGH CONTACT FACES

DEFINITION

In the broadest sense, the term passive earth pressure indicates the resistance of a mass of soil against displacement by lateral pressure. The object that exerts the lateral pressure may consist of the foundation of a retaining wall, the outer face of the buried part of a sheet pile bulkhead, or a block of masonry such as the abutment of a loaded arch. It may also consist of a mass of soil that exerts a horizontal pressure because it supports a vertical load. The soil beneath a loaded footing acts in this manner. Since the stability of almost any lateral earth support and the

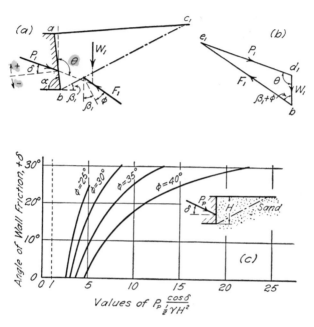

FIG. 69.   (*a* and *b*) Diagrams illustrating assumptions on which Coulomb's theory of passive earth pressure is based; (*c*) chart that furnishes coefficients for computation of passive earth pressure.

bearing capacity of every shallow foundation depend to some extent on the passive earth pressure, the problem of computing this pressure is of outstanding practical importance.

The surface of contact between the soil and the object that exerts the lateral pressure is called the *contact face*. Coulomb computed the passive earth pressure against rough contact faces on the simplifying assumption that the surface of sliding is plane (see Figures 69*a* and *b*). The error due to this assumption is always on the unsafe side. If the angle of wall friction δ is small, the surface of sliding is really almost plane, and the error is tolerable. However, if δ is large, the error is excessive, and Coulomb's method should not be used.

Coulomb's Theory of the Passive Earth Pressure of Sand

The Coulomb value of the passive earth pressure can be determined graphically by Culmann's method. The procedure is identical with that described in Article 26 except that the slope line bS, Figure 65c, must be drawn at an angle ϕ below the horizontal instead of above.

Figure 69c shows the influence of the angle of wall friction δ on the Coulomb value of the passive earth pressure. According to this chart, the earth pressure increases rapidly with increasing values of the angle of wall friction. However, if δ is greater than about $\phi/3$, the surface of sliding is strongly curved (Figure 64c). As a consequence, the error due to Coulomb's assumption of a plane surface increases rapidly. For $\delta = \phi$ it may be as great as 30 per cent. Hence, for values of δ greater than $\phi/3$, the curvature of the surface of sliding must be taken into consideration.

Passive Earth Pressure of Cohesive Soils

In order to illustrate the methods for determining the passive earth pressure without assuming a plane surface of sliding, the problem illustrated by Figure 70 will be solved. In this figure ab is a section through a contact face that is pushed toward a mass of ideal cohesive soil. The shearing resistance of the soil is determined by the equation,

$$s = c + p \tan \phi \qquad (15.2)$$

The surface of the soil is horizontal. The angle of wall friction is denoted by δ, and the total adhesion between the soil and the contact face by C_a. The real surface of sliding is bde. It consists of a curved part bd and a straight part de. According to Article 25, the soil within the isosceles triangle ade is in the passive Rankine state. Therefore, the shearing stresses on the vertical section df are zero, and the pressure P_d on this section is horizontal. It can be computed by means of equation 24.16. The body of soil $abdf$ is acted on by the following forces: its weight W; the pressure P_d; the resultant C of the cohesion along bd; the adhesion C_a along ab; the resultant F of the normal and frictional stresses along bd; and the resultant P_P of the normal and frictional components of the passive earth pressure.

Since the point of application of P_P is not known, we make use of the approximations discussed at the end of Article 24 and replace P_P by the two forces, $P_P{}'$ and $P_P{}''$. Each of these forces acts at an angle δ with the normal to the contact face. One force $P_P{}'$ maintains equilibrium with the weight of the mass $abdf$ and the friction due to the weight. The other, $P_P{}''$, maintains equilibrium with the cohesion on the surface of

sliding and the friction due to forces other than the weight. The force
P_P' acts at the lower third-point of ab, whereas P_P'' acts at the mid-
point. Since the point of application and the direction of each of these
forces are known, we may compute each force individually. The resultant of these two forces represents the total passive earth pressure P_P.

The methods for determining the real shape of the surface of sliding
are so involved that they are unsuitable for practical purposes. However,
sufficiently accurate results can be obtained on the simplifying assump-

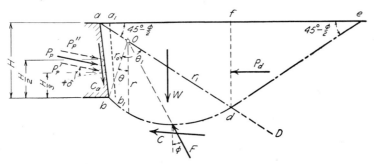

FIG. 70.   Diagram illustrating assumptions on which theory of passive earth pressure
against rough contact faces is based.

tion that the curved portion bd of the real surface of sliding is either an
arc of a circle or a logarithmic spiral that has the equation,

$$r = r_0 \epsilon^{\theta \tan \phi} \qquad (28.1)$$

In the following paragraphs, the curved part of the surface of sliding is
assumed to be a logarithmic spiral. Since the spiral is tangent at d to the
straight part de of the surface of sliding, the center O of the spiral must
be located on the line aD, Figure 70, which is inclined at $45° - \phi/2$ to
the horizontal. According to equation 28.1, every radius of the spiral
makes an angle ϕ with the normal to the spiral at the point where it
intersects the curve. Since ϕ is the angle of internal friction, the resultant
dF of the normal stress and the frictional resistance on any element of
the surface of sliding also makes an angle ϕ with the normal to the element, and its direction coincides with that of the radius that subtends
the element. Since every radius of the spiral passes through point O,
the resultant F of the normal and frictional forces on bd also passes
through the center O. This fact is utilized in the following calculations.

In order to compute P_P' (the value of P_P if $c = 0$), we arbitrarily
select a surface of sliding bd_1e_1, Figure 71a, consisting of the logarithmic
spiral bd_1 with its center at O_1, and the straight line d_1e_1 which makes an
angle of $45° - \phi/2$ with the horizontal. The lateral pressure required

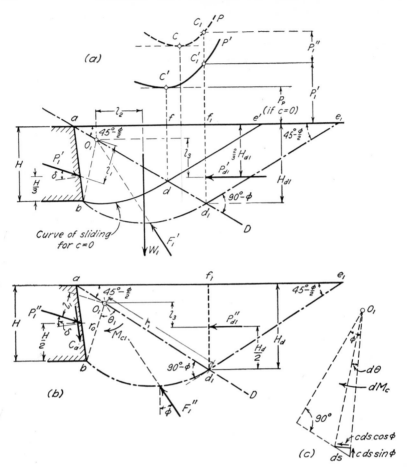

FIG. 71. Logarithmic spiral method for determining passive earth pressure. (a) Forces entering into computation of component due to weight of soil, neglecting cohesion; (b) forces entering into computation of component due to friction and cohesion, neglecting weight of soil; (c) diagram illustrating computation of moment due to cohesion.

to produce a slip on this surface is designated as P_1'. We then evaluate the force P_{d_1}', which acts at the lower third-point of $f_1 d_1$, by means of the equation,

$$P_{d_1}' = \tfrac{1}{2}\gamma H_{d_1}{}^2 N_\phi$$

Finally, we take moments of the forces P_1', P_{d_1}', W_1, and F_1' about O_1. Since the moment of F_1' about O_1 is zero,

$$P_1' l_1 = W_1 l_2 + P_{d_1}' l_3$$

whence

$$P_1' = \frac{1}{l_1}[W_1 l_2 + P_{d_1}' l_3] \tag{28.2}$$

The value of P_1' is plotted to scale above f_1. It is represented by the point C_1'. Similar computations are performed for other arbitrarily selected surfaces of sliding, and a curve P' is drawn through the points C_1', etc. If the soil has no cohesion ($c = 0$), the second component P_P'' of the passive earth pressure P_P is equal to zero, and the value of P_P is represented by the minimum ordinate of the curve P', at point C'. The surface of sliding passes through the point d which is located on aD vertically below C'.

If the soil possesses cohesion, we must also compute P_P'' (the value of P_P if $\gamma = 0$). In order to calculate the value P_1'' which corresponds to the arbitrary surface of sliding bd_1e_1, we must consider the forces involved in the computation (see Figure 71b). The value of P_{d_1}'' is obtained by making $\gamma = 0$, $q = 0$, and $H = H_{d_1}$ in equation 24.15. Hence,

$$P_{d_1}'' = 2cH_{d_1}\sqrt{N_\phi}$$

The point of application of this force is at the mid-height of d_1f_1. The influence of the cohesion along the curve bd_1 may be evaluated by considering an element having a length ds, Figure 71c. The cohesion along the length ds is equal to $c\,ds$. The moment of $c\,ds$ about O_1 is

$$dM_c = rc\,ds\cos\phi = rc\,\frac{r\,d\theta}{\cos\phi}\cos\phi = cr^2\,d\theta$$

and the moment of the total cohesion along bd_1 is

$$M_{c_1} = \int_0^{\theta_1} dM_c = \frac{c}{2\tan\phi}(r_1^2 - r_0^2) \tag{28.3}$$

The force F_1'' passes through O_1. By taking moments about this point, we obtain

$$P_1'' l_1 = M_{c_1} + P_{d_1}'' l_3$$

whence

$$P_1'' = \frac{1}{l_1}[M_{c_1} + P_{d_1}'' l_3] \tag{28.4}$$

In Figure 71a the value P_1'' is plotted to scale at C_1 above point C_1'. Since P_1' and P_1'' represent the forces required to overcome the two parts of the resistance against sliding along the same surface bd_1e_1, the ordinate of point C_1 represents the total force required to produce a slip along this surface. Similarly, values of P'' are obtained for other arbitrary surfaces of sliding, and a curve P is drawn through the points C_1, etc. The passive earth pressure P_P is represented by the minimum ordinate of the curve P, and the surface of sliding passes through a point on aD directly below the point C at which curve P is closest to ae_1. The total pressure on the contact face is equal to the resultant of P_P and the adhesion force C_a.

The shape of the curved part of the real surface of sliding is intermediate between that of an arc of a circle and that of a spiral. Since the difference between the shape of these two curves is small, the error due to replacing the real curve by either a circle or a logarithmic spiral is negligible. As a matter of fact, comparisons between the approximate and the exact methods have shown that values of the passive earth pressure computed by means of the approximate methods are at least as accurate as values of the active earth pressure computed by Coulomb's method in which it is assumed that the real slightly curved surface of sliding is a plane.

The preceding investigations are based on the assumption that the mass of soil adjoining the contact face is pushed into a position located entirely beyond a_1b_1, Figure 70. If the upper part of the contact face does not advance so far as a_1b_1, the surface of sliding is curved throughout its full length, and only the lowest part of the sliding mass passes into the passive Rankine state. If the lower part of the face stops short of a_1b_1, the soil adjoining this part does not pass into a state of plastic equilibrium at all. In these instances, the total passive earth pressure and its distribution over the contact face depend on the type of restriction imposed on the movement of the contact face.

PROBLEMS

1. Construct a logarithmic spiral for $\phi = 36°$. The value of r_0 should be taken as 1 in., with values of θ ranging from $-30°$ to $270°$.

2. Compute by the logarithmic-spiral method the total passive earth pressure against a vertical face in contact with a sand fill having a level surface. The contact face is 20 ft high, and the angle of wall friction is $+20°$. The fill has a unit weight of 112 lb per cu ft and an angle of internal friction of $36°$. In order to facilitate use of the spiral constructed in problem 1, the graphical solution should be laid out on tracing paper. Use the scale 1 in. = 10 ft. $20° > \frac{36}{3}$

   Ans.   175,000 lb per lin ft.

3. Compute the value of passive earth pressure in problem 2, assuming a plane surface of sliding. CULMANN'S GRAPHICAL METHOD

   Ans.   200,000 lb per lin ft.

4. Compute the passive earth pressure against the contact surface of problem 2 if, in addition to frictional resistance, the soil possesses a cohesion of 500 lb per sq ft. The adhesion between the soil and the contact face is also 500 lb per sq ft. Locate the resultant earth pressure P_P.

   Ans.   255,000 lb per lin ft;   8 ft above base.

ART. 29. BEARING CAPACITY OF SHALLOW FOOTINGS

Fundamental Assumptions

When a load is applied on a limited portion of the surface of a soil, the surface settles. The relation between the settlement and the average load per unit of area may be represented by a *settlement curve*, Figure 72. If the soil is fairly dense or stiff, the settlement curve is similar to curve C_1. The abscissa q_d of the vertical tangent to the curve represents the *bearing capacity* of the soil. If the soil is loose or fairly soft, the settlement curve may be similar to C_2, and the bearing capacity is not always well defined. The bearing capacity of such soils is commonly assumed to be equal to the abscissa q_d' of the point at which the settlement curve becomes steep and straight.

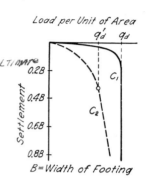

Fig. 72.   Relation between intensity of load and settlement of a footing on (C_1) dense or stiff and (C_2) loose or soft soil.

In practice, loads are transmitted to the soil by means of footings, as shown in Figure 73. The footings may be *continuous*, having a long rectangular shape, or they may be *spread footings*, which are usually square or circular. The *critical load* is the load per unit of length of a continuous footing or the total load on a spread footing at which the soil support fails. The distance from the level of the ground surface to the base of the footing is known as the *depth of foundation* D_f. A footing that has a width B equal to or greater than D_f is considered a *shallow footing.* In computations dealing with shallow footings, the weight of the soil above the base level of the foundation may be replaced by a uniform surcharge,

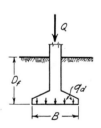

Fig. 73.   Section through continuous shallow footing.

$$q = \gamma D_f \qquad (29.1)$$

This substitution simplifies the computations. The error involved is small and on the safe side.

States of Plastic Equilibrium beneath Shallow Continuous Footings

Mathematical investigations concerning the state of plastic equilibrium beneath continuous footings have led to the following general conclusions. If the base of the footing is perfectly smooth, the loaded soil fails, as shown in Figure 74a, by plastic flow within the region located

above the composite curve $fede_1f_1$. This region can be divided into five
zones, one zone marked *I* and two pairs of zones marked *II* and *III*.
The shear patterns for these zones are shown on the left side of the
figure. Zone *I* represents an *active Rankine zone*, and the zones *III* are
passive Rankine zones, because the shear patterns within these zones are
identical with those for the active and passive Rankine states, Article 23.
The boundaries of the active Rankine zone rise at an angle of $45° + \phi/2$,

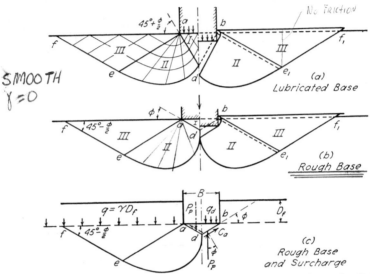

FIG. 74. Boundaries of zone of plastic equilibrium after failure of soil beneath
continuous footing.

and those of the passive Rankine zone at $45° - \phi/2$ with the horizontal.
The zones *II* located between *I* and *III* are known as *zones of radial
shear*, because the lines that constitute one set in the shear pattern in
these zones radiate from the outer edge of the base of the footing. These
lines are fairly straight. The lines of the other set resemble logarithmic
spirals with their centers located at the outer edge of the base of the
footing. If the weight of the soil located within the zone of plastic
equilibrium is disregarded ($\gamma = 0$), the radial lines are perfectly straight,
and the concentric lines are true logarithmic spirals, as shown in Figure
74a. Finally, if the unit weight of the soil is taken into consideration
($\gamma > 0$) but $\phi = 0°$, the radial lines are straight, the concentric lines are
arcs of circles, and the corresponding bearing capacity of the footing is
given by the equation,

$$q_d = (2 + \pi)c = 5.14c = 2.57q_u \qquad (29.2)$$

wherein c is the cohesion and q_u the unconfined compressive strength,

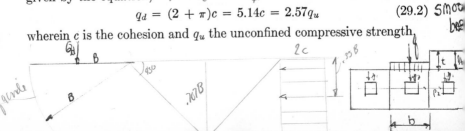

The right side of Figure 74a shows the deformation of the soil located within the zones of plastic flow. The soil located within zone *I* spreads in a horizontal direction. The soil in zones *III* is compressed laterally. Its surface rises and terminates at the side of the footing in a sharp edge that conveys the impression that the soil has been punched. This apparent punching effect has sometimes been called *edge action*.

 If the base of the footing is rough, the friction and adhesion between the soil and the base of the footing prevent the lateral spreading. Therefore, the soil within the region *adb*, Figure 74b, remains in an elastic state. It acts as if it were part of the footing and it penetrates the soil like a wedge. Since the wedge moves vertically downward, every curved surface of sliding within the zones of radial shear must possess a vertical tangent at the inclined face of the wedge. The inclined faces themselves are planes of radial shear rising at an angle ϕ to the horizontal. Therefore, if the base of the footing is rough, the inner boundaries of the zones of radial shear rise not at $45° + \phi/2$ with the horizontal, as shown in Figure 74a, but at an angle ϕ, as shown in Figure 74b. However, the shear pattern in these zones and in the passive Rankine zones *III* is identical with that in the corresponding zones in Figure 74a. If $\phi = 0°$, the curved lines of sliding in the zones of radial shear are arcs of circles, and the corresponding bearing capacity is given by the equation,

$$q_d = 5.70c = 2.85q_u \qquad (29.3)$$

The deformations of the soil associated with the sinking of the footing are shown on the right side of Figure 74b.

APPROXIMATE METHODS FOR COMPUTING THE BEARING CAPACITY OF CONTINUOUS FOOTINGS

 The bases of real footings are rough. Therefore the soil beneath the footings fails as indicated in Figure 74b. Accurate methods for computing the bearing capacity of rough footings are not yet available, but for practical purposes no other than approximate methods are needed. The approximate methods are based on the fact that the wedge *adb* in Figure 74b cannot penetrate the soil unless the pressure on its inclined sides *ad* and *bd* is equal to the passive earth pressure of the adjoining soil. As a consequence, the bearing capacity can be estimated by the methods described in Article 28. The procedure is illustrated by Figure 74c which shows a section through a shallow continuous footing with a width *B*. Since the base of every footing is rough, the soil located between it and the two surfaces of sliding *ad* and *bd* remains in a state of elastic equilibrium and acts as if it formed part of the footing. The surfaces ad and bd rise at ϕ to the horizontal. The unit weight of the soil is γ, and the soil located above the level of the base of the footing is replaced by an equivalent continuous surcharge γD_f per unit of area. At the instant of failure, the pressure on each of the surfaces ad and bd is equal to the resultant of the passive earth pressure P_P and the cohesion force C_a. Since slip occurs along these faces, the resultant earth pressure acts at an angle ϕ to the normal on each face and, as a consequence, in a vertical direction. If the weight of the soil within adb is disregarded, the equilibrium of the footing requires that

$$Q_d = 2P_P + 2C_a \sin\phi = 2P_P + Bc \tan\phi \qquad (29.4)$$

The problem, therefore, is reduced to determining the passive earth pressure P_P.

The passive earth pressure required to produce a slip on def can be divided into two parts, $P_P{}'$ and $P_P{}''$ (see Article 28). The force $P_P{}'$ represents the resistance due to the weight of the mass $adef$. The point of application of $P_P{}'$ is located at the lower third-point of ad. The second part $P_P{}''$ of the passive earth pressure can itself be resolved into two parts. One part, P_c, is due to cohesion. It corresponds to the rectangle $abcd$ in Figure 63b. The second part, P_q, is due to the surcharge $q = \gamma D_f$. It corresponds to the rectangle cc_1d_2d in Figure 63b. Since both pressures P_c and P_q are uniformly distributed, their point of application is located at the mid-point of the contact face ad in Figure 74c, corresponding to the mid-point of ab in Figure 63b.

Hence, the value of the bearing capacity may be calculated by replacing P_P in equation 29.4 by $P_P{}' + P_c + P_q$. Thus,

$$Q_d = 2(P_P{}' + P_c + P_q + \tfrac{1}{2}Bc \tan\phi)$$

By introducing into this equation the symbols,

$$N_c = \frac{2P_c}{Bc} + \tan\phi$$

$$N_q = \frac{2P_q}{\gamma D_f B}$$

$$N_\gamma = \frac{4P_P{}'}{\gamma B^2}$$

we obtain

$$Q_d = B(cN_c + \gamma D_f N_q + \tfrac{1}{2}\gamma B N_\gamma) \qquad (29.5)$$

The quantities N_c, N_q, and N_γ are called the *bearing-capacity factors*. They are dimensionless quantities that depend only on the value of ϕ. Therefore, they can be computed once for all by the methods explained in Article 28 and plotted in a chart. The solid curves in Figure 75 represent the relation between the bearing-capacity factors and the values of ϕ.

The use of the chart, Figure 75, greatly facilitates the computation of the bearing capacity Q_d. The results are only approximate, because the surfaces of sliding that correspond to the components $P_P{}'$, P_c, and P_q,

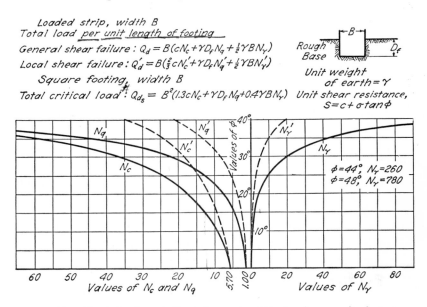

FIG. 75.   Chart showing relation between ϕ and the bearing capacity factors.

computed separately, are not identical with that corresponding to the resultant passive pressure P_P. However, the error is small and on the side of safety.

The soil does not fail as shown in Figure 74c unless it is fairly dense or stiff, so that its settlement curve resembles C_1 in Figure 72. Otherwise, the footing sinks into the ground before the state of plastic equilibrium spreads beyond e and e_1, Figure 74, and the corresponding settlement curve has no well-defined break, curve C_2 in Figure 72. An approximate value for the bearing capacity Q_d of continuous footings on such soils can be obtained by assuming that the cohesion and friction of the soil are equal to two-thirds of the corresponding values in Coulomb's equation, or that

$$c' = \tfrac{2}{3}c \qquad (29.6a)$$

and

$$\tan \phi' = \tfrac{2}{3} \tan \phi \qquad (29.6b)$$

If the angle of shearing resistance is ϕ' instead of ϕ, the bearing-capacity factors assume values N_c', N_q', and N_γ'. These values are given by the dash curves in Figure 75. The bearing capacity is then obtained from the equation,

$$\boxed{Q_d' = B(\tfrac{2}{3}cN_c' + \gamma D_f N_q' + \tfrac{1}{2}\gamma B N_\gamma')} \qquad (29.7)$$

Experience has shown that even uniformly loaded foundations always fail by tilting. This fact, however, does not invalidate the reasoning in the preceding paragraphs. It merely demonstrates that there are no perfectly uniform subgrades. With increasing load the settlement above the weakest part of the subgrade increases more rapidly than that above the rest. Because of the tilt, the center of gravity of the structure shifts toward the weak part and increases the pressure on that part, whereas the pressure on the stronger parts decreases. These factors almost exclude the possibility of a failure without tilting.

BEARING CAPACITY OF CIRCULAR AND SQUARE FOOTINGS

All the preceding discussions refer to continuous footings. For computing the bearing capacity of spread footings with square or circular bases, not even an approximate theory is available. On the basis of experiments the following semiempirical equation has been derived for the bearing capacity Q_{dr} of a circular footing with a radius r resting on a fairly dense or stiff soil.

$$\# \text{ or } \#/_{FT} \quad Q_{dr} = \pi r^2 (1.3cN_c + \gamma D_f N_q + 0.6\gamma r N_\gamma) \qquad (29.8)$$

or

$$\#/_{FT}{}^2 \quad q_{dr} = 1.3cN_c + \gamma D_f N_q + 0.6\gamma r N_\gamma \qquad (29.9)$$

The corresponding value for square footings, $B \times B$, on dense or stiff soil, is

$$\#/_{FT}{}^2 \quad q_{ds} = 1.3cN_c + \gamma D_f N_q + 0.4\gamma B N_\gamma \qquad (29.10)$$

The values of N are given by the ordinates of the solid curves in Figure 75. If $c > 0$, $\phi = 0$, and $D_f = 0$ we obtain for the bearing capacity the value, $\quad$ USE $q_{dr} = 5.7c$

$$q_{dr} = q_{ds} = 7.4c = 3.7q_u \qquad (29.11) \text{ SQUA}$$

which is considerably greater than the value $q_d = 5.70c$, equation 29.3. On the other hand, if $c = 0$ and $D_f = 0$, the bearing capacity q_{dr} per unit of area is considerably smaller than q_d for a continuous footing with a width equal to the diameter of the circular footing.

If the supporting soil is fairly loose or soft, the values of N must be replaced by the values N', determined from the dash curves in Figure 75, and the value of c must be replaced by c', equation 29.6a.

PRACTICAL USE OF EQUATIONS AND DIAGRAMS

The bearing capacity of footings on soft clay is determined by equation 29.3 (continuous footings) or equation 29.11 (square footings). The value q_u contained in these equations represents the average unconfined compressive strength of the clay located within the zone of potential plastic flow. The bearing capacity of footings on cohesionless or cohesive sand is obtained by means of equation 29.5 (continuous footings) or equation 29.10 (square footings). The values N_c, N_q, and N_γ contained in these equations depend on the angle of internal friction ϕ of the sand. The value of ϕ can be estimated on the basis of the numerical data contained in Article 15. Once the value of ϕ has been chosen, the corresponding values of N_c, N_q, and N_γ can be determined without any computation by means of the diagram, Figure 75.

The ultimate bearing capacity of footings on dry cohesionless sand is determined by the equations,

$$q_d = \gamma(D_f N_q + 0.5BN_\gamma) \quad \text{(continuous footings)}$$

and

$$q_{ds} = \gamma(D_f N_q + 0.4BN_\gamma) \quad \text{(square footings)}$$

In these equations γ represents the unit weight of the dry sand. If the water table rises from a depth of more than about B below the base of the footing to the surface of the sand, the effective unit weight of the sand is reduced to its submerged unit weight γ'. According to Article 12, the submerged unit weight is roughly equal to one half of γ. Hence the rise of the water table to the surface of the ground reduces the bearing capacity of the footings by about 50 per cent.

DISTRIBUTION OF SOIL PRESSURE ON BASE OF FOOTINGS

The distribution of the critical load Q_d on the base of the footing depends on the relation between normal stress and shearing resistance for the soil and on the depth of foundation D_f. It may be determined approximately by a procedure similar to that used for determining the point of application of the resultant passive earth pressure (see Article 24). The procedure is illustrated by Figure 76 which refers to a continuous footing on soil for which ϕ is greater than zero.

The first step is to determine the distribution of that part Q'' of Q_d which is due only to the cohesion c and to the surcharge γD_f. The unit weight of the soil located below the base of the footing is assumed to be zero. The corresponding part P_P'' of the passive earth pressure on the inclined face db, Figure 76a, acts at the mid-point of db. Similarly, the reaction P_E'' on the vertical section Od acts near the mid-point of Od. Therefore, the forces P_P'', P_E'', and C_a are practically concurrent at e.

For equilibrium the line of action of Q'' must pass through e. Since the adhesion on Ob causes Q'' to be inclined, the vertical component of Q'' must act to the right of the mid-point of Ob, and, as a consequence, the distribution of pressure on the base of the footing must be similar to $Obsr$. According to equation 29.5, the total magnitude of Q'' is equal to $BcN_c + B\gamma D_f N_q$.

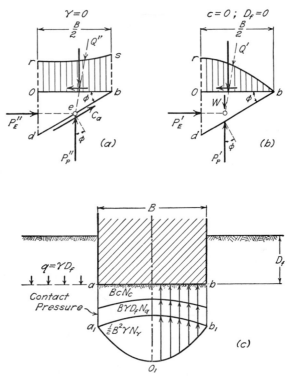

FIG. 76. Distribution of contact pressure at instant of failure beneath continuous footing (a) on weightless cohesive soil; (b) on cohesionless soil with weight; (c) on cohesive soil with weight.

The second step is to determine the distribution of that part Q' of Q_d which is due only to the weight of the soil located below the level of the base of the footing. Since in this step it is assumed that $c = 0$ and $q = \gamma D_f = 0$, the corresponding part P_P' of the passive earth pressure acts at the lower third-point of db, Figure 76b, and the distribution of the contact pressure is similar to Obr. The total magnitude of Q' is $\frac{1}{2}B^2\gamma N_\gamma$. The distribution of the total critical load Q_d is obtained by combining the two partial pressures represented in Figures 76a and b. It is shown in Figure 76c.

The reasoning that leads to Figure 76c is based on the assumption that the shearing resistance of the soil is fully active. Therefore, the conclusions are not valid if the load on the footing is less than the critical value. The distribution of the pressure on the base of moderately loaded footings is discussed in Article 37.

PROBLEMS

1. Compute the bearing capacity per unit of area of a continuous footing 8 ft wide, supported on a soil for which $c = 400$ lb per sq ft, $\phi = 17°$, and $\gamma = 120$ lb per cu ft. The load–settlement curve resembles C_1 in Figure 72, and the relation between normal stress and shearing resistance is $s = c + p \tan \phi$. The depth of foundation is 6 ft.

  Ans. 11,000 lb per sq ft.

2. Compute the bearing capacity per unit of area of a footing 10 ft square on dense sand ($\phi = 37°$), if the depth of foundation is, respectively, 0, 2, 5, 10, and 15 ft. The unit weight of the soil is 126 lb per cu ft.

  Ans. 30,000; 45,000; 68,000; 106,000; 144,000 lb per sq ft.

3. A load test was made on a bearing plate 1 ft square on the surface of a cohesionless deposit of sand having a unit weight of 110 lb per cu ft. The load–settlement curve approached a vertical tangent at a load of 4000 lb. What was the value of ϕ for the sand?

  Ans. 38°.

4. A load test was made on a plate 1 ft square on a dense cohesionless sand having a unit weight of 115 lb per cu ft. The bearing plate was enclosed in a box surrounded by a surcharge 2 ft deep. Failure occurred at a load of 12,000 lb. What would be the failure load per unit of area of the base of a footing 5 ft square located with its base at the same depth in the same material?   TRIAL & ERROR   for Nq & Nγ

  Ans. 19,800 lb per sq ft.

5. A structure was built on a mat foundation 100 ft square. The mat rested at the ground surface on a stratum of uniform soft clay which extended to a depth of 150 ft. If failure occurred at a uniformly distributed load of 4500 lb per sq ft, what was the average value of c for the clay? Because of the great depth of the zone of plastic equilibrium, the consolidation of the clay prior to failure can be disregarded, and it can be assumed that $\phi = 0°$.

  Ans. 910 lb per sq ft.

ART. 30. BEARING CAPACITY OF PIERS AND PILES

Definitions

A pier is a slender prismatic or cylindrical body of masonry that transfers a load through a poor stratum onto a better one. A pile is essentially a very slender pier that transfers a load either through its lower end onto a firm stratum or else through side friction onto the surrounding soil. The relation between the load on a pier or pile and the corresponding settlement is very similar to that for footings. The load–settlement curve approaches either a vertical or an inclined tangent, as shown in Figure 72. The definition of the *critical load* on piers and piles is identical with that of the bearing capacity of footings (see Article 29).

Bearing Capacity of Cylindrical Piers

Since the diameter of a pier is small compared to its depth, at least a small part of the load is carried by friction and adhesion between the sides of the pier and the surrounding soil. The critical load Q_d on a pier with depth D_f can be expressed by the equation,

$$Q_d = Q_{pr} + 2\pi r f_s D_f \tag{30.1}$$

in which Q_{pr} represents the critical load on the circular base of the pier, r is the radius of the base, and f_s is the sum of the friction and adhesion, per unit of contact area between the pier and the soil.

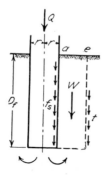

Figure 77 represents a vertical section through such a pier. The pier cannot fail without displacing at least part of the mass of soil located beneath it. The displacement takes place in an outward or in an outward and upward direction as indicated by the curved arrows. It is resisted by the weight W of the mass of soil that surrounds the pier and by the shearing stresses on the inner and outer boundaries of this mass. The intensity of these shearing stresses depends on the compressibility of the soil and on various other factors. If these shearing stresses were equal to zero, the value Q_{pr} in equation 30.1 would be identical with Q_{dr}, equation 29.8. Since the evaluation of the shearing stresses and of their influence on the bearing capacity is very uncertain, it is preferable to disregard them and to compute Q_{pr} by means of equation 29.8. The error is on the safe side, and experience indicates that it is usually small.

Fig. 77.   Section through cylindrical pier.

The second term on the right-hand side of equation 30.1 contains the skin friction f_s. However, the value of f_s cannot be determined even approximately by means of laboratory tests, because the stress conditions at the contact surface are unknown. Therefore, f_s is commonly estimated on the basis of empirical data derived from field observations (see Article 57).

Bearing Capacity of Piles

Since piles are essentially very slender cylindrical piers, their bearing capacity can be estimated by an equation similar to equation 30.1. If

Q_d is the resistance of a pile to penetration into the ground under a static load,

$$Q_d = Q_{pr} + 2\pi r f_s D_f = Q_p + Q_f \qquad (30.2)$$

The quantity $Q_{pr} = Q_p$ is called the *point resistance*, whereas the quantity $2\pi r f_s D_f = Q_f$ is known as the *skin friction*. If Q_p is large compared to Q_f, the pile is said to be *point-bearing*. On the other hand, if Q_p is relatively insignificant, the pile is known as a *friction pile.*

The principal difference between piles and piers lies in the method of installation. The construction of piers is preceded by excavation, whereas the driving of piles, which usually consist either of solid bodies or of shells closed at the lower end, involves a displacement of the soil. Occasionally the driving is facilitated by removing part of the soil located in the path of the pile by means of a water jet or a pre-excavator, but the volume of the soil so removed is small compared to the total volume of the piles.

A lower limiting value for the point resistance Q_p of piles having a circular cross section can be obtained by means of equation 29.8, and of piles having a square cross section by equation 29.10. These equations determine the bearing capacity of point-bearing piles. The bearing capacity of friction piles depends on the skin friction f_s (see equation 30.2). The evaluation of the skin friction on the basis of laboratory tests is even more unreliable for piles than it is for piers, because the computation of the stresses produced by the partial or total displacement of the soil during the process of pile driving is beyond the power of analysis. Therefore, the bearing capacity Q_d of a friction pile can be determined only by load tests on piles in the field or else, less accurately, on the basis of empirical values for f_s. Values of f_s corresponding to the principal types of soil are given in Article 56. In those cities where friction piles are extensively used, empirical values for f_s, derived from local experience, are likely to be quite reliable.

Pile Formulas

The bearing capacity Q_d of a point-bearing pile is approximately equal to the resistance Q_{dy} of the soil against rapid penetration of the pile under the impact of the falling ram of the pile driver. There is at least a theoretical possibility of estimating Q_{dy}, known as the *dynamic resistance*, from the average penetration S of the pile under the last few blows of the hammer, provided the weight W_H of the ram and the height of fall H are known. Therefore, many efforts have been made to compute the bearing capacity on the basis of this information. The results of these efforts are

known as *pile formulas*. The following paragraphs deal with the fundamental concepts on which the pile formulas are based.

The work performed by the falling hammer is $W_H H$, and the work
required to increase the penetration of the pile by S against a resistance
Q_{dy} is $Q_{dy}S$. If the entire work of the falling hammer served to increase
the penetration of the pile, we could write

$$W_H H = Q_{dy}S$$

whence

$$Q_{dy} = \frac{W_H H}{S}$$

This is Sanders' pile formula, published about 1850. The values obtained
by means of this formula are too great, because part of the energy of the
falling hammer is converted into heat and into elastic deformations.

If the energy loss did not occur, the pile would penetrate under the
hammer blow not only the actual distance S but also an additional
distance c. Hence

$$Q_{dy} = \frac{W_H H}{S + c} \tag{30.3}$$

Wellington (1898) tried to evaluate c on the basis of whatever empirical
data he had at his disposal. He arrived at the conclusion that c is approximately equal to 1 in. for piles driven by a drop hammer, and 0.1 in.
for piles driven by a steam hammer. Since he realized the uncertainties
involved in his estimate, he proposed that the allowable load Q_a per pile
should not exceed one sixth of the computed ultimate load Q_{dy}. By expressing H in feet and S in inches, he obtained

$$Q_a = \frac{1}{6} Q_{dy} = \frac{12}{6} \frac{W_H H}{S + c} = \frac{2W_H H}{S + c} \tag{30.4}$$

This equation is known as the *Engineering News formula*.

In order to evaluate the degree of accuracy of equation 30.4, a comparison has been made between the allowable load Q_a, equation 30.4, and
the real ultimate bearing capacity Q_d of 18 piles selected at random. The
real bearing capacity was determined by means of load tests. For these
piles it was found that Q_d ranged between $2Q_a$ and $12Q_a$. According to
the laws of probability, the values of Q_d for 100 or 1000 piles should range
between considerably wider limits. In a few instances, Q_d might even be
less than $1.0 \, Q_a$, involving failure of the pile under the design load. For
these reasons many engineers have tried to develop more reliable formulas. A few of these are discussed in the following paragraphs.

If equation 30.3 is written in the form,

$$W_H H = Q_{dy} S + Q_{dy} c$$

it becomes obvious that the term $Q_{dy} c$ represents a loss of energy. At least part of this loss is due to the work that must be expended in producing a temporary elastic compression S_e of the pile and the adjoining soil. If the force Q_{dy} were applied at one end of a column, it would perform a work equal to $\frac{1}{2} Q_{dy} S_e$. Although the analogy between a pile and a column is not perfect, it seems justifiable to assume that $Q_{dy} c$ in equation 30.3 is at least roughly equal to $\frac{1}{2} Q_{dy} S_e$, whence

$$Q_{dy} = \frac{W_H H}{S + \frac{1}{2} S_e} \tag{30.5}$$

If the dimensions and elastic properties of the pile and the pile cap are known, the value of S_e can be estimated at least crudely. This has been done by the authors of some of the pile formulas. However, S_e can also be measured in the field by holding a pencil against a piece of cardboard fastened to the pile. Since about 1910 various pile-driving contractors have practiced this method and claim that it has been fairly successful. The measured values of S_e are certainly more accurate than the computed ones. Yet, even if S_e has been measured, equation 30.5 cannot be expected to apply to all piles under all conditions, because it does not take account of the inertia forces involved in the process of pile driving.

If the ratio between the weight W_P of the pile and the weight W_H of the hammer is very small, equation 30.5 may be reasonably accurate. However, if the weight of the pile is very much greater than that of the hammer, the fall of the hammer merely produces a deformation of the head of the pile, comparable to the deformation of a large rock when it is struck by a small stone. Hence, if W_P/W_H is very large, failure of the pile to penetrate deeper into the ground does not indicate a high bearing capacity of the pile. This fact can roughly be taken into consideration by multiplying the right-hand side of equation 30.5 by the factor $1/(1 + W_P/W_H)$, whence

$$Q_{dy} = \frac{W_H H}{S + \frac{1}{2} S_e} \cdot \frac{1}{1 + \dfrac{W_P}{W_H}} = \frac{W_H H}{S + \frac{1}{2} S_e} \frac{W_H}{W_H + W_P} \tag{30.6}$$

This is the general pattern of the more elaborate pile formulas. However, since the reasoning that leads to this pattern involves various arbitrary assumptions with unknown practical implications, it is not surprising that even the most elaborate pile formulas are far from accurate. As a matter of fact, [there is no evidence that the bearing capacity computed by means of any pile formula is likely to be more reliable than that computed by means of equation 30.4.]

The principal defect in the derivation of equation 30.6 is the arbitrary manner in which the effect of the ratio W_P/W_H on Q_{dy} has been evaluated. The effect of the impact on the penetration of the pile depends on several factors other than the weights W_P and W_H, but none of these other factors has been considered. In order to reduce the corresponding error, attempts have been made in recent years to derive pile formulas on the basis of the theory of longitudinal impact on rods. From a scientific point of view, this new approach is a great improvement over the older methods, but the investigations are in an experimental stage, and it is still uncertain whether or not they will lead to results of practical value. Hence, for the present, the designer of a point-bearing pile foundation must choose between two alternatives. Either he may use one of the many pile formulas at the risk of driving two or three times more piles than the foundation requires, or else he may go to the expense of making load tests on full-size test piles in the field. The choice between the alternatives depends on the available time and the relation between the cost of the tests and that of the entire foundation.

PROBLEMS

1. A reinforced-concrete pile with a cross section 16 by 16 in. was driven through a deposit of fine loose sand and soft clay 65 ft thick and into a stratum of dense sand for a distance of 2.5 ft. The water table was located near the ground surface. The loose sand and soft clay had a submerged unit weight of 45 lb per cu ft, and the angle of internal friction of the dense sand in a submerged state was 35°. Compute the point resistance of the pile.

    Ans. 114 tons. By means of a loading and a pulling test, the point resistance was found to be 115 tons.

2. The pile referred to in the preceding problem was driven by means of a steam hammer having a weight $W_H = 4$ tons and a stroke $H = 2$ ft. The penetration of the pile under the last blow was $S = 0.056$ in. According to the Engineering News formula, what is the ultimate bearing capacity of the pile?

    Ans. 616 tons. According to the load test, the real ultimate bearing capacity, equal to the sum of the point resistance (115 tons) and the skin friction (110 tons), was 225 tons.

3. A test pile of the type described in problem 1 was driven at another point of the area to be occupied by the structure. Soil conditions were identical, except that the sand encountered at a depth of 65 ft was loose ($\phi = 30°$). Compute the point resistance of the pile.

    Ans. 21 tons. (No load test was made, but the pile penetrated the sand so easily under the blows of the hammer that it was decided to change the type of foundation over the entire area underlain by the loose sand.)

ART. 31. STABILITY OF SLOPES

INTRODUCTION

The failure of a mass of soil located beneath a slope is called a *slide*. It involves a downward and outward movement of the entire mass of soil that participates in the failure.

Slides may occur in almost every conceivable manner, slowly or suddenly, and with or without any apparent provocation. Usually, slides are due to excavation or to undercutting the foot of an existing slope. However, in some instances, they are caused by a gradual disintegration of the structure of the soil, starting at hair cracks which subdivide the soil into angular fragments. In others, they are caused by an increase of the pore-water pressure in a few exceptionally permeable layers, or by a shock that liquefies the soil beneath the slope, Article 49. Because of the extraordinary variety of factors and processes that may lead to slides, the conditions for the stability of slopes usually defy theoretical analysis. Stability computations based on test results can be relied on only when the conditions specified in the different sections of this article are strictly satisfied. Moreover, it should always be remembered that various undetected discontinuities in the soil, such as systems of hair cracks, remnants of old surfaces of sliding, or thin seams of water-bearing sand, may completely invalidate the results of the computations.

In the following paragraphs, it is assumed that seepage forces are negligible. The effect of these forces on stability are considered in Article 42.

SLOPES ON DRY COHESIONLESS SAND

A slope underlain by clean dry sand is stable regardless of its height, provided the angle β between the slope and the horizontal is equal to or smaller than the angle of internal friction ϕ for the sand in a loose state. The factor of safety of the slope with respect to sliding may be expressed by the equation,

$$G_s = \frac{\tan \phi}{\tan \beta} \tag{31.1}$$

No slope on clean sand can exist with a slope angle greater than ϕ, irrespective of its height.

Since very few natural soils are perfectly cohesionless, the remainder of this article deals with slopes underlain by cohesive materials.

GENERAL CHARACTER OF SLIDES IN HOMOGENEOUS COHESIVE SOIL

A cohesive material having a shearing resistance,

$$s = c + p \tan \phi$$

can stand with a vertical slope at least for a short time, provided the height of the slope is somewhat less than H_c, equation 24.8. If the height of a slope is greater than H_c, the slope is not stable unless the slope angle β is less than 90°. The greater the height of the slope, the smaller must be the angle β. If the height is very great compared to H_c, the slope will fail unless the slope angle β is equal to or less than ϕ.

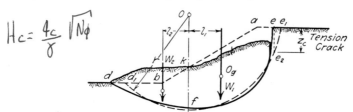

$$H_c = \frac{4c}{\gamma} \sqrt{N_\phi}$$

FIG. 78.   Deformation associated with slope failure.

The failure of a slope in a cohesive material is commonly preceded by the formation of tension cracks behind the upper edge of the slope, as shown in Figure 78. The force which produces the tension cracks behind the edge of a vertical slope is represented by the triangle *ace* in Figure 62*b*. Sooner or later, the opening of the cracks is followed by sliding along a curved surface, indicated by the full line in Figure 78. Usually the radius of curvature of the surface of sliding is least at the upper end, greatest in the middle, and intermediate at the lower end. The curve,

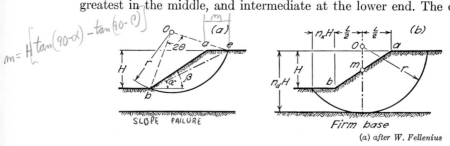

$$m = H \tan(90-\alpha) - \tan(90-\beta)$$

FIG. 79.   Position of critical circle for (*a*) slope failure; (*b*) base failure.

therefore, resembles the arc of an ellipse. If the failure occurs along a surface of sliding that intersects the slope at or above its toe (see Figure 79*a*), the slide is known as a *slope failure*. On the other hand, if the soil beneath the level of the toe of the slope is unable to sustain the weight of the overlying material, the failure occurs along a surface that passes at some distance below the toe of the slope. A failure of this type, shown in Figure 79*b*, is known as a *base failure*.

In stability computations the curve representing the real surface of sliding is replaced either by an arc of a circle or of a logarithmic spiral.

Either procedure is as legitimate as Coulomb's assumption of a plane surface of sliding in connection with retaining wall problems, Article 26. In the following discussions only the circle will be used as a substitute for the real surface of sliding.

Purpose of Stability Computations

In engineering practice stability computations serve as a basis either for the redesign of slopes after a failure, or else for choosing slope angles in accordance with specified safety requirements in advance of construction.

Local failures on the slopes of cuts or fills are common during the construction period. They indicate that the average value of the minimum shearing resistance of the soil has been overestimated. Since such failures constitute large-scale shear tests, they offer excellent opportunities for evaluating the real minimum shearing resistance and for avoiding further accidents on the same job by changing the design in accordance with the findings. The general procedure is to determine the position of the surface of sliding by means of test borings or shafts, to estimate the weights of the various parts of the sliding mass that tended to produce or to oppose the slide, and to compute the average shearing resistance s of the soil necessary to satisfy the conditions for equilibrium of the mass.

In order to design a slope in a region where no slides have occurred, the average shearing resistance s must be estimated or determined in advance of construction. Methods for evaluating the shearing resistance are discussed in Article 15. After the value of s has been determined, the slope angle can be chosen on the basis of theory in such a manner that the slope satisfies the specified safety requirements. It is obvious that this method can be used only if the soil conditions permit a fairly reliable determination of s on the basis of the results of soil tests.

Computation of Shearing Resistance from Slide Data

The method for determining the average shearing resistance of soils on the basis of slide data is illustrated by Figure 78. The depth z_c of the tension cracks and the shape of the surface of sliding are ascertained by field measurements. The line of sliding is then replaced by the arc of a circle having a radius r and its center at O. Equilibrium requires that

$$W_1 l_1 = W_2 l_2 + sr \, \overset{\frown}{d_1 e_2}$$

from which

$$s = \frac{W_1 l_1 - W_2 l_2}{r \, \overset{\frown}{d_1 e_2}}$$

where W_1 is the weight of the slice *akfe* which tends to produce failure, and W_2 is the weight of slice kbd_1f which tends to resist it.

[If the shape of the surface of sliding is such that it cannot be represented even approximately by an arc of a circle, the procedure must be modified according to the method described subsequently in connection with composite surfaces of sliding.]

PROCEDURE FOR INVESTIGATING STABILITY OF SLOPES

In order to investigate whether a slope on soil with known shear characteristics will be stable, it is necessary to determine the diameter and position of the circle that represents the surface along which sliding will occur. This circle, known as the *critical circle*, must satisfy the requirement that the ratio between the moment of the forces tending to resist the slide and the moment of the forces tending to produce it must be a minimum. Hence, the investigation belongs to the category of maximum and minimum problems exemplified by Coulomb's theory, Article 26, and the theory of passive earth pressure, Article 28.

After the diameter and position of the critical circle have been determined, the factor of safety G_s of the slope with respect to failure may be computed by means of the relation (see Figure 78),

$$G_s = \frac{\text{moment of resisting forces}}{\text{moment of driving forces}} = \frac{W_2 l_2 + sr \overparen{d_1 e_2}}{W_1 l_1} \qquad (31.2)$$

wherein r represents the radius of the critical circle and $d_1 e_2$ the length of the surface of sliding.

Like the passive earth pressure of a mass of soil, the stability of a slope may be investigated by trial or, in simple cases, by analytical methods. To make the investigation by trial, different circles are selected, each representing a potential surface of sliding. For each circle, the value G_s, equation 31.2, is computed. The minimum value represents the factor of safety of the slope with respect to sliding, and the corresponding circle is the critical circle.

The analytical solutions can rarely be used to compute the factor of safety of a slope under actual conditions, because they are based on greatly simplified assumptions. They are valuable, however, as a guide for estimating the position of the center of the critical circle and for ascertaining the probable character of the failure. In addition, they may serve as a means for judging whether a given slope will be unquestionably safe, unquestionably unsafe, or of doubtful stability. If the stability appears doubtful, the factor of safety with respect to failure should be computed according to the procedure described in the preceding paragraph.

The analytical solutions are based on the following assumptions: Down to a given level below the toe of the slope, the soil is perfectly homogeneous. At this level, the soil rests on the horizontal surface of a stiffer stratum, known as the *firm base*, which is not penetrated by the surface of sliding. The slope is considered to be a plane, and it is located between two horizontal plane surfaces, as shown in Figure 79. Finally, the weakening effect of tension cracks is disregarded, because it is more than compensated by the customary margin of safety. The following paragraphs contain a summary of the results of the investigations.

SLOPES ON SOFT CLAY

The average shearing resistance s per unit of area of a potential surface of sliding in homogeneous soft clay is roughly equal to one-half the unconfined compressive strength q_u of the clay. This value of s is referred to briefly as the cohesion c. That is,

$$s = \tfrac{1}{2}q_u = c \qquad (22.1)$$

If c is known, the critical height H_c of a slope having a given slope angle β can be expressed by the equation,

$$H_c = N_s \frac{c}{\gamma} \qquad (31.3)$$

In this equation the *stability factor N_s* is a pure number. Its value depends only on the slope angle β and on the *depth factor n_d,* Figure 79b, which expresses the depth at which the clay rests on a firm base. If a slope failure occurs, the critical circle is usually a *toe circle* that passes through the toe b of the slope, Figure 79a. However, if the firm base is located at a short distance below the level of b, the critical circle may be a *slope circle* that is tangent to the firm base and that intersects the slope above the toe b. This type of failure is not shown in Figure 79. If a base failure occurs, the critical circle is known as a *mid-point circle*, because its center is located on a vertical line through the mid-point m of the slope, Figure 79b. The mid-point circle is tangent to the firm base.

The position of the critical circle with reference to a given slope depends on the slope angle β and the depth factor n_d. Figure 80 contains a summary of the results of pertinent theoretical investigations. According to this figure, the failure of all slopes rising at an angle of more than 53° occurs along a toe circle. If β is smaller than 53°, the type of failure depends on the value of the depth factor n_d and, at low values of n_d, also on the slope angle β. If n_d is equal to 1.0, failure occurs along a slope circle. If n_d is greater than about 4.0, the slope fails along a mid-point circle tangent to the firm base, regardless of the value of β. If n_d is intermediate in value between 1.0 and 4.0, failure occurs along a slope circle if the point representing the values of n_d and β lies above the shaded area in Figure 80. If the point lies within the shaded area, failure occurs along a toe circle. If the point is below the shaded area, the slope fails along a mid-point circle tangent to the firm base.

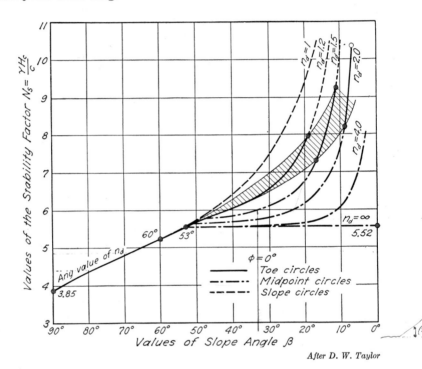

After D. W. Taylor

FIG. 80.   Relation for frictionless material between slope angle β and stability factor N_s for different values of depth factor n_d.

If the slope angle β and the depth factor n_d are given, the value of the corresponding stability factor N_s, equation 31.3, can be obtained without computation from Figure 80. The value of N_s determines the critical height H_c of the slope.

If failure occurs along a toe circle, the center of the critical circle can be located by laying off the angles α and 2θ, as shown in Figure 79a. Values of α and θ for different slope angles β are given in Figure 81a. If failure occurs along a mid-point circle tangent to the firm base, the position of the critical circle is determined by the horizontal distance $n_x H$

from the toe of the slope to the circle (see Figure 79b). Values of n_x can be estimated for different values of n_d and β by means of the chart, Figure 81b.

[If the clay beneath a slope consists of several layers with different average cohesion c_1, c_2, etc., or if the surface of the ground is irregular

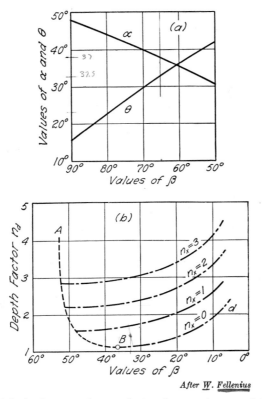

After W. Fellenius

FIG. 81.   (a) Relation between slope angle β and parameters α and θ for location of critical toe circle when β is greater than 53°; (b) relation between slope angle β and depth factor n_d for various values of parameter n_x.

(see Figure 82), the center of the critical circle must be determined by trial and error. It is obvious that the longest part of the real surface of sliding will be located within the softest stratum. Therefore, the trial circle should also satisfy this condition. If one of the upper layers is relatively soft, the presence of a firm base at considerable depth may not enter into the problem, because the deepest part of the surface of sliding is likely to be located entirely within the softest stratum. For example, if the cohesion c_2 of the second stratum in Figure 82 is much smaller than the cohesion c_3 of the underlying third layer, the critical circle will be tangent to the upper surface of the third stratum instead of the firm base.

For each trial circle we compute the average shearing stress t which must act along the surface of sliding to balance the difference between the moment $W_1 l_1$ of the driving weight and the resisting moment $W_2 l_2$. The value of t is

$$t = \frac{W_1 l_1 - W_2 l_2}{r \, \widehat{ab}}$$

Then, on the basis of the known values of c_1, c_2, c_3, etc., we compute the average value of the cohesion c of the soil along the sliding surface. The factor of safety of the slope against sliding along the circular trial surface is

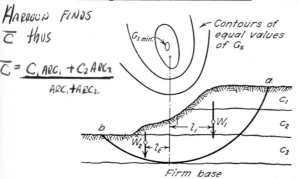

FIG. 82. Base failure in stratified cohesive soil.

$$G_s = \frac{c}{t} \qquad (31.4)$$

The value of G_s is inscribed at the center of the circle. After values of G_s have been determined for several trial circles, curves of equal values of G_s are plotted (see Figure 82). These curves may be considered as contour lines of a depression. The center of the critical circle is located at the bottom of the depression. The corresponding value $G_{s\,min}$ is the factor of safety of the slope with respect to sliding.

SLOPES ON SOILS WITH COHESION AND INTERNAL FRICTION

The shearing resistance of dry or moist cohesive soils located above the water table can be expressed approximately by the equation,

$$s = c + p \tan \phi$$

The values of c and ϕ are likely to change with the seasons. Therefore, the instances in which the lower limiting values for c and ϕ can be evaluated reliably are rather rare. Nevertheless, the method for investigating the stability of slopes on such soils deserves attention, because the same method can also be used for investigating the stability of slopes on fine sand acted on by seepage pressures, as shown in Article 42. Furthermore, the results of the investigations strikingly illustrate the important influence of the value ϕ on the stability of slopes, and they permit one to decide whether or not the shearing resistance of a mass of soil which failed by sliding was partly due to internal friction.

The procedure is illustrated by Figure 83a. The forces acting on the sliding mass are its weight W, the resultant cohesion C, and the resultant F of the normal and frictional forces acting along the surface of sliding. The resultant cohesion C acts in a direction parallel to the chord de and is equal to the unit cohesion c multiplied by the length L of the chord. The distance x from the center of rotation to C is determined by the condition that

$$Cx = cLx = c\,\widehat{de}\,r$$

whence $x = \widehat{de}\,r/L$. Therefore, the force C is known. The weight W is also known. Since the forces C, W, and F are in equilibrium, the force F must pass through the point of intersection of W and C. Hence, the magnitude and line of action of F can be determined by constructing the polygon of forces.

If the factor of safety against sliding is equal to unity, the slope is on the verge of failure. Under this condition each of the elementary reactions dF in Figure 83a must be inclined at the angle ϕ to the normal to the circle of sliding. As a consequence, the line of action of each elementary reaction is tangent to a circle, known as the *friction circle*, having a radius,

$$r_f = r \sin \phi$$

and having its center at the center of the circle of sliding. The line of action of the resultant reaction F is tangent to a circle having a radius slightly greater than r_f, but as a convenient approximation we assume that at a factor of safety equal to unity the line of action of F is also tangent to the friction circle. The corresponding error is small and is on the safe side.

For a given value of ϕ the critical height of a slope which fails along a toe circle is given by the equation,

$$H_c = N_s \frac{c}{\gamma}$$

which is identical with equation 31.3, except that N_s depends not only on β but also on ϕ. Figure 83b shows the relationship between β and N_s for different values of ϕ. At a given value of the slope angle β, N_s increases at first slowly and then more rapidly with increasing values of ϕ. When $\phi = \beta$, N_s becomes infinite.

See TAYLOR p443 for friction circle correction factors

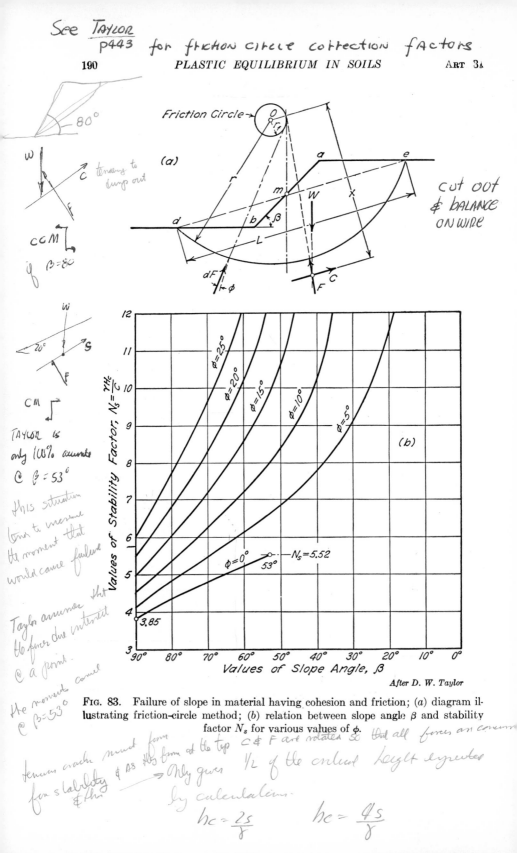

80°

w

c tendency to dump out

(a)

Friction Circle →

cut out & balance on wire

ccM if β=80

w
20° S
F

CM

TAYLOR is only 100% accurate @ β=53°

this situation tends to increase the moment that would cause failure

Taylor assumes that the forces due interior @ a point.

the moments cancel @ β=53°

FIG. 83. Failure of slope in material having cohesion and friction; (a) diagram illustrating friction-circle method; (b) relation between slope angle β and stability factor N_s for various values of ϕ.

After D. W. Taylor

tension cracks must form for stability & as they form at the top C & F are rotated so that all forces are concurrent → only gives ½ of the critical height expected by calculation.

$$h_c = \frac{2s}{\gamma}$$

$$h_c = \frac{4s}{\gamma}$$

All the points on the curves shown in Figure 83*b* correspond to failures along toe circles, because theory has shown that the possibility of a base failure does not exist unless the value of ϕ is smaller than 3°. Therefore, if a typical base failure has occurred in a fairly homogeneous soil in the field, it can be concluded that the value of ϕ for the soil at the time of the slide was close to zero.

COMPOSITE SURFACES OF SLIDING

If the subsoil contains one or more thin exceptionally weak strata, the surface of sliding is likely to consist of three or more sections that do not merge smoothly one into another. In stability computations such a surface cannot be replaced by a continuous curve without the introduction of an error on the unsafe side.

Figure 84 represents a slope underlain by a thin layer of very soft clay with cohesion c. If such a slope fails, the slip occurs along some composite surface *abcd*. In the right-hand part of the sliding

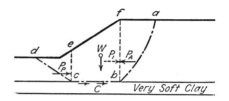

FIG. 84.   Failure of slope underlain by thin layer of very soft clay.

mass, represented by the area *abf*, active failure must be expected, because the earth stretches horizontally under the influence of its own weight. The central part *bcef* moves to the left under the influence of the active pressure on *bf*. The left-hand part of the sliding mass *cde* experiences passive failure due to the thrust of the advancing central part *bcef*.

The first step in investigating the conditions for the stability of the slope is to compute the passive earth pressure P_P of the soil located on the left side of a tentatively selected vertical section *ec* located near the toe of the slope. It is conservative to assume that P_P acts in the horizontal direction. The next step is to estimate the position of the right-hand boundary b of the horizontal part *cb* of the potential surface of sliding and to compute the active earth pressure P_A on a vertical section *fb* through b. The tendency for the mass *bcef* to move to the left is resisted by the passive earth pressure P_P and the total cohesion C along *bc*. If the slope is stable, the sum of these resisting forces must be greater than the active earth pressure P_A which is assumed to act in a horizontal direction. The factor of safety against sliding is equal to the ratio between the sum of the resisting forces and the force P_A. The investigation must be repeated for different positions of the points c and b until the surface of least resistance to sliding is found that corresponds to the least factor of safety.

$$\text{Slices}$$
$$F.S. = \frac{\Sigma \, N \tan \phi + cL}{\Sigma \, T}$$

PROBLEMS

1. A wide cut was made in a stratum of soft clay that had a level surface. The sides of the cut rose at 30° to the horizontal. Bedrock was located at a depth of 40 ft below the original ground surface. When the cut reached a depth of 25 ft, failure occurred. If the unit weight of the clay was 120 lb per cu ft, what was its average cohesive strength? What was the character of the surface of sliding? At what distance from the foot of the slope did the surface of sliding intersect the bottom of the excavation?

    Ans.   500 lb per sq ft;   mid-point circle;   18 ft.

2. The rock surface referred to in problem 1 was located at a depth of 30 ft below the original ground surface. What were the average cohesive strength of the clay and the character of the surface of sliding?

    Ans.   450 lb per sq ft;   toe circle.

3. A cut is to be excavated in soft clay to a depth of 30 ft. The material has a unit weight of 114 lb per cu ft and a cohesion of 700 lb per sq ft. A hard layer underlies the soft layer at a depth of 40 ft below the original ground surface. What is the slope angle at which failure is likely to occur?

    Ans. $\beta = 69°$.

4. A trench with sides rising at 80° to the horizontal is excavated in a soft clay which weighs 120 lb per cu ft and has a cohesion of 250 lb per sq ft. To what depth can the excavation be carried before the sides cave in? At what distance from the upper edge of the slope will the surface of sliding intersect the ground surface?

    Ans.   9 ft;   8 ft.

5. A bed of clay consists of three horizontal strata, each 15 ft thick. The values for c for the upper, middle, and lower strata are, respectively, 600, 400, and 3000 lb per sq ft. The unit weight is 115 lb per cu ft. A cut is excavated with side slopes of 1 (vertical) to 3 (horizontal) to a depth of 20 ft. What is the factor of safety of the slope against failure?

    Ans.   1.2.

6. To what depth can the trench in problem 4 be excavated without bracing if the soil has, in addition to its cohesion, an angle of internal friction of 20°?

    Ans.   14.2 ft.

ART. 32. EARTH PRESSURE AGAINST BRACING IN CUTS

DEFORMATION CONDITIONS IMPOSED BY BRACING

Figure 85 illustrates one of several methods for bracing an open cut. A row of H-piles is driven along each side of the proposed excavation to a depth of several feet below grade. The sides of the cut between H-piles are lined by horizontal boards placed directly against the soil as the cut is deepened. The two ends of each board are wedged against the inner flanges of the H-piles. The piles themselves are supported by horizontal steel or timber struts inserted as excavation proceeds. In order to design the struts, we must know the magnitude and the distribution of the earth pressure.

In Article 23 it was shown that the earth pressure depends not only on the properties of the supported soil but also on the restrictions that the construction procedure imposes on the freedom of the support to

yield. Hence, the first step in investigating the earth pressure against an open cut is to examine the nature of these restrictions. When the first row of struts I, Figure 85, is placed, the amount of excavation is still so insignificant that the original state of stress in the soil is practically unaltered. Therefore, the first row of struts is in position before any appreciable yielding of the soil mass occurs. As excavation proceeds to the level of the next set of struts II, the rigidity of set I prevents further horizontal yielding of the soil located near the ground surface on each side of the cut. However, the H-piles are acted on by the lateral pressure of the soil outside the cut. Under the influence of this pressure, they yield inward by rotating about a line at the level of the uppermost set of struts. Hence, the place-ment of the second row of struts is pre-ceded by a horizontal yielding of the soil located outside the cut at the level of this set. With increasing depth the yielding increases, because the height of the banks on either side of the cut increases. There-fore, while excavation proceeds, the ver-tical section ab, Figure 85, advances into the position ab_1. Since the strut at the top of the cut prevents the stretching of the upper part of the sliding wedge, the

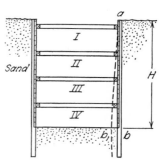

Fig. 85. Diagram illustrating deformation condition for lateral pressure against bracing in open cut.

soil can fail only as indicated in Figure 58. Because of this, the active earth pressure against the bracing in the cut cannot be computed by means of Coulomb's or Rankine's theory. A method must be developed that takes into consideration the influence of the deformation conditions on the type of failure.

It has been shown that the deformation conditions represented by line ab_1 in Figure 85 involve a failure of the type illustrated in Figure 58. It has also been shown, Article 23, that the failure cannot occur unless the lower edge b of the lateral support, Figure 85, yields more than a certain distance bb_1. This distance depends on the depth of the cut and on the physical properties of the soil. In the following discussion, we shall assume that this deformation condition is satisfied. The observa-tions on which the assumption is based and the necessary qualifications are presented in Article 48.

Cuts in Dry or Drained Sand

Figure 86 shows a vertical section through one side of a cut with depth H in dry or drained sand. The initial position of the H-piles is indicated by the plain line ab and the final position by the dash line ab_1. The earth pressure on the bracing, per unit of length of the cut, is designated by P_a to distinguish it from the active earth pressure P_A exerted by a similar mass of sand against a retaining wall of height H. Since the upper part of the sliding wedge, Figure 86a. cannot move laterally, the surface of sliding intersects the ground surface at a right angle (see also Figure

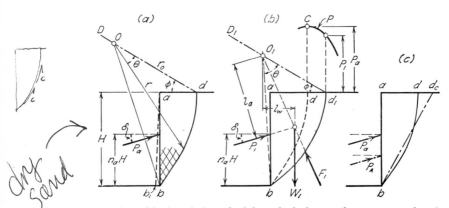

Fig. 86.   Logarithmic spiral method for calculating earth pressure against bracing of open cuts.   (a) Diagram illustrating assumptions on which computation is based; (b) forces acting on sliding wedge; (c) comparison of surface of sliding with that assumed in Coulomb's theory.

58). The real curve of sliding can be closely approximated by a logarithmic spiral having the equation,

$$r = r_0 \epsilon^{\theta \tan \phi} \qquad (32.1)$$

The center of the spiral is located on a straight line that passes through d and makes an angle ϕ with the horizontal. Since the yield of the lateral support causes the wedge to move downward along the back of the support, the resultant earth pressure acts at an angle δ to the horizontal. Theoretical investigations beyond the scope of this book have shown that the point of application of the earth pressure is determined by the shape of the surface of sliding and vice versa. If the curve of sliding is similar to bd in Figure 86, theory indicates that the distribution of the sand pressure against the bracing is roughly parabolic, as indicated in Figure 58b, and that the elevation of the point of application $n_a H$ should be between $0.45H$ and $0.55H$. This theoretical conclusion has been confirmed by pressure measurements in full-sized cuts. Therefore, in the following computation n_a is assumed to be known.

In order to determine the position of the surface of sliding, an arbitrary point d_1, Figure 86b, is selected on the horizontal surface adjoining the upper edge of the cut. Through this point and through the lower edge b of the bank, a logarithmic spiral bd_1 is traced with its center on d_1D_1. The reaction F_1 on the surface of sliding represented by bd_1 passes through the center O_1. Taking moments about O_1, we obtain

$$P_1 l_a = W_1 l_w$$

whence

$$P_1 = \frac{W_1 l_w}{l_a} \tag{32.2}$$

A similar computation is made for spirals through $d_2, d_3 \cdots$ (not shown). By plotting the values $P_1, P_2 \cdots$, etc., as ordinates above $d_1, d_2, \cdots$, the curve P is obtained. The active earth pressure P_a is equal to the maximum ordinate, corresponding to point C, and the surface of sliding passes through d. The width ad of the top of the wedge which exerts the maximum pressure P_a is always much smaller than the width of the top of the corresponding Coulomb wedge abd_c, Figure 86c.

The value of P_a depends to a certain extent on n_a. It increases slightly with increasing values of n_a and is always greater than the corresponding Coulomb value P_A. For the values $\phi = 38°$ and $\delta = 0°$, an increase of n_a from 0.45 to 0.55 increases P_a from $1.03 P_A$ to $1.11 P_A$. If we assume $n_a = 0.55$, any error is on the safe side because this value is the greatest which has so far been obtained by field measurements. The angle δ has very little influence on the ratio P_a/P_A. Hence, for a preliminary estimate, it is sufficiently accurate to assume

$$\boxed{P_a = 1.1 P_A} \tag{32.3}$$

The next step in the investigation is to determine the pressure in individual struts. The distribution of the lateral pressure against the bracing in cuts is roughly parabolic as shown in Figure 58b, but from section to section in a given cut it deviates somewhat from the statistical average because of variations in soil conditions and in details of the construction procedure. As a consequence, for a given value of P_a the pressure in individual struts at a given elevation varies. The procedure for estimating the maximum pressure that may have to be resisted by the struts in any given row is described in Article 48.

CUTS IN SOFT CLAY

For soft clay, the value of ϕ is equal to zero, and equation 32.1 becomes identical with that of a circle having the radius $r = r_0$. Since the circle must intersect the ground surface at a right angle, its center must be located at the level of the surface. The computation of P_a is made by taking moments about the center of the circle of the forces that act upon the sliding wedge. The driving moment is produced by the weight of the wedge. The resisting moment is equal to the sum of the moment of the forces of cohesion that act along the surface of sliding and the moment of the resultant earth pressure P_a. Measurements in full-sized cuts excavated in such clays have shown that n_a varies between 0.4 and 0.55, and that the corresponding distribution of lateral pressure, like that for sand, is roughly parabolic. The method for estimating the maximum pressure which may act on an individual strut is described in Article 48.

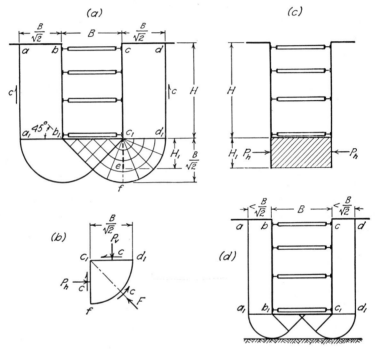

Fig. 87.   Stability of bottom of open cut in soft clay.   (a) Stability conditions if no hard stratum interferes with flow of clay; (b) forces acting on wedge c_1d_1f; (c) section through cut in which sheet piles extend below bottom of excavation; (d) stability conditions if hard stratum is located at shallow depth below bottom of cut.

Heave of the Bottom of Cuts in Soft Clay

In connection with open cuts in soft clay, we must consider the possibility that the bottom may fail by heaving, because the weight of the blocks of clay beside the cut tends to displace the underlying clay toward the excavation. Figure 87a represents a cross section through a cut in soft clay. The width of the cut is B, and the depth is H. The two strips a_1b_1 and c_1d_1 at the level of the bottom of the cut carry a surcharge due to the weight of the blocks of clay located above them. If this surcharge is equal to the bearing capacity of the strips, the clay located beneath the level of the bottom of the cut passes into a state of plastic equilibrium. Since the struts prevent the blocks of clay from moving laterally, the shearing resistance of the clay along the strips a_1b_1 and c_1d_1 prevents the clay immediately below the strips from spreading horizontally. The strips a_1b_1 and c_1d_1 act, therefore, like footings with rough bases. The boundaries of the zones of elastic equilibrium located beneath the loaded strip should rise at the angle ϕ to the horizontal, as indicated in Figure 74b. However, since $\phi = 0°$, there is no zone of elastic equilibrium. The zone of radial shear starts at the loaded strip and extends to the boundary of the passive Rankine zone which rises at 45° to the horizontal. Therefore, the region of plastic equilibrium must have the characteristics shown in Figure 87a, and the total width of the region is $B + \sqrt{2}B$. According to equation 29.3, the bearing capacity of the strips is $q_d = 5.70c$.

The weight of the mass of soil that tends to move downward at one side of the cut is $\frac{1}{2}\sqrt{2}B\gamma H$. Since the downward movement is resisted by the cohesion cH along the vertical surface dd_1, the total load P on c_1d_1 is

$$P = \tfrac{1}{2}\sqrt{2}B\gamma H - cH$$

The intensity of the load on c_1d_1 is

$$p_v = \gamma H - \frac{\sqrt{2}cH}{B} \tag{32.4}$$

To avoid risk, the factor of safety against heaving should be at least 1.5. Hence, the pressure p_v, equation 32.4, should not exceed $q_d/1.5 = 5.7c/1.5 = 3.8c$.

If sheet piling extends below the bottom of the cut for an additional distance, $c_1f = \frac{1}{2}\sqrt{2}B$, the horizontal pressure against the embedded portion of the sheet pile, per foot of length of sheeting along the axis of the cut, can be computed by considering the equilibrium of the wedge c_1d_1f, Figure 87b. Taking moments about c_1 gives

$$p_h \frac{\sqrt{2}}{2}B\frac{\sqrt{2}B}{4} = p_v\frac{\sqrt{2}}{2}B\frac{\sqrt{2}B}{4} - \frac{c\pi\sqrt{2}B}{8}\sqrt{2}B$$

whence

$$p_h = p_v - \pi c \tag{32.5}$$

The total pressure P_h exerted against the sheet piles is then

$$P_h = (p_v - \pi c)\frac{\sqrt{2}}{2}B \tag{32.6}$$

If the sheeting extends only to a depth H_1 below c_1, the pressure P_h is carried partly by the sheeting and partly by the soil which occupies the gap ef, Figure 87a. If the distance H_1 is greater than about two thirds of c_1f, the rigidity of the sheet piles causes most of the pressure on ef to be transferred by arching, Article 33, to the sheet piles. Hence, the total pressure against the piles is still given approximately by equation 32.6. If H_1 is less than about two thirds of c_1f, the quantity $1.5H_1$ may be substituted for $\frac{1}{2}\sqrt{2}B$ in equation 32.6. The load P_h can be assumed to be uniformly distributed over the buried part of the sheet piles.

The horizontal load P_h is resisted by the unconfined compressive strength $2cH_1$ of the block of clay represented by the shaded area in Figure 87c and by the bending strength of the buried part of the sheet piles. Hence, the sheet piles must be capable of resisting a load of $P_h - 2cH_1$. Otherwise, the piles fail by bending, and the bottom of the cut heaves.

If the lower ends of the sheet piles are driven into a hard stratum, the effectiveness of the sheet piles is increased in two ways. Support of the lower edge of the piles reduces the maximum bending moments in the embedded portion of the piles to about one quarter of the value for unsupported piles. In addition, the vertical load on section c_1d_1, Figure 87a, is reduced by the weight transferred by adhesion to the sheet piles. If the point resistance of the sheet piles is greater than the adhesion, the reduction is equal to the adhesion between the clay and the sheet piles. If it is smaller, the reduction is equal to the point resistance.

If the hard stratum is located a short distance below the bottom of the cut, as indicated in Figure 87d, the lower boundary of the zone of plastic equilibrium is tangent to the upper surface of the hard layer. The general character of the shear pattern, however, remains unchanged. Since the depth of the plastic zone is limited by the presence of the hard stratum at a shallow depth, the width of the mass of soil aa_1b_1b, which constitutes a surcharge on each side of the cut, is less than $\frac{1}{2}\sqrt{2}B$. Yet the shearing resistance along aa_1 is the same as the resistance along aa_1 in Figure 87a. Therefore, the intensity of the vertical load on a_1b_1 in Figure 87d is less than that in Figure 87a, and the tendency for the bottom to heave is reduced.

PROBLEMS

① By means of the logarithmic-spiral method, determine the total pressure P_a against the bracing of a cut 30 ft deep in cohesionless sand for which $\gamma = 115$ lb per cu ft and $\phi = 30°$. The value of δ is assumed to be zero. The center of pressure is 16 ft above the bottom of the cut. Determine also the Coulomb value P_A.

    Ans   18,400;   17,300 lb per lin ft.

(2.) An open cut is made to a depth of 40 ft in clay having a unit weight of 127 lb per cu ft and a cohesion of 635 lb per sq ft. The values of ϕ and δ are assumed to be zero. The point of application of the resultant earth pressure against the bracing is 18 ft above the bottom. Find the value of the resultant earth pressure.

    Ans. 59,700 lb per lin ft.

(3.) A cut 50 ft wide is made for a depth of 36 ft in soft clay having a value of $c = 300$ lb per sq ft and a value of $\gamma = 114$ lb per cu ft. The value of ϕ is zero. If sheeting does not extend below the bottom of the cut, what is the factor of safety against heaving of the bottom? If sheet piles having a section modulus of 46.8 cu in. per ft of wall extend to a depth of 10 ft below the bottom of the cut, what is the factor of safety against heave? Assume that struts are located at the bottom of the cut, that the compressive strength of the clay is 600 lb per sq ft, and that the steel sheet piles are stressed to their yield point of 36,000 lb per sq in.

    Ans. 0.45; 1.12.

ART. 33. ARCHING IN SOILS

The earth pressure on the lateral support shown in Figure 85 is greatest at about mid-height of the sides of the cut. Yet, if a few of the horizontal boards supporting the soil at mid-height are removed, the exposed part of the sides of the cut remains stable, provided the soil has at least a trace of cohesion. In order to explain this fact, we are compelled to assume that the pressure formerly exerted on the boards that were removed was transferred onto those that remained in place. This phenomenon of pressure transfer is known as *arching*.

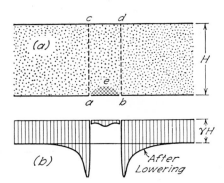

FIG. 88. (*a*) Apparatus for investigating arching in layer of sand above yielding trap door in horizontal platform; (*b*) pressure on platform and trap door before and after slight lowering of door.

The essential features of arching can be demonstrated by the test illustrated by Figure 88*a*. A layer of dry cohesionless sand with unit weight γ is placed on a platform that contains a trap door *ab*. The trap door is mounted on a scale (not shown) that permits measurement of the pressure on the door. The depth *H* of the layer of sand is several times greater than the width of the trap door.

As long as the trap door occupies its original position, the pressure on the trap door as well as that on the adjoining platform is equal to γH per unit of area. However, as soon as the trap door is allowed to yield in a downward direction, the pressure on the door decreases to a small fraction of its initial value, whereas the pressure on the adjoining parts of the platform increases. This is due to the fact that the descent of the prism of sand located above the yielding trap door is resisted by shearing stresses along its lateral boundaries, ac and bd.

Theory, as well as the results of tests and experience in tunneling, indicates that the ultimate pressure on the yielding trap door is practically independent of the depth H of the layer of sand. It does not exceed the weight of a body of sand having approximately the dimensions indicated by the shaded area abe in Figure 88. Hence, if the sand has a trace of cohesion, the trap door can be removed entirely, and the sand will not drop out of the gap.

CHAPTER V

SETTLEMENT AND CONTACT PRESSURE

ART. 34. INTRODUCTION

PURPOSE OF SETTLEMENT INVESTIGATIONS

The term *settlement* indicates the sinking of a building due to the compression and deformation of the underlying soil.

The design of the framework of a building or other structure is, with rare exceptions, based on the assumption that the structure rests on an unyielding base. In reality, the weight of every structure compresses and deforms the underlying soil, and, as a consequence, the design assumption is never strictly satisfied. If the base of the structure remains plane, the settlement is irrelevant because the stresses in the framework are not altered. On the other hand, if the weight of the structure causes the loaded area to warp, the base of the structure also becomes warped, and the entire structural framework is distorted. The supplementary stresses caused by this distortion are not considered in the design of the super-structure. Yet in many instances they are important enough to impair the appearance of a building or to cause permanent and irreparable damage.

Because of the complexity of the mechanical properties of soils and the disturbing influences of stratification, the settlement of buildings can be accurately predicted only under exceptional conditions. Nevertheless, a theoretical analysis of settlement phenomena is indispensable because the results permit the engineer at least to recognize the factors that determine the magnitude and the distribution of the settlement. Knowledge of these factors constitutes the prerequisite for converting construction experience into semiempirical rules for the design of foundations, Article 53.

THEORETICAL APPROACH TO SETTLEMENT PROBLEMS

The theoretical methods for dealing with settlement problems must be chosen in accordance with the mechanical properties of the subsoil and the nature of the stratification. If a proposed structure is located above one or more layers of very compressible soil, buried beneath and separated by layers of relatively incompressible soil such as sand, the settlement depends only on the physical properties of the soft strata and on the intensity and distribution of the vertical pressure on these strata. Experience has shown that the vertical pressures can be computed with sufficient accuracy on the assumption that the subsoil of the building is perfectly elastic and homogeneous.

Likewise, if a structure rests on a fairly homogenous subsoil, the distribution of the vertical stresses on horizontal sections can be estimated on the assumption that the subgrade is perfectly elastic. However, the intensity and distribution of all the other stresses are likely to be very different from those in an equally loaded perfectly elastic subgrade, and, in addition, the determination of the stress–strain relations for the soil is commonly impracticable. Hence, in such instances it may be necessary to investigate the relation of intensity of loading, settlement, and size of loaded area by semiempirical methods.

COMPUTATION OF CONTACT PRESSURE

After the designer has laid out the foundation in such a manner that the unequal settlement will not be great enough to injure the superstructure, he must design the foundation. The design requires a computation of the bending moments and shearing stresses in those parts of the foundation, such as footings or rafts, that transfer the weight of the building onto the subgrade. The pressure that acts on the base of footings or rafts is known as *contact pressure*.

The distribution of the contact pressure on the base of some foundations resembles that on the base of a similar foundation supported by an elastic isotropic material, but more often it is entirely different. Furthermore, if the supporting material is clay, the distribution of the contact pressure may change considerably with time. To simplify design, the computation of the bending moments in footings is commonly based on the arbitrary assumption that the footings rest on a uniformly spaced bed of springs. The procedure is described in Article 37. Experience has shown that it is usually accurate enough for practical purposes. Therefore, the designer needs to be familiar only with the general relationships between the type of soil and the character of the pressure distribution. If the difference between the computed and the real pressure distribution is likely to be large and on the unsafe side, the risk is eliminated by increasing the factor of safety.

ART. 35. VERTICAL PRESSURE IN SOIL BENEATH LOADED AREAS

BOUSSINESQ'S EQUATIONS

The application of a concentrated vertical load to the horizontal surface of any solid body produces a set of vertical stresses on every horizontal plane within the body. It is obvious, without computation, that the intensity of the vertical pressure on any horizontal section through the loaded soil decreases from a maximum at the point located directly beneath the load to zero at a very large distance from this point. A pressure distribution of this kind can be represented by a bell- or dome-shaped space, as indicated in Figure 92b. Since the pressure exerted by the load spreads out in a downward direction, the maximum pressure on any horizontal section, represented by the maximum height of the corresponding bell-shaped pressure space, decreases with increasing depth below the loaded surface. Yet equilibrium requires that the total increase of pressure on any horizontal section must be equal to the applied load. Therefore, with increasing depth below the surface, the pressure bells become lower but wider.

Both theory and experience have shown that the shape of the pressure bells is more or less independent of the physical properties of the loaded subgrade. Therefore, in connection with practical problems, it is customary and justifiable to compute these stresses on the assumptions that the loaded material is elastic, homogeneous, and isotropic. On these assumptions, a concentrated vertical load Q, Figure 89a, acting on the horizontal surface of a mass of very great extent produces at point N within the mass a vertical pressure having the intensity,

$$p_v = \frac{3Q}{2\pi z^2}\left[\frac{1}{1 + (r/z)^2}\right]^{5/2} \tag{35.1}$$

In this equation z represents the vertical distance between N and the surface of the mass, and r the horizontal distance from N to the line of action of the load.

Equation 35.1 is one of a set of stress equations, known as *Boussinesq's equations*, that determine the entire state of stress at point N, Figure 89a. However, in contrast to the vertical pressure p_v, most of the other components of stress at point N depend to a large extent on the stress-deformation characteristics of the loaded material. Since soils are not even approximately elastic and homogeneous, the other stress equations of Boussinesq are not suitable for the computation of stresses in soils.

PRESSURE DISTRIBUTION ON HORIZONTAL SECTIONS BENEATH LOADED AREAS

In computing the vertical pressures in the soil beneath a building, it is commonly assumed that the building is perfectly flexible. If an area on the surface of a very large mass carries a uniformly distributed and perfectly flexible load of intensity q, the intensity of the vertical pressure at any point N, Figure 89b, within the mass may be computed by divid-

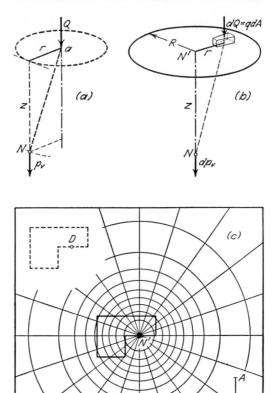

FIG. 89. (a) Intensity of vertical pressure at point N in interior of semi-infinite solid acted on by point load Q; (b) vertical pressure at point N beneath center of circular area acted on by load q per unit of area; (c) diagram illustrating use of influence chart for computing vertical pressure.

ing the loaded area into small parts dA, each of which sustains a load,

$$dQ = q\,dA$$

This load is considered to be concentrated at the centroid of the elementary area dA. According to equation 35.1, each concentrated load produces at point N a vertical pressure,

$$dp_v = \frac{3q}{2\pi z^2}\left[\frac{1}{1 + (r/z)^2}\right]^{5/2} dA \qquad (35.2)$$

The intensity of the vertical pressure at N due to the entire load is computed by integrating equation 35.2 over the loaded area. For example, if the point N is located at depth z beneath the center N' of a loaded area having the shape of a circle with radius R, the vertical pressure is found to be

$$p_v = q \left[1 - \left(\frac{1}{1 + (R/z)^2} \right)^{3\!/\!2} \right] \tag{35.3}$$

If the load of intensity q is distributed over an area with a shape other than circular, the stress p_v at an arbitrary point N at depth z below this area can be computed readily with the aid of the chart, Figure 90. The chart represents a set of lines located on the ground surface. It is drawn to such a scale that the distance AB is equal to the depth z. The point N is located directly below the center of the concentric circles. The chart is so constructed that a load of intensity q distributed over any one of the smallest subdivisions bounded by two adjacent radial lines and two adjacent circles produces a pressure $p_v = 0.005q$ at point N. Each subdivision is, therefore, an *influence area*, with the value 0.005, for the stress p_v at point N.

To illustrate the use of the chart, we shall compute the value of p_v at a depth of 50 ft below point D of the building shown in plan in Figure 89c. The weight of the building constitutes a uniformly distributed load of 3000 lb per sq ft covering the area occupied by the building. The first step in the computation is to draw on tracing paper a plan of the building to such a scale that the depth, 50 ft, is equal to the distance AB on the chart. We then place the tracing over the chart so that point D is directly above point N' on the chart and count the number of influence areas enclosed by the outline of the loaded area. In this example the number of influence areas is 31.5, and the corresponding stress p_v at a depth of 50 ft below D is $31.5 \times 0.005 \times 3000 = 473$ lb per sq ft. The stress p_v at any other point at the same depth is obtained by the same procedure after shifting the tracing until the new point is directly above N'. In order to determine the stresses on a section at a different depth z_1, we draw a tracing to a different scale, such that the depth z_1 is equal to the distance AB on the chart.

Change of Pressure with Depth

The intensity of vertical pressure along any vertical line beneath a distributed load decreases with increasing values of the depth z below the surface. Therefore, if the compressible layer is very thick, the vertical pressure in the layer decreases appreciably from the top to the bottom. However, the compression of a thin layer depends merely on the average

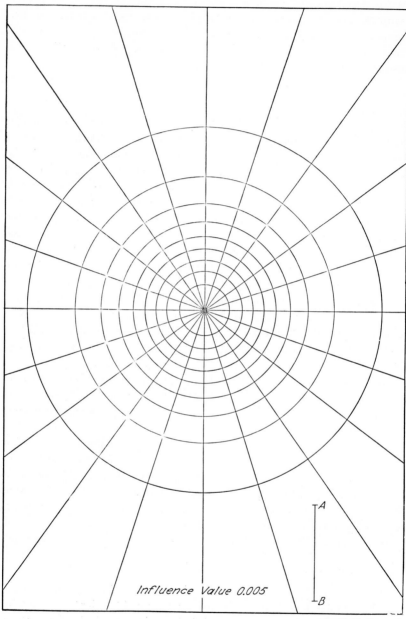

Influence Value 0.005

After N. M. Newmark

FIG. 90.   Influence chart for vertical pressure.

vertical pressure, which is roughly equal to the vertical pressure at mid-height of the layer. (Therefore, if the compressible layer is relatively thin, the change of pressure with depth can be disregarded, and it may be sufficiently accurate to compute the intensity and distribution of the pressure on a horizontal plane at mid-height of the layer.)

In Figure 91 the abscissas of the curve C_a represent the intensity of vertical pressure at different depths below the center of a square area $B \times B$ which carries a uniformly distributed load q per unit of area. If the total load B^2q is represented by a concentrated load $Q = B^2q$ acting at the center of the square area, the curve C_q is obtained instead of C_a. The figure shows that the curves become almost identical at a depth of about $3B$. At any depth greater than $3B$, the pressure on a horizontal section produced by loading a square area is practically the same as the pressure produced by an equivalent point load acting at the center of the loaded area. Hence, the stresses p_v on horizontal sections at a depth of more than $3B$ can be computed by means of equation 35.1.

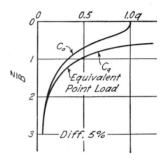

Fig. 91.   Diagram illustrating effect on vertical pressure of replacing uniformly distributed load on square area by equivalent point load at center of square.   Curves represent stress along vertical line beneath center of square.

The removal of soil from the space to be occupied by a basement reduces the vertical pressure at every point below the bottom of the excavation. In order to compute the resulting change in the stresses, it is assumed that the surface of the soil is located at the level of the bottom of the excavation, and that the weight of the excavated material acts in an upward direction at this level.

PROBLEMS

1. A point load of 5300 lb acts on the surface of an elastic mass of very great extent. What is the intensity of vertical pressure, due to the load, at a depth of 20 ft directly below the load? at a depth of 40 ft? at a depth of 200 ft? What is the intensity of vertical pressure at the same depths at a horizontal distance of 50 ft from the line of action of the point load?

Ans.   6.33, 1.58, 0.06; 0.045, 0.150, 0.054 lb per sq ft.

2. A circular area on the surface of an elastic mass of great extent carries a uniformly distributed load of 2500 lb per sq ft. The radius of the circle is 10 ft. What is the intensity of vertical pressure at a point 15 ft beneath the center of the circle? at a point at the same depth beneath the edge of the circle?

Ans.   1060;   640 lb per sq ft.

3. A building of very great length has a width of 120 ft. Its weight constitutes a practically uniform surcharge of 5000 lb per sq ft on the ground surface. Between the

depths of 70 and 90 ft there is a layer of soft clay. The rest of the subsoil is dense sand. Compute the intensity of vertical pressure due to the weight of the building, at the following points located in a horizontal plane at mid-height of the compressible layer: directly below edge of building; 20 ft from edge toward center line; 40 ft from edge toward center line; directly below center line.

   Ans.   2300;   2960;   3430;   3570 lb per sq ft.

   4. If the building in problem 3 is 120 ft square, compute the stresses at the same points along a section midway between the ends of the building.

   Ans.   1690;   2250;   2610;   2750 lb per sq ft.

   5. The excavation for a rectangular building 200 by 120 ft in plan is 20 ft deep. The excavated material is a moist sand having a unit weight of 115 lb per cu ft. What is the reduction in vertical pressure, due to the removal of weight from the excavated area, at a point 70 ft below the original ground surface, at one corner of the building?

   Ans.   560 lb per sq ft.

ART. 36.   SETTLEMENT OF FOUNDATIONS

FOUNDATIONS ABOVE CONFINED STRATA OF SOFT CLAY

The following paragraphs describe the procedure for estimating the settlement of a building located above a confined layer of soft clay. The weight of the building is transferred by a reinforced-concrete mat founda-

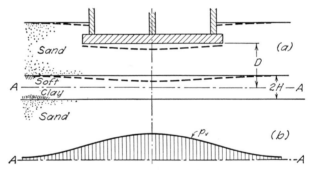

FIG. 92.   (*a*) Settlement of building having mat foundation supported by subsoil that contains compressible stratum at depth D; (*b*) distribution of vertical pressure on horizontal plane at mid-height of compressible layer.

tion, Figure 92*a*, onto a stratum of sand that contains a layer of soft clay at a depth D below the mat. The weight of the building is assumed to be uniformly distributed over the area occupied by the mat.

   Inasmuch as sand is almost incompressible in comparison with soft clay, the settlement is caused almost entirely by the compression of the clay stratum. Since the clay is confined, the compression produced by a given pressure can be computed by the method described in Article 13. However, it is necessary to compute the settlement for several points on the base of the building, because the principal object of the settlement computation is to estimate the amount of warping that the base will experience. If the thickness of the clay stratum is small compared to the depth of the overburden, it can be assumed that the average intensity of vertical pressure p_v in the clay beneath a given point of the foundation is equal to the intensity of vertical pressure beneath this point at mid-height of the stratum. This pressure may be evaluated by means of the chart, Figure 90.

The next step is to compute the compression S of the clay layer below each of the selected points. According to equation 13.2, the change Δn in the porosity is given by the expression,

$$\Delta n = m_v \Delta p \qquad (13.2)$$

The quantity m_v represents the average coefficient of volume compressibility, equation 13.3, for the range in pressure from the original value p_0 to the final value $p_0 + \Delta p$. The added pressure Δp is equal to the vertical pressure p_v computed as outlined in the preceding paragraph. Since the thickness of the compressible layer is $2H$, the change in thickness S due to the pressure p_v is

$$S = 2H \Delta n = 2H m_v p_v \qquad (36.1)$$

The value S represents not only the decrease in thickness of the stratum below the given point but also the settlement of the base of the foundation at that point. If the subsoil contains several compressible layers, the settlement of a given point on the foundation is equal to the sum of the compressions of each of the layers along the vertical line through the point.

If a clay stratum is relatively thick, or if p_v and m_v cannot be considered approximately constant through its entire thickness, we may resolve the stratum into several layers and determine p_v and m_v for each layer individually. On the other hand, we may replace equation 36.1 by the more general equation,

$$S = \int_0^{2H} m_v p_v \, dz$$

in which m_v and p_v are, respectively, the coefficient of compressibility and the added vertical pressure at any depth z below the point at which the settlement is to be computed. The integration is performed graphically, as shown in Figure 93. The added vertical pressure p_v at any depth z beneath the given point is represented by the width of the shaded area in Figure 93a. In order to determine the right-hand boundary of the shaded area, the value of p_v must be computed for several values of z below each point. By plotting the values of m_v as abscissas and the depth as ordinates, the curve in Figure 93*b* is obtained. The width of the shaded area in Figure 93*c* at depth z is made equal to the product $m_v p_v$. Therefore, the entire shaded area in c represents the settlement S.

The compression of the clay stratum involves a decrease of the water content of the clay. Because of the low permeability of the clay, the excess water escapes very slowly and retards the compression (see Article 14). The methods for computing the rate of settlement are presented in Article 41. At any given time, however, the settlement of a

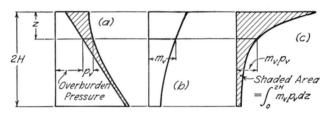

Fig. 93.   Diagram illustrating graphical method for computing settlement of compressible layer if both vertical pressure p_v and coefficient of compressibility m_v vary with depth.

uniformly loaded area is trough- or dish-shaped, because the vertical pressure on the compressible layers is a maximum near the center and decreases toward the edges of the area (see Figure 92*b*).

Foundations on Unstratified Soil

If the subsoil of a foundation is fairly homogeneous, the weight of the building causes not only a compression of the underlying soil but also a lateral yield. Therefore, one part of the settlement may be regarded as a vertical shortening of the loaded stratum due to volume decrease, and the other as an additional shortening due to lateral bulging.

If the subgrade were perfectly elastic and homogeneous to a very great depth, the settlement due to bulging would be considerably greater than that due to volume decrease. At a given intensity of loading, the settlement of loaded areas having the same shape would increase in simple proportion to the widths of the areas.

In connection with the settlement of loaded areas on soils, a distinction must be made between loads that rest on clay and those that rest on sand. If the subsoil consists of clay, the settlement due to lateral bulging is usually small compared to the total settlement. For this reason, even the settlement of foundations on thick strata of clay can be evaluated at least roughly by the method described under the preceding subheading. On the other hand, if the foundation rests on strata of inorganic silt or sand, the second part of the settlement is likely to be much greater than the first.

In order to determine the influence of the size of the loaded area and the position of the water table on the settlement of footings on cohesionless sand, we must consider the factors that determine the stress–strain properties of the sand, Article 18. Theoretical investigations of these relations as well as laboratory tests and field observations have led to the following conclusions.

The settlement of a footing with width B decreases with increasing average value of the initial tangent modulus E_i of the sand located between the base of the footing and a depth of about B below the base. According to Figure 42, the initial tangent modulus of sand increases with increasing effective confining pressure. At any given depth below the surface of the sand, the effective confining pressure is roughly proportional to the effective overburden pressure. If the water table rises to the surface of the sand from a depth greater than B below the base of the footing, the effective confining pressure decreases by roughly 50 per cent, Article 12. Therefore, the settlement increases approximately 100 per cent.

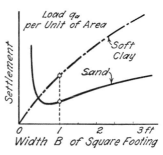

Fig. 94.   Relation between width of square footing and settlement under same load per unit of area.

At a given load per unit of area of the base of a footing, the depth of the body of sand subject to intense compression and deformation increases as the width of the footing increases. On the other hand, the ultimate bearing capacity of the footing and the average initial tangent modulus of the sand also increase. As a consequence of these several factors, the settlement varies with the width of the footing approximately as shown by the plain curve in Figure 94.

In practice, the magnitude of the settlement of footings on sand cannot be predicted on the basis of the results of laboratory tests on soil specimens. However, it can be estimated roughly, by means of semi-empirical rules based partly on the aforementioned general relations and partly on the observed relation between settlement and the results of simple field tests such as penetration tests, Articles 54 and 55.

PROBLEMS

1. The layer of soft clay referred to in problem 3, Article 35, has a natural water content of 45 per cent. The unit weight of the solid matter of the clay is 2.70 gm per

cu cm, and the unit weight of the dense sand is 130 lb per cu ft. The free-water level is at the ground surface. From the results of consolidation tests it has been ascertained that C_c is equal to 0.50. Compute the settlement of the edge and of the center of the building.

> *Ans.* 8.5; 12.3 in.

2. A uniform load of 3000 lb per sq ft is distributed over a very large area on the surface of the ground. The subsoil consists of a bed of dense sand containing two strata of clay each 10 ft thick. The top of the upper stratum is 20 ft deep, and of the lower 70 ft deep. The value of C_c is 0.35 for both layers; the natural water content and the unit weight of the solid constituents are 34 per cent and 2.75 gm per cu cm, respectively. The sand weighs 125 lb per cu ft and is completely submerged. What is the settlement of the ground surface due to the uniform load?

> *Ans.* 15 in.

ART. 37. CONTACT PRESSURE AND THEORIES OF SUBGRADE REACTION

CONTACT PRESSURE ON BASE OF RIGID FOOTINGS

Since the settlement of the base of a perfectly rigid footing is by necessity uniform, the distribution of the pressure on the base of such a footing is identical with the distribution of the load required to produce uniform settlement of the loaded area. If the subgrade consists of a

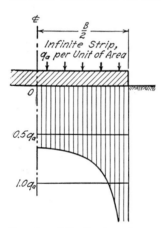

FIG. 95. Distribution of contact pressure on base of uniformly loaded rigid footing of very great length, resting on perfectly elastic, homogeneous, and isotropic subgrade.

perfectly elastic material, of clay, or of sand containing thick layers of soft clay, a uniformly loaded area assumes the shape of a shallow bowl or trough. In order to obtain uniform settlement it would be necessary to shift part of the load from the center of the loaded area toward the edges. Hence, the contact pressure on the base of a rigid footing resting on such a subgrade increases from the center of the base toward the rim. On the other hand, if a uniformly loaded area is underlain by sand, the settlement is greater at the edges than at the center. Uniform settlement can be obtained only by distributing the load so that its intensity decreases from a maximum at the center to a minimum at the rim. Hence, the distribution of the contact pressure on the base of a rigid footing on sand has the same characteristics.

Figure 95 is a section through a rigid continuous footing with a width B resting on a perfectly elastic and homogeneous subgrade of very great depth. The load on the footing is $q_a B$ per unit of length. Computations based on the theory of elasticity have shown that the contact pressure increases as shown in the figure from less than $0.7q_a$ at the center line to an infinite value at the edges. If the footing rests on a real elastic material, the pressure along the edges cannot exceed a certain finite value q_c at which the material passes from the elastic into a semiplastic or plastic state. The corresponding distribution of the contact pressure is shown in Figure 96a by the curve C_1.

If the load on the footing in Figure 96a is increased, the state of plastic equilibrium spreads from the edges, and the distribution of contact pressure changes. If the base of the footing is smooth, the distribution

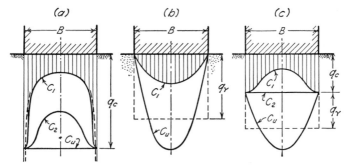

Fig. 96.   Distribution of contact pressure on base of smooth rigid footing supported by (a) real, elastic material; (b) cohesionless sand; (c) soil having intermediate characteristics.   Curves C_u refer to contact pressure when footing is loaded to ultimate value.

becomes perfectly uniform at the instant when the subgrade fails by plastic flow. The curve C_u represents the distribution at this stage, and the curve C_2 at an intermediate stage. If the base adheres to the subgrade, the final distribution is similar to that shown in Figure 76a.

If either a rigid or a flexible footing rests on the surface of a mass of dry cohesionless sand, theory indicates that the intensity of the contact pressure at any load decreases from a maximum at the center to zero at the edges, as shown in Figure 96b. Experimental investigations have led to the same conclusion.

Figure 96c represents the distribution of contact pressure on the base of a footing supported by a subgrade intermediate in character between purely cohesive and purely cohesionless soils. At small loads the contact pressure increases from the center toward the edges of the footing, curve C_1. As the load increases, the pressure at the center increases whereas that at the edges remains unaltered. At the point of failure the pressure decreases from the center toward the edges, as indicated by curve C_u.

DEFINITION OF SUBGRADE REACTION

Figure 96 demonstrates that the relation between the stress–deformation characteristics of the subgrade and the contact pressure on the base of a perfectly rigid footing is by no means simple. If the footing is not rigid, the relation becomes even more complicated. Therefore, even a rough evaluation of the distribution of the real contact pressure is very cumbersome. Yet without some knowledge of the contact pressure footings or mats cannot be designed. Therefore, it is customary and necessary to estimate the contact pressure on the basis of simplifying assump‑ tions and to compensate for the error due to these assumptions by an adequate factor of safety.

The simplified procedures are based on the arbitrary and incorrect assumption that the settlement S of any element of a loaded area is entirely independent of the load on the adjoining elements. It is further assumed, at variance with reality, that the ratio,

$$K_s = \frac{p}{S} \qquad (37.1)$$

between the intensity p of the pressure on the element and the corresponding settlement S is a constant K_s (grams per cubic centimeter). In contrast to the real contact pressure that acts on the base of the footing, the fictitious pressure p that satisfies equation 37.1 is called the *subgrade reaction*. In the following paragraphs of this article the symbol p is strictly reserved for the subgrade reaction. It is not used with reference to the real contact pressure. The coefficient K_s is known as the *coefficient of subgrade reaction*, and the theories based on the aforementioned assumptions are the *theories of subgrade reaction*.

SUBGRADE REACTION ON RIGID FOUNDATIONS

In connection with a rigid foundation, equation 37.1 leads to the conclusion that the distribution of the subgrade reaction p over the base of the foundation must be planar, because a rigid foundation remains plane when it settles. Hence, in order to design a rigid foundation in accordance with equation 37.1, we merely assume that the subgrade reaction has a planar distribution. In addition, we must satisfy the requirements of statics that (1) the total subgrade reaction is equal to the sum of the vertical loads that act on the subgrade, and (2) the moment of the resultant vertical load about an arbitrary point is equal to the moment of the total subgrade reaction about that point.

As an example, the rigid gravity retaining wall shown in Figure 97 is considered. The width of the base is B, and the resultant Q of the vertical loads on the base acts at the distance a from the toe. The subgrade reaction at the toe is p_a, and at the heel it is p_b. According to the previous paragraph, the distribution of the reaction is assumed to be linear between these two points. By statics we obtain the two equations,

$$Q = \tfrac{1}{2}B(p_a + p_b) \tag{37.2}$$

and

$$Qa = \tfrac{1}{6}B^2 p_a + \tfrac{1}{3}B^2 p_b \tag{37.3}$$

These equations can be solved for p_a and p_b.

It should be noted that equations 37.2 and 37.3 do not contain the coefficient of subgrade reaction K_s. In other words, the distribution of subgrade reaction on the base of a rigid footing is independent of the degree of compressibility of the subgrade. This fact makes it easy to visualize the difference between the subgrade reaction and the real contact pressure. If the resultant Q of the load on a footing passes through the centroid of the loaded area A, the subgrade reaction is distributed uniformly over the base of the footing and is everywhere equal to Q/A. On the other hand, the distribution of the real contact pressure on the base of the same footing may be far from uniform, as shown by Figure 96. It depends on the stress–deformation characteristics of the subgrade and on the intensity of the load.

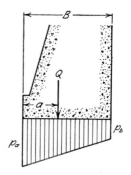

FIG. 97.   Subgrade reaction on base of rigid gravity retaining wall.

In spite of these obvious discrepancies between theory and reality, the theories of subgrade reaction can be used safely in connection with the routine design of footings, because the errors are within the customary margin of safety, and, as a rule, they are also on the safe side.

SUBGRADE REACTION ON FLEXIBLE FOUNDATIONS

If a footing or a mat is not rigid, the distribution of the subgrade reaction depends on both the numerical value of K_s and the flexural rigidity of the foundation. The influence of the latter is illustrated by Figure 98, which represents a cross section through a long rectangular elastic slab. The longer axis of the slab carries a line load q' per unit of length. The slab rests on an elastic subgrade. Because of the flexibility of the slab, the settlement decreases from the center line toward the edges. As a consequence, the subgrade reaction also decreases from a maximum at the center to a minimum at the edges. If the slab is very flexible, the edges may rise, and the subgrade reaction beneath the outer portions of the slab may become zero. In any event, for a given line load q' and a given width B of the slab the maximum bending moment in a flexible slab is very much smaller than that in a rigid one.

The subgrade reaction on the base of a relatively flexible member in a foundation can be computed by means of the *theory of elastic beams on a continuous elastic support*. The theory is based on the obvious fact that the vertical displacement of the loaded member due to settlement and bending must at every point be equal to the settlement of the ground surface at the same point. The computa-

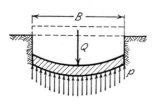

tion of the settlement of the ground surface is based on equation 37.1. In contrast to equations 37.2 and 37.3, which pertain to a rigid foundation, the equations for computing the subgrade reaction on an elastic foundation always contain the value K_s, equation 37.1.

FIG. 98.   Elastic footing of great length acted on by line load and supported by elastic subgrade.   (a) Deformation of footing under load; (b) distribution of subgrade reaction.

Since the theory of elastic beams on a continuous elastic support is based on equation 37.1, it is no more accurate than the theory of subgrade reaction for rigid footings.

It can be even less accurate, because it involves the error associated with evaluating K_s. Since the computations are always cumbersome, the investigation is not justified unless it leads to a considerable saving in the cost of the structure.

In all the theories of subgrade reaction, the coefficient K_s, which is the ratio between the intensity of load on the fictitious subgrade and the corresponding vertical displacement, is assumed to be a constant that depends only on the physical properties of the subsoil. However, the ratio between the average intensity of pressure on the surface of a given solid and the corresponding settlement is not a constant. For circular footings on an elastic isotropic base the ratio decreases as the radius of the footings increases. For a footing of given size resting on soil it also decreases with increasing values of the intensity of the load. Furthermore, it is different for different points at the base of the same footing. Therefore, the evaluation of K_s involves many uncertainties, and the customary procedure for determining K_s on the basis of small-scale load tests is subject to all of the limitations of the load-test method described in Article 54.

PROBLEMS

1. A gravity retaining wall has a base width of 8 ft. The line of action of the resultant of the vertical and horizontal forces intersects the base at a point 3 ft from the toe of the wall. The vertical component of the resultant force is 12,000 lb per ft. What is the subgrade reaction at the toe? at the heel?

Ans.   2625 lb per sq ft;   375 lb per sq ft.

2. A footing with a trapezoidal base is 12 ft long, 3 ft wide at one end, and 6 ft wide at the other. It supports two columns along its center line, one at a distance of 2 ft from the narrow end and the other 3 ft from the wide end. The load on the first column is 18 tons, and on the second 36 tons. Assuming that the footing is rigid, what is the subgrade reaction at each end?

Ans.   2000 lb per sq ft.

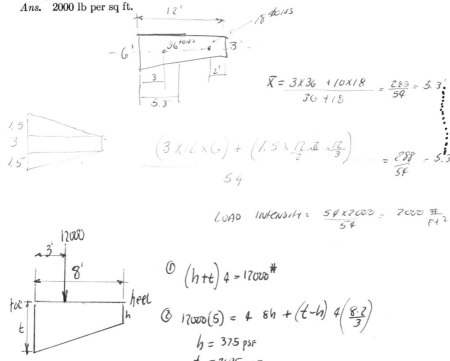

$$\bar{X} = \frac{3 \times 36 + 10 \times 18}{36 + 18} = \frac{288}{54} = 5.3'$$

$$(3 \times 12 \times 6) + \left(1.5 \times \frac{12}{2} \times 8 \times \frac{12}{3}\right)$$

$$54 = \frac{288}{54} = 5.3'$$

$$LOAD \ \ INTENSITY = \frac{54 \times 2000}{54} = 2000 \frac{\#}{F^2}$$

$$① \ \left(h + t\right) 4 = 12000^{\#}$$

$$② \ 12000(5) = 4 \cdot 8h + \left(t - h\right) 4 \left(\frac{8 \cdot 2}{3}\right)$$

$$h = 375 \ psf$$

$$t = 2625 \ psf$$

Chapter VI

HYDRAULICS OF SOILS

ART. 38. SCOPE OF HYDRAULIC PROBLEMS

The preceding chapters of Part B have dealt with soils that are dry, moist, or submerged in stationary water. The interaction between soils and percolating water has not yet been considered. However, there are three groups of problems in earthwork engineering that cannot be solved without a knowledge of the laws governing this interaction. One group involves the estimate of the quantity of water that will enter a pit during construction, or the quantity of stored water that will be lost by percolation through a dam or its subsoil, Article 39. A second group deals with the effect of the seepage pressure on the stability of slopes and foundations, Articles 40 and 42. The third deals with the influence of the permeability on the rate at which the excess water drains from loaded clay strata, Article 41.

The theoretical solution of each of these problems is based on the assumption that the mass of soil through which the water percolates is homogeneous or that it is composed of a few homogeneous strata with well-defined boundaries. Similar assumptions have been made in the derivation of all the theories presented in the first two chapters of Part B. However, in hydraulic problems the practical implications of the assumptions are fundamentally different.

Earth pressure, stability, and settlement depend merely on the average values of the soil properties involved. Therefore, even a considerable scattering of the values from the average is of little practical consequence. On the other hand, in connection with hydraulic problems, apparently insignificant geological details may have a decisive influence on both the amount of seepage and the distribution of the seepage pressures throughout the soil. The following example illustrates this point.

If a thick deposit of sand contains a few thin layers of dense fine silt or stiff clay, the presence of these layers has practically no effect on the lateral pressure exerted by the sand against the bracing of an open cut above the water table, on the ultimate bearing capacity of the sand, or on the settlement of a structure resting on the sand. Hence, in connection with the problems considered in the preceding chapters of Part B, the

218

presence of such layers can safely be ignored, and it makes no difference whether or not the boring foreman noticed them.

On the other hand, in connection with any practical problem involving the flow of water through the sand, for instance from a pond on the upstream side of a row of sheet piles to the downstream side, the presence or absence of thin layers of relatively impermeable soil is of decisive importance. If one of the layers is continuous and located above the lower edge of the sheet piles, it intercepts the flow almost completely. If the layers are discontinuous, it is impossible to estimate their influence on the amount and direction of the seepage without knowing the degree of their continuity. Yet, this degree cannot be determined by any practicable means. As a matter of fact, the test borings may not even disclose the presence of the layers at all.

Every natural soil stratum and every man-made earth fill contain undetected or undetectable inclusions of material with exceptionally high or low permeability, and the location of the horizontal boundaries of these inclusions can only be a matter of conjecture. Therefore, the difference between reality and the results of any investigation involving the flow of water through soil can be very important, irrespective of the thoroughness and care with which the subsoil is explored. Yet, if no investigation is made at all, the engineer is entirely at the mercy of chance. Therefore, sound engineering calls for the following procedure in dealing with hydraulic problems. The design should be based on the results of a conscientious hydraulic investigation. However, during the entire period of construction and, if necessary, for several years afterwards, all the field observations should be made that are required for finding out whether and to what extent the real hydraulic conditions in the subsoil differ from the assumed ones. If the observations show that the real conditions are less favorable than the designer anticipated, the design must be modified in accordance with the findings. By means of this procedure, which is illustrated by several examples in Part C, many dam failures could have been avoided.

ART. 39. SEEPAGE COMPUTATIONS

Fundamental Relationships

In the following analysis, it is assumed that the flow of water through the soil follows Darcy's law, equation 11.6, and that the soil consists of relatively incompressible material such as sand, silty sand, or rock flour.

In order to compute the rate of flow of water through such soils, it is necessary to determine the intensity and distribution of the neutral stresses, commonly known as the *pore-water pressures.* These stresses can be determined by constructing a graph called the *flow net*, which represents the flow of water through an incompressible soil. To illustrate the method, we shall compute the quantity of water which escapes out of a pond by percolation through the subsoil of the single sheet-pile coffer-dam shown in Figure 99a. The row of sheet piles is assumed to be impermeable. The piles are driven to a depth D into a homogeneous sand stratum having a depth D_1. The sand rests on a horizontal impermeable

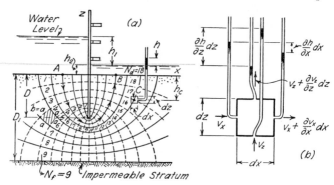

Fig. 99. (*a*) Flow of water around lower edge of single row of sheet piles in homogeneous sand; (*b*) hydrostatic pressure conditions at four faces of element of sand shown in (*a*).

base. The hydraulic head h_1 (see Article 11) is kept constant. Water entering the sand at the upstream surface travels along curves known as *flow lines*. Curve AB, marked by arrows, is one such flow line.

Figure 99b shows a prismatic element of the permeable layer drawn to a larger scale. The lengths of the sides of this element in the plane of the paper are dx and dz. The length perpendicular to the paper is dy. Let

v_x = component of discharge velocity in horizontal direction
$i_x = \partial h/\partial x$, hydraulic gradient in horizontal direction
v_z, and $i_z = \partial h/\partial z$, corresponding values for vertical direction
h = hydraulic head at place occupied by element

The total quantity of water that enters the element per unit of time is

$$v_x \, dz \, dy + v_z \, dx \, dy$$

The quantity that leaves it is

$$v_x \, dz \, dy + \frac{\partial v_x}{\partial x} \, dx \, dz \, dy + v_z \, dx \, dy + \frac{\partial v_z}{\partial z} \, dz \, dx \, dy$$

If the liquid is perfectly incompressible, and the volume of voids occupied by the water is constant, the quantity of water which enters the element is equal to that which leaves it. Therefore,

$$\left(v_x \, dz \, dy + \frac{\partial v_x}{\partial x} \, dx \, dz \, dy + v_z \, dx \, dy + \frac{\partial v_z}{\partial z} \, dz \, dx \, dy \right)$$

$$- (v_x \, dz \, dy + v_z \, dx \, dy) = 0$$

or

$$\frac{\partial v_x}{\partial x} + \frac{\partial v_z}{\partial z} = 0 \tag{39.1}$$

Equation 39.1 is known as the *continuity condition* for flow parallel to the XZ plane. Since both water and soil are at least slightly compressible, the flow of water through soil does not strictly satisfy the continuity condition. However, in connection with practical seepage problems this fact can usually, although not always, be disregarded.

By combining equation 39.1 with equation 11.6, we obtain

$$v_x = ki_x = k \frac{\partial h}{\partial x} \quad \text{and} \quad v_z = ki_z = k \frac{\partial h}{\partial z}$$

It may be seen from these equations that the velocities v_x and v_z can be regarded as the partial derivatives with respect to x and z of a quantity,

$$\Phi = kh$$

known as a *velocity potential*. Substituting the values,

$$v_x = \frac{\partial \Phi}{\partial x} \quad \text{and} \quad v_z = \frac{\partial \Phi}{\partial z}$$

into equation 39.1, we obtain

$$\frac{\partial^2 \Phi}{\partial x^2} + \frac{\partial^2 \Phi}{\partial z^2} = 0 \tag{39.2}$$

This expression, known as *Laplace's equation*, governs the flow of every incompressible fluid through an incompressible porous material when the flow can be considered two-dimensional. Graphically, the equation can be represented by two sets of curves that intersect at right angles. The curves of one set are called *flow lines*, whereas the curves of the other set are known as *equipotential lines*. At all points along an equipotential line the water would rise in a piezometric tube to a certain elevation known as the *piezometric level*, Article 11, corresponding to the given equipotential line. The water particles travel along the flow lines, in a direction at right angles to the equipotential lines.

In the problem illustrated by Figure 99a the upstream surface of the sand is one of the equipotential lines, and the downstream surface is another. On the other hand, the surface of the impermeable base of the sand is a flow line. These are called the *hydraulic boundary conditions* of the problem. By solving equation 39.2 in accordance with these boundary conditions, we obtain the data required for constructing the flow net shown in Figure 99a. Every strip located between two adjacent flow lines, as shown in the figure, is called a *flow channel*, and every section of a flow channel located between two equipotential lines is known as a *field*. It is convenient to construct the equipotential lines such that the difference between the piezometric levels for any two adjacent equipotential lines is a constant. This difference is called the *potential drop* Δh. If h_1 is the total hydraulic head and N_d is the number of potential drops ($N_d = 18$ in Figure 99a), the potential drop is equal to

$$\Delta h = \frac{h_1}{N_d} \tag{39.3}$$

Once the flow net has been constructed, the pore-water pressure at any point located within the flow net, such as point C in Figure 99a, can be determined readily on the basis of the following reasoning. If there were no flow, that is, if the downstream ground surface were perfectly impervious, the neutral pressure at point C would be equal to the sum of the hydraulic head h_1 and the position head $h_2 + h_c$. However, as a consequence of the flow that does occur, there is a drop in head between the upstream ground surface and point C. Since C is located on the right-hand boundary of the 16th equipotential drop and $N_d = 18$, this drop in head is equal to $16h_1/18$. Therefore, the pressure in the water at point C is

$$u_w = (h_1 + h_2 + h_c - \tfrac{16}{18} h_1)\gamma_w$$

That part,

$$(h_1 - \tfrac{16}{18} h_1)\gamma_w = h\gamma_w$$

due only to the flow of the water, is known as the *excess hydrostatic pressure*.

COMPUTATION OF SEEPAGE AND OF SEEPAGE PRESSURE

In order to derive the equations necessary to compute the quantity of seepage, we shall consider the field indicated by the shaded area in Figure 99a. The length of its side in the direction of the flow lines is a. The hydraulic gradient across the field is

$$i = \frac{\Delta h}{a}$$

and the discharge velocity is

$$v = ki = k\frac{\Delta h}{a} = \frac{k}{a}\frac{h_1}{N_d}$$

If the width of the field measured at right angles to the flow lines is taken equal to an arbitrary value b, the quantity of water that flows through the field, per unit of width of the sheet piles, is

$$\Delta Q = bv = k\frac{b}{a}\frac{h_1}{N_d}$$

In order to simplify the computation of seepage, flow nets are constructed such that $b = a$, or, in other words, such that every field is square. On this assumption we obtain

$$\Delta Q = k\frac{ah_1}{aN_d} = k\frac{h_1}{N_d} \tag{39.4}$$

If N_f is the total number of flow channels ($N_f = 9$ in Figure 99a), the seepage Q per unit of width of sheet piles and per unit of time is

$$Q = N_f\,\Delta Q = kh_1\frac{N_f}{N_d} \tag{39.5}$$

By means of this equation the seepage can be computed readily, after the flow net has been constructed.

The total excess hydrostatic pressure on the upstream side of the cubical element with side a is

$$a^2 \times 15\Delta h\gamma_w$$

and on the downstream side is

$$a^2 \times 14\Delta h\gamma_w$$

The difference between these two pressures,

$$p_s = a^2\Delta h\gamma_w = a^3\frac{\Delta h}{a}\gamma_w$$

is transferred by the water onto the soil grains. Since $\Delta h/a$ is equal to the hydraulic gradient i, and a^3 is the volume of the element, the water exerts a force against the soil equal to

$$p_s = i\gamma_w \tag{39.6}$$

per unit of volume. This force is known as the *seepage pressure.* It has the dimension of a unit weight, and at any point its line of action is tangent to the flow line.

Construction of Flow Net

The data required for plotting a flow net can be obtained by solving equation 39.2, but a mathematical solution is not practicable unless the boundary conditions are very simple. The boundary conditions corresponding to most hydraulic structures do not satisfy this condition. Although flow nets for such structures can be obtained by various experimental methods, by far the most convenient and least expensive of the procedures is to construct the flow net graphically by trial and error.

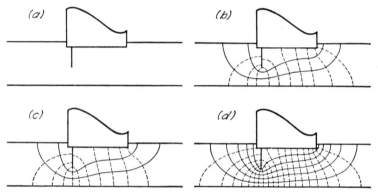

Fig. 100.   Steps in constructing a flow net.   (a) Cross section through pervious stratum; (b) result of first attempt to construct flow net; (c) result of adjusting flow net constructed in (b); (d) final flow net.

The steps in performing the graphical construction are illustrated in Figure 100. In this figure a represents a vertical section through an overflow dam with a sheet-pile cutoff wall.

Before starting the construction of the flow net, we must examine the hydraulic boundary conditions of the problem and ascertain their effect on the shape of the flow lines. The upstream and downstream ground surfaces in Figure 100a represent equipotential lines. The base of the dam and the sides of the cutoff wall represent the uppermost flow line, and the base of the pervious stratum represents the lowest flow line. The other flow lines lie between these two, and their shapes must represent a gradual transition from one to the other. Furthermore, all the flow lines must be vertical where they meet the upstream and downstream ground surfaces. The first step in constructing the flow net is to draw several smooth curves representing flow lines (plain curves in Figure 100b) that satisfy these requirements. Then several equipotential lines, which should intersect the flow lines at right angles, are drawn so that the fields are at least roughly square. In this manner a first rough approximation to the flow net is obtained.

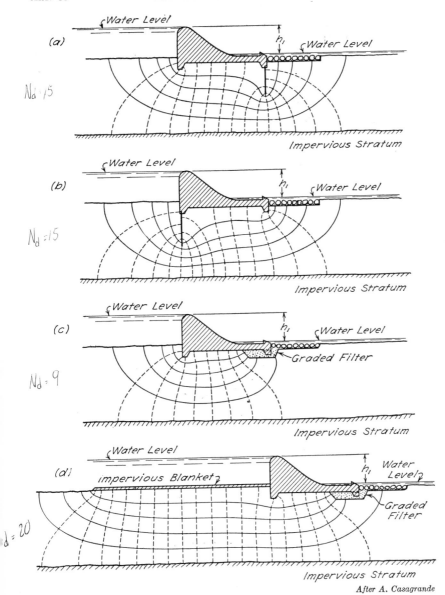

After A. Casagrande

FIG. 101.   Seepage through homogeneous sand beneath base of concrete dam.

The next step is to examine the trial flow net carefully in order to detect the most conspicuous defects. In the trial flow net shown in Figure 100*b*, the flow lines and the equipotential lines do intersect at approximately right angles, but several of the fields are not yet square.

Therefore, a new flow net is drawn in which the fields are more nearly square. The process of adjustment is continued until all of the fields are roughly square. The flow net at this stage is represented by Figure 100c.

Finally, the fields in Figure 100c are subdivided, and the flow net is adjusted until each small field is square. The result is shown in Figure 100d. Each field in Figure 100c has been subdivided into four small fields, and minor inaccuracies have been eliminated.

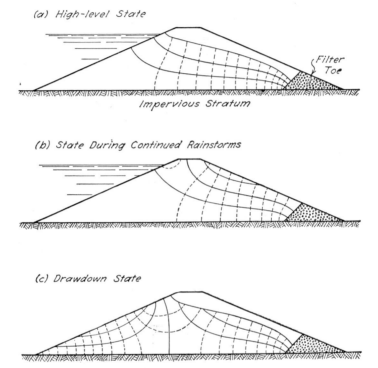

Fig. 102. Seepage through imaginary homogeneous dam consisting of very fine clean sand.

For all practical purposes the flow net is satisfactory as soon as all of the fields are roughly square. Even an apparently inaccurate flow net gives remarkably reliable results. Figures 101 and 102 may serve as a guide for constructing flow nets that satisfy various hydraulic boundary conditions. The flow net in Figure 102a contains one line that represents a free-water surface located entirely within the pervious medium. Along this surface, the vertical distance between each adjacent pair of equipotential lines is a constant and is equal to Δh.

Every flow net is constructed on the assumption that the soil within a given stratum through which the water percolates is uniformly permeable. In a natural soil stratum, the permeability varies from point to point, especially along lines at right angles to the boundaries of the stratum. Therefore, the difference between even a very roughly sketched flow net and an accurate one is commonly small compared to the difference between the flow pattern in the real soil and that indicated by the accurate flow net. Because of this universal condition, refinements in the construction of flow nets or elaborate model studies are entirely unwarranted.

The use of models based on the analogy between the flow of water in a pervious medium and the flow of electricity in a conductor affords a convenient means for constructing a flow net such as Figure 102a that contains a free-water surface. However, the assembling of the necessary equipment is not warranted unless many flow nets of this type have to be drawn.

SEEPAGE THROUGH SOILS WITH TRANSVERSE ISOTROPY

The flow nets shown in Figures 99 to 102 have been constructed on the assumption that the soil is hydraulically isotropic. In nature every mass of soil is more or less stratified. Therefore, as stated in Article 11, the average permeability k_I in a direction parallel to the planes of stratification is always greater than the average permeability k_{II} at right angles to these planes. To construct a flow net for such a stratified mass of soil, we substitute for the real soil a homogeneous material having horizontal and vertical permeabilities equal, respectively, to k_I and k_{II}. A medium with such properties is said to possess *transverse isotropy* (see Article 7).

In order to prepare a flow net for a homogeneous medium with transverse isotropy, we proceed as follows: A drawing is made showing a vertical section through the permeable layer parallel to the direction of flow. The horizontal scale of the drawing is reduced by multiplying all horizontal directions by $\sqrt{k_{II}/k_I}$. For this transformed section we construct the flow net as if the medium were isotropic. The horizontal dimensions of this flow net are then increased by multiplying them by $\sqrt{k_I/k_{II}}$. The quantity of seepage is obtained by substituting the quantity,

$$k = \sqrt{k_I k_{II}}$$

into equation 39.5. The expression for the quantity of seepage per unit width of the medium is then

$$Q = h_1 \frac{N_f}{N_d} \sqrt{k_I k_{II}} \tag{39.7}$$

The procedure is illustrated by Figure 103.

The preceding method has been developed on a purely mathematical basis without any simplifying assumptions. Therefore, the results are as reliable as Darcy's law and the values of k_I and k_{II} that enter the computation.

The average value of k_I for almost all natural soil strata is considerably greater than k_{II}. However, the ratio k_I/k_{II} ranges from about two or three to several hundred, and there is no way to determine the value accurately for a given deposit. Therefore, it is advisable to sketch two flow nets, one on the basis of the greatest probable value for k_I/k_{II}, and

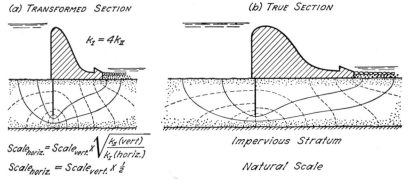

(a) TRANSFORMED SECTION   (b) TRUE SECTION

$k_I = 4k_{II}$

$Scale_{horiz.} = Scale_{vert.} \times \sqrt{\dfrac{k_{II}\ (vert)}{k_I\ (horiz.)}}$

$Scale_{horiz.} = Scale_{vert.} \times \dfrac{1}{2}$

Impervious Stratum

Natural Scale

FIG. 103.   Construction of flow net if coefficients of permeability of sand stratum are different in horizontal and vertical directions.   (a) Transformed section; (b) true section.

the other on the basis of the least probable one. In selecting these values, consideration should be given to the fact that k_I/k_{II} cannot be less than unity, nor greater than the ratio between the coefficients of permeability of the most and least permeable layers. For design purposes, that flow net should be retained which represents the most unfavorable conditions, or else provisions should be made to ascertain during construction whether the difference between the real and the anticipated seepage conditions is on the side of safety.

PROBLEMS

1. The sand beneath the dams shown in Figure 101 has a permeability in every direction of 4.2×10^{-3} cm per sec. The head h_1 is 25 ft. Compute the seepage loss in cubic feet per second, per lineal foot along the axis of each dam.

   Ans.   (a) 1.15×10^{-3}; (b) 1.15×10^{-3}; (c) 1.91×10^{-3}; (d) 0.86×10^{-3} cu ft per sec.

2. Estimate the hydrostatic uplift pressure in excess of that at tail-water level, at a point midway between the upstream and downstream faces of the concrete base of the dams of problem 1.

   Ans.   (a) 15; (b) 9; (c) 6; (d) 2.5 ft of head.   *that is feet of water*

3. The subsoil of the dam shown in Figure 101*b* contains a horizontal layer of silt, 1 in. thick, that intersects the row of sheet piles a short distance above the bottom of the piles. There are no means for detecting the presence of such a layer by any practicable method of soil exploration. The coefficient of permeability of the sand is 4.2×10^{-3} cm per sec, whereas that of the silt is 2.1×10^{-6} cm per sec. The total thickness of the sand stratum upstream from the dam is 55 ft, and the lower edge of the sheet piles is located 25 ft above the base of the sand. (*a*) Describe how the influence of the silt layer on the seepage loss could be evaluated on the assumption that the silt layer is continuous over a large area. (*b*) Describe the effect on the seepage loss of gaps in the silt layer. (*c*) How can the degree of continuity of the silt layer be determined in advance?

> *Ans.* (*a*) The silt layer has the same effect as increasing the thickness of the sand layer from 55 to 221 ft, and the penetration of the sheet piles from 30 to 196 ft. Therefore, the seepage loss could be evaluated by sketching a flow net for these fictitious soil conditions. Since the gap beneath the sheet piles in the fictitious profile is small compared to the depth of sheet-pile penetration, the loss of water computed on the basis of this flow net would be only a small fraction of that through the sand without a silt layer. (*b*) Depending on the size and location of the gaps in the layer, a discontinuous silt layer may have any effect varying from almost nothing to that of a continuous layer. (*c*) It cannot.

4. Compute the seepage loss per foot of length of the dam shown in Figure 208*b*, assuming $k = 1 \times 10^{-3}$ cm per sec. Estimate the uplift pressure on the base of the dam at the back of the high masonry section. $p5 11$

> *Ans.* 1.1×10^{-3} cu ft per sec per lin ft; 64 ft of head.

5. The average coefficient of permeability of the sand beneath the dam shown in Figure 103 is 16×10^{-4} cm per sec in the horizontal direction and 4×10^{-4} cm per sec in the vertical direction. What is the seepage loss per lineal foot of dam, when the head is 30 ft?

> *Ans.* 2×10^{-4} cu ft per sec.

6. Construct the flow net for the dam shown in Figure 103*b*, if the value of k is equal to 36×10^{-4} cm per sec in the horizontal direction and 4×10^{-4} cm per sec in the vertical direction. The base width of the dam is 83 ft, the thickness of the pervious layer is 38 ft, and the length of the sheet piles is 29 ft. The head is 30 ft. What is the seepage loss per lineal foot of dam? Compare this value with the seepage loss beneath the same dam if k is equal to 12×10^{-4} cm per sec in every direction.

> *Ans.* 3.9×10^{-4}; 2.5×10^{-4} cu ft per sec.

7. What is the approximate intensity of the horizontal hydrostatic excess pressure against the left-hand side of the sheet-pile wall in Figure 208*a*, at the lowest point of the wall?

> *Ans.* 2620 lb per sq ft.

ART. 40. MECHANICS OF PIPING

DEFINITION OF PIPING

Many dams on soil foundations have failed by the apparently sudden formation of a pipe-shaped discharge channel or tunnel located between the soil and the foundation. As the stored water rushed out of the reservoir into the outlet passage, the width and depth of the passage increased rapidly until the structure, deprived of its foundation, collapsed and broke into fragments that were carried away by the torrent. An event of this type is known as a *failure by piping.*

Failures by piping can be caused by two different processes. They may be due to scour or subsurface erosion that starts at springs near the downstream toe and proceeds upstream along the base of the structure or some bedding plane. Failure occurs as soon as the upstream or intake end of the eroded hole approaches the bottom of the reservoir. The mechanics of this type of piping defy theoretical approach. However, piping failures have also been initiated by the sudden rise of a large body of soil adjoining the downstream toe of the structure. A failure of this kind occurs only if the seepage pressure of the water that percolates upward through the soil beneath the toe becomes greater than the effective weight of the soil. Failures of the first category will be referred to as *failures by subsurface erosion,* and those of the second as *failures by heave.* The following paragraphs deal exclusively with failures by heave.

The magnitude and distribution of the excess hydrostatic pressure are determined by the flow net. In Article 39 it has been emphasized that the theoretical flow net is never identical with the one that represents the flow of water through the real soil strata. Indeed, the two flow nets may have no resemblance whatsoever. Therefore, the results of theoretical investigations into the mechanical effects of the flow of seepage serve merely as a guide for judgment and as a basis for planning appropriate installations for surveillance during and after construction.

Mechanics of Piping Due to Heave

The mechanics of failure by piping due to heave are illustrated by Figure 104a, which represents a vertical section through one side of a single-wall sheet-pile cofferdam. To a depth h_1 below the water level, the soil outside the cofferdam consists of coarse gravel, whereas the gravel within the cofferdam has been removed by dredging. The gravel rests on a bed of uniform sand. The loss of head in the gravel is so small that it can be disregarded. We wish to compute the factor of safety G_s with respect to piping, after the water level on the inside has been pumped down to the surface of the sand.

Before making this computation, we shall consider the hydrostatic conditions at the instant of failure. As soon as the water level within the cofferdam is lowered by pumping, water begins to flow downward through the sand on the left side of the sheet piles and upward on the right. The excess hydrostatic pressure on a horizontal section such as Ox, Figure 104b, reduces the effective pressure on that section. As soon as the average effective pressure on and above a portion of Ox near the sheet piles becomes equal to zero, the water that flows through the sand can straighten and widen the flow channels without meeting any resistance. This process greatly increases the permeability of the sand adjoining the sheet piles, as explained in Article 12, and it diverts an additional part of the seepage toward this zone. The surface of the sand then rises (see Figure 104a). Finally, the sand starts to boil, and a mixture of water and sand rushes from the upstream side of the sheet piles, through the space below the lower edge of the sheet piles, and toward the zone where the boiling started.

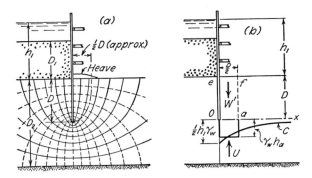

FIG. 104. Use of flow net to determine factor of safety of row of sheet piles in sand with respect to piping. (a) Flow net; (b) forces acting on sand within zone of potential heave.

By model tests it has been found that the rise of the sand occurs within a distance of about $D/2$ from the sheet piles. The failure, therefore, starts within a prism of sand having a depth D and a width $D/2$. At the instant of failure the effective vertical pressure on any horizontal section through the prism is approximately equal to zero. At the same time the effective lateral pressure on the sides of the prism is also approximately zero. Therefore, piping occurs as soon as the excess hydrostatic pressure on the base of the prism becomes equal to the effective weight of the overlying sand.

In order to compute the excess hydrostatic pressure a flow net must be constructed. After this has been done, Figure 104a, the intensity of this pressure can be determined readily at every point on the base of the prism at depth D by means of the procedure described in Article 39. In Figure 104b these values are represented by the ordinates of curve C with reference to a horizontal axis through O. Within the distance $D/2$ from the sheet piles the average excess hydrostatic pressure on the base of the prism has the value $\gamma_w h_a$, and the total excess hydrostatic pressure on the base is $U = \frac{1}{2}D\gamma_w h_a$. Failure by piping occurs as soon as U becomes equal to the effective weight of the sand which, in turn, is equal to the submerged weight $W' = \frac{1}{2}D^2\gamma'$. Therefore, the factor of safety with respect to piping is

$$G_s = \frac{W'}{U} = \frac{D\gamma'}{h_a\gamma_w} \qquad (40.1)$$

In a similar manner, we may compute the factor of safety for a dam with a sheet-pile cutoff.

Uplift Compensation by Loaded Filters

If the factor of safety against failure by piping is too small, it may be increased by establishing on top of the prism $Oafe$, Figure 104b, an inverted filter which has a weight W. The presence of the filter does not alter the excess hydrostatic pressure U, but it increases the effective weight of the prism from W' to $W' + W$. Hence, it increases the factor of safety with respect to piping from G_s, equation 40.1, to

$$G_s' = \frac{W + W'}{U} \qquad (40.2)$$

The stabilizing effect of loaded inverted filters has been demonstrated repeatedly by experiment and by experience with filter-protected structures. In order to be effective, the filters must be coarse enough to permit the free outflow of the seepage water, but fine enough to prevent the escape of soil particles through their voids. The design of filters to satisfy both requirements is discussed in Article 11.

PROBLEMS

1. In Figure 104 the head h_1 is 25 ft. The penetration of the sheet piles into the sand layer is 19 ft. If the saturated unit weight of the sand is 113 lb per cu ft, what is the weight of an inverted filter required to increase the factor of safety with respect to piping to 2.5?

Ans. 340 lb per sq ft.

2. The sand in the experiment illustrated in Figure 204a had a saturated unit weight of 115 lb per cu ft. At what head should piping by heave occur?

3. The sand layer mentioned in problem 1 contains a seam of clay too thin to be detected by the boring crew, but thick enough to constitute a relatively impermeable membrane. The numerical data regarding the head and the depth of sheet piles are identical with those given in problem 1. The clay seam is located a few feet above the lower edge of the sheet piles. Its left-hand boundary is located a few feet upstream from the sheet piles, and on the downstream side it is continuous. On the downstream side the sand stratum carries an inverted filter weighing 340 lb per sq ft which provides a factor of safety of 2.5 on the assumption that the sand contains no obstacle against

flow. (*a*) To what value does the clay seam reduce the factor of safety? (*b*) What procedure could be used to detect the danger?

    Ans.   (*a*) 0.83. The sand at the downstream side of the sheet piles would blow up as soon as the head reached 21 ft. (*b*) Install a single observation well on the downstream side of the sheet piles, with its lower end a few feet below the level of the bottom of the sheet-pile wall.

ART. 41. THEORY OF CONSOLIDATION

PROCESS OF CONSOLIDATION

If the load on a layer of highly compressible porous saturated soil such as clay is increased, the layer is compressed, and excess water drains out of it. This constitutes a process of consolidation, Article 14. During the process the quantity of water that enters a thin horizontal slice of the soil is smaller than the quantity that leaves it. Therefore, the continuity condition expressed by equation 39.1, on which the theory of flow nets and seepage is based, is no longer applicable.

The added load or pressure per unit of area that produces consolidation is known as the *consolidation pressure* or *consolidation stress*. At the instant of its application, the consolidation pressure is carried almost entirely by the water in the voids of the soil (see Article 14). Therefore, at the beginning of a process of consolidation, there is an initial excess pressure in the water almost exactly equal to the consolidation stress. As time goes on, the excess water pressure decreases, and the corresponding average effective pressure in the layer increases. At any point in the consolidating layer, the value u of the excess hydrostatic pressure at a given time may be determined by equation 12.1, written in the form,

$$u = \gamma_w h \qquad (41.1)$$

in which h is the hydraulic head with respect to the ground-water level above the consolidating layer. After a very great time the excess hydrostatic pressure u becomes equal to zero, and the entire consolidation pressure becomes an effective stress transmitted from grain to grain. If the consolidation pressure at any point is denoted by Δp, equilibrium requires that

$$\Delta p = \Delta \bar{p} + u \qquad (41.2)$$

where $\Delta \bar{p}$ represents that portion of the consolidation stress which, at a given time, is transmitted from grain to grain, and u is the corresponding excess hydrostatic pressure.

GRAPHICAL REPRESENTATION OF PROGRESS OF CONSOLIDATION

Since Δp in equation 41.2 is a constant, the progress of consolidation at a given point can be visualized by observing the variation of u at that point or, according to equation 41.1, by observing the variation in h by means of an imaginary standpipe rising from that point.

Figure 105 illustrates the consolidation of the compressible layer shown in Figure 92a, due to the weight of the building which rests on the surface of the ground. It is assumed that the layer can drain freely at both its upper and lower surfaces and that within the layer the water flows only in a vertical direction. Furthermore, it is assumed that the consolidation stress Δp does not vary from top to bottom of the layer.

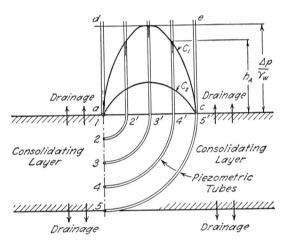

Fig. 105.   Diagram illustrating consolidation of compressible layer of clay.

The progress of consolidation within the layer can be studied by observing the position of the water level in a series of standpipes. The lower ends of the pipes are located on a vertical line through the layer as shown in Figure 105. Since the excess hydrostatic pressure is independent of the position of the water table, the water table is assumed to be identical with the top surface of the consolidating layer. If the standpipes are arranged in such a manner that the horizontal distances 1–2′, 1–3′ etc., are equal to the corresponding vertical distances 1–2, 1–3 etc., as shown in the figure, the curve that represents the locus of the water levels in the standpipes at a given time represents the *isochrone* (see Article 14). The hydraulic gradient i at any depth d below a is equal to the slope of the isochrone at a horizontal distance d from a. Furthermore, if the slope at any point of the isochrone is upward toward the right, the flow is upward at the corresponding point in the layer.

The distribution of the initial excess hydraulic head over vertical sections through the clay layer is represented by the horizontal line de

located at an elevation $\Delta p / \gamma_w$ above the free-water surface. This line is the initial isochrone. According to Article 14, the consolidation of a layer of clay proceeds from the drainage surface or surfaces toward the interior. Hence, at an early stage of consolidation the piezometric levels for the central part of the layer are still unchanged while those for the outer parts have already dropped as shown by the isochrone C_1. In an advanced stage, represented by C_2, all of the levels have dropped, but the elevations decrease from the central part toward zero at the drainage surfaces. Finally, after a very long time, all the excess hydrostatic pressure has disappeared, and the final isochrone is represented by the horizontal line ac.

Figure 106 shows the isochrones for different processes of consolidation. If the consolidating layer is free to drain through both its upper and lower surfaces, the layer is called an *open layer*, and its thickness is denoted by $2H$. If the water can escape through only one surface, the layer is called *half-closed*. The thickness of half-closed layers is denoted by H. In Figure 106, the layers labeled a, b, c, and e are open, whereas the layers d and f are half-closed.

Figure 106a is a simplified replica of Figure 105. The piezometric tubes are not shown. The diagram represents the consolidation of an open layer of clay under the influence of a consolidation stress that is uniform from top to bottom of the layer.

If the consolidating layer is fairly thick with respect to the width of the loaded area, the consolidation pressure due to the weight of a structure or a fill decreases with depth in a manner similar to that indicated by the curve C_a, Figure 91. Under the simplifying assumption that the decrease of the pressure with depth is linear, the initial isochrone may be represented by the line de in Figure 106b, and the consolidation pressures at the top and bottom of the layer are Δp_t and Δp_b, respectively.

If the consolidating layer is very thick compared to the width of the loaded area, the pressure Δp_b is likely to be very small compared to Δp_t. Under this condition it can be assumed with sufficient accuracy that $\Delta p_b = 0$. The corresponding isochrones are shown in Figure 106c for an open layer, and in Figure 106d for a half-closed layer. It should be noticed that the consolidation of the half-closed layer in Figure 106d is associated with a temporary swelling of the clay in the lower part of the layer.

Figures 106e and f illustrate the consolidation of hydraulically placed layers acted on by no force other than their own weight. The water table is assumed to be located at the top surface of the layers, and the consolidation that occurs during construction is disregarded. The fill shown in Figure 106e rests on a stratum of sand (open layer), whereas that in

Figure 106*f* rests on an impermeable stratum (half-closed layer). At a
time $t = 0$, the entire submerged weight of the soil in either layer
(γ' per unit of volume) is carried by the water, and the consolidation

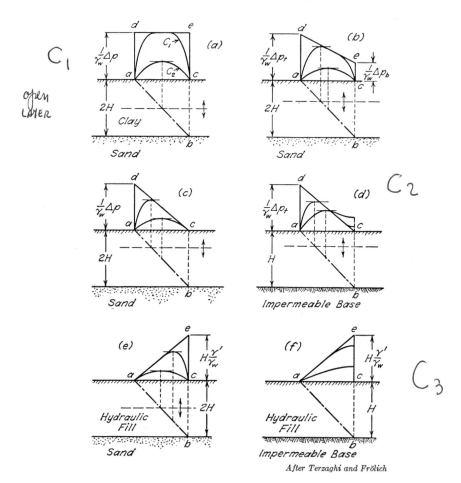

Fɪɢ. 106. Isochrones representing progress of consolidation of a layer of ideal clay
for different types of drainage and different distributions of consolidation pressure
in the vertical direction.

pressure increases from zero at the surface to $H\gamma'$ at the base. Therefore,
the final result of the consolidation is the same for both layers. However,
the difference in the shape of the isochrones for intermediate stages of
consolidation indicates that the rate at which the final stage is approached is very different for the two layers.

Computation of Rate of Consolidation

In order to compute the rate of consolidation and the degree of consolidation U per cent, equation 14.1, for the processes illustrated in Figure 106, we make the following simplifying assumptions:

——➤(a) The coefficient of permeability k, equation 11.6, is the same at every point in the consolidating layer and for every stage of consolidation.

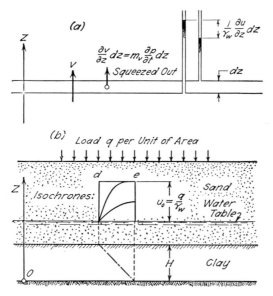

FIG. 107.   (a) Vertical section through thin horizontal slice of consolidating layer showing hydraulic pressure conditions at boundaries of slice; (b) section through consolidating layer, showing hydraulic boundary conditions.

——➤ (b) The coefficient of volume compressibility m_v, equation 13.3, is the same at every point in the layer and for every stage of consolidation.

——➤ (c) The excess water drains out only along vertical lines.

——➤ (d) The time lag of the compression is caused exclusively by the low permeability of the material. Thus, the secondary time effect discussed in Article 14 is disregarded.

Figure 107a represents a vertical section through a thin horizontal slice of a consolidating layer. The thickness of the slice is dz. Water flows through the layer at a rate v. The unbalanced hydrostatic pressure is $(\partial u/\partial z)dz$. Darcy's law, Article 11, requires that

$$v = ki = -k\frac{\partial h}{\partial z} = -k\frac{1}{\gamma_w}\frac{\partial u}{\partial z} \qquad (41.3)$$

If the layer were incompressible, the quantity of water flowing out of the layer would equal that which flows in, and we could write

$$\frac{\partial v}{\partial z} = 0 \qquad (41.4)$$

This condition is identical with the continuity condition expressed by equation 39.1. However, in a consolidating compressible layer with a thickness equal to unity, the quantity of water that leaves the layer per unit of time exceeds that which enters it by an amount equal to the corresponding volume decrease of the layer. Hence, by making use of equation 13.2, we can write

$$\frac{\partial v}{\partial z} = m_v \frac{\partial(\Delta \bar{p})}{\partial t}$$

Since Δp is a constant, equation 41.2 leads to

$$\frac{\partial(\Delta \bar{p})}{\partial t} = -\frac{\partial u}{\partial t}$$

whence

$$\frac{\partial v}{\partial z} = -m_v \frac{\partial u}{\partial t}$$

By combining this equation with equation 41.3, we obtain

$$\frac{\partial v}{\partial z} = -m_v \frac{\partial u}{\partial t} = -\frac{k}{\gamma_w} \frac{\partial^2 u}{\partial z^2}$$

or

$$\frac{\partial u}{\partial t} = \frac{k}{\gamma_w m_v} \frac{\partial^2 u}{\partial z^2} \qquad (41.5)$$

Equation 41.5 is the differential equation of every process of consolidation that involves linear drainage. It can be simplified by substituting

$$c_v(\text{cm}^2/\text{sec}) = \frac{k(\text{cm/sec})}{\gamma_w(\text{gm/cm}^3)m_v(\text{cm}^2/\text{gm})} \qquad (41.6)$$

The coefficient c_v represents the coefficient of consolidation, equation 14.2. Hence,

$$\frac{\partial u}{\partial t} = c_v \frac{\partial^2 u}{\partial z^2} \qquad (41.7)$$

The solution of this equation must satisfy the hydraulic boundary conditions. These conditions depend on the loading and drainage conditions as shown in the diagrams in Figure 106. The boundary conditions that determine the consolidation of a half-closed layer and a uniform pressure distribution may serve as an example. According to Figure 107b, the boundary conditions are as follows:

(1) At $t = 0$ and at any distance z from the impervious surface, the excess hydrostatic pressure is equal to Δp.

(2) At any time t at the drainage surface $z = H$, the excess hydrostatic pressure is zero.

(3) At any time t at the impervious surface $z = 0$, the hydraulic gradient is zero (that is $\partial u / \partial z = 0$).

(4) After a very great time, at any value of z, the excess hydrostatic pressure is zero.

Equation 41.7 combined with the boundary conditions determines the degree of consolidation U per cent for a given time t. The equation for U per cent is

$$U\% = f(T_v) \tag{41.8}$$

In this expression,

$$\boxed{T_v = \frac{c_v}{H^2} t} \tag{41.9}$$

is a pure number called the *time factor*. Since the soil constants and the thickness of the compressible layer enter equation 41.8 only in the combination represented by the dimensionless time factor T_v, the value $U\% = f(T_v)$ is the same for every layer that consolidates under specified conditions of loading and drainage. It has been determined for every condition of practical importance by means of the differential equation 41.7. The results have been presented in the form of graphs or tables. By means of these graphs and tables, all the problems likely to be met in practice can be solved without any computation other than the evaluation of equation 41.9. Figure 108 represents the solutions of the problems illustrated in Figure 106. The following instructions serve as a guide for using the graphs.

For every open layer (thickness $2H$) the relationship between U per cent and T_v is determined by the curve C_1, regardless of the slope of the zero isochrone de. Therefore, the curve C_1 represents the solution for all the consolidation problems represented by Figure 106a, b, c, and e. If the zero isochrone is horizontal, indicating a uniform distribution of the consolidation pressure throughout the consolidating layer, curve C_1 also represents the process of consolidation for a half-closed layer with thickness H. The following example illustrates the procedure for using the graph, Figure 108a.

The coefficient of consolidation of an open layer with thickness $2H$, Figure 92, is c_v. We wish to determine the time t at which the degree of

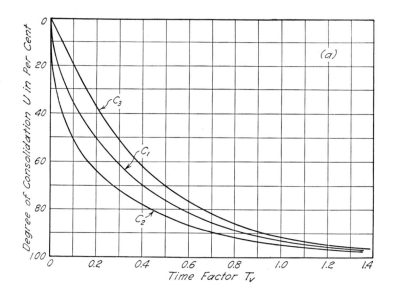

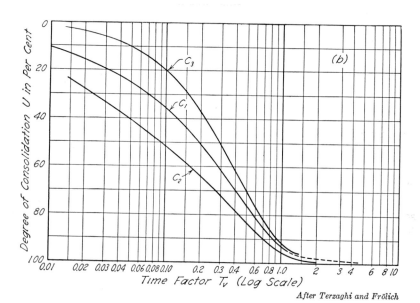

After Terzaghi and Frölich

FIG. 108. Relation between time factor and degree of consolidation. In (a) the time factor is plotted to an arithmetic and in (b) to a logarithmic scale. The curves C_1, C_2, and C_3 correspond to different conditions of loading and drainage, represented by a, d, and f, respectively, in Figure 106.

consolidation of the layer due to the weight of the superimposed building becomes equal to 60 per cent. From equation 41.9 we obtain

$$t = T_v \frac{H^2}{c_v}$$

C_v *see p 76*

According to curve C_1 in Figure 108a, a degree of consolidation of 60 per cent corresponds to the time factor 0.28, whence

$$t = 0.28 \frac{H^2}{c_v} \tag{41.10}$$

regardless of the slope of the zero isochrone. If the zero isochrone for a half-closed layer of clay with thickness H is horizontal, the degree of consolidation of this layer after time t, equation 41.10, will also be equal to 60 per cent.

If the consolidation pressure for a half-closed layer decreases from some value Δp_t at the top to zero at the bottom, as shown in Figure 106d, the relation between U and T_v is given by the curve C_2. If it increases from zero at the top to Δp_b at the bottom, as in Figure 106f, curve C_3 furnishes the required information. For intermediate types of vertical distribution of consolidation pressure, sufficiently accurate results can be obtained by interpolation. Figure 108b shows the curves C_1 to C_3 plotted to a semilogarithmic scale. Small values of U can be obtained somewhat more accurately from the semilogarithmic curves. The semilogarithmic plot of C_1 corresponds to the solid curve in Figure 28b.

On account of the simplifying assumptions listed at the outset of the preceding analysis, the computation of the rate of settlement has the character of a crude estimate. The most important discrepancy between theory and reality has been referred to as the secondary time effect, Article 14. According to the theory of consolidation, the time–settlement curve should approach a horizontal asymptote whereas in reality it merges into an inclined tangent as shown in Figure 28a. At present the secondary settlement cannot be predicted on the basis of test results. Experience shows that the rate of the secondary settlement of buildings resting on normally loaded clay ranges, during the first decades after construction, between $\frac{1}{8}$ and $\frac{1}{2}$ in. per year. Exceptional rates as high as one inch per year have been observed.

It is obvious that the results of a settlement computation are not even approximately correct unless the assumed hydraulic boundary conditions are in accordance with the drainage conditions in the field. Every continuous sand or silt seam located within a bed of clay acts like a drainage layer and accelerates consolidation of the clay, whereas lenses of sand and silt have no effect. If the test boring records indicate that a bed of clay contains partings of sand or silt, the engineer is commonly unable to find out whether or not these partings are continuous. In such instances the theory of consolidation can be used only for determining an upper and a lower limiting value for the rate of settlement. The real rate remains unknown until it is observed.

PROBLEMS

1. Representative samples were obtained from a layer of clay 20 ft thick, located between two layers of sand. By means of consolidation tests, it was found that the average value of c_v for these samples was 4.92×10^{-4} sq cm per sec. By constructing a building above the layer, the average vertical pressure in the layer was everywhere increased and the building began to settle. Within how many days did half the ultimate settlement occur?

    Ans.   438 days.

2. If the clay layer in problem 1 contained a thin drainage layer located 5 ft below its upper surface, how many days would be required to attain half the ultimate settlement?

    Ans.   127 days.

3. A layer of clay 30 ft thick rests on an impermeable rock base. The consolidation stress along a given vertical line is assumed to vary uniformly from a maximum at the top of the layer to zero at the rock surface. The value of c_v for the clay is 9.5×10^{-5} sq cm per sec. How many years will elapse after the construction of a building until the settlement becomes equal to 30 per cent of the final value? Solve the same problem on the assumption that the clay rests on a pervious sand bed instead of rock.

    Ans.   6.5; 4.9 years.

ART. 42. STABILITY OF EARTH DAMS

HIGH-LEVEL AND DRAWDOWN STATES

If the upstream slope of an earth dam is partly or wholly submerged, the soil in the dam is acted on not only by its own weight but also by the seepage pressure of the water that percolates through the dam. The seepage pressure p_s, equation 39.6, is due to the friction between the percolating water and the walls of the voids, and, as a consequence, it acts in the direction of flow. This direction is indicated by the flow lines in the flow net, Figure 102a. Since the water seeps from the upstream toward the downstream slope, the seepage pressure increases the stability of the upstream slope. At the same time, it reduces the factor of safety of the downstream slope to the smallest value that it is likely to assume under normal operating conditions. Hence, for the downstream slope the hydraulic state corresponding to a full reservoir represents the critical condition, known as the *high-level state*.

Theoretically, the factor of safety of the downstream slope can be reduced to less than the value for the high-level state if, in addition to seepage from a full reservoir, water enters the dam through its crest and the upper part of the downstream slope. A flow net corresponding to this condition is shown in Figure 102b. Such a condition might conceivably occur during heavy rainstorms of long duration or the melting of a thick blanket of snow, but experience with railway and highway fills indicates that it is exceptional. The air content of the fill material located between the normal line of seepage and the surface of the fill seems to prevent complete saturation of the material. Therefore, in the following discussions, the influence of rain or melt water on the stability of the downstream slope will be disregarded.

During the high-level state the line of seepage of a properly constructed dam is located entirely beneath the downstream slope (see Figure 102a). The upstream slope represents an equipotential line, whereas the line of seepage is a flow line. If the water level in the reservoir is instantaneously lowered to the elevation of the base of the dam, the flow net assumes the character indicated in Figure 102c. At the instant of drawdown, the line of seepage retains its original position, but the upstream slope represents not an equipotential line but a free surface. The hydraulic conditions represented by this flow net are referred to as the *drawdown state*. During the transition from the high-level to the drawdown state the downstream slope becomes more stable than it was before, but the sliding tendency of the upstream slope is considerably increased. As time goes on, the free water stored in the voids of the fill gradually seeps out, and, as a consequence, the stability of both slopes increases. Hence, for the upstream slope the drawdown state represents the critical condition.

In order to evaluate the factor of safety of the slopes of a proposed embankment or earth dam that will be acted on by seepage pressures, it is necessary to select representative samples of the borrow-pit material, to estimate in advance of construction the average unit weight, relative density, permeability, and water content of the fill material after it is placed and compacted, and to make the fundamental assumptions for the stability computation in accordance with field conditions. These preliminary investigations as well as the preparation of the program for soil testing require experience and judgment. The following paragraphs deal merely with the theoretical part of the problem, the stability computation.

Stability Computation for Sudden Drawdown, Rigid Fill

Figure 109a represents a cross section of a fill. Before drawdown both slopes of the fill are completely submerged, and at the instant of drawdown the free-water level is lowered from the elevation of the crest to that of the base. Furthermore, the fill material is assumed to be practically incompressible, such as well-compacted sand, and the height of capillary rise is negligible compared to the height of the dam.

The flow net for the drawdown state in such a fill is shown in Figure 109a. It satisfies the following hydraulic boundary conditions: The entire

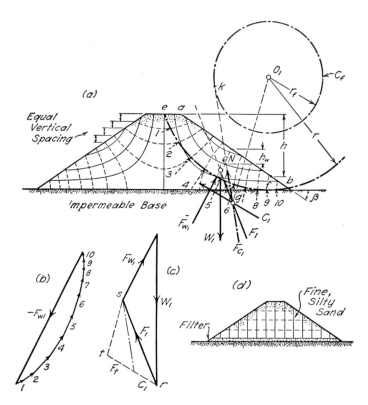

Fig. 109. (a) Seepage conditions in embankment of fine sand immediately after sudden drawdown; (b) and (c) force polygons required for stability computations; (d) seepage through embankment after sudden drawdown if coarse-grained filter underlies fill.

flow net is symmetrical about the center line of the dam; the center line and the base of the dam are flow lines; the crest of the dam is an equipotential line; and the slopes represent free surfaces. According to Article 39, the water would rise in a piezometric tube from any point N to the elevation of the point at which the equipotential line through N intersects the slope, at a distance h_w above N. The pore-water pressure at N is, therefore,

$$u_w = \gamma_w h_w \tag{12.1}$$

The circular arc *efb* with center at O_1 represents a first approximation to the surface of sliding, and the circle C_f is the corresponding friction circle. If r is the radius of the circle of sliding and ϕ the angle of internal friction of the fill material, the radius r_f of the friction circle is equal to $r \sin \phi$.

The force W_1 that tends to produce a slide along *efb* is equal to the weight of the soil located above *efb*, solid and water combined. The sliding movement is resisted by the friction along *efb*, which is equal to the coefficient of internal friction, $\tan \phi$, times the total effective pressure on *efb*. The total effective pressure at any point of this surface is equal, in turn, to the difference between the total and the neutral pressure on the surface at that point. Since the quantity h_w in equation 12.1 can be scaled from the drawing for any point of *efb*, the resultant neutral pressure F_{w_1} on *efb* can be obtained readily by means of a polygon of forces, Figure 109b. The resultant F_1 of the effective pressure on *efb* is obtained by combining the total force W_1 and the neutral force F_{w_1} in the force diagram, Figure 109c. The line of action of F_1 passes, Figure 109a, through the point of intersection of W_1 and F_{w_1}.

Since F_1 in Figure 109a neither intersects nor touches the friction circle, the sudden drawdown would cause a failure of the slopes of the dam unless the slide were resisted not only by friction but also by cohesion. In order to estimate the cohesion required to prevent the slip along *efb*, the line of action of the resultant cohesion C_1 is determined as explained in Article 31. It intersects the line of action of the force F_1 at point g, Figure 109a. In order to comply with the conditions for the stability of the slope *ab*, the resultant F_{c_1} of the forces C_1 and F_1 must pass through point g and be tangent to the friction circle C_f. The required magnitude of the force C_1 is obtained by drawing additional lines in the force polygon, Figure 109c, parallel to the lines of action of these forces in Figure 109a.

In order to estimate the factor of safety with respect to sliding, we trace *st* in Figure 109c parallel to O_1g. If the surface of sliding were perfectly frictionless, the total cohesion required to prevent a slide would be $rt = F_t + C_1$. Hence, if the available cohesion is C_a, the factor of safety with respect to sliding may be expressed by

$$G_s = \frac{F_t + C_a}{F_t + C_1} \tag{42.1}$$

If the slope is stable without the assistance of cohesion, C_1 in equation

42.1 is negative. If, in addition, the soil is cohesionless, C_a is zero. On these assumptions, we obtain

$$G_s = \frac{F_t}{F_t - C_1} \tag{42.2}$$

This value is 10 to 15 per cent greater than the value obtained by means of equation 31.1 for the factor of safety of slopes on cohesionless soils. More accurately, the safety with respect to sliding can be judged on the basis of the concept represented by equation 31.2.

Since *efb*, Figure 109a, may not be the critical circle, the procedure must be repeated for different circles that intersect the crest and are tangent to the base of the fill. The slide would occur along the circle for which G_s is the smallest.

If a highway embankment subject to periodic inundation consists of well-compacted relatively incompressible soil, the reduction in stability of the slopes due to rapid subsidence of the floods can be avoided by the insertion of a gravel filter between the fill and its base, as shown in Figure 109d. Since the water drains downward into the filter, the seepage pressure acts in a downward direction instead of outward. If such a filter is to be constructed beneath a storage dam, its continuity must be broken by a strip of relatively impermeable soil that divides the filter layer into upstream and downstream halves. A discontinuous filter of this type was installed (1941) in the Arkabutla dam in Mississippi.

SIMPLIFIED STABILITY COMPUTATION FOR SUDDEN DRAWDOWN, RIGID FILL

In Article 38 the reader was warned that every computation involving seepage effects is likely to be very inaccurate, because the real shape of the equipotential curves depends to a large extent on local variations in the permeability of the soil. Hence, simplified methods serve their purpose as well as or even better than the rather cumbersome procedure just described, provided the error is on the safe side and does not exceed 10 or 15 per cent.

One such simplified method, applicable to slopes flatter than about 1:2.5, is illustrated by Figure 110. The flow net for the drawdown state is shown in Figure 110a. It can be seen that most of the equipotential curves, represented by dash lines, are nearly vertical. Hence, it can be assumed without excessive error that all of them are really vertical, as shown in Figure 110b.

If this assumption is made, the resultant F_w of the neutral stresses on the surface of sliding passes almost through the center of gravity O_g of the sliding segment *abfe*. Furthermore, the line O_gO represents almost exactly the direction of F_w. It makes an angle α with the vertical. The vertical component of F_w is equal to the weight of a body of water that has a volume equal to that of the sliding segment. Hence, if A is the

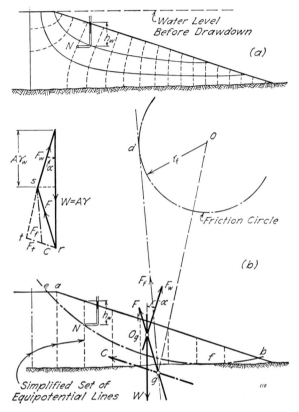

FIG. 110. Diagram illustrating simplified method of making stability computation for drawdown state if fill material is incompressible. (*a*) Flow net for drawdown state; (*b*) simplified set of equipotential lines; (*c*) force polygon required for stability computation.

volume of the segment per unit of length of the fill and γ_w is the unit weight of water, the vertical component of F_w is equal to $A\gamma_w$ and

$$F_w = \frac{A\gamma_w}{\cos \alpha}$$

Thus F_w is obtained without drawing a force polygon. The remainder of the investigation is identical with that illustrated by Figure 109. The factor of safety with respect to sliding along *efb* is determined by equation

42.1, and the factor of safety with respect to a slope failure is equal to the smallest value obtained by repeating the investigation with different circles.

The real factor of safety of the slope is greater than the computed one because, on account of the difference between the real and the assumed equipotential lines, Figures 110a and b, the real magnitude of F_w is less than that of F_w in Figure 110b. For steep slopes the difference is quite large. However, it decreases with decreasing slope angles β, and for values of β less than about 15° it can be disregarded.

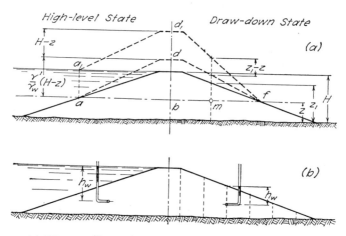

FIG. 111. (a) Diagram illustrating change in state of stress in compressible fill immediately after sudden drawdown; (b) equipotential lines corresponding to draw-down state.

STABILITY COMPUTATION FOR SUDDEN DRAWDOWN, COMPRESSIBLE FILL

If the fill material is not practically incompressible, as assumed in the preceding paragraphs, the flow-net method cannot be used for computing the neutral stresses (see Article 39). Yet, it is necessary to consider the hydraulic effects of the change in the state of stress of the fill produced by the drawdown. The change produced by an instantaneous drawdown is illustrated by Figure 111a. The left-hand side of this figure shows the approximate distribution of vertical stresses on a horizontal section af before drawdown. The effective normal pressure on the section is represented by the area adb, and the neutral pressure by the area add_1a_1. The ordinates of the upper boundary of each area with reference to the lower are equal to the vertical pressure divided by the unit weight γ_w of water. At every point on the horizontal section, the neutral stress is equal to $\gamma_w(H - z)$.

The sudden drawdown reduces the total normal pressure on the horizontal section to the value represented by the area bd_1f on the right-hand side of the center line, Figure 111a. Since the water content of the fill immediately after drawdown remains unchanged, the effective pressure on the horizontal section is practically unaltered. This is indicated by the equality of the areas bfd and abd. As a consequence, after draw-down the neutral stress at any point m on the horizontal section ab is equal to

$$u_w = \gamma_w(z_1 - z)$$

The piezometric head is $z_1 - z$, and the hydrostatic head with reference to the base of the fill is

$$h = z_1$$

The equipotential lines that satisfy this condition are vertical. In other words, the equipotential pattern is identical with the simplified pattern for the rigid fill shown in Figure 110b. Therefore, the stability computation can be made by the method illustrated by Figure 110b, and the factor of safety can be computed by means of equation 42.1.

It was pointed out on page 248 that the simplified method for computing the factor of safety of rigid fills, Figure 110b, involves an error on the safe side. When the method is used in connection with compressible fills, it is nearly correct. This fact leads to the conclusion that the compressibility of the fill increases the tendency of its slopes to fail after a sudden drawdown. If the slope angle β is 36°, the minimum angle of internal friction ϕ compatible with the equilibrium of slopes on cohesionless soil increases with increasing compressibility of the fill material from about 48° to about 57°, and, if $\beta = 18°$, the value of ϕ increases from about 33°30' to about 36°.

Effect of Speed of Drawdown on Stability

If the permeability of an incompressible fill is as high as that of a coarse sand, the water drains out of the voids of the fill almost as fast as the outside water level goes down. On the other hand, if the permeability of an incompressible fill is low, the voids of the soil are so small that most of the water is retained in the fill by capillary forces. While the outside water level goes down, the pore-water pressure changes within the zone of capillary saturation from positive to negative (see Article 21). Hence, at the end of the drawdown period such a fill is likely to be more stable than it was at the outset. Therefore, if a fill is incompressible, the gradual descent of the adjoining water level practically eliminates the danger of a drawdown failure, and, if the permeability of such a fill is low, the drawdown even increases the stability of the slopes.

The permeability of compressible embankments also is commonly low, and most of the water is retained in the fill by capillary forces. However, the drawdown is associated with and followed by a decrease of the volume of the fill due to consolidation. On account of the slowness with which consolidation proceeds, the hydraulic conditions illustrated by Figures 110b and 111b are likely to develop even during a slow drawdown. Hence, if a fill consists of compressible material the stability conditions after a slow drawdown are almost as unfavorable as after a rapid one. This accounts for the fact, demonstrated by experience, that drawdown failures occur almost exclusively on slopes underlain by fine-grained relatively compressible soils such as silt or mixtures of silt and clay. Because of the decisive influence of the compressibility on the effects of a gradual drawdown, thorough compaction of the fill material is of paramount importance.

In practice, drawdowns always occur more or less gradually. Complete drawdowns requiring less than a few days are very rare. If the water level descends gradually, the conditions for the equilibrium of the fill depend not only on the degree of compressibility but also on the permeability of the fill material and its water-holding capacity. Therefore, the effect on the stability conditions of the properties of the fill material is even more important during gradual drawdown than after sudden drawdown.

Stability of Storage Dams

In Figures 109 to 111, it has been assumed that the fills are symmetrical with respect to the center line and that the drawdown is preceded by complete submergence of both slopes of the dam. In contrast to these simple conditions, the upstream slope of an earth dam for storage purposes is commonly somewhat flatter than the downstream slope, and the downstream toe is provided with a toe filter, as shown in Figure 102. Furthermore, only the upstream slope is submerged before the drawdown. These differences influence the details of the stability analysis, but not the general principles.

The stability computations for the downstream slope of a storage dam must be preceded by the construction of a flow net representing the seepage through the dam at the high-level stage, inasmuch as this stage is the critical one for the downstream slope. The flow net for this stage is shown in Figure 102a. Since the equipotential lines are curved, the investigation should be made by the method illustrated by Figure 109.

The critical stage for the upstream slope is the drawdown state. However, the danger of failure of the slope due to drawdown can be disregarded unless the fill material constituting the upstream part of the dam consists of soil with low permeability and at least moderate compressibility. The magnitude and distribution of the pore-water pressure in the upstream part of the dam after drawdown depend not only on the rate of drawdown and the consolidation characteristics of the fill material but also on the air content and on the density and permeability patterns of the fill. Since these latter factors are purely accidental, they cannot be precisely evaluated, and the designer is compelled to make a rough estimate of the pore-water pressures on the basis of simplifying assumptions. The discussion on page 249 exemplifies the reasoning which should enter into the estimate.

Shearing Resistance of Fill Material

In connection with the investigation of the stability of an embankment or dam acted on by seepage pressures, the question arises whether the shearing resistance of the fill material should be determined by means of slow, consolidated-quick, or quick tests (see Article 15). The answer to this question depends on several factors which must be considered individually. The most important of these are the state of consolidation of the fill at the end of the construction period and the state of stress in the fill just before the critical conditions are established.

If the dam consists of well-compacted and practically incompressible soil with a coefficient of permeability of more than about 10^{-6} cm per sec, it can safely be assumed that consolidation will be complete by the end of the construction period. It can also be assumed that the water content of the fill material will adapt itself to the changes of stress during the filling of the reservoir and the subsequent drawdown. Therefore, it is usually safe to make the stability computations for such dams on the basis of the slow-shear values. The cohesion should be disregarded. The errors are likely to be on the safe side, because at low and medium normal pressures the consolidated-quick-shear values are likely to be higher than the slow values.

If a dam consists of clay, entirely different conditions prevail. The permeability of clay is so low that the water content of the clay will not decrease appreciably during construction. Therefore, the stability of the dam immediately after construction should be investigated on the basis of quick-shear tests performed on samples of clay in the same state at which the clay will be placed in the dam. However, the critical period in the life of a clay dam may not necessarily occur immediately after construction. In the course of the years the water content of the central part of the dam is likely to decrease on account of further consolidation, whereas that beneath the upstream slope and near the downstream toe may increase. The effect of these changes in water content on the shearing resistance of the clay must be considered. It is advisable to evaluate the changes and to make stability computations not only for the ultimate state of the dam but also for one or two intermediate states.

If a dam consists of a soil intermediate between sand and clay, such as a compressible variety of silt, a consolidation computation may show that the fill material is permeable enough to permit consolidation during construction. If this is the case, it can be taken for granted that the water content will adapt itself to the shearing stresses that develop along the potential surfaces of sliding during the construction period. In exchange, the effects of drawdowns must be considered, because they may subsequently produce an increase of the shearing stresses at practically unaltered water content. Hence, the stability computation should be based on the most unfavorable combination of slow and consolidated-quick-shear values compatible with the contemplated operating conditions. The details of such investigations, as well as those mentioned in the preceding paragraph, cannot be classified as routine procedures and are beyond the scope of this book.

Part C
PROBLEMS OF DESIGN AND CONSTRUCTION

The contents of Parts A and B represent what is now known as soil mechanics. Soil mechanics, in turn, constitutes a small subdivision of the broad field of applied mechanics.

History shows that there is hardly a single concept of practical importance in the field of structural engineering that was not instinctively anticipated and used with success in design and construction by individuals or groups of engineers many centuries before applied mechanics came into existence. This is testified by daring bridges, aqueducts, and domes of great age that still command respect and admiration for their designers and builders. Yet progress was painful and very slow, because outstanding achievement called for the rare gift of intuition.

Conditions did not change until the advent of applied mechanics, when the art of structural engineering was subjected to the attack of science. Once a field of human activity is successfully invaded by science, even the average worker acquires the capacity to adapt his methods and designs to the immutable laws of nature, whereupon his degree of efficiency increases tremendously. This is demonstrated by the unprecedented advances of structural engineering during the last century.

Foundation and earthwork engineering lagged behind the other branches of civil engineering, because the laws that interconnect cause and consequence in this field are not so simple and lucid as those in the others. Furthermore, many of the problems cannot be solved adequately by theory alone because of the complexity of the physical properties and of the structure of natural soil deposits.

In spite of these inherent difficulties, an intimate knowledge of the relations between cause and effect increases the capacity of the average engineer for rational design in the field of foundation and earthwork engineering as effectively as it does in other branches of civil engineering, although in a different manner. This can be recognized by comparing the contents of Part C of this book with the chapters on the design of foundations in any book published 20 or more years ago.

The first chapter of Part C contains a discussion of the properties of natural soil deposits and the methods for investigating them. The following two are concerned with the empirical rules that pertain to the different branches of foundation and earthwork engineering. By correlating these rules with the information contained in Parts A and B, the limits for their validity are ascertained, and supplementary semi-empirical rules are established. The final chapter deals with the effect on adjoining structures of such construction operations as excavating and pumping.

Chapter VII

SOIL EXPLORATION

Art. 43. Purpose and Scope of Soil Exploration

Definition of Soil Exploration

The design of a foundation, an earth dam, or a retaining wall cannot be made in an intelligent and satisfactory manner unless the designer has at least a reasonably accurate conception of the physical properties of the soils involved. The field and laboratory investigations required to obtain this essential information constitute the *soil exploration*.

Until a few decades ago soil exploration was consistently inadequate because rational methods for soil testing had not yet been developed. On the other hand, at the present time the amount of soil testing and the refinements in the techniques for performing the tests are often quite out of proportion to the practical value of the results. In order to avoid either of these extremes, it is necessary to adapt the exploratory program to the soil conditions and to the size of the job.

Influence of Soil Conditions on Exploratory Program

If the foundation of an important structure is to be established above a fairly homogeneous layer of clay, a considerable amount of soil testing by expert laboratory technicians may be justified because the test results permit a relatively accurate forecast of both the amount and the time rate of settlement. On the basis of such a forecast, it may be possible to eliminate the danger of harmful differential settlement at reasonable expense by appropriate distribution of the loads or by suitable adjustment of the depths of subbasements beneath different parts of the structure. On the other hand, if a similar structure is to be located above a deposit composed of pockets and lenses of sand, clay, and silt, the same amount of testing would add very little to the information that could be obtained merely by determining the index properties of several dozen representative samples extracted from exploratory drill holes. Additional data of far greater significance than those obtainable from extensive soil tests could be secured in a shorter time and at less expense by

255

means of simple subsurface soundings along closely spaced vertical lines, because such soundings would disclose whatever weak spots might be located between drill holes. The discovery of such spots is more important than an accurate knowledge of the properties of random samples.

The preceding remarks demonstrate that, if the soil profile is complex, an elaborate program of soil testing is likely to be out of place. Hence, the methods of soil exploration must be chosen in accordance with the type of soil profile at the site of the construction operations. The following paragraphs describe the significant characteristics of the principal types of soil profiles commonly encountered in the field.

The term *soil profile* indicates a vertical section through the subsoil that shows the thickness and sequence of the individual strata. The term *stratum* is applied to a relatively well-defined layer of soil in contact with other layers of conspicuously different character. If the boundaries between strata are more or less parallel, the soil profile is said to be *simple* or *regular*. If the boundaries constitute a more or less irregular pattern, the soil profile is called *erratic*.

From the ground surface to a depth of about 6 ft, and exceptionally to a greater depth, the physical properties of the soil are influenced by seasonal changes of moisture and temperature and by such biological agents as roots, worms, and bacteria. The upper part of this region is known as the A-horizon. It is subject primarily to the mechanical effects of weathering and to the loss of some constituents due to leaching. The lower part is referred to as the B-horizon, where part of the substances washed out of the A-horizon are precipitated and accumulate.

The properties of the soils in the A- and B-horizons are chiefly the concern of agronomists and road builders. Foundation and earthwork engineers are interested primarily in the underlying parent material. Beneath the B-horizon the character of the soil is determined only by the raw material from which it is derived, by the method of deposition, and by subsequent geological events. The individual strata that constitute the soil profile beneath the B-horizon may be fairly homogeneous, or they may be composed of smaller elements having properties that depart more or less from the average. The shape, size, and arrangement of these smaller elements determine the *primary structure* of the deposit. Since most soils have been deposited under water, the most common primary structure is *stratification*. If the individual layers are not thicker than about 1 in. and are of roughly equal thickness, the soil is called *laminated*. For example, the varved clays described in Article 2 are laminated soils. The action of ice, landslides, torrential streams, and several other agents leads to the formation of deposits with an *erratic structure.* Such deposits have no well-defined pattern. The more the structure of a mass of soil approaches the erratic type, the more difficult it is to determine the average values of the soil constants, and the more uncertain is the result.

In stiff clays and other soils with great cohesion the primary structure may be associated with a *secondary structure* that develops after the soil is deposited. Most important among the secondary structural characteristics are systems of hair cracks, joints, or slickensides (see Article 7). Hair cracks and joints occur commonly in flood-plain clays consisting of layers, each of which was temporarily exposed to the atmosphere after deposition. Shrinkage caused cracks to form during the period of exposure. Slickensides are smoothly polished surfaces that may be the result of volume changes produced by chemical processes or of deformations produced by gravity or tectonic forces involving slippage along the walls of existing or newly formed joints.

If a cohesive stratum has a well-developed secondary structure, the results of laboratory tests may give an erroneous conception of its mechanical properties. Therefore, in connection with such soils, the only guide on which the engineer can rely is his judgment based on field experience with similar materials.

INFLUENCE OF SIZE OF PROJECT ON EXPLORATORY PROGRAM

In the preparation of a program for soil exploration the magnitude of the job must also be considered. If the proposed construction operation involves only a small expenditure, the designer cannot afford to include more in the investigation than a small number of exploratory borings and a few classification tests on representative soil samples. The lack of accurate information concerning the subsoil conditions must be compensated by the use of a liberal factor of safety in design. On the other hand, if a large-scale construction operation of the same kind is to be carried out under similar soil conditions, the cost of even a thorough and elaborate subsoil investigation is usually small compared to the savings that can be realized by utilizing the results in design and construction, or compared to the expenditures that would arise from a failure due to erroneous design assumptions. Hence, on large projects extensive subsoil investigations are likely to be justified.

In order to adapt the exploratory program to the requirements of a given job and obtain the essential data at minimum expenditure of time and money, the engineer in charge must be familiar with the tools and processes available for exploring the soil, with the methods for analyzing and digesting the results of laboratory and field tests, and with the uncertainties involved in the results obtained by the different methods of soil exploration. These subjects are discussed in the following two articles.

ART. 44. METHODS OF SOIL EXPLORATION

Boring, Sampling, and Sounding

The first step in investigating the subsoil is to drill a few holes into the ground by an expedient method, and to obtain fairly intact samples of soil from every stratum encountered by the drilling tools. These drill

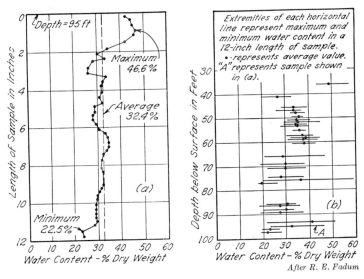

After R. E. Fadum

Fig. 112. Variation in natural water content of clay from one drill hole in Boston. (a) Variation within vertical distance of one foot; (b) variation throughout entire boring.

holes are known as *exploratory borings*. In addition, field tests, undisturbed sampling operations, or both may be required. The field tests, such as subsurface soundings or pumping tests, supply direct information concerning the details of the soil profile and the properties of the soil *in situ*. Undisturbed sampling operations furnish the material for an investigation of the soil properties by means of laboratory tests.

In recent years geophysical methods of exploration have been adapted to the purposes of civil engineering. By means of observations at the ground surface they provide information regarding the position of the boundary between soil and rock. If the rock is sound and its upper surface is not too uneven, the position and topography of the rock surface can be determined more cheaply and rapidly than by means of borings. Attempts have also been made by geophysical methods to determine the location of the boundaries between different soil strata and to obtain information about the physical properties of these strata. However, these attempts are still in an experimental stage.

Experience has shown that the physical properties of almost every natural soil stratum vary to a considerable extent in the vertical direction and to a smaller degree in horizontal directions. This fact is strikingly demonstrated by the variation in natural water content of clays that appear on visual inspection to be homogeneous. The results of an investigation of the variation in water content within a layer of clay in Boston are shown in Figure 112. The variations within a 1-ft layer are shown in Figure 112a, and those within a 60-ft layer in Figure 112b. If a mass of clay appears to be nonhomogeneous, its water content is likely to vary with depth in a manner as erratic as that shown in Figure 113.

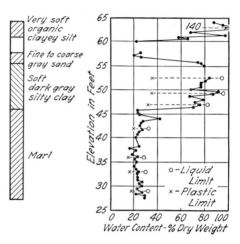

FIG. 113.   Variation in natural water content of samples from boring in composite shore deposit.

If a soil stratum is of the erratic type, adequate information concerning the variations in the soil properties can be obtained only by securing continuous cores from top to bottom of the stratum and performing soil tests on every part of the core material, or else by performing suitable tests in the field. Field tests of one type, exemplified by subsurface soundings, furnish continuous records of the variations in penetration resistance of the stratum. Those of a second type, represented by pumping tests for determining the coefficient of permeability, furnish average values of the soil property under investigation.

The average physical properties of a clay stratum can be determined conveniently by laboratory tests on continuous cores extending from top to bottom of the stratum. The cores are commonly removed from the ground in thin-walled steel sampling tubes with a diameter of 2 or $2\frac{1}{2}$ in., and the borings from which the samples are obtained are referred to as *tube-sample borings*. The tubes that contain the cores are sealed on the job and shipped to the laboratory where they are not opened until the clay is to be tested.

If an accurate estimate must be made of the settlement of a proposed structure located above a clay stratum, or if a structure is to be built above a stratum of extrasensitive or heavily precompressed clay, consolidation tests must be made on samples with a diameter of at least 4 in. Since the boring equipment for obtaining tube samples is usually unsuitable for taking samples with a diameter of more than $2\frac{1}{2}$ in., the consolidation test samples must be secured by independent operations such as sampling in test shafts or in large-diameter drill holes. The latter are commonly referred to as *undisturbed sample borings*, although the samples obtained from such borings are in many instances no less disturbed than 2-in. cores obtained by means of thin-walled tube samplers.

To obtain reliable average values for the physical properties of a sand stratum by means of laboratory tests, it would also be necessary to test all parts of practically continuous cores. However, the tools commonly used for sampling in clay are not suitable for extracting samples of cohesionless soils located below the water table. Excessive loss of core cannot be avoided without recourse to one of the expensive and cumbersome procedures described on page 272. Hence, it is preferable to investigate cohesionless or almost cohesionless soil strata by means of field tests, such as penetration or pumping tests, that eliminate the need for obtaining continuous cores.

The following sections of this article deal with the techniques of the procedures used in connection with soil exploration.

EXPLORATORY BORINGS

Methods of drilling. The cheapest and most expedient procedures for making borings are the wash-boring process and drilling by means of an auger. Shallow holes up to about 10 ft deep are commonly made with augers. To make deeper borings either method can be used.

Wash borings. The equipment for making a wash boring commonly includes a set of 5-ft lengths of pipe $2\frac{1}{2}$ in. in diameter, known as *casing*, which serves to support the walls of the hole; a weight for driving the casing into the ground; a derrick for handling the weight and casing; and wash pipe, 1 in. in diameter, in 5-ft or 10-ft lengths. A hose connection is made through a swivel head to the top of the wash pipe, and the lower end of the pipe is fitted with a chopping bit, Figure 115d, provided with water ports so that the wash water can be pumped down the wash pipe and forced out of the ports. The equipment also includes a tub to store the water and a hand- or power-operated pump.

In order to start a wash boring, Figure 114, the derrick is erected, and a 5-ft length of casing is driven about 4 ft into the ground. A tee is attached to the top of the casing with its stem in a horizontal position, and a short pipe is inserted horizontally in the stem. The tub is placed under the end of the short pipe and filled with water. The wash pipe is lifted to a vertical position by means of a hand rope that passes over a

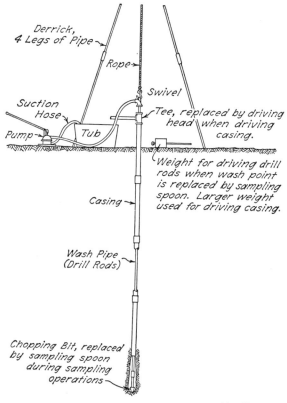

After H. A. Mohr

Fig. 114.   Apparatus for making wash boring.

pulley at the top of the derrick and is lowered into the top of the casing. The pump is started, and water is circulated from the tub through the swivel head into the wash pipe, whence it emerges at the chopping bit and rises in the annular space between the wash pipe and the casing. It returns to the tub, carrying cuttings of soil, through the tee and horizontal pipe at the top of the casing. As the water circulates, the wash pipe is churned up and down and is rotated at the bottom of each stroke to cut the soil loose. The hole is advanced by the churning and washing, and additional casing is driven as needed.[44.1]

While drilling proceeds, the drillman observes the color and general appearance of the mixture of soil and water that comes out of the hole. Whenever a conspicuous change is noticed, the wash water is turned off, and a spoon sample (see page 263) is taken. Spoon samples are also secured, one for each 5 ft of depth, if the character of the subsoil appears to remain unaltered. Departures from this procedure should not be tolerated, because they may lead to serious misjudgment of the subsoil conditions. Even if the sampling is conscientiously done, the presence of clay strata with a thickness of several feet, located between sand strata, may remain unnoticed.

When the boring operations are discontinued for the purpose of taking a spoon sample, the water should be allowed to rise in the casing until the water level becomes almost stationary. At this stage the elevation of the water table should be determined and recorded. It is not uncommon for water to rise from deeper strata to very much higher elevations than from the upper strata. Failure to recognize such a condition may be of serious consequence. In rare instances the reverse condition may be encountered.

Auger borings. The scrapings washed from the casing in a wash boring give such a vague indication of the character of the soil that the foreman may fail to notice the passage of the wash bit from one stratum into another. Therefore, some engineers prefer auger borings even for deep drill holes, in spite of their greater cost.

Types of augers used for extracting the soil from the bottom of a drill hole are shown in Figures 115a and b. The boring is made by turning the auger into the soil for a short distance, withdrawing the auger and the soil which clings to it, and removing the soil from the auger for examination. The auger is again inserted into the hole and turned further. If the hole fails to stand open to permit the insertion of the auger because of squeezing from the sides or because of caving, it must be lined with a casing having an inside diameter somewhat larger than the diameter of the auger. The casing should be driven to a depth not greater than that of the top of the next sample and should be cleaned out by means of the auger. The auger is then inserted into the clean hole and turned below the bottom of the casing to obtain the sample. Auger borings cannot be made in sand below the water table because the material will not adhere to the auger.

The diameter of the casing for deep auger holes is commonly 4 in., but in order to drill through coarse gravel or through soils containing large stones, it may be necessary to use 8- or even 10-in. casing. Stones that interfere with the driving of the casing can be broken up by means of a chopping bit.

Cohesive soil brought to the surface by the auger contains all its solid constituents, but the structure of the soil is completely destroyed, and the water content is likely to be greater than that of the soil in place. Hence, the use of augers as drilling tools does not eliminate the necessity for obtaining spoon samples whenever the drill hole reaches a new stratum. Only the spoon samples should be considered representative of the character of the undisturbed soil.

If a relatively firm stratum such as a layer of gravel is located above a very soft one, it is not uncommon for an auger boring to fail to disclose the real position of the boundary between the two strata. In one instance the existence of an 8-ft stratum of soft clay between two thick gravel layers was overlooked. In another the boundary between a bed of gravel and an underlying stratum of soft clay was reported 10 ft below its real position. Errors of this type are caused by driving the casing below the level at which the auger is operating. The casing pushes or drags stony material into the clay layer. The errors can be avoided by keeping the cutting tool as far in advance of the casing as the character of the soil permits.

Sampling in exploratory drill holes. In order to obtain soil samples from exploratory drill holes, a *sampling spoon* is attached to the bottom of the wash pipe or the drill rod in place of the bit and is lowered to the bottom of the hole. It is forced or driven into the soil to obtain a sample and is then removed from the hole.

Sampling spoons for exploratory borings commonly consist of a pipe with an inside diameter of about $1\frac{1}{2}$ in. and a length of 1 to 2 ft. The pipe is split lengthwise, as shown in Figure 115*f*. As a consequence the sampler is called a *split spoon*. While the sample is being taken, the two halves of the spoon are held together at the ends by short pieces of threaded pipe. One piece serves to couple the spoon to the wash pipe. The other, which has been sharpened, serves as the cutting edge while the spoon is driven into the soil.

According to the usual practice, the soil is extracted from the spoon by the foreman, who inspects and classifies the material and places a small portion of it in a glass jar that is covered tightly and shipped to the engineer for visual inspection. Preferably, fairly large samples should be removed from the spoon, sealed in airtight jars, carefully identified, and shipped to a laboratory for determination of the index properties.

If the sample consists of clay, the deformation of the sample due to the transfer from the sampling spoon into the jar is likely to reduce the strength to such an extent that the sample is not suitable for laboratory tests to determine its consistency. To avoid the transfer, split spoons have been constructed that contain a thin-walled cylindrical liner of brass or steel. The inner walls of the liner are flush with the cutting edge. After the sample has been taken, the liner with its contents is taken out of the shell, the ends are scraped out and sealed, and the sample is shipped to the laboratory in the liner.

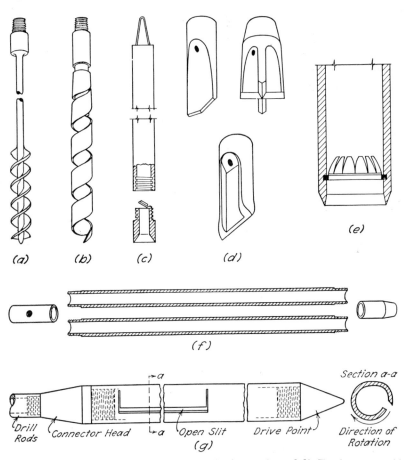

Fig. 115. Sampling tools for exploratory borings. (*a* and *b*) Earth augers; (*c*) bailer; (*d*) chopping bits; (*e*) spring core catcher; (*f*) split spoon sampler; (*g*) scraper bucket.

Whatever the type of sampler may be, only part of the sample should be used for tests. The remainder should be transferred into jars with air-tight covers, to be available for inspection by the bidders.

Clay samples obtained by means of a sampling spoon retain at least part of the characteristics of the undisturbed soil. On the other hand, samples of soils with a high permeability are always thoroughly compacted, regardless of whether the soil *in situ* is loose or dense. Hence, the samples fail to inform the investigator on the relative density of the soil although, as a rule, this property is far more significant than the character of the soil grains themselves.

The simplest method of obtaining at least some information concerning the degree of compactness of the soil *in situ* consists of counting the number of blows of the drop weight required to drive the sampling spoon into the soil for a distance of 1 ft. A weight of 140 lb and a height of fall of 30 in. are considered standard. The spoon has the dimensions shown in Figure 116. It is attached to the drill rods and lowered to the bottom of the drill hole after the hole has been cleaned by means of a

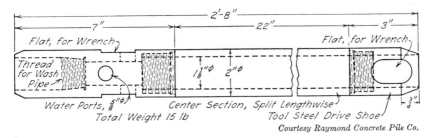

Courtesy Raymond Concrete Pile Co.

Fig. 116.   Dimensions of sampling spoon for standard penetration test.

water jet or an auger. After the spoon reaches the bottom, the drop weight is allowed to fall on the top of the drill rods until the sampler has penetrated about 6 in. into the soil, whereupon the penetration test is started, and the foreman records the number of blows required to produce the next foot of penetration. This procedure is referred to as the *standard penetration test*. Since this test furnishes vital information with very little extra effort, it should never be omitted.

In cohesionless or nearly cohesionless sand located below the water table, the sand is likely to drop out of the spoon while it is being lifted from the bottom of the drill hole. Bailers, Figure 115c, are unsatisfactory, because the churning operation required to fill them washes the fine particles out of the sand. In order to secure sand samples which contain all their constituents, it is necessary to experiment with other devices such as a sampling spoon equipped with a core catcher made of spring steel, Figure 115e. The core catcher is attached to the walls of the lower end of the sampling spoon. As the spoon is lifted, the springs bend in toward the center of the sample, and, if no coarse particle becomes caught between them, they join to form a dome-shaped bottom that supports the sample.

If the sampling spoon equipped with core catcher fails to retain the sand, reasonably complete samples can be obtained from 4-in. holes by means of the scraper bucket shown in Figure 115g. It has an internal diameter of $2\frac{1}{2}$ in. and a length of 30 in. The lower end is plugged with a conical shoe. The upper half of the bucket is provided with a vertical slit. One side of the wall adjoining the slit is bent out and sharpened to form a cutting edge. The sampler is driven for its full length into the bottom of the hole and rotated in the direction shown in the figure, whereupon the cutting edge scrapes off the adjoining soil. The scraped-off material accumulates first in the lower half of the sampler and later in the upper part. The sample is thoroughly disturbed and partly segregated, but the loss of fines is very small.

If a stratum of gravel is encountered, no samples can be secured from exploratory drill holes with a diameter as small as $2\frac{1}{2}$ in. It may even be impossible to drive the casing through the stratum, whereupon the hole must be abandoned. The next hole should be lined with a casing having a diameter of at least 4 in.

Field records of exploratory borings. Regardless of the procedure used for making an exploratory boring, the field notes kept by the foreman or the supervising engineer should contain the date when the boring was made, the location of the boring with reference to a permanent system of co-ordinates, and the elevation of the ground surface with respect to a permanent bench mark. They should include the elevations at which the water table and the upper boundary of each of the successive soil strata were encountered, the foreman's classification of the layers, and the values of the penetration resistance obtained by means of the standard penetration test. The type of tools used in making the boring should be recorded. If the tools are changed, the depth at which the change was made and the reason for change should be noted. Incomplete or abandoned borings should be described with no less care than successfully completed drill holes. The notes should contain everything of significance observed on the job, such as the elevations at which wash water was lost from the hole.

If the base of a foundation is to be located below the water table, it is advisable to transform at least one drill hole into an observation well and to record the movement of the water table during construction. If concrete is to be placed beneath the water table, water samples of about 1 gal should be taken from several drill holes for a chemical analysis to determine whether the water contains detrimental constituents in sufficient quantity to attack the concrete (see Article 63). If there are any indications that the water contains gas, the analysis should be made at the site immediately after the samples are taken.

The information contained in the field notes should be assembled in the form of boring logs in which the boundaries between the strata are plotted at their correct elevation on a suitable vertical scale.

Methods for Obtaining Undisturbed Samples

Tube-sample borings. Tube-sample borings must be made if the project calls for reliable information concerning the water content, shearing resistance, and sensitivity of a clay stratum.

Since the standard casing for lining exploratory drill holes has an internal diameter of $2\frac{1}{2}$ in., the largest sampling tube that can be used with standard equipment has a diameter of 2 in. Samples obtained in tubes of larger diameter are seldom more satisfactory than those obtained in 2-in. tubes, but their cost is considerably greater. Therefore, 2-in. sampling tubes commonly satisfy all requirements.

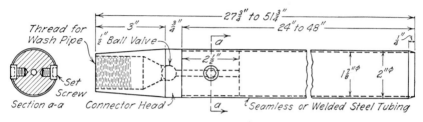

Fig. 117.   Two-inch tube sampler.

In order to obtain information on the consistency of clay in its original state, any unnecessary disturbance of the clay by the sampling tool should be avoided. Under the next subheading it is shown that the degree of disturbance of a sample with a given diameter increases quite rapidly with increasing thickness of the walls of the sampler. Therefore, the walls should be as thin as possible. On the other hand, they must be strong enough to withstand the resistance of the soil to penetration without buckling. All these requirements are satisfied by samplers consisting of tubing 2 in. in diameter, made of no. 16 or no. 18 gage steel. The tubes commonly have a length of 30 or 36 in. The lower ends are beveled to a cutting edge, and the upper ends are fitted for attachment to the drill rods (see Figure 117).

In order to take a sample, the foreman attaches a tube to the bottom of the drill rods and lowers it into the hole that has previously been cleaned by a cleaning spoon or by washing. The sampler is then pushed downward from the bottom of the hole for a distance about 6 in. less than the length of the tube. Preferably, the sampler is forced down in one rapid continuous movement by means of a block-and-tackle arrangement using the casing to provide the reaction, or with the aid of a hydraulic jack. Driving with a hammer should be avoided. When the sampler has been forced down, the drill rods are rotated to shear the end of the sample, and the sampler is removed. The material at each end of the tube is carefully cleaned out for a short distance and smoothed so that metal disks can be inserted to protect the faces of the soil sample. Paraffin is then poured against the metal disks to form a seal.

Usually, after two samples have been recovered, the casing is advanced to within a few inches of the bottom of the hole and is cleaned out by a spoon or a water jet. The next two samples are then taken. By repeating this procedure, an almost continuous core record of the clay strata can be obtained. During all these processes the hole should remain filled with water. The casing should not be driven into the clay below a given level until the sampling operations have been carried out for at least the length of one sampling tube below this level. Otherwise, the sample consists not of relatively undisturbed soil but of material that has been forced into the casing. If the clay is very soft, it may squeeze into the hole left by the sampler so rapidly that casing must be driven before the next sample can be obtained. If the soil is fairly stiff, several samples can be taken in succession before additional casing is needed.

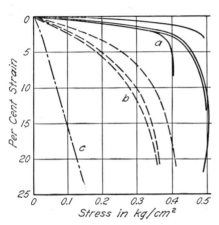

Fig. 118. Stress–strain curve obtained by means of unconfined compression tests on Chicago clay. (*a*) Undisturbed samples cut from bench in tunnel; (*b*) 2-in. tube samples of same clay; (*c*) completely remolded samples.

If tube samples have been taken on a given job, it is always desirable to investigate the extent to which the consistency of the clay has been affected by the sampling operations. However, such information can be obtained only at sites where the clay is exposed, either in open excavations or on the bottom of shafts. Several sampling tubes are pushed into the clay on the bottom of the excavation and are allowed to remain in the soil while a bench containing the tubes is cut in the clay. A large sample is then carefully carved from the bench, and finally the filled sampling tubes are recovered.

Investigations of this kind were carried out in clays of various consistencies in tunnels of the Chicago subway. The results of tests at one location are shown in Figure 118, in which the plain curves *a* represent the stress–strain relations obtained by means of unconfined compression tests on the hand-carved samples, and the dash curves *b* those on the tube samples. The dash–dotted curve c represents the relation for one of the samples completely remolded at unaltered water content. On the basis of the results of a great number of tests of this kind, it was concluded that the unconfined compressive strength of 2-in. tube samples of the clay was roughly equal to 75 per cent of that of the hand-cut samples, whereas complete remolding reduced the strength of the hand-cut samples to 30 per cent of its original value. On rare occasions the disturbance of 2-in. tube samples may be excessive, regardless of the care with which the sampling is done. Under these circumstances it may be necessary to resort to large-diameter samples.

Large-diameter samples from clay strata. If the exploratory borings indicate that the subsoil of a proposed structure contains a stratum of extrasensitive clay, or if the nature of the problem demands an exceptionally accurate settlement computation, undisturbed samples are required with a diameter of at least 4 in. Such samples can be carved from a bench in a test shaft, or they can be obtained from drill holes.

The process of securing large-diameter samples from drill holes is identical with that of taking 2-in. tube samples, but the sampling tool is somewhat more elaborate. It commonly consists of a thin cylindrical metal shell that receives the sample, and a heavy outer barrel provided at the lower end with a cutting shoe. When a sample has been recovered, the outer barrel is disassembled. The metal liner that contains the sample is sealed at both ends and shipped to the laboratory.[44.2]

Whatever type of sampler is used, a certain amount of disturbance of the soil is inevitable. Since the disturbance is greatest near the edges, the outer portion of the samples should be trimmed away before testing. The distortion of the layers in a stratified soil becomes visible when the sample is split lengthwise and allowed to dry very slowly. The silty and sandy layers reach the shrinkage limit and assume a light color while the plastic clay layers are still saturated and dark in color. At this stage of desiccation the stratification is very apparent.

The degree of disturbance depends on the manner in which the sampler is forced into the soil and on the dimensions of the sampler. The greatest disturbance is caused by driving the sampler into the soil by successive blows of a hammer, and the best results can be obtained if the sampler is pushed into the ground at a high and constant speed. For samples of a given diameter forced into the soil by the same process, the degree of disturbance depends on the area ratio,

$$A_r(\%) = 100 \frac{D_e^2 - D_i^2}{D_i^2}$$

in which D_e is the external diameter, and D_i the internal diameter of the sampler. For 2-in. thin-walled steel tubes A_r is about 10 per cent. It does not exceed 40 per cent in properly designed samplers for recovering 4-in. undisturbed samples. Figure 119a shows the upper end, and

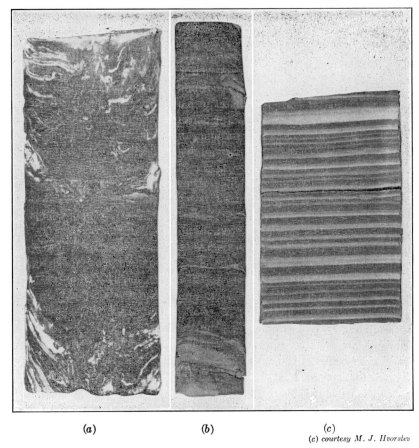

(a)   (b)   (c)
(c) courtesy M. J. Hvorslev

Fig. 119.   Photographs of soil specimens taken in 4-in. sampling spoons.   (a) Sample badly distorted owing to drilling ahead of casing before introducing sampler; (b) distorted sample obtained by driving poorly designed sampler into soil by blows of hammer; (c) excellent sample obtained by forcing well-designed sampler into soil by single rapid stroke.

Figure 119b the lower end of a 4-in. sample, 5 ft long, that was obtained by driving a very unsatisfactory sampler (area ratio 180 per cent) by the blows of a hammer into a stratified sedimentary clay. The violent disturbance of the upper part was caused by drilling 2 ft ahead of the casing before introduction of the sampler, so that the clay squeezed into the hole from all sides. Figure 119c shows an untrimmed specimen of laminated clay. The excellence of the sample is due to the use of a good technique and a well-designed sampler. The sampler had an area ratio of 40 per cent and a diameter of 4 in. It was forced rapidly into the clay by static pressure.

The effects of a given disturbance on the different physical properties of a clay are very different. They have been discussed in Part A.

In order to obtain a large-diameter undisturbed sample in an open excavation or tunnel, the clay around the location of the proposed sample is carefully carved away, leaving a block somewhat larger than the sample standing in the form of a pedestal. Soft clay is usually carved with the aid of a tightly drawn piano wire or a loop of thin strap steel. In stiffer materials a knife or spatula may be more suitable.

The container for the sample consists of a thin-walled metal can with no projecting lugs or rim. When the pedestal has been carved into a size several inches larger than the final dimensions of the sample, the container, with top removed, is inverted and placed on top of the pedestal. The pedestal is carefully trimmed to the diameter of the container, a few inches at a time. As carving proceeds, the container is forced down. When it is full, the pedestal is cut off below the can by means of the piano wire. The soil is trimmed flush with the end of the container, and any voids left between the sample and the container are filled by pouring paraffin around the periphery of the sample. Finally a metal top is placed on the container and sealed.

Undisturbed sand samples. A distinction must be made between sampling in sand above and below the water table. Above the water table the soil moisture imparts to the sand a trace of cohesion, Article 20. Samples of the slightly cohesive sand can be secured from drill holes by means of sampling spoons equipped with core catchers, Figure 115e, or from test shafts.

Samples obtained from drill holes contain all of the solid constituents of the sand in its natural state, but the permeability of sand is so great that the sampling operation is likely to cause a compaction of the material that enters the sampler. Hence, if the nature of the job requires information concerning the natural void ratio of the sand, satisfactory samples can be obtained only from shafts.

Before a sample is taken from a shaft, a bench is cut in the sand at the bottom. The surface of the sand is carefully leveled, and on it is placed a cylindrical metal shell with its axis in a vertical direction. The shell commonly has a diameter of 5 or 6 in. and a length of about 6 in. It consists of thin sheet steel. The shell is pushed gently into the sand for its full length so that it encases a cylinder of sand. The surrounding sand is trimmed away, and the top of the sample is sealed with a metal cap that fits over the shell. If the surface of the sample is not level with the top of the shell, the space is filled with paraffin before the cap is attached. A shovel is used to cut off the sample several inches below the shell, and the sample is inverted. The surplus sand is removed so that the surface now on top can also be sealed with a metal cap.

If samples are needed from below the water table, it is usually worth while to attempt to recover them by means of a sampling tool similar to that shown in Figure 115e. If this attempt fails, or if the job requires information concerning the natural void ratio of the sand, satisfactory samples can be obtained either by lowering the water table to a level below the base of the sand stratum and excavating a shaft in the drained sand, or else by sampling in large-diameter drill holes after transforming the sand below the drill hole into a cohesive material by one of the procedures described in the following paragraphs.

If a shaft is unwatered by pumping from a sump, the water that flows toward the sump is likely to loosen the structure of the sand, or, if the sand is already loose, the shaft may be invaded by a mixture of sand and water. Because of this fact, satisfactory results can be obtained only if the water table is lowered by pumping from well points, Article 21. The water level should be maintained several feet below the bottom of the shaft.

The transformation of water-bearing cohesionless sand below the bottom of a drill hole into a cohesive material has been accomplished by three different methods:

(a) Solidification of the sand by injection of asphalt emulsion. After solidification, a sample is taken from the injected sand. Until it is ready for testing, the sample can be handled like a cohesive material. The binder is then removed by a solvent.[44.3]

(b) Freezing the sand below the lower end of the casing, and taking a sample of the frozen material.

(c) Freezing the lower end of the sample, thus plugging the lower part of the sampling tube. The sampling tubes with freezing equipment have a diameter of 3 in., and the casing a diameter of 6 in. In order to take a sample, the sampler is gently forced into the soil ahead of the casing. The soil around the sampler is then removed by the cutting action of an annular auger combined with that of a water jet, and the casing is lowered at the same time by jetting. When the bottom of the casing reaches a level about 2 in. above that of the cutting edge of the sampler, the auger is replaced by an annular freezing chamber through which is pumped alcohol or acetone cooled by dry ice. After the lower end of the sample is frozen solid, the sampler is removed.[44.4]

All of these methods for sampling sand below the water table are rather expensive and require elaborate equipment. In the United States method *c* has been used almost exclusively. Fortunately, undisturbed samples of sand located below the water table are rarely needed except for finding out whether or not a stratum of very fine sand beneath the site of a proposed structure is excessively loose and unstable. Method *b* was developed and used in connection with the investigation of some of the notorious quicksand strata referred to in Article 17.

Undisturbed sample borings without casing.   The holes from which tube samples and most large-diameter samples are obtained are lined with casing. To avoid the necessity for casing, the walls of the holes can be plastered with a thin layer of cohesive material called *drilling mud*. The mud lining usually prevents the caving of the walls of those parts of the hole that are located in soil with little or no cohesion.

The drilling mud is introduced into the hole in suspension through a set of hollow drill rods. The core barrel is located within a larger barrel provided with cutting teeth on the lower end. While drilling proceeds, the outer barrel rotates. The drilling mud flows downward through the annular space between the two barrels. It escapes through the openings between the cutting teeth and rises between the outer barrel and the walls of the hole into the upper part of the drill hole.

This procedure is used extensively by the United States Army Engineers and the United States Bureau of Reclamation in combination with a sampling tool known as the *Denison sampler*. The sampler has a length of 24 in. and an inner diameter of 6 in. It contains a thin cylindrical lining within which the sample may be removed from the tool, and it is equipped with a spring core catcher similar to that shown in Figure 115e. While drilling proceeds, the sampler is pushed into the ground by means of jacks exerting a pressure between one and two tons. The jacks react against the drilling rig.[44.5]

Clay samples obtained by means of the Denison sampler are as satisfactory as those extracted by any other sampling tools for use in drill holes. Furthermore, the degree of disturbance of sand samples is usually, but not always, unimportant, because the sampler is pushed into the ground and not driven. However, when used in clean sand below the water table, the sampler may come out of the hole empty. Strata of gravel may interfere with the drilling operations to such an extent that the drill hole must be abandoned.

If successful, the drilling operations furnish a continuous set of 6-in. samples with very small gaps between them. However, these samples require much storage space and encourage large-scale soil testing at an expenditure of time and money that may be entirely out of proportion to the practical value of the results. Therefore, the instances are rather rare in which the hydraulic rotary method deserves preference over the ordinary methods of drilling and sampling.

Subsurface Soundings

Purpose of subsurface soundings. Subsurface soundings are made for exploring layers of soil with an erratic structure. They are also used to make sure that the subsoil does not contain exceptionally soft spots located between drill holes and to get information on the relative density of soils with little or no cohesion.

Experience shows that erratic soil profiles are far more common than regular ones. The results of test borings in subsoils with an erratic structure leave a dangerously wide margin for interpretation unless the spacing between drill holes is very small, and the cost of a set of closely spaced drill holes is likely to be prohibitive unless the area under investigation is also very small. However, significant changes in the character of the subsoil are commonly associated with a change in the resistance of the soil against the penetration of a pile or of a pipe equipped with a drive point.

The effect of the relative density of sand on the penetration resistance is well known to every engineer experienced in pile driving. If the sand is very dense, a pile cannot be driven deeper than 10 or 15 ft. Driving is very hard, and the number of blows per foot increases rapidly with depth. If the sand is very loose, cylindrical piles can be driven to any depth, and the increase of resistance with depth is small.

The variation of the penetration resistance of a soil along vertical lines can be determined rapidly at moderate expense by tests known as *subsurface soundings.* The tool used to make the tests is the *penetrometer.* Whereas the standard penetration test described on page 265 furnishes only one resistance value for about 5 ft of depth, subsurface soundings yield continuous or almost continuous penetration records.

Improvised sounding methods. For several generations engineers have made crude attempts to ascertain the consistency of the subsoil by driving rods, pipes, or railroad rails into the ground and recording the penetration produced by each blow of the drive weight. If this method is intelligently used in combination with at least a few exploratory borings, it can be very successful in spite of its simplicity. The following incident is an example.

The preliminary borings for a pile foundation disclosed an erratic deposit consisting principally of loose and medium sand with a few pockets of soft silt or clay. During construction of the foundation, it was noticed that the depth at which the piles met refusal varied between surprisingly wide limits. It was feared that the shorter piles might have met refusal in resistant deposits located above large pockets of soft silt or clay. To find out without undue loss of time whether or not this apprehension was justified, the sounding method was used. The only equipment available on short notice was a supply of 86-lb steel rails and a

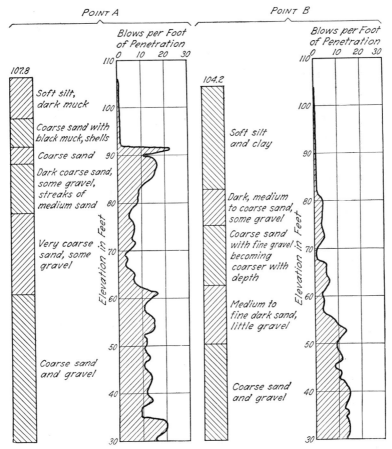

FIG. 120.   Penetration record for steel rails driven at two points 42 ft apart through soft silt and clay into coarse-grained glacial outwash, Port Alberni, Vancouver, British Columbia.

drop hammer weighing 2500 lb. The procedure consisted in driving the rails by dropping the hammer 30 in. per blow, and in recording the number of blows per foot of penetration. The soundings disclosed extremely erratic variations in the resistance of the soil against penetration of the rail. These variations are shown in Figure 120 which represents the records of two soundings 42 ft apart. By means of the soundings it was

possible to determine in a short time the boundaries of all the exceptionally soft pockets in the subsoil. After this information was secured,
a few exploratory drill holes were made where the softest pockets were

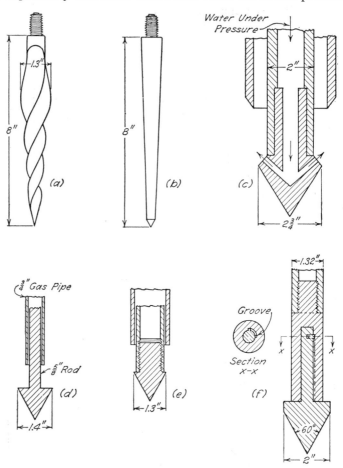

Fig. 121.   Penetrometers.   (*a*) Swedish penetrometer; (*b*) Danish penetrometer;
(*c*) wash-point penetrometer; (*d*) Dutch penetrometer; (*e*) Swiss penetrometer;
(*f*) conical drive point.

located. They showed that most of the pockets contained clean, well-
graded, but very loose sand instead of compressible silt or clay. The
variation in the lengths of the piles was due only to erratic and very
large variations in the density of the sand.

   If the sounding method is to be used to full advantage, the technique
must be adapted to the subsoil conditions. For this reason a great many

different procedures have been developed. They can be divided into two large groups, static and dynamic. In the static methods the sounding rod is pushed into the ground by static pressure. The dynamic methods consist of driving the rod by the impact of a drop hammer.

Static Sounding Methods. About 1917 the Swedish State Railways developed a sounding tool consisting of an auger-shaped point, Figure 121a, 8 in. long, with a maximum diameter of 1.3 in. It is attached to the

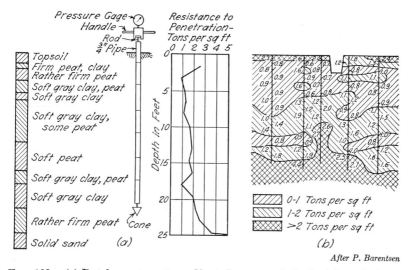

After P. Barentsen

Fig. 122. (a) Dutch penetrometer. Chart shows record obtained from single test hole; (b) soil profile along route of highway, showing variation in penetration resistance.

lower end of a solid stem. The device is used for obtaining information regarding the relative consistency of clay.[44.6] After the rod will sink into the clay no further under its own weight, it is loaded by increments up to 220 lb, and the penetration produced by each load increment is measured. Finally the rod, with all weights attached, is screwed into the ground, and the penetration for each 50 full turns is recorded.

A similar procedure has been used since about 1927 by the Danish Railways to estimate the depth to which foundation piles should be driven. However, the point forced into the ground has the shape of a slender truncated pyramid, as shown in Figure 121b.[44.7]

Figure 121d shows the point of a sounding device that has been used by the Department of Public Works of the Netherlands since about 1935. A 60° cone with a diameter of 1.4 in. is attached to the lower end of a $\frac{5}{8}$-in. rod surrounded by a $\frac{3}{4}$-in. gas pipe, Figure 122a. The cone is pushed 20 in. into the ground at a rate of 0.4 in. per sec by one or two men who apply part of their weight to a crossbar attached to the upper end of the rod. The pressure exerted on the rod is registered by a Bourdon gage built into the rod below the crossbar. After each downward stroke, the pipe is pushed down 20 in., and the stroke is repeated. The pressure exerted on the rod during each stroke is plotted against depth, Figure 122a. The individual penetration records furnish the data for constructing consistency profiles, Figure 122b. The procedure is used to obtain information concerning the bearing capacity of layers of soft clay and peat prior to the construction of road fills. One sounding to a depth of 40 ft requires about 15 min.[44.8]

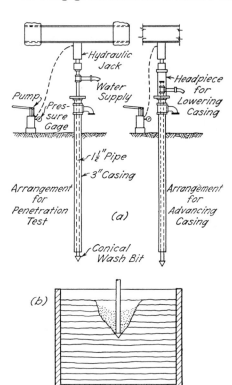

The penetration methods described in the preceding paragraphs are used chiefly in soft clay. The resistance of sand or other cohesionless soils against the static penetration of sounding rods with drive points is likely to depend not only on the relative density of the sand but also on the depth below the surface. To eliminate the influence of depth, a wash-point method was developed in 1928 for use on a subway job in New York. The subsoil consisted of clean medium-to-coarse sand. In the application of this method, a conical point, Figure 121c, with a diameter of $2\frac{3}{4}$ in. is attached to the lower end of a heavy wash pipe with an external diameter of 2 in. The pipe, with the cone attached, is introduced into a casing with an inner diameter of 3 in., Figure 123a. The cone is forced into the soil to a depth of 10 in. by means of a hydraulic jack acting on the upper end of the pipe. The water is then turned on. It leaves the cone

FIG. 123. (a) Penetration device for investigating relative density of sand; (b) sketch from photograph showing wash point at beginning of a downward stroke. In cone-shaped space above point, structure of sand was destroyed by jet action.

through holes pointing upward and transforms a cone-shaped body of soil, Figure 123*b*, located above the top of the conical point into a semiliquid. Part of the soil is washed out through the space between the wash pipe and the casing. While the water circulates, a slight push is sufficient to press the casing down through a distance equal to the preceding stroke of the cone. Then the water is turned off, and the conical point is again forced down through a distance of 10 in. The pressure exerted by the jack during each downward stroke of the cone is read on a Bourdon gage attached to the oil conduit of the jack and is plotted on a diagram as a function of the depth. By using this procedure on the job in New York, a great many soundings were made in a short time. The results of the observations were calibrated against the results of loading tests on bearing plates 1 ft square, resting on the bottom of an open shaft. The tests were made at different depths below the surface as the shaft was excavated. The results of the calibration tests are shown in Figure 124. During both the penetration and the loading tests the reaction for the jack was furnished by the base of the foundations of existing buildings.[44.9]

Dynamic Methods. The dynamic sounding methods consist of driving a rod with a drive point into the ground by means of a drop hammer and measuring the number of blows per foot of penetration. The diameter of the drive point is commonly close to 1.5 in., and the weight of the hammer ranges between 120 and 140 lb.

To drive the rod the Ohio State Highway Department uses a minia-ture pile driver operated by a two-cylinder motorcycle engine.[44.10] The sounding procedure serves chiefly to determine the depth to which the foundation piles for bridge piers and abutments should be driven.

In Switzerland a similar procedure is employed for exploring the subsoil for building foundations. The drive point has a diameter of about 1.3 in. When the soundings are made in soft ground the rod is surrounded by a casing with a diameter of about 1.7 in., Figure 121*e*, and the casing and the rod are alternately driven.[44.11]

Selection of method of sounding. No one sounding method is equally suitable under all the soil conditions that may be encountered in the field. This fact is indicated by the great variety of methods that have come into existence. The method must also be chosen in accordance with the type of information called for by the project. Whenever a new method is used, a certain amount of experimentation is required to adapt the procedure to local soil conditions.

The most common deposits with erratic structure are river or shore deposits consisting of lenses of silt or clay embedded in sand or sand and gravel with variable relative density. General information on the structure of such deposits can be obtained by driving a 1-in. extra-strong steel pipe with a 2-in. conical drive point, Figure 121f. The pipe is composed of 5-ft sections with flush joints. Each section of pipe weighs 11 lb.

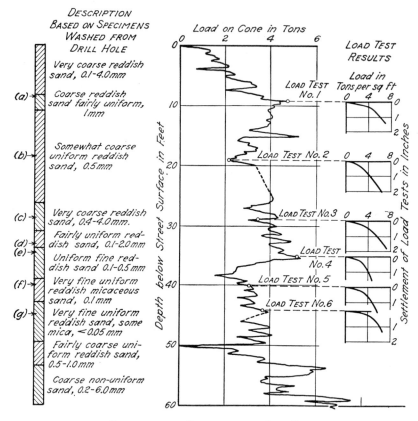

Fig. 124. Results of investigation of sand deposit at Houston Street subway, New York, by means of wash-point penetrometer and by means of load tests conducted in test shaft after penetration record was obtained.

Attached to the cone is a short stem fitting a $\frac{1}{2}$-in. hole in a plug that is screwed into the lower end of the string of pipes. The pipe is driven into the ground by means of a 160-lb drive weight that falls 30 in., and a record is kept of the number of blows per foot. Since the diameter of the cone is larger than that of the pipe, the side friction is likely to be small compared to the point resistance. After the pipe is driven to refusal, it is recovered whereas the drive point remains in the ground.

By means of such a simple penetrometer, several soundings per day can be made to a depth of 60 or 80 ft. Further increase of the output can be obtained by means of mechanically operated driving equipment with an automatic device for recording the penetration per blow.

GEOPHYSICAL METHODS

At the beginning of this article it was mentioned that various kinds of information regarding subsoil conditions can be obtained by means of geophysical methods, without the aid of borings or soundings.

Some of the geophysical methods are based on the fact that the geometry of every field of force depends on the location of the boundaries between the substances that occupy the field. The field of force may already exist, as for example the gravitational or the magnetic field of the earth, or it may be created artificially, for instance by sending an electric current through the ground located between two electrodes embedded in the ground.

The geometry of any field of force in a perfectly homogenous medium is independent of the physical properties of the medium. It is simple and can be determined accurately by theory. The distortion of the field produced by the existence of an internal boundary depends on those physical properties of the substances located on either side of the boundary that create the field or that have a decisive influence on its intensity. Hence the most suitable method for locating the boundary between two types of rock is determined by the type of field of force that will be distorted most conspicuously by the difference between the properties of these rocks. If their unit weights are very different, a gravitational method may be indicated. If their unit weights are almost equal, but their electric conductivities are very different, the electric potential method may be used to advantage.

To locate the position of an internal boundary the pattern of the real field of force at the surface of the ground is determined by suitable surface observations. This pattern is compared with the one determined by computation based on the assumption that the seat of the field is perfectly homogenous. The position of the internal boundary is ascertained on the basis of the difference between the real and the ideal patterns.

A second group of geophysical methods, known as seismic methods, is based on the fact that the rate of propagation of elastic waves is a function of the elastic constants of the media through which the waves travel. If a wave arrives at the boundary between two media with different elastic properties, part of it is reflected, and another part is refracted. In order to determine the position of an internal boundary, for instance between hard and soft rock or between soil and rock, a small charge of an explosive is fired at a short distance below the surface, and the time is measured at which the reflected or the refracted waves arrive at different points on the surface. On the basis of the results of the observations the position of the internal boundary can be computed, provided the boundary is well defined and not too uneven.

In connection with civil-engineering problems, only the electric potential and the seismic methods are successfully practiced. Their field of application is still limited to the location of the surface of the bedrock. If the thickness of the weathered top layer of the rock is small and the rock surface is not too uneven, the results are commonly reliable, and the cost of a geophysical survey of the bedrock topography is very much lower than that of a similar survey by boring. If the sedimentary overburden contains many boulders, the survey by boring may be almost impracticable, whereas the geophysical survey may be as simple and reliable as if the boulders did not exist.

The electric potential and the seismic methods have been successfully used for many years by various state highway departments and other public institutions engaged in design and construction. On private jobs the survey is commonly made by commercial firms, because such work requires elaborate equipment, and the interpretation of the results of the observations calls for considerable experience. Although the results of the survey of well-defined rock surfaces are commonly reliable, it is always necessary to investigate their degree of accuracy by means of a few check borings.[44.12]

Since about 1920 various attempts have been made in Germany to determine the properties of soils on the basis of their performance under the influence of periodic impulses produced by mechanically operated vibrators. The frequency of the vibrations can be regulated within wide limits. The investigations furnished valuable information regarding the effect of pulsating loads on settlement of foundations on cohesionless soils, Article 19, and the procedure has been successfully used for determining the degree of compaction of artificial fills. By combining the vibrator and seismic methods, it was even found possible under favorable conditions to determine the location of the boundary between soil strata with very different elastic properties, such as that between dense sand and soft clay. However, all these procedures are still in an experimental stage, and the theoretical principles on which they are based are somewhat controversial, since they involve assumptions that constitute radical simplifications of the elastic properties of the different members of the vibrating systems.

Pumping Tests

Pumping tests serve to determine the permeability of sand or gravel strata located below the water table without the performance of permeability tests in the laboratory. The principle of the method is illustrated by Figure 125.

Figure 125a is a vertical section through a sand stratum located between two relatively impervious strata. A well is drilled to the bottom

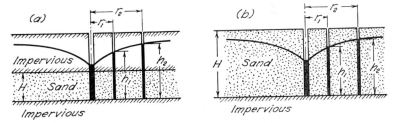

Fig. 125.   Diagram illustrating flow of water toward well during pumping test (a) if piezometric level lies above pervious layer; (b) if free water surface lies within pervious layer.

of the sand layer, and water is pumped from the well at a constant rate (cubic centimeters per second) until the water level in the well becomes almost stationary. Once this state has been established, the total flow across the boundary of any cylindrical section having a radius r is, according to equation 11.6,

$$Q = kiA = k_I \frac{dh}{dr} 2\pi r H$$

whence, by integration

$$\frac{2\pi H k_I}{Q} h_1 + C = \log_e r_1$$

and

$$\frac{2\pi H k_I}{Q} h_2 + C = \log_e r_2$$

Therefore, the coefficient of permeability k_I is

$$k_I = \frac{Q}{2\pi H (h_2 - h_1)} \log_e \frac{r_2}{r_1} \tag{44.1}$$

$$\frac{\pi k}{Q} h_1^2 + C = \log_e h_1$$

$$\frac{\pi k h_2^2}{Q} + C = \log_e h_2$$

If the free-water surface is located below the top of the sand stratum, as shown in Figure 125b, equation 11.6 leads to

$$Q = kiA = k_I \frac{dh}{dr} 2\pi rh \qquad N = h \, i$$

whence

$$\frac{Q\pi k}{Q} h \, dh = \frac{dr}{r}$$

$$k_I = \frac{Q}{\pi (h_2^2 - h_1^2)} \log_e \frac{r_2}{r_1} \qquad (44.2)$$

A pumping test requires the construction of one test well, commonly 10 or 12 in. in diameter, and at least eight observation wells located on two straight lines through the center of the mouth of the test well. One of these is located approximately in the direction of the ground-water flow, and the other at right angles to it. Details concerning the installation of the test wells, the layout and installation of the observation wells, and the testing procedure can be found in reference 44.13.

REFERENCES

44.1. H. A. MOHR, *Exploration of Soil Conditions and Sampling Operations*, Harvard University, Graduate School of Engineering, Soil Mechanics Series 21, third revised edition, Nov. 1943. Description of the most common methods of drilling and sampling supplemented by case records.

44.2. M. JUUL HVORSLEV, *The Present Status of the Art of Obtaining Undisturbed Samples of Soils*, Harvard University, Graduate School of Engineering, Soil Mechanics Series 14, Mar. 1940. Detailed description of sampling operations and sampling tools, and analysis of the factors that determine the degree of disturbance of the soil samples. This paper will be superseded by a report to be issued by the Soil Mechanics Division of the American Society of Civil Engineers.

44.3. J. P. VAN BRUGGEN, Sampling and Testing Undisturbed Sands from Boreholes, *Proc. Intern. Conf. Soil Mech.*, Cambridge, Mass. (1936), Vol I, pp 3–6. Description of asphalt emulsion method for undisturbed sampling in sand.

44.4. F. E. FAHLQUIST, New Methods and Technique in Subsurface Explorations, *J. Boston Soc. Civil Engrs.*, Vol 28 (1941), pp 144–160. Description of freezing method for undisturbed sampling in sand.

44.5. H. L. JOHNSON, Improved Sampler and Sampling Technique for Cohesionless Materials, *Civil Eng.*, Vol 10 (1940), pp 346–348. Description of the method of using the Denison sampler combined with the hydraulic rotary method of drilling.

44.6. Statens Järnvägars Geotekniska Commission, 1914–1922 (in Swedish), *Slutbetänkande*, 31. Maj 1922, Stockholm.

44.7. O. GODSKESEN, Investigation of the Bearing-Power of the Subsoil (especially moraine) with 25 × 25-mm Pointed Drill without Samples, *Proc. Intern. Conf. Soil Mech.*, Cambridge, Mass. (1936), Vol I, pp 311–314.

44.8. P. BARENTSEN, Short Description of a Field-Testing Method with Cone-Shaped Sounding Apparatus, *Proc. Intern. Conf. Soil Mech.*, Cambridge, Mass. (1936), Vol I, pp 7–10.

44.9. K. TERZAGHI, The Bearing Capacity of Pile Foundations (in German), *Bautechnik*, 1930, Heft 31 and 34. Description of wash-point penetrometer.

44.10. K. V. Taylor et al, The Predetermination of Piling Requirements for Bridge Foundations, *Ohio State Eng. Exp. Sta. Bull.* 90, July 1935.

44.11. R. Haefeli, Soil Mechanics in the Light of Snow Research (in German), *Mitt. Versuchsanst. Wasserbau, Eidgenöss. Polyt. Hochsch.*, Zürich, No. 7 (1944). Description of Swiss penetrometer, with examples for application.

44.12. C. A. Heiland, *Geophysical Exploration*, Prentice-Hall, New York, 1940.

44.13. L. K. Wenzel, Methods for Determining Permeability of Water-Bearing Materials, *Water Supply Paper* 887, pp 1–191. U. S. Department of the Interior, Washington, D. C., 1942. Pages 74 to 191 deal with the theory and practice of pumping tests.

ART. 45. PROGRAM FOR SUBSOIL EXPLORATION

Type and Sequence of Operations

Whatever the project may be, the engineer should never forget that most subsoils were formed by geological processes that changed at random in space and time. Because of the decisive influence of geological factors on the sequence, shape, and continuity of the soil strata, the first step in any subsoil exploration should always be an investigation of the general geological character of the site. The more clearly the geology of the site is understood, the more efficiently can the program for soil exploration be laid out. The second step is to make exploratory drill holes that furnish more specific information regarding the general character and the thickness of the individual strata. These two steps are obligatory. All others depend on the size of the job and the character of the soil profile.

On routine jobs, such as the design and construction of foundations for apartment houses of moderate size in districts with known foundation conditions, no further investigations are called for. The soil testing can be limited to the determination of the index properties (see Table 5, page 38) of spoon samples obtained from the exploratory borings. The test results serve to correlate the soils with others previously encountered on similar jobs. Hence, they make it possible to utilize past experience. The gaps in the information obtained from the exploratory drill holes are compensated by a liberal factor of safety. Wherever information can be obtained by inspection of existing structures in the vicinity, this opportunity should not be overlooked.

The soil exploration on large projects may call for the determination of one or several of the following: relative density of sand strata, permeability of sand strata, shearing resistance and bearing capacity of clay strata, or compressibility of clay strata. In every instance the program of the exploration should be prepared in accordance with the amount of useful information that can be derived from the results of laboratory tests. With increasing complexity of the soil profile the usefulness of elaborate soil investigations rapidly decreases. If the soil profile is erratic, the efforts should be concentrated not on obtaining accurate data regarding the physical properties of individual soil samples, but on obtaining reliable information regarding the structural pattern of the subsoil. Attempts to obtain this information by means of boring and testing are commonly wasteful, provided they are successful at all. Since erratic soil profiles are far more common than simple and regular ones, the instances are relatively rare in which elaborate and large-scale soil testing is justified from a practical point of view. In the following discussion of the means for obtaining reliable information concerning the subsoil conditions, the influence of the degree of complexity of the soil profile on the practical value of soil testing is consistently emphasized.

GEOLOGICAL CONSIDERATIONS

Most natural soil deposits represent one of the following principal types: river-channel deposits, flood-plain deposits, delta deposits, shore deposits, glacial deposits, wind-laid deposits (dune sand or loess), and deposits formed by sedimentation in standing water. The only ones likely to have a fairly regular structure are the flood-plain and wind-laid deposits and those formed in large bodies of standing water at a considerable distance from the shore. All the others are likely to be distinguished by important and erratic variations, at least in consistency or relative density, and usually in grain size as well.

In the upper reaches of river systems the *river-channel deposits* commonly occupy the bottoms of valleys carved out of rock. In the lower reaches they may be laid down in winding and interlaced channels eroded out of the broad sheet of fine-grained sediments that have previously been deposited by the river under different conditions of sedimentation. The average grain size decreases with increasing distance from the source, and at any one point it is likely to increase in a general way with increasing depth below the surface. However, the details of stratification are always erratic, and both grain size and relative density vary in an unpredictable manner. Still more abrupt and conspicuous are the variations in the so-called *glacial outwash* deposited by the melt waters along the rim of the continental ice sheets. The variations in the relative density of a fluvioglacial sand stratum are illustrated in Figure 124, and those of a fluvioglacial sand and gravel stratum capped by a blanket of soft silt in Figure 120.

Flood-plain deposits are laid down during the high-water season on both sides of the lower courses of rivers. They commonly consist of continuous layers of silt or clay of fairly uniform thickness, separated from each other by equally persistent layers of coarser sediments. However, at any point or line the continuity of these strata can be broken by bodies of other sediments occupying troughs or abandoned river channels. If such a body is located between two drill holes, its presence may escape attention. Several well-known foundation accidents were due to this cause.

Delta deposits are formed at the points where water courses enter bodies of standing water. The main features of deltas are simple but the details of their structure can be very complex, as shown in Figure 126, because the currents which transport the sediments shift continually.

Shore deposits are composed of sediments that were eroded by waves or carried into a body of standing water by rivers and transported and deposited by shore currents. They commonly consist of sand and gravel. However, as a result of important fluctuations in the lake or sea level combined with the shifting of the water courses which cross the coastal belt, the sand and gravel deposits may alternate in an intricate manner with layers or pockets of silt, clay, or peat. Shore deposits of this kind are referred to as *composite shore deposits*. Figure 122b and the upper half of Figure 113 illustrate the structure of deposits of this type.

The constituents of *glacial deposits* were picked up and transported by ice and laid down when the ice melted. The wasting away of ice sheets always alternates with periods of temporary growth and advancement. The advancing ice plows up or deforms previously deposited layers of glacial material. Furthermore, at the ice rim random sorting and shifting are carried on by the streams of water that emerge from beneath the ice. Hence, glacial deposits are among the most erratic with which the engineer has to deal. Irregular pockets and lenses of fine- and coarse-grained materials intermingled with boulders may follow each other in a chaotic manner.

In contrast to glacial deposits, *wind-laid sediments* invariably are remarkably uniform. However, the shape of their boundaries may be very irregular, because the wind may drop its burden in irregular heaps on very uneven surfaces. Furthermore, the fine-grained varieties known as loess (see Article 2) may completely lose their original homogeneity on account of local leaching or weathering. Many faulty foundations on loess have been caused by the failure of the designers to recognize the existence of these partial alterations.

The various transporting agencies, running water, ice, and wind, deposit only part of their solid burden on their way or at the end of their path. The remainder is carried into large bodies of standing water such as lakes, bays, or the open ocean. Once they get beyond the narrow zone in which the shore currents travel, they are acted on by no force other than gravity. Therefore, in contrast to all other sedimentary deposits, those which are formed in large bodies of standing water commonly have a relatively simple structure. This structure reflects merely the periodic or progressive changes in the character of the material that

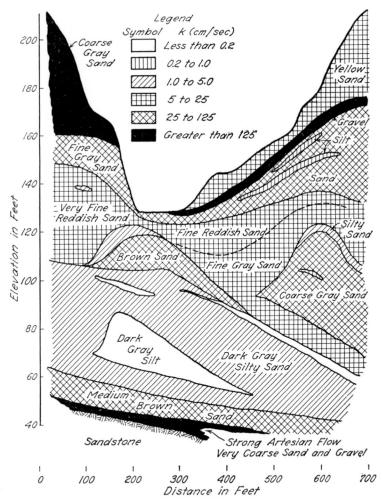

Fig. 126. Permeability profile of relatively homogeneous glacial delta deposit near Chicopee, Mass.

enters the region of sedimentation. It is also influenced to some extent by the chemical composition of the water.

The effect of the seasonal changes in the character of the suspended material is disclosed by the water-content diagram, Figure 112b. On account of this effect, the scattering of the water content from the average is as important for vertical distances as small as a few inches as it is for the entire depth. Still more conspicuous is the effect of seasonal changes on the structure of sediments that were laid down in fresh-water lakes under arctic conditions such as those which prevailed in the northern United States and in Canada during the ice age. In the summertime, the suspended material in the offshore parts of the lakes consisted of silt and clay, because the coarser materials such as sand and gravel had already been laid down at the mouths of the rivers, building up delta deposits. The silt particles settled out during the summer. During the winter, however, no new material was carried into the lakes because the rivers were completely frozen. Hence, beneath the ice crust, only clay particles which did not settle during the summer were deposited. Therefore, the sediment is composed of light-colored summer layers consisting of silt, and dark-colored winter layers consisting chiefly of clay. Each double layer represents the deposit of one year. These deposits are the varved clays, Figure 119c, mentioned in Article 2. The thickness of the double layers is commonly less than 1 in., but exceptionally as much as several feet. It depends on the amount of material washed into the lake during the summer season. Deposits of such clay are very common in both North America and Europe north of the 40th parallel. They are a prolific source of serious construction difficulties.

If similar arctic rivers enter a bay of the ocean instead of a fresh-water lake, the segregation according to particle size is much less perfect because the salts contained in the sea water cause flocculation of the clay particles. As a consequence, most of the clay is deposited simultaneously with the silt. In some localities, such as several sections of the shore districts in the Great Lakes region, the fine-grained glacial sediments seem to have dropped out of the melting ice which floated on the lakes toward the end of the last period of glaciation. The resulting clay strata are among the most homogeneous in existence. Figure 127 refers to such a deposit.

The preceding review has shown that nature created an infinite variety of structural patterns ranging from the simple stratification of offshore deposits formed in large lakes to the utterly complex structure of masses of gravel, sand, and silt that were laid down, plowed up, distorted, locally eroded, and redeposited along the rim of a continental ice sheet. If borings are made in a mass of soil at two points 100 or 200 ft apart, the engineer knows the character and the sequence of the strata along two vertical lines. Between these two lines the strata may be continuous. However, they may also wedge out at a short distance from each line, and the sequence of strata halfway between the two borings may not have the remotest resemblance to that at either one. An intelligent program for supplementary soil investigations can be prepared only by an engineer who is thoroughly familiar with the elements of physical geology and with the geology of the region in which the site is located.

A description of the geological history of the subsoil of large cities can usually be found in the publications of the local museum of natural

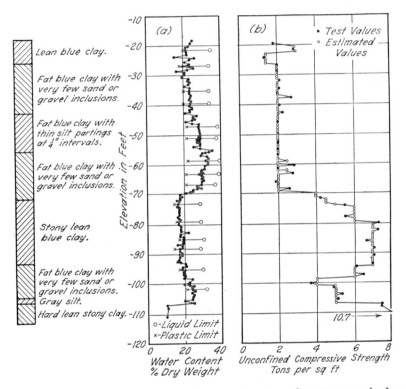

FIG. 127. Results of water-content and compressive strength tests on samples from tube-sample boring in moderately precompressed glacial clay in Cleveland, Ohio.

history or of some similar institution. If the job is located in the open country, it is advisable to find out whether or not a geological study of the region has been made. References should be looked for in the following bibliographies:

Geologic Literature on North America, bibliographic bulletins of the U. S. Geological Survey, published every two years. Cumulative bibliographies are available for the years 1785–1918 and 1919–1928.

Bibliography and Index of Geology Exclusive of North America, published annually since 1930 by the Geological Society of America.

Catalogue of Published Bibliographies in Geology 1896–1920, Bulletin National Research Council, Vol 6, Pt 5, No. 36, 1923.

R. F. LEGGET, Geological Surveys of the English Speaking World, Appendix B in *Geology and Engineering*, New York, 1939. Contains brief discussions of the geological surveys of North America and the British Empire, and their publications.

R. F. LEGGET, Geological Societies and Periodicals, Appendix C in *Geology and Engineering*.

P. C. PUTNAM, *Guide to the Literature of Geology and Kindred Subjects*, mimeographed. Copy in library of Department of Mineralogy and Petrography, Harvard University.

Geologic maps and brief descriptions of a few regions have been published in the Folios of the U. S. Geological Survey. Descriptions and maps of many other regions are scattered throughout the periodical literature. These are listed in the bibliographic bulletins of the U. S. Geological Survey.

A large amount of useful information regarding regional geology is given in the *Water Supply Papers* published from time to time since 1896 by the U. S. Geological Survey.

If no specific information regarding the geology of the site of the job is available, the engineer must rely on his own capacities for geological observation and interpretation. On large projects a detailed geological survey of the site and its vicinity is imperative. It calls for the services of a professional geologist.

SPACING AND DEPTH OF EXPLORATORY BORINGS

At the present time the spacing between exploratory drill holes is still governed primarily by convention and not by rational considerations. On building sites the borings are commonly spaced at about 50 ft in both principal directions. On subway or earth-dam projects a spacing of 100 ft is generally considered the minimum. However, if the line is very long or the site very large, it may be necessary to increase the spacing to 200 ft. Even at that spacing the required amount of drilling and testing may be very large, and it may cause undesirable delays in starting construction on the project.

The standardization of the spacing of exploratory drill holes has obvious disadvantages. If the soil profile is very simple, the customary spacing is too small, whereas, if the profile is erratic, the spacing is excessive. In order to avoid the loss of time and money due to drilling superfluous bore holes, the method of subsurface soundings can often be used to advantage. A sounding, which is cheaper and more expedient than a drill hole, may be made at each point where the conventional regulations call for a drill hole. If all the penetration diagrams are similar to each other, the soil profile is likely to be simple. Exploratory drill holes are required only near those few points where the penetration diagrams indicate maximum deviations from the statistical average. If the geology of the site involves the possibility that the continuity of the strata may be disrupted locally by channel fillings or other bodies of foreign material, supplementary soundings should be made wherever there is any surface indication of the presence of a compressible inclusion, such as a shallow depression on the surface of the ground. If a sounding strikes such an inclusion, an exploratory drill hole should be made near by to determine the type of soil of which the inclusion consists.

If the penetration diagrams obtained from the exploratory soundings are consistently very different, the soil profile is likely to be erratic, and intermediate soundings should be made until the penetration data are complete enough to leave no doubt concerning the general shape and trend of the boundaries between the fine-grained and coarse-grained, and the loose and dense parts of the deposit. Yet, no more drill holes are required than those few needed to determine the types of soil located between the different surfaces of discontinuity or to find out whether a body of exceptionally resistant or nonresistant soil consists of sand or clay. Such a question arose when the sounding shown on the right-hand side of Figure 120 was made. It was doubtful whether the soil between El. 80 and 60 consisted of very loose sand or of clay. To answer this question a boring was made next to the line of sounding. The boring record left no doubt that there was no clay below El. 80. The low resistance to penetration within this range of depth was due exclusively to the exceptionally loose structure of the sand.

The depth to which exploratory drill holes should be made is likewise more or less standardized. This practice is not only wasteful but also dangerous. Many buildings have been seriously damaged by settlement due to the consolidation of soft clay strata located below the depth to which the subsoil was explored. Yet, no general rules can be established for selecting this depth, because for a given weight and given dimensions of a structure the depth at which the seat of settlement is located depends to a large extent on the soil profile. The following paragraphs illustrate the factors that should be considered before the depth of the drill holes is specified.

If it is certain for geological reasons or from the results of previous borings in the vicinity that the subsoil of a group of buildings does not contain any strata of clay or soft silt, it is sufficient to explore the subsoil at the site of each building to a depth between 20 to 30 ft below subgrade, depending on the size and weight of the building. The size of the area occupied by the group does not require any consideration because each building settles almost as if the others did not exist. This is due to the fact that the compressibility of sand strata decreases rapidly with increasing depth, Article 18.

On the other hand, if the subsoil of a group of buildings contains soft strata, the seat of settlement may be located at a depth greater than the width of the entire area occupied by the buildings because, even at a depth of 150 or 200 ft, a moderate increase of the pressure on a thick stratum of soft clay may produce a settlement of more than 1 ft, Article 55. Hence, the depth to which the subsoil should be explored depends primarily on the absence or presence of compressible strata such as clay or plastic silt.

If the geology of the site indicates that clay or silt strata may be located at great depth below the surface, or if nothing whatsoever is known concerning the subsoil conditions, a rough estimate should be made of the intensity and distribution of the pressures that will be produced in the subsoil by the proposed group of buildings. The procedure has been described in Article 35. On the basis of this estimate, the greatest depth D_{max} can be evaluated at which the presence of a thick layer of soft clay with a high liquid limit may still have a significant influence on settlement. The first drill hole should be made to this depth. All the other borings and subsoil soundings can be discontinued at a depth of about 10 ft below the base of the lowest clay stratum that was encountered within the depth D_{max}. This procedure should be followed, regardless of whether the character of the upper soil strata may call for a footing, raft, or pile foundation.

The following example illustrates the possible consequences of disregarding the recommended procedure. A group of factory buildings was constructed on a tidal flat. None of the buildings was more than 40 ft wide. The subsoil was explored by borings to a depth of 90 ft. Within this depth there was a gradual transition from soft silt near the surface to sand with variable density at a depth of more than 65 ft. Because of the high compressibility of the top strata it was decided to support the buildings on piles 70 to 90 ft long. To the surprise of the engineers in charge of the job, the buildings started to settle during construction, and in the course of three years the settlement increased to more than 2 ft. Subsequent soil investigations showed that the settlement was due to the consolidation of a stratum of soft clay 30 ft thick, located at a depth of about 115 ft below yard level.

If bedrock is encountered within the depth D_{max}, the topography of the rock surface must be determined at least approximately by sounding or boring, because the depressions in the rock surface may be filled with very compressible sediments that are encountered in only the deepest drill holes. The omission of this precaution also has repeatedly been the cause of important settlement.

The results of the exploratory borings and subsurface soundings should be assembled in a report containing all the information that was secured concerning the geology of the site, a list of the index properties of all the spoon samples that were taken, and a record of the results of the standard penetration tests. On the basis of this report it can be decided whether or not supplementary investigations are required concerning the relative density and permeability of the sand strata and the shearing resistance and compressibility of the clay strata.

RELATIVE DENSITY OF SAND STRATA

The relative density of sand strata has a decisive influence on the angle of internal friction of the sand, Article 15; on the ultimate bearing capacity, Article 29; and on the settlement of footings resting on the sand.

TABLE 10

RELATIVE DENSITY OF SANDS
ACCORDING TO
RESULTS OF STANDARD PENETRATION TEST

No. of Blows N	Relative Density
0–4	Very loose
4–10	Loose
10–30	Medium
30–50	Dense
Over 50	Very dense

If a submerged sand is very loose, a sudden shock may transform it temporarily into a sand suspension with the properties of a thick viscous liquid, Article 17. In a dense state the same sand is insensitive to shock and is perfectly suitable as a base for even very heavy structures. For this reason the relative density of a sand is far more important than any of its other properties, except possibly its permeability.

While the exploratory borings are being made, some information regarding the relative density of the sand strata encountered in the drill holes can be obtained by performing the standard penetration test (page 265) whenever a spoon sample is taken. Considering the outstanding importance of the relative density, the standard penetration test should be considered an essential part of the boring operation. Table 10 gives the approximate relation between the number of blows N and the relative density.

In any sand with grain size intermediate between coarse and fine, the value of N is not significantly different above and below the water table unless the relative density also differs. However, in very fine or silty sand having an effective grain size between 0.1 and 0.05 mm, the number of blows per foot on the sampling spoon may change at the upper boundary of the zone of complete saturation. If the sand is loose, the number decreases below this boundary; if it is dense, it increases very considerably. This is due to the relatively low permeability of these soils. Because the permeability is low, the shearing resistance of the soil, which opposes the penetration of the sampling spoon, is approximately equal to the consolidated-quick value. This value of the shearing resistance varies much more with the relative density than does the slow shear value, Article 15.

On account of the abnormally high penetration resistance of a moderately dense very fine or silty sand below the water table, the relative density of such a material may be overestimated. Hence, in such soils the standard penetration test should be supplemented by more reliable procedures such as loading tests on the bottom of large-diameter drill holes.

On important jobs the information obtained from the standard penetration tests concerning the relative density of the sand should be supplemented by subsurface soundings. These soundings furnish continuous records, such as those shown in Figures 120 and 124, of the variations of the penetration resistance with depth. However, the resistance against the penetration of a penetrometer into sand, or the energy required to produce a given penetration, depends not only on the relative density of the sand but also on the dimensions of the drive point and the stem and to some extent on the shape of the grains and the grain-size distribution. Hence, every new method of subsurface sounding and every use of the method in an unexplored locality call for a set of calibration tests that furnish the data for interpreting the penetration records.

A rough calibration can be achieved by making a subsurface sounding next to a drill hole in which standard penetration tests were performed. More cumbersome but also more reliable are surface load tests at different depths below a point close to the location of a subsurface sounding. The tests are made on a bearing plate 1 ft square, resting on a horizontal surface of the sand. No backfill or surcharge is placed within 3 ft of the plate. The relation between load and settlement for such tests on several different sands is shown in Figure 128a. Curves 1 and 2 were obtained from tests on very dense sand, curve 4 on sand of medium density, and curve 5 on loose sand. With increasing relative density the bearing capacity increases rapidly, and the settlement under a given load decreases. Figure 128a shows, in accordance with field experience and in contrast to a widespread opinion, that the grain size has no influence on the relative density and bearing capacity of a sand.

On the right-hand side of Figure 124 are shown the results of load tests made for the purpose of calibrating the wash-point penetrometer, Figure 121c. The procedure was described on page 278.

On the basis of the results of standard load tests, such as those shown in Figure 128a, the relative density of the sand can be determined by

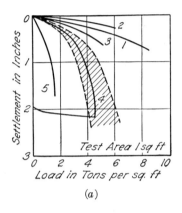
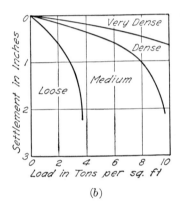

Fig. 128. (a) Relation between load and settlement of bearing plate 1 ft square resting on the surface of a sand. Curve 1 represents dense clean fine sand in caisson 26 ft below river bottom; 2 represents very dense very fine sand in open excavation 26 ft below ground surface in Lynn, Mass; 3 represents damp sand of medium density hand-compacted by tamping in layers; 4 represents medium-dense sand at bottom of shaft 30 ft deep in Houston Street, New York. Shaded area indicates range for curves obtained between depths of 20 and 60 ft; 5 represents loose, coarse, clean, and very sharp sand at bottom of open excavation near Muskegon, Mich; (b) chart for estimating relative density of sand on basis of results of standard load test on bearing plate 1 ft square.

means of the diagram, Figure 128b. For this purpose the curves obtained from the calibration tests are introduced into the diagram. Each curve corresponds to a definite penetrometer reading. The position of the curve with reference to the boundaries shown in the figure indicates the relative density of the sand penetrated by the drive point.

Still more accurate information regarding the relative density of sand strata can be obtained by laboratory tests on undisturbed samples secured by means of the freezing or asphalt injection method, Article 44. All the sample borings are made near points at which subsurface soundings were previously performed. By correlating the test results with the corresponding resistances to penetration, the data are obtained for accurate interpretation of the results of all the other subsurface soundings. However, the instances are very rare in which such refinements are warranted.

Permeability of Sand Strata

Reliable information on the permeability of sand strata may be required for either of two purposes. It may be necessary to estimate the quantity of water that will flow toward an excavation with specified dimensions, at a given position of the water table. Or it may be required to determine the depth to which the cutoff beneath a dam on a permeable foundation must be made in order to reduce the seepage losses from the reservoir to less than a specified amount.

The data for estimating the flow of water toward an excavation are obtained most conveniently by means of pumping tests, Article 44. The results of the tests make it possible to compute the average coefficient of permeability of the subsoil in horizontal directions. Once this coefficient is known, all the problems concerning the flow of water toward the proposed excavation can be solved on the basis of the laws of hydraulics. If the project calls for lowering the water table by means of filter wells, Article 47, the well system can be laid out, and an estimate can be made of the capacity of the pumps required for maintaining the water table below the bottom of the excavation during construction.

In order to solve cutoff and seepage problems, it is necessary to determine not only the average permeability of the subsoil but also the major variations of the permeability within the sand strata located beneath and beside the water-retaining structure. This can be done only by means of permeability tests on fairly continuous series of samples obtained from a considerable number of drill holes. Actual performance of the tests on all the samples shipped to the laboratory may be prohibitive. However, after a laboratory technician has made 15 or 20 permeability tests on samples from a given stratum, he should be able to estimate the coefficient of permeability of the others on the basis of their texture and general appearance. Once the technician is familiar with the material, no more than occasional check tests are required.

The samples are obtained from 4-in. to 6-in. drill holes by means of a sampling spoon equipped with a core catcher, Figure 115e. Before testing, each sample should be remolded because the rate of flow through undisturbed samples at right angles to the bedding planes depends not on the average permeability of the sample but on that of its least permeable constituents. The relative density of the remolded sample is likely to be different from that of the sand *in situ*. Furthermore, the temperature in the laboratory is likely to be higher than that of the ground water. Hence, when an estimate is made of the k-value of natural sand strata, the effect of the differences in temperature and relative density must be considered. The required information is contained in Article 11.

On account of the technical difficulties associated with sampling operations in cohesionless material, it is almost inevitable that some parts of the sand strata will not yield any samples at all. The gaps in the cores may be the source of important errors in the evaluation of the permeability of the stratum. The process of remolding the samples in the laboratory introduces a further error into the estimate. Hence, if part of the sand stratum is located below the water table, the results of the laboratory investigations should be checked by those of a pumping test. If the discrepancies are large, the laboratory value of the coefficient of permeability should be corrected.

Various attempts have been made to evaluate the permeability of sand strata located above the water table on the basis of the quantity of water that percolates out of drill holes into the adjoining soil through the openings in a perforated casing. This method is not recommended because the formation of a filter skin at the entrance surface can hardly be avoided.

The results of the permeability tests and estimates are represented in permeability diagrams such as that shown in Figure 126.[45.1, 45.2]

In Article 11 it was pointed out that the average coefficient of permeability k_{II} of natural soil strata in directions at right angles to the bedding planes is always smaller and commonly very much smaller than the corresponding coefficient k_I in directions parallel to these planes. The results of both pumping and permeability tests furnish information only about k_I. An estimate of k_{II} is necessarily based on the assumption that the permeability of the sand stratum is the same at every point on any plane parallel to the bedding planes. This assumption is very seldom justified. For this reason, it is not even admissible to estimate the ratio k_I/k_{II} on the basis of the results of two sets of permeability tests, in one of which the water percolates through the samples parallel to the stratification and in the other at right angles to it. Furthermore, the cores are never perfectly continuous. A single seam of silt located between two adjoining samples of sand eliminates the validity of the computation of k_{II}. The occurrence of such seams is not uncommon (see Figure 129).

The only method which, under favorable conditions, permits the evaluation of k_I/k_{II} is to lower the water table by pumping from several wells under a large area, to construct a flow net on the basis of the results of piezometer readings at a great number of points within the mass of sand through which the water percolates toward the wells, and to compare this empirical flow net with a theoretical one constructed on the assumption that $k_I/k_{II} = 1.$[45.3] This method is based on the same principle as that of constructing the flow net for a stratified sand deposit with a known value of the ratio k_I/k_{II} (see Article 39). Under normal

Fig. 129.   Silt seams in medium uniform sand.   The presence of the seams could not be detected by ordinary test borings.   Yet they reduce the permeability of the sand stratum in a vertical direction to a small fraction of that in horizontal directions.

circumstances this method is very expensive and cumbersome. Fortunately, accurate information concerning the value of k_I/k_{II} is seldom required.

Shearing Resistance of Soft Clay Strata

If a project involving clay soils calls for an investigation of the stability of slopes, the computation of the lateral pressure against the bracing of open cuts, or an estimate of the ultimate bearing capacity of footings or rafts, the shearing resistance of the clay must be determined. In Article 15 it is shown that the shearing resistance of clay under field conditions is roughly equal to one-half the unconfined compressive strength q_u of tube samples obtained by means of thin-walled sampling tubes that are pushed rapidly into the soil. The compressive strength of homogeneous clay strata commonly increases to some extent with the depth below the surface, but there are many exceptions to this rule.

During the drilling of the exploratory holes the shearing resistance of the clay can be crudely estimated on the basis of the record of the standard penetration test. Table 11 shows the approximate relation between the unconfined compressive strength and the number of blows per foot of penetration of the sampling spoon. However, at a given number N of blows per foot, the scattering of the corresponding values of q_u from the average is very large. Therefore, compression tests should

TABLE 11

RELATION OF CONSISTENCY OF CLAY, NUMBER OF BLOWS N
ON SAMPLING SPOON, AND UNCONFINED COMPRESSIVE STRENGTH

q_u in tons per sq ft

Consistency	Very Soft	Soft	Medium	Stiff	Very Stiff	Hard
N	<2	2–4	4–8	8–15	15–30	>30
q_u	<0.25	0.25–0.50	0.50–1.00	1.00–2.00	2.00–4.00	>4.00

always be made on the spoon samples. The other routine tests on the spoon samples, listed in Table 5, are also obligatory because their results are required for correlating the clay with others previously encountered on similar jobs. The values of q_u obtained by means of compression tests are likely to be somewhat too low because spoon samples are appreciably disturbed. The supplementary investigations required on important jobs depend on the character of the soil profile.

If the soil profile is simple and regular, it is commonly possible to evaluate the average shearing resistance of the clay strata on the basis of the results of laboratory tests. The samples are secured by means of tube sample borings, Article 44, which furnish continuous 2-in. cores. To obtain fairly reliable average values, the spacing between the sample borings should not exceed 100 ft. If it is known in advance that the soil profile is fairly regular and that tube sample borings will be required, continuous samples are taken in all those sections of the exploratory holes that are located within clay strata. In the sections located between clay strata spoon samples are extracted, and standard penetration tests are made. This combination is practicable because the tube-sampling procedure does not require a larger casing than that with which the walls of the exploratory drill holes are lined.

The samples are delivered at the laboratory in sealed tubes. Preferably, all the clay samples from one hole should be tested in the sequence in which they followed each other in the drill hole in a downward direction. The sampling tubes are commonly 30 or 36 in. long. They are cut into

6-in. sections with a hack saw, a band saw, or a motor-driven abrasive disk. The soil itself is cut by means of a wire saw. The sample is then ejected from its container by means of a close-fitting plunger.

If the uppermost clay-core section appears to be relatively undisturbed, it is submitted to an unconfined compression test first in its natural state and then in a completely remolded state at the same water content. The ratio between the two values of the compressive strength is a measure of the sensitivity of the clay, Article 8. After the test the sample is divided lengthwise into two parts. One half is used for a water-content determination, and the other is stored in a jar with an airtight cover. The same set of tests is made during subsequent operations whenever a sample is encountered that differs noticeably from its predecessor in consistency, color, or general appearance. A change in consistency is revealed by a noticeable change of the resistance of the clay to deformation between the fingers. The uppermost samples in each tube may be appreciably more disturbed than the others. If this is the case, the compression tests should be performed on one of the other less disturbed samples.

The samples following the first one are split lengthwise. One entire half is used for a water-content determination. The other half should be set aside in a fairly humid atmosphere with its plane surface facing upward, whereupon it starts to dry slowly. At an intermediate state of desiccation the details of stratification become clearly visible. At that state a record should be made of the details of stratification, indicating the color and approximate thickness of the individual layers, the degree of perfection of the stratification, and other visible features. The records are later used for preparing a general description of the characteristics of the stratification of the clay. A few representative specimens are photographed.

The following 6-in. sections are also used only for water-content determination and visual inspection. If the experimenter tests five or six samples in this manner without noticing a conspicuous change, the next section is submitted to an unconfined compression test in its natural state, as well as to the water-content determination. This procedure is continued until a sample is encountered that differs materially from its predecessor. This sample is submitted to the same tests as the very first one, whereupon the routine procedure is resumed.

After all the tests on samples from one drill hole have been made, the Atterberg limits are determined on representative specimens of those samples that were submitted to compression tests in both the natural and remolded states. The results of the tests are represented in diagrams such as that shown in Figure 127. The diagrams should be accompanied by a brief description of the stratification characteristics of the clay (not shown in the figure).

If the investigation is made for the purpose of estimating the factor of safety of slopes with respect to sliding or of fills with respect to spreading, the knowledge of the details of stratification is at least as important as that of the strength of the clay, because the major part of the potential surface of sliding is located in one or more seams of fine sand or coarse silt and not in the clay. In such instances a detailed and well-illustrated description of the characteristics of the stratification should be prepared. A few typical samples of the stratified layers should be set aside for further investigation. This investigation consists of determining the natural water content and the Atterberg limits of each of the layers of which the sample is composed. Figure 130 shows the results of such an investigation.

In any event the opportunity should be sought to investigate the degree of disturbance of the tube samples as described in Article 44.

All the preceding discussions referred to the investigation of fairly homogeneous clay strata. If the clay strata contained in the subsoil have a variable thickness and consistency, the method of investigation must be modified. Instead of concentrating on soil tests, the engineer should make efforts to investigate the topography of the upper and lower boundaries of the clay layers and to locate the softest and hardest parts of the layers. The most expedient method to get this information is to make numerous subsurface soundings supplemented by exploratory drill holes. After the results of these investigations are assembled, two or three tube-sample borings are made. These borings should be located at the best and the worst spots of the site. Within the bodies of soil located between the clay strata, spoon samples are taken and standard penetration tests are made, whereas within the clay strata continuous tube samples are secured. Figure 131 represents a boring of this type. The boring was made in a composite shore deposit located on one of the slopes of a drowned valley. On the left side is shown an abstract of the foreman's record. The first diagram is the penetration record of a subsurface sounding made a few feet from the drill hole. The last two diagrams contain the results of the soil tests.

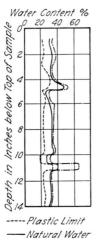

Water Content %

----- Plastic Limit

——— Natural Water Content

—·— Liquid Limit

After A. Casagrande

Fig. 130.   Diagram showing variations of index properties within a 1-ft layer of a soft glacial clay.

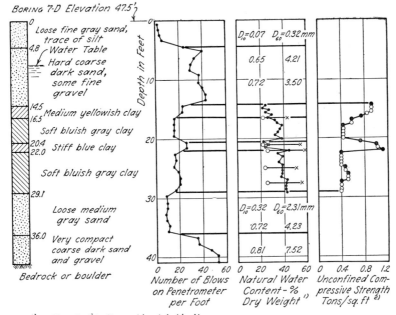

FIG. 131.   Diagram representing boring record, penetration record, and results of soil tests on samples from drill hole through composite shore deposit.

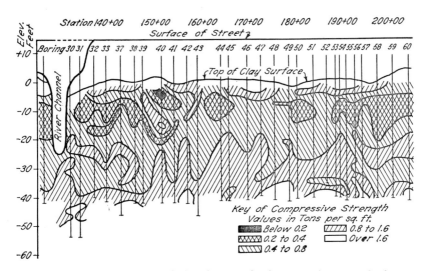

FIG. 132.   Diagram showing variations in unconfined compressive strength of somewhat erratic glacial clay deposit in Chicago.

Figure 132 represents the results of a survey of the unconfined compressive strength of a glacial clay deposit intermediate between regular and erratic. The individual clay strata were not homogeneous enough to justify assigning definite average values to their physical properties. Yet the project called for general information concerning the compressive strength of the clay and its variations in both horizontal and vertical directions. To satisfy these demands tube sample borings were made at points 200 ft apart, and the cores obtained from these borings were submitted to the same tests that are made on continuous cores from homogeneous strata. Subsequent tunneling operations showed that the profiles actually disclosed the general character of the clay strata encountered in the different tunnel sections. As would be expected, between drill holes the scattering of the properties of the clay from the average was important and called for continual vigilance during construction, but a more detailed subsoil investigation would have been impracticable and uneconomical.[45.4]

Compressibility of Clay Strata

The compressibility of clay strata is of interest as a source either of progressive settlement or else of delay in the increase of shearing resistance produced by superimposed load. Whatever the practical implications of the compressibility may be, a reliable forecast of its effects can be made only if the clay strata are continuous and fairly homogeneous.

If the subsoil contains a continuous and fairly homogeneous clay stratum, the settlement of the surface due to superimposed loads is at every point roughly proportional to the average pressure that the loads produce in the clay beneath this point. The intensity and distribution of the pressure in the clay can be computed by means of the methods described in Article 35. On the basis of the results of the computations and those of soil tests, the settlement due to the loads can be computed, and the curves of equal settlement can be constructed.

On minor jobs involving foundations above homogeneous clay strata, no soil investigations are required other than routine tests on the spoon samples. For clay these tests include the liquid-limit determination. The statistical relation between the liquid limit and the compression index C_c is given by equation 13.11. For a normally loaded clay of ordinary sensitivity the value obtained by means of this equation is accurate enough for most practical purposes. However, if the clay is extrasensitive, the correct value of C_c is likely to be higher than the computed one, and, if it is precompressed, the correct value is considerably lower. The degree of sensitivity is indicated by the effect of remolding on the compressive strength of the spoon samples. The existence of precompression can commonly be inferred from the geological character of the site.

On important jobs that call for accurate settlement forecasts, supplementary investigations are required. These consist, first of all, of tube-sample borings spaced not more than 100 ft. The continuous samples obtained from these borings are submitted to the same tests as those prescribed for the investigation of the shearing resistance of homogeneous clay strata. However, the unconfined compression tests need be performed on representative samples from only one hole in order to get reliable information concerning the sensitivity of the clay.

After the water-content profiles for all the tube-sample borings have been plotted in diagrams similar to Figure 127a, one representative boring is selected. Near this boring an undisturbed-sample boring is made that furnishes samples with a diameter of at least 4 in. to be submitted to consolidation tests.

Because of the great amount of time and labor involved in the performance of consolidation tests, these tests cannot be made on more than 10 or 15 samples without undue delay. Yet, even in relatively homogeneous clay strata the physical properties of the clay are likely to change to a considerable extent from point to point. As a consequence the compressibility characteristics of a clay can be determined at a reasonable expense only on the basis of statistical relationships between the compressibility and the index properties of the clay.

Of all the tests listed in Table 5 as routine tests on clay, the cheapest and most convenient is the water-content determination. Furthermore, the natural water content is more closely related to the compressibility of the different parts of a clay stratum than any of the other index properties. Hence, the evaluation of the average compressibility of a clay stratum is most conveniently based on the statistical relation between the natural water content and the compressibility of the components of the stratum.

The settlement due to the consolidation of a normally loaded layer of clay with an average void ratio e_0 depends on the compression index C_c of the clay, provided all other conditions are equal. Experience has shown that the relation between the natural water content and the *compression ratio* $C_c/(1 + e_0)$ for such clays can be represented approximately by a linear equation. In order to take advantage of this relation, consolidation tests are performed on samples of the clay, and the values of $C_c/(1 + e_0)$ are plotted against the natural water content. Figure 133 shows such a diagram. All the points representing individual test results are located close to a straight line. The vertical distance between the dash lines represents the scattering of the values of $C_c/(1 + e_0)$ from the average corresponding to a given natural water content.

After the relation between the compression ratio and the natural water content has been determined, the next step is to make use of the relation to estimate the values of the compression ratio corresponding to the natural water content of all the 2-in. tube samples that have been tested. Finally, the average value of $C_c/(1 + e_0)$ is determined by a suitable arithmetic or graphical procedure. This value can be used directly in equation 13.8 to compute the settlement.

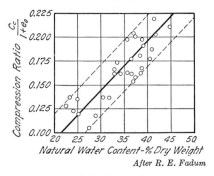

FIG. 133. Statistical relation between natural water content and compression ratio for samples of clay from boring in Boston, Mass.

If a clay is precompressed, equation 13.8 cannot be used, and the method of settlement computation must be adapted to the consolidation characteristics of the clay. Yet, whatever method may be used, an accurate settlement forecast is commonly impracticable. The reasons have been explained in Article 13.

Figure 194 illustrates the degree of accuracy that can be achieved in computing the distribution of the settlement over the base area of a building located above fairly homogeneous clay strata. The real distribution is shown on the left-hand side, and the computed on the right. The structure itself is complex but symmetrical. No such results can be obtained if the profile of the subsoil of a building is erratic, because the settlement of buildings on such subsoils depends not only on the intensity and the distribution of the loads but also on the variations in the compressibility of the subsoil in horizontal directions. In addition, the rate of settlement depends on the degree of continuity of layers and pockets of cohesionless material present in the subsoil. As a consequence it can change from place to place. Figure 134 illustrates such a profile. It represents the results of test borings in a composite shore deposit located at the south shore of Lake Erie. More than 100 borings were made, and the spacing between drill holes did not exceed 100 ft. Yet the boring records did not indicate whether or not the layers of clay encountered in the drill holes were continuous.

If the profile of the subsoil of a proposed structure is erratic, undisturbed sample borings and elaborate soil investigations are entirely out of place. Information of far more practical value can be obtained by means of numerous subsurface soundings supplemented by exploratory drill holes. The results of such investigations at least inform the designer of the location of the softest and the most resistant spots beneath the base of his building. At two or three points tube-sample borings may be made to get information on the details of stratification and on the sensitivity of the clay that was encountered in the exploratory holes. The maximum settlement is roughly estimated on the basis of the statistical

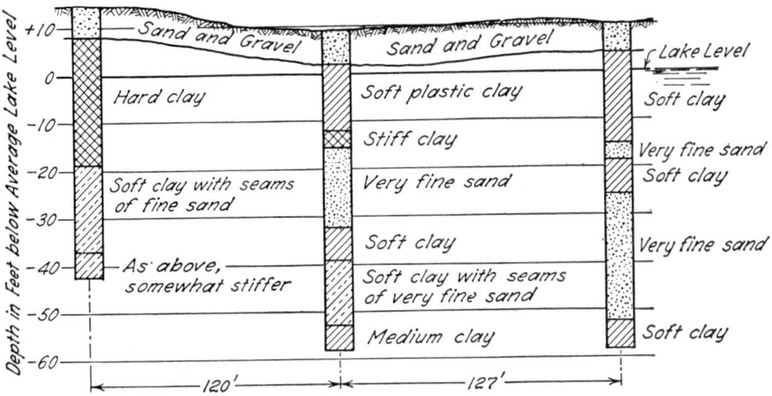

FIG. 134.   Erratic shore deposit, Lake Erie near Cleveland.

relation between the liquid limit and the compression index C_c. In judging whether or not the proposed structure can stand the estimated settlement, the spacing between the hardest and the softest spots of the subsoil is taken into consideration. The results of even very elaborate soil investigations would hardly add anything to the information obtained by the recommended procedure.

SUMMARY OF PROCEDURES IN SUBSOIL RECONNAISSANCE

According to the preceding discussions, a subsoil reconnaissance involves several successive stages. The first step is to decide on the depth and spacing of the exploratory borings.

If the proposed structure is a building, current practice calls for about one drill hole for every 2500 sq ft of the area covered by the building. If a retaining wall is to be constructed or an open cut to be made, it is customary to make at least one drill hole for every 100 ft of length of the wall or the cut. However, these rules are based on convention rather than rational considerations. If the subsoil is erratic, more useful information can commonly be obtained in less time and at a smaller expense by combining the exploratory borings with subsurface soundings.

The depth to which the exploratory drill holes should be made depends on whether the subsoil may contain layers of soft clay. If the local geological conditions or the conditions revealed by earlier test borings in the vicinity exclude this possibility, the drill holes do not need to be made to a depth of more than 20 or 30 ft below subgrade. On the other hand, if the subsoil may contain layers of soft clay at an unknown depth, a sound decision regarding the minimum depth of the test borings can be made only on the basis of the results of a rough estimate of the maximum depth at which the presence of clay strata may still have a significant influence on the performance of the proposed structure.

The subsequent investigations depend on the size of the job, the nature of the design problems, and the subsoil conditions.

On routine jobs such as the foundations of ordinary buildings or bridges, no investigations are needed beyond the routine tests on the spoon samples (see Table 5, page 38). Large or unusual jobs may call for one or more of the supplementary investigations described under the preceding subheadings. After the results of these investigations are digested, the engineer must then judge whether the conclusions based on the data can be considered final or whether the remaining uncertainties require an observational procedure during construction. Because of the important practical implications of these uncertainties, they are discussed in detail at the end of this article.

The preceding summary of operations demonstrates that subsoil reconnaissance is seldom a simple procedure requiring only conscientious adherence to a set of hard and fast rules. Unless the investigator is guided by mature judgment and has had a varied practical experience in this field, much time and money may be wasted.

In connection with each step, a thorough knowledge of the geology of sedimentary and other unconsolidated masses is an asset of inestimable value, because factual knowledge is always limited to soil conditions along vertical lines spaced far apart. It has already been mentioned, Article 43, that the results of interpolation and the estimate of possible scattering can be very misleading, unless the investigator has a fairly clear conception of the anatomy of the body of soil under investigation. A knowledge of the geology of the region is also needed to determine whether clay beds beneath the building site have ever been subjected to greater loads than at present and, if so, to provide a basis for estimating the magnitude of the additional pressure.

The larger the job, the more necessary it is to supplement the results of the soil investigations by information obtained from purely geological sources, because on large jobs a detailed soil survey is likely to be a physical impossibility.

DISCREPANCIES BETWEEN REALITY AND ASSUMPTIONS BASED ON SUBSOIL RECONNAISSANCE

The results of the subsoil reconnaissance for every job, large or small, are ultimately condensed into a set of assumptions that constitute the basis for design. The steps that lead to this final result involve various processes of interpolation and correlation based on statistical relationships. Therefore, the assumptions are always to some extent at variance with reality. However, the importance of these inevitable discrepancies is very different for different types of assumptions. This fact is explained in detail in the following paragraphs.

Assumptions regarding the angle of internal friction of sandy soils, the relative density of sand strata, or the average compressibility of clay strata belong in one category. The errors associated with these assumptions depend chiefly on the number and quality of the field tests which furnish the basic data. Hence, faulty assumptions in this category can safely be blamed on inadequate soil reconnaissance, provided the soil profile is relatively simple. The dangerous character of some submerged or partly submerged very loose sands cannot be demonstrated reliably by tests of any kind, Article 17. Therefore, it should always be assumed that loose submerged sands may liquefy on slight provocation unless they are compacted by artificial means.

The accurate determination of the average coefficients of permeability k_I and k_{II} for soil strata of any kind on the basis of the results of soil tests is impracticable, because the values k_I and k_{II} depend on structural details of the strata that cannot be detected by any method of soil exploration. However, if the method for investigating the permeability is judiciously selected and intelligently used, fairly reliable limiting values can be obtained under almost any circumstances. The difference between the limiting values and the real average value cannot be determined, but for many practical purposes only a knowledge of the limiting values is needed.

By far the most unreliable information is obtained when attempts are made to predict the pore-water pressures in stratified sand layers or in beds of clay containing thin seams or layers of more permeable material. This is due to the fact that the intensity and distribution of pore-water pressures, under given hydraulic boundary conditions, depend on unexplorable structural details, even more than do the average coefficients of permeability of such strata. Hence, if the factor of safety of a foundation with respect to failure, or that of a mass of soil with respect to sliding, depends on pore-water pressures, the fundamental assumptions regarding the pore-water pressures should not be trusted under any circumstances, regardless of the care with which the subsoil has been explored.

In such instances the assumptions on which the design is based should be considered as nothing more than the expression of a working hypothesis, subject to revision on the basis of the results of observations made in the field during construction. Practically all the failures of the foundations of dams and other hydraulic structures can be attributed to unjustified confidence in assumptions of some kind, and many of the failures could have been avoided by appropriate field observations during the construction period. Considering the loss of life and capital involved in the failure of an important hydraulic structure, reliance on the assumptions on which the original design was based and omission of the field observations required for investigating the real conditions must, at the present state of our knowledge, be classified as unpardonable neglect.

In spite of the fact that computed values of the pore-water pressure cannot be relied on, the computations should always be made because the results serve a vital purpose. They constitute the basis for evaluating the possible dangers, for preparing the program of field observations needed to detect impending dangers during construction, and for interpreting the results of these observations.

REFERENCES

45.1. K. TERZAGHI, Soil Studies for the Granville Dam at Westfield, Mass., *J. New Engl. Water Works Assoc.*, Vol 43 (1929), pp 191–223. Permeability survey of glacial outwash adjoining a reservoir site. The capillary rise method used in this study has been superseded by other procedures.

45.2. F. S. BROWN, Foundation Investigations for the Franklin Falls Dam, *J. Boston Soc. Civil Engrs.* Vol 28 (1941), pp 126–143. Abstract of results of permeability survey of fluvio-glacial sand deposits beneath dam site.

45.3. H. GRAFTIO, Some Features in Connection with the Foundation of Svir 3 Hydro-Electric Power Development, *Proc. Intern. Conf. Soil Mech.*, Cambridge, Mass. (1936), Vol I, pp 284–290. Determination of ratio between horizontal and vertical permeability of a stratified deposit by means of flow-net method.

45.4. K. TERZAGHI, Liner-Plate Tunnels on the Chicago Subway, *Trans. ASCE*, Vol 108 (1943), pp 970–1007. Investigation of physical properties of semierratic stratum of glacial clay for tunneling purposes.

45.5. See Ref. 44.6. Numerous examples of the exploration of slopes on soft clay by boring and testing combined with subsurface soundings with Swedish penetrometer.

45.6. G. L. FREEMAN, Soil Survey of the Flushing Meadow Park Site, Long Island, N. Y., *Proc. Intern. Conf. Soil Mech.*, Cambridge, Mass. (1936), Vol I, pp. 25–30. Technique and results of investigations of foundation conditions for proposed structures on tidal marsh.

45.7. G. TSCHEBOTAREFF, Settlement Studies of Structures in Egypt, *Trans. ASCE*, Vol 105 (1940), pp 919–972. Subsoil exploration at site of buildings on fine-grained flood-plain deposits, disclosing important variations of soil properties at least in the vertical direction.

45.8. WM. P. KIMBALL, Settlement Records of the Mississippi River Bridge at New Orleans, *Proc. Intern. Conf. Soil Mech.*, Cambridge, Mass. (1936), Vol I, pp 85–92. Technique and results of subsoil exploration for bridge piers on clay in river channel of Mississippi River.

Chapter VIII

EARTH PRESSURE AND STABILITY OF SLOPES

ART. 46. RETAINING WALLS

Design of Retaining Walls

The procedure for the design of retaining walls, like that of many other types of engineering structures, consists essentially of the successive repetition of two steps: (1) the tentative selection of the dimensions of the structure, and (2) the analysis of the ability of the selected structure to resist the forces that will act on it. If the analysis indicates that the structure is unsatisfactory, the dimensions are altered and a new analysis is made.

In making the first tentative selection of the dimensions of a retaining wall, the designer is guided by his experience and by various tables giving the ratio of base width to height of ordinary walls. In order to make the analysis, he first estimates the magnitude of all the forces that act above the base of the wall, including the pressure exerted by the backfill and the weight of the wall itself. Next, he investigates the stability of the wall with respect to overturning. He then estimates the adequacy of the underlying soil to prevent failure of the wall by sliding along a plane at or below the base, to withstand the pressure beneath the toe of the foundation without failing and allowing the wall to overturn, and to support all the vertical forces, including the weight of the backfill, without excessive settlement, tilting, or outward movement.

Soil mechanics may enter into the design of retaining walls in two of these operations: the estimate of the pressure exerted against the wall by the backfill; and the estimate of the adequacy of the foundation soil to support the structure. These two subjects are discussed independently.

Estimate of Pressure Exerted by Backfill

Introduction. Theoretical methods for computing the earth pressure against retaining walls are presented in Articles 24 and 26. These methods are based on three assumptions:

(1) The wall can yield by tilting or sliding through a distance sufficient to develop the full shearing resistance of the backfill.

(2) The pressure in the pore water of the backfill is negligible.

(3) The soil constants appearing in the earth-pressure equations have definite values that can be determined reliably.

The use of earth-pressure theory to estimate the pressure of the backfill against a retaining wall is justified only if these three assumptions are satisfied. Every retaining wall not rigidly supported at its crest is able to yield far enough to comply with the first assumption. However, in order to satisfy the second, the drainage system in the backfill must be designed and constructed with the same care as the wall itself, and in order to satisfy the third, the backfill material must be selected and investigated before the wall is designed. Furthermore, it must be carefully placed, because the shearing resistance of a backfill which is merely dumped into position cannot be determined reliably by any practicable means.

If the latter two requirements are not satisfied, the wall will be acted on by various agents and forces beyond the scope of any earth-pressure theory. If a backfill is loosely deposited or inadequately drained, its properties change from season to season, and during the course of each year it passes through states of partial or total saturation alternating with states of drainage or even partial desiccation. All these processes cause seasonal changes in the earth pressure that receive no consideration in the classical earth-pressure theories. For example, pressure cell measurements on the back of a reinforced-concrete retaining wall 34 ft high indicated that within one year the pressure varied from the average value by ±30 per cent.[46.1]

The maximum value of the earth pressure of backfills subject to seasonal changes is greater than the Coulomb or Rankine value. Yet, on routine jobs such as the construction of retaining walls along railroads or highways, it would be both uneconomical and impracticable to eliminate the seasonal pressure variations by design and construction in strict accordance with theoretical requirements. For the sake of economy and expediency, such walls are designed on the basis of simple semiempirical rules for estimating the backfill pressure. In their original form these rules were based chiefly on analyses of the stability of actual retaining walls, only a few of which had failed. Since the underlying causes of failure were not taken into consideration in formulating the rules, the design of walls by this procedure leads on rare occasions to failure, but in the great majority of cases the walls are safer than necessary.

On the other hand, if a retaining wall constitutes the major part of a large job, or if the height of a wall exceeds about 20 ft, it is likely to be more economical to determine the properties of the backfill, to carry out such construction procedures as are necessary to satisfy the theoretical requirements for applying an earth-pressure theory, and to design the wall to withstand only the theoretical value of the earth pressure.

Semiempirical methods for estimating pressure of backfills. For many years most retaining walls have been designed by empirical or semiempirical methods. Perhaps the oldest of these methods is the use of charts or tables giving suitable values of the ratio of base width to height for various types of walls and backfills. The principal defect of this approach is that the foundation cannot be investigated adequately because the forces that act on it are unknown. A second procedure in common use is the *equivalent-fluid method,* in which the wall is designed to withstand the pressure of a liquid that is assumed to exert the same pressure against the wall as the real backfill. In spite of its widespread use, the equivalent-fluid concept has not led to generally accepted values for the unit weight of the equivalent fluid. Many designers prefer to use the theoretical equations for calculating the pressure of cohesionless earth and to substitute such values for the angle of internal friction as have usually led to satisfactory design in the past. However, a great diversity of opinion exists as to the proper values to use for ϕ under different circumstances, and attempts to use the procedure for cohesive backfills cannot be justified even on a theoretical basis.

TABLE 12

Types of Backfill for Retaining Walls

1. Coarse-grained soil without admixture of fine soil particles, very permeable (clean sand or gravel).
2. Coarse-grained soil of low permeability due to admixture of particles of silt size.
3. Residual soil with stones, fine silty sand, and granular materials with conspicuous clay content.
4. Very soft or soft clay, organic silts, or silty clays.
5. Medium or stiff clay, deposited in chunks and protected in such a way that a negligible amount of water enters the spaces between the chunks during floods or heavy rains. If this condition cannot be satisfied, the clay should not be used as backfill material. With increasing stiffness of the clay, danger to the wall due to infiltration of water increases rapidly.

Nevertheless, each of the various empirical or semiempirical procedures represents a body of valuable experience and summarizes much useful information. Today our knowledge of the physical properties of soils permits us to eliminate the most unreasonable values assigned to the soil constants or to the unit weight of the equivalent fluid. Furthermore, a knowledge of earth-pressure theory can be used to take proper account of the cohesion and to estimate the influence of a surcharge carried by the backfill or of a backfill that has an irregularly shaped surface. A summary of all this information, in the form of an approximate design procedure for practical use, is given in the following paragraphs.

In the use of this procedure, it should be emphasized that every approximate method for the design of retaining walls involves two features: It must be based on more or less arbitrary assumptions, and it cannot apply to all cases encountered in practice. Therefore, the following suggestions for the design of small retaining walls should serve merely as a basis for extrapolating from the stipulated simple conditions to the conditions encountered in specific instances in the field.

The first step in the design of a wall on a semiempirical basis is to assign the available backfill material to one of the five categories listed in Table 12.

If the wall must be designed before the nature of the backfill material can be learned, the estimate of the backfill pressure should be based on the most unsuitable material that may be used by the construction forces, or else alternative designs should be prepared. Each design should be accompanied by clear and simple statements indicating to which of the five soil types in Table 12 it pertains. The engineer in the field should then select the design appropriate for the existing field conditions.

The practical conditions likely to be encountered in the design of retaining walls can be divided into four categories, depending on the shape of the surface of the backfill and the surcharge which it carries. These are:

(a) The surface of the backfill is plane and carries no surcharge.

(b) The surface of the backfill rises on a slope from the crest of the wall to a level at some elevation above the crest.

(c) The surface of the backfill is horizontal and carries a uniformly distributed surcharge.

(d) The surface of the backfill is horizontal and carries a uniformly distributed line load parallel to the crest of the wall.

If the surface of the backfill is plane (case a), the backfill pressure may be estimated by means of the chart, Figure 135. The first step in using the chart is to determine the height H of a vertical section passing through the heel of the wall, extending from the bottom of the base to the surface of the backfill. The total pressure against this section is $\frac{1}{2}k_hH^2$, and the total vertical force on it is $\frac{1}{2}k_vH^2$. Values of k_h and k_v are given on the right-hand side of Figure 135, in terms of the slope angle β, for each of the given types of backfill material. The backfill pressure is assumed to increase in simple proportion to the depth below point a. Hence the point of application of the resultant backfill pressure is at the lower third-point of H. If the material consists of clay chunks, type 5, the value of H should be reduced by 4 ft, and the resultant pressure considered to act at a height above the base equal to $\frac{1}{3}(H-4)$ ft.

If the surface of the backfill rises at an angle β to the horizontal for a limited distance and then becomes horizontal (case b), values of k_h and

k_v may be estimated from the curves in Figure 136. As before, the chart gives values of the pressure against a vertical section ab through the heel of the wall. If the backfill is of types 1 to 4, the point of application of the resultant pressure is taken at the lower third-point of H. For ma-

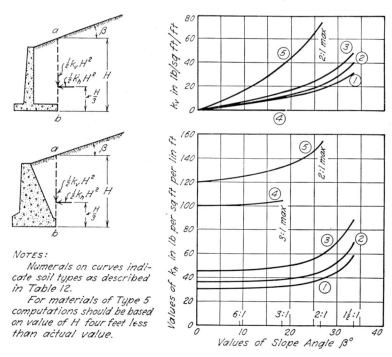

Fig. 135.   Chart for estimating pressure of backfill against retaining walls supporting backfills with plane surface.

terials of type 5, the value of H is reduced 4 ft in calculating the total pressure, and the resultant pressure is considered to act at a height above the base equal to $\frac{1}{3}(H - 4)$ ft.

If the surface of the backfill is horizontal and carries a uniformly distributed surcharge q per unit of area (case c), the pressure per unit of area against the vertical section ab at any depth is increased because of the surcharge by an amount,

$$p_q = Cq \qquad (46.1)$$

where C is a coefficient depending on the type of soil. Values of C are given in Table 13.

If the surface of the backfill carries a line load, q' per unit of length, parallel to its crest (case d), the line is considered to exert against the

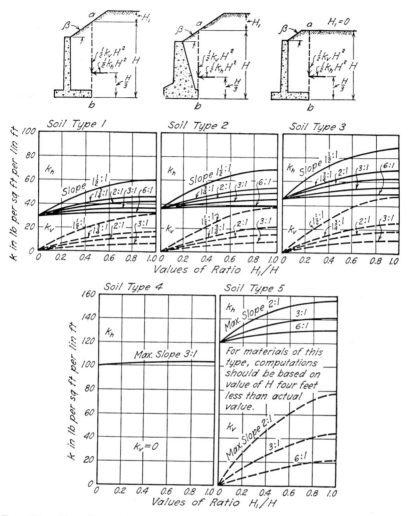

FIG. 136. Chart for estimating pressure of backfill against retaining walls supporting backfill with surface which slopes upward from crest of wall for limited distance and then becomes horizontal.

vertical section ab a horizontal force,

$$p_q' = Cq' \qquad (46.2)$$

per unit of length of the wall. The point of application d of the force p_q', Figure 137a, can be obtained by drawing a straight line from point c, which represents the point of application of the force q', at an angle of $40°$ to the horizontal until it intersects the back of the wall at point d_1.

If point d_1 is located below the base of the wall, the influence of the line load on the surcharge can be disregarded. If point c is located to the left of the vertical plane ab, the rule remains unaltered.

The line load q' also produces an additional vertical pressure on the upper surface of the heel of the wall. It may be assumed that the pressure p'' at this level is uniformly distributed over the base $\overline{ef}$ of an equilateral triangle with apex at c. Hence, the intensity of the pressure is

$$p'' = \frac{q'}{\overline{ef}} \tag{46.3}$$

Only that part of p'' acting directly on the heel of the wall should be considered in the stability computation.

TABLE 13
VALUES OF C IN EQUATIONS 46.1 AND 46.2

Type of Soil	C
1	0.27
2	0.30
3	0.39
4	1.00
5	1.00

The procedures described in the preceding paragraphs refer to walls on relatively unyielding foundations. Hence, the wall friction and adhesion tend to pull the wall down and to reduce the earth pressure. However, if a wall rests on a very compressible foundation, the settlement of the wall with respect to that of the backfill is likely to reverse the direction of these forces. This increases the earth pressure very considerably (see Article 26 and Figure 64). Therefore, if a wall rests on such a compressible foundation as soft clay, the values of backfill pressure computed for materials of types 1, 2, 3, and 5 should be increased by 50 per cent.

The backfill pressures computed by means of the semiempirical procedures just outlined include the effect of seepage pressures and various time-conditioned changes in the backfill. In spite of this fact, however, provisions must be made to prevent the accumulation of water behind the wall, and to reduce the effect of frost action.

For removing water that seeps into the backfill during rainstorms outlets known as weep holes or back drains are provided. *Weep holes* are commonly made by embedding 4-in. pipes in the wall, as shown in Figure 137a. The vertical spacing between horizontal rows of weep holes should not exceed 5 ft. The horizontal spacing in a given row depends on the provisions made to direct the seepage water toward the weep holes. The cheapest but least effective method is to dump about one cubic foot of crushed stone or gravel at the intake end of each weep hole. If this method is used, the horizontal spacing of the weep holes should not exceed about 5 ft. The water that emerges from the weep holes seeps into the ground at the toe of the retaining wall where the soil should be kept as dry as possible. This undesirable condition can be avoided by substituting for every horizontal row of weep holes a longitudinal *back drain* that extends for the full length of the back of the wall. The outlets of the back drains are located beyond the ends of the wall. The most elaborate

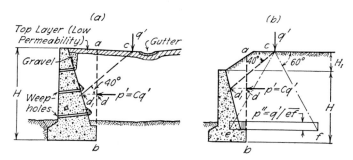

FIG. 137. Diagrams illustrating method for estimating magnitude and line of action of force against vertical section through heel of retaining wall, due to surcharge q' per unit of length parallel to crest of wall.

system of drainage in common use is the *continuous back drain*, which consists of a vertical layer of gravel covering the entire back of the wall. Outlets are provided at each end of the wall.

These drainage provisions prevent the accumulation of water behind the wall. However, regardless of which method is used, the water flows out of the backfill toward the drains. Theoretical studies based on the flow net have shown that the seepage pressure associated with this process of percolation may considerably increase the lateral pressure exerted by backfills with low permeability. The values given in Figures 135 and 136 take account of this temporary increase in earth pressure, because they are based on experience with retaining walls with the customary imperfect drainage provisions.

To prevent the saturation of backfills of types 2 and 3, Table 12, during the wet season, the surface should be covered by a layer of soil with a permeability considerably smaller than that of the backfill. The surface should be given a slope toward a conveniently located gutter, as indicated in Figure 137a.

If a water or sewer pipe is to be buried in the backfill, the pipe should be surrounded by a gravel drain with an outlet located in such a position that a break in the pipe cannot escape attention.

Since the semiempirical method given here takes into account the forces exerted by the earth, by water percolating toward the back drains, and by various other time-conditioned agencies, the only factor that requires independent consideration is frost action. If a backfill of types 2 and 3 in Table 12 is saturated, the freezing of the pore water adjoining the back of the wall draws more water out of the fill toward the zone of freezing, and ice layers may be formed parallel to the back of the wall (see Article 21). If the backfill is permanently separated from the water table by a very permeable or very impermeable soil stratum, it constitutes a closed system. In such a backfill the formation of ice layers involves merely a migration of water from the central part of the back-

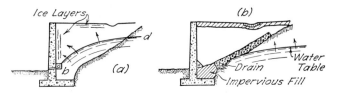

Fig. 138.   (*a*) Frost action in backfill of retaining wall provided only with backdrain; (*b*) method of draining backfill to prevent formation of ice layers.

fill toward the zone of freezing, but the volume and shape of the backfill remain practically unaltered and the corresponding movement of the retaining wall is likely to be imperceptible. However, if the ground water rises into the backfill, the system is an open one, and the formation of ice layers produces an energetic outward movement of the wall, because no retaining wall is heavy enough to withstand the pressure of crystallization of ice. It has been suggested that the condition may be remedied by the installation of a continuous gravel drain at the intersection *b* of the back of the wall and the original ground surface, Figure 138*a*. Such a drain would lower the water table into the position *bd*, but it would not prevent the water from being drawn by capillarity toward the zone of freezing, as indicated by the arrows in Figure 138*a*. However, the backfill can be transformed into a closed system by covering the entire area of contact between the backfill and its base, up to the highest position of the water table, with a blanket of gravel or some other highly permeable material (see Figure 138*b*). The collector drain *d* should be installed beyond the inner boundary of the zone of freezing, and its outlets should be protected against obstruction by ice. No serious frost action need be feared if the backfill constitutes a closed system, or if it consists of soils of the types 1, 4, or 5.

Estimate of earth pressure by means of theory.   The magnitude of the earth pressure computed on the basis of theory is smaller than the backfill pressure estimated by means of the semiempirical procedure described in the preceding paragraphs. However, as stated previously, the design of a retaining wall on the basis of theory is justifiable only if the physical constants of the backfill material are reliably known, and if provisions are made to take care that the pore-water pressure in the backfill will be permanently negligible. The cost of satisfying these requirements more than offsets the benefits from the use of the theoretical earth pressure in design, unless the retaining wall is of greater than ordinary height or length. In this event, however, it may prove more economical to investigate the properties of the backfill, take suitable measures to assure that the properties will remain constant, eliminate the possibility of excess pore-water pressure, and design the wall to withstand only the theoretical value of the earth pressure.

The physical soil properties that enter into the theoretical earth-pressure computations are the unit weight, the angle of internal friction, and the cohesion. No elaborate theoretical calculations are justified unless the values of these constants are determined by means of laboratory tests on representative samples of the backfill material compacted to a density equal to that after deposition and compaction in the field. The following three paragraphs summarize the procedure for getting the required information.

The unit weight of soils of types 1 to 3 in Table 12 should be determined by weighing samples that are first saturated and then allowed to drain by gravity for about 30 min through perforations in the bottom of their containers. The samples should be about 4 in. high. Clay is weighed at the water content at which it is placed in the fill.

The angle of internal friction of fairly permeable soils, such as types 1 to 3 in Table 12, can be determined by means of slow-shear tests, because the void ratio of these materials in the field can adapt itself during construction to the change in stresses. The cohesion should be disregarded. The coefficient of wall friction tan δ can be assumed equal to two thirds of tan ϕ. If the fill will be subjected to traffic vibrations, or if it will sustain heavy surcharges of variable intensity, such as the loads on the floor of storage-warehouse docks, the values of tan ϕ and tan δ should be reduced by 20 per cent. If there is a possibility that the wall may settle more than the backfill, the wall friction should be assumed to act against the wall in an upward direction.

The angle of internal friction of clay soils, such as types 4 and 5 in Table 12, should be considered equal to zero. The cohesion c is roughly equal to one-half the unconfined compressive strength q_u of the backfill material as deposited behind the wall. The adhesion between the clay backfill and the back of the wall should be disregarded, and the value of δ taken equal to zero. The effect of traffic vibrations does not require consideration. Stiff clay should not be used as a backfill material unless conditions permit the complete and permanent exclusion of water from the fill; however, this can seldom be accomplished.

During rainstorms water percolates through the backfill toward the back of the wall as shown in Figure 139a. The seepage pressure, Article 39, exerted by the percolating water increases the earth pressure exerted by backfills with medium permeability, types 2 and 3, Table 12, as

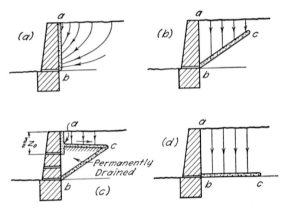

Fig. 139. Diagram showing provisions for drainage of backfill behind retaining walls. (a) Vertical drainage layer; (b) inclined drainage layer for cohesionless backfill; (c) horizontal drain and seal combined with inclined drainage layer for cohesive backfill; (d) bottom drain to accelerate consolidation of cohesive backfill.

long as percolation continues. This should be prevented by means of inclined drainage layers, such as that shown in Figure 139b. The drainage layers serve the double function of drains and protection against frost action. In addition, the surface of backfills of medium permeability should be covered with a well-compacted layer of less permeable soil, as shown in Figure 137a.

A clay backfill is likely to pull away from the back of the wall to a depth of about z_0, equation 24.6. In order to prevent the accumulation of water in the open fissure during rainstorms, a drainage layer should be inserted between the wall and the backfill to a depth of $1.5z_0$ below the crest. Since the uppermost layer of a clay backfill is likely to break up and become fairly permeable as the result of alternate wetting and drying, the vertical drainage layer should be connected to an inclined drainage layer by a gently sloping top filter, Figure 139c. This filter collects the water that percolates through the top layer of clay. The physical properties of the wedge-shaped body of clay located between the top filter and the inclined drainage layer can be expected to remain fairly constant throughout the year.

The quantity of water that percolates through a well-constructed backfill is so small that there is no danger of the drains becoming obstructed by washed-out soil particles. Therefore, it is not necessary that the grain size of the materials in the drainage layers should satisfy the requirements for filter layers, Article 11.

Earth pressure against nonyielding retaining walls. Rigid walls in a fixed position, such as the front part of U-shaped bridge abutments or the side walls of deep basements, are acted on not by the active earth pressure but by the earth pressure at rest. The magnitude of the earth pressure at rest is greater than the active value. It depends not only on the physical properties of the backfill, but also, to a large extent, on the method of placing the fill. Hence, the intensity of the earth pressure against a fixed wall can be estimated only on the basis of experience. As yet, very little empirical information exists on this subject. The pressure exerted by a loose fill against a low fixed wall appears to be smaller than that of the same backfill in a compacted state.[46.2] The results of pressure-cell measurements on two U-shaped bridge abutments in northwestern Germany indicated that the pressure of the well-compacted medium-sand backfill was roughly equal to the Coulomb value at any depth plus a constant value of about 0.13 ton per sq ft.[46.3]

FOUNDATIONS FOR RETAINING WALLS

Introduction. Experience has shown that most retaining wall failures are caused by inadequacy of the foundations. Since an adequate foundation cannot be designed without at least some knowledge of the type of soil located beneath the base of the proposed wall, the subsoil must be investigated at least by primitive means. The minimum requirement for exploring the soil beneath the base of any retaining wall is to drill with a post-hole digger or some other convenient tool to a depth below the base equal to the height of the wall. If a firm stratum is encountered at a smaller depth, the boring can be discontinued after drilling about 2 ft into the stratum, provided local experience or readily available geological evidence leaves no doubt that soft strata do not exist at greater depth. On the other hand, if a soft stratum extends to a depth greater than the height of the wall, the boring should be continued until the bottom of the soft stratum is encountered, or until the stiffness of the soil increases perceptibly. The designer should also know the depth of frost penetration and the depth to which the soil is broken up by seasonal volume changes, so that he can establish the base of the foundation below both of these depths (see Article 53). If no information can be obtained in advance, the dimensions for the foundation should not appear on the plans, and simple instructions should be given to the engineer on the job for selecting the dimensions after the required information is available.

Foundations for retaining walls must satisfy at least two conditions: The factor of safety against sliding must be adequate, and the soil pressure beneath the toe of the foundation should be equal to or smaller than the allowable soil pressure (see Article 54). To prevent excessive tilting, it is quite properly considered good practice to require that the resultant of all the forces acting on the wall above its base should intersect the base within the middle third. In addition, if the subsoil is compressible, the further requirement must be satisfied that the differential settlement of the foundation should not be excessive. Hence, not only should the resultant pressure be made to fall within the kern of the base, but also the adequacy of every retaining wall foundation should be investigated with respect to sliding, maximum value of soil pressure, and settlement.

Safety against sliding. The sliding of a retaining wall on its base is resisted by the friction between the soil and the base and by the passive earth pressure of the soil in contact with the outer face of the foundation. It is commonly required that the factor of safety against sliding be at least 1.5.

The friction between the base and a fairly permeable soil such as a clean or silty sand is equal to the total normal pressure on the base times the coefficient of friction f between soil and base. For a coarse-grained soil containing no silt or clay the value of f may be taken as 0.55; for a coarse-grained soil containing silt $f = 0.45$.

If the wall rests on silt or clay, special precautions are required. Immediately before the footing is poured, about 4 in. of soil should be removed over the area to be covered by concrete and replaced by a 4-in. layer of well-compacted sharp-grained sand or sand and gravel. The coefficient of friction between the sand and the underlying soil can be assumed as $f = 0.35$. However, if the unconfined compressive strength q_u of the underlying soil is less than twice the frictional resistance beneath any part of the base, the slip will take place by shear in the soil at some distance below the base. If the normal pressure increases from zero at the heel to p at the toe, as shown in Figure 140a, failure between a_2 and d would occur by sliding along the contact between the sand layer and the underlying soil, and between d and a_1 by shear in the soil itself. If the pressure on the base has a uniform value p per unit of area, the sliding resistance per unit of area of the base is equal to the smaller of the two values fp and $q_u/2$.

The second force that resists the sliding of the base is the passive earth pressure of the soil in front of the buried part of the wall. Within the zone of seasonal changes of moisture and temperature, the passive earth pressure is a rather unreliable resistance. The presence of root holes may make the soil so compressible that the passive resistance does not become effective until the wall has advanced through a considerable distance. If the subsoil contains silt and the water table is close to the surface, ice layers may be formed during the winter in the upper part of the soil (see Article 21). During the subsequent thaw the soil may be-

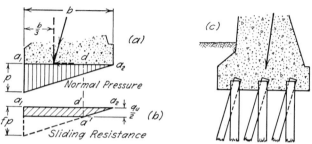

FIG. 140. (a) Approximate distribution of contact pressure on base of retaining wall if resultant force intersects base at outer third-point; (b) diagram showing resistance to sliding if unconfined compressive strength of soil beneath base is less than twice the frictional resistance between base and underlying soil; (c) base of retaining wall supported by vertical and batter piles.

come so soft that its passive resistance is negligible. Because of these possibilities, the passive earth pressure should be disregarded unless local conditions permit reliable evaluation of its lower limiting value.

If the factor of safety with respect to sliding cannot be raised to 1.5 without the construction of an excessively heavy foundation, it is likely to be more economical to establish the wall on a pile foundation, as shown in Figure 140c. The vertical forces are carried by vertical piles, and the horizontal ones by *batter piles*, driven at an angle to the vertical. The practice of driving some of the piles beneath the foundations of retaining walls on a batter is by no means universal, because vertical piles can be driven more cheaply. However, since the resistance against horizontal displacement offered by the upper part of vertical piles in soft soil is very small, the absence of batter piles is likely to be associated with a gradual outward movement of the wall. Some bridge abutments supported by pile foundations without batter piles have advanced in the course of time until the tension members have started to buckle owing to axial compression.[46.4] If the weight of the backfill exceeds about one-half the bearing capacity of the subsoil, the progressive movement of the retaining wall or abutment is likely to be excessive, even if the foundation is provided with enough batter piles to resist the backfill pressure. Under these circumstances, it may be necessary to substitute lightweight material for the ordinary types of backfill, or even to alter the layout of the entire project to eliminate the fill. Solid bridge abutments, for example, may be less desirable than open abutments through which the backfill extends on a slope. The roadway immediately behind the abutment is then carried on a structure rather than on a fill.

Allowable soil pressure and settlement. If the resultant of all the forces acting on the wall above its base intersects the base of the foundation at the outer third-point, the contact pressure on the base increases roughly from zero at the heel to twice the average pressure at the toe. Therefore, the process of backfilling commonly produces an outward tilt of the wall. If the wall rests on a firm soil, such as a dense sand or a stiff sand–clay mixture, the tilt of the wall will be imperceptible provided the pressure · beneath the toe does not exceed the allowable pressure for the given soil (see Article 54). On the other hand, if the wall rests on a very compressible soil, such as soft clay, the tilt can become very large. Progressive consolidation of the clay beneath the toe may cause the tilt to increase for many years. The increased tilt causes the center of gravity of the wall to advance and the soil pressure under the toe to increase further, until finally the wall may fail by overturning. Hence, if a wall rests on a very compressible soil, the foundation must be designed in such a way that the point of application of the resultant pressure is located close to the midpoint of the base.

If a retaining wall serves as a bridge abutment, a tilt of the wall changes the clearance between the abutments. At some bridges, the clearance decreases until the superstructure acts as a spacer,[46.4] whereas at others the clearance increases and threatens to exceed the span of the superstructure. A movement of the second type can occur only if the subsoil of the backfill contains a fairly thick layer of compressible soil such as peat or soft clay. Under the weight of the fill the layer compresses, and the area beneath the backfill settles. Since the abutment is located near the edge of the loaded area, its base becomes inclined, and the wall tilts toward the backfill. The backward tilt due to this cause may be much greater than the forward tilt caused by the pressure of the backfill.

These considerations serve to indicate that the foundation of a retaining wall requires even more careful attention than that of an ordinary building. The general principles that govern the design of foundations are discussed in Articles 53, 54, and 56.

FIELD OBSERVATIONS

Further improvement in the design and construction of retaining walls cannot be anticipated until information is available concerning the actual performance of ordinary retaining walls backfilled in the customary manners and concerning the effectiveness of drains intended to eliminate the pore-water pressure in compacted backfills. Hence, field observations are needed to provide data of both kinds.

No empirical rules can be more reliable than the observations on which they are based. Yet the observational data which form the basis of the existing empirical rules for estimating backfill pressures are meager and inadequate. Records concerning the behavior of actual retaining walls seldom contain more than a vague description of the backfill material, and the data concerning displacements are generally limited to evidence every casual observer can see. Hence, the important field of estimating backfill pressures on a semiempirical basis still contains much room for improvement. Progress can be made only by observing retaining walls in the field for a number of years and by publishing and interpreting the results.

The records of observations made for the purpose of improving the semiempirical basis of design should contain an adequate description of the soil used as a backfill, the method of constructing the backfill, the provisions for drainage, the time of year when the backfill was placed, the average annual rainfall, and the depth of frost penetration. This information should be accompanied by a sketch that shows a cross section of the wall and a profile of the subsoil that leaves no doubt regarding the foundation conditions. The backfill samples can be obtained by means of a post-hole digger, and the description of the backfill material should contain the results of all of the pertinent identification tests listed in Table 5, page 38. The observations on the wall should include measurements of the tilt and of the horizontal displacement of the crest. The measurements should be made at least four times each year, at the end of every season.

The displacement of retaining walls due to frost action is practically an unexplored phenomenon. Yet, periodic measurements of tilt or displacement for a period of a few years could determine whether the observed movements are caused by frost action. If frost action is found to be the responsible agent, the structure of the ice in the frozen zone should be investigated by excavating along the back of the wall before the spring thaw.

The records of observations on large retaining walls designed on the basis of earth-pressure theory should also include the results of all soil tests made prior to construction and of the periodic measurement of the pore-water pressure at several suitably located points in the backfill. Measurements of earth pressure against the back of the wall are desirable but not essential.

No satisfactory basis will be found for the design of rigid walls that cannot yield at the crest until numerous records are available of the earth pressure exerted against such walls in the field. The few available data have been obtained by means of pressure cells that had a small area compared to that of the back of the wall, and, as a consequence, the results are rather erratic. More reliable information could be secured by the use of devices that measure the average pressure on fairly large areas.

SUMMARY

In connection with the design of retaining walls, the planning of adequate drainage provisions and a careful consideration of the foundation conditions are more important than a correct evaluation of the earth pressure. The pressure exerted by the backfill can be estimated either on the basis of semiempirical rules or else by means of earth-pressure theory. The first method has the same drawbacks as the evaluation of the safe load on piles by means of pile formulas, Article 56. Some walls designed according to this method are excessively safe, others are barely stable, and occasionally a wall fails. Nevertheless, for routine jobs the first method is cheaper and preferable. The second method requires that the backfill and the drainage system be constructed in strict compliance with the conditions imposed by the theory. The time and labor involved in this process are not justified, unless the retaining wall constitutes a prominent part of an individual job or has a height exceeding about 20 ft.

Further progress in the design and construction of retaining walls cannot be expected without observations made on full-sized retaining walls in the field, to determine the seasonal variations in the condition of the backfill and their effect on the wall.

REFERENCES

Examples of the various semiempirical procedures mentioned in this article may be found in the following references:

(a) TRAUTWINE, Design on basis of ratio of base width to height, *Civil Engineer's Reference-Book*, twenty-first edition, Ithaca, 1937, pp 603–606.

(b) TURNEAURE AND MAURER, Design by equivalent fluid method, *Principles of Reinforced Concrete Construction*, second edition, New York, 1913, pp 370–373.

(c) Design by theory, using fictitious values of ϕ, *Manual of the American Railway Engineering Association*, Chicago, 1946, pp 8-82–8-86. The values recommended for ϕ are excessive.

Other references containing useful information are the following:

46.1. J. V. McNARY, Earth Pressure against Abutment Walls Measured with Soil Pressure Cells, *Public Roads*, Vol 6 (1925), pp 102–106. This paper contains the results of observations on two walls.

46.2. K. Terzaghi, Large Retaining-Wall Tests, *Eng. News-Record*, Vol 112 (1934), pp 136–140, 259–262, 316–318, 403–406, 503–508. Large-scale tests demonstrating the effect of the movement of a retaining wall on the intensity and distribution of earth pressure.

46.3. P. Müller, Measurements of the Earth Pressure Exerted by Mechanically Consolidated Backfills of Abutments (in German), *Bautechnik*, Vol 17 (1939), pp 195–203. Results of observations demonstrating that the earth pressure on the front part of U-shaped bridge abutments can be very much greater than the Coulomb pressure.

46.4. K. Terzaghi, The Mechanics of Shear Failures on Clay Slopes and the Creep of Retaining Walls, *Public Roads*, Vol 10 (1929), pp 177–192.

46.5. Benjamin Baker, The Actual Lateral Pressure of Earthwork, *Min. Proc. Inst. Civil Engrs.* Vol 65 (1881), pp 140–186, discussions pp 187–241. This paper contains a graphic description of the causes and types of failure of retaining walls. The theoretical discussions and proposed design methods are out of date.

46.6. K. Terzaghi, Retaining-Wall Design for Fifteen-Mile Falls Dam, *Eng. News-Record*, Vol 112 (1934), pp 632–636. Design of gravity retaining wall 170 ft high.

46.7. Use of Portable Cribbing in Place of Rigid Retaining Walls and the Utility of the Different Kinds of Cribbing, Committee Report, *Proc. Am. Rwy. Eng. Assoc.*, Vol 34 (1933), pp 139–148. Digest of maintenance experience.

ART. 47. DRAINAGE PRIOR TO EXCAVATION

Introduction

On many jobs, such as the installation of underground utilities, the construction of deep basements for buildings, and the preparation of foundations for dams, the soil must be excavated to a level beneath the water table, and the flow of water into the excavation must be eliminated or reduced to an inconsequential amount. To control the inflow of water, a system of drains must be established either during or, preferably, before removal of the soil. The sides of the excavation are given a slope adequate to maintain stability, or else they are made vertical and are braced with some type of lateral support, Article 48.

In an excavation with given dimensions, extending to a given depth below the water table, the quantity of water that must be disposed of and the time required for draining the surrounding soil depend on the permeability and the compressibility of the soil. On average jobs the planning of the drainage provisions does not require accurate information concerning the permeability of the subsoil. Hence, on such jobs no soil investigations need be made other than the routine tests (Table 5, page 38) on spoon samples obtained from the exploratory drill holes. On large jobs pumping tests are commonly made. On every job, regardless of size, the method of drainage and the location of the points at which water will be pumped require careful consideration.

METHODS OF DRAINAGE

To obtain satisfactory results at least expense, the method of drainage should be adapted to the average permeability of the soil surrounding the site, to the depth of the cut with reference to the water table, and, on small jobs, to the type of equipment most readily available at the site. The permeability of the soils that constitute most natural deposits, with the probable exception of those that are wind-laid, varies consider-

TABLE 14

COEFFICIENT OF PERMEABILITY OF COMMON NATURAL SOIL FORMATIONS

Formation	Value of k (cm/sec)
River Deposits	
Rhone at Genissiat	Up to 0.40
Small streams, eastern Alps	0.02 to 0.16
Missouri	0.02 to 0.20
Mississippi	0.02 to 0.12
Glacial Deposits	
Outwash plains	0.05 to 2.00
Esker, Westfield, Mass.	0.01 to 0.13
Delta, Chicopee, Mass.	0.0001 to 0.015
Till	Less than 0.0001
Wind Deposits	
Dune sand	0.1 to 0.3
Loess	0.001 ±
Loess loam	0.0001 ±
Lacustrine and Marine Offshore Deposits	
Very fine uniform sand, $U = 5$ to 2	0.0001 to 0.0064
Bull's liver, Sixth Ave., N. Y., $U = 5$ to 2	0.0001 to 0.0050
Bull's liver, Brooklyn, $U = 5$	0.00001 to 0.0001
Clay	Less than 0.0000001

ably from point to point. The extreme limits within which the coefficient of permeability k has been found to vary in individual representative deposits of the most common types are given in Table 14.

According to their coefficients of permeability soils may be divided into five groups as indicated in Table 15. Soils of high permeability are rarely encountered, and, when they are, they commonly alternate in the ground with less permeable layers. Practically impervious soils, such as clays, are very common.

Until the end of the last century the drainage of open excavations was generally accomplished by conducting the water that seeped into the excavation to shallow pits or timbered shafts called *sumps* and by pumping it out of these pits. On small jobs this method of sumping is still practiced. The principle of the method is illustrated by the left-hand side of Figure 141, which represents a vertical section through a wide excavation with sloping sides. Most of the water emerges from the toes of the slopes. It is diverted through drainage ditches into one or several sumps *S*. At each sump a pump is installed that lifts the water into a discharge pipe.

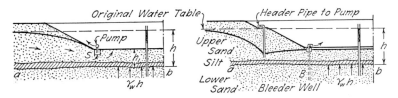

Fig. 141.   Position of water table while pumping from sumps (left) and from well points (right).   Soil conditions lead to failure by heave in spite of pumping unless bleeder wells *B* are installed.

The method of pumping from sumps has several disadvantages. First of all, it invites softening and sloughing of the lower part of the slopes, because in this region the seepage velocity and, as a consequence, the seepage pressures are greatest, Articles 39 and 40. Second, since every natural soil stratum is more or less nonuniform, the water emerges in the form of springs. If the soil contains layers or pockets of fine sand or

TABLE 15

CLASSIFICATION OF SOILS ACCORDING TO THEIR
COEFFICIENTS OF PERMEABILITY

Degree of Permeability	Value of k (cm/sec)
High	Over 10^{-1}
Medium	10^{-1} to 10^{-3}
Low	10^{-3} to 10^{-5}
Very low	10^{-5} to 10^{-7}
Practically impermeable	Less than 10^{-7}

coarse silt, the springs are likely to discharge a mixture of soil and water instead of clear water. Springs of this type located on the bottom of the excavation are known as *boils*. Starting at the boils, underground erosion may work backward and form tunnels. The collapse of the roofs of these tunnels leads to subsidence of the ground surface surrounding the excavation, to slumping of the slopes, or to failure of the lateral supports, Articles 59 and 61.[47.1]

The probability of the formation of boils can be reduced by surrounding the excavation with a row of sheet piles driven to some distance below grade. The sheet piles intercept the seepage through all the strata located above the lower edge of the sheet-pile wall and reduce the hydraulic gradient at which the water rises toward the bottom of the excavation. Yet, if the soil conditions are unfavorable, even sheet piles may not prevent the formation of boils with all their undesirable consequences. On small jobs, such as the excavation of shallow timbered cuts in fine-grained water-bearing soils, attempts are often made to prevent the formation of boils by dumping gravel into the cut wherever the soil has a tendency to rise with the water, but this procedure is slow and hazardous. On a large job, such as the excavation for the foundation of a dam, it may be entirely impracticable.

Accidents and serious delays may also be caused by the hydrostatic pressure acting on the base of a continuous relatively impervious layer, such as ab in Figure 141, located beneath the bottom of the excavation. The seepage toward the excavation lowers the piezometric level of only the body of water located above ab, whereas that below ab remains unchanged. If a piezometric tube is installed at a point located below ab, the water rises in this tube to the level of the original water table. If

h = vertical distance between ab and the original water table
h_1 = vertical distance between ab and the bottom of the excavation
γ_w = unit weight of water
γ = unit weight of soil, solid and water combined

the pressure on ab due to the weight of the overlying soil is γh_1, and the hydrostatic upward pressure is $\gamma_w h$. If $\gamma_w h$ is greater than γh_1, and if ab is fairly horizontal, the bottom of the excavation rises bodily. This phenomenon is known as a *heave*. On the other hand, if ab is very uneven, the ground heaves only in those places where h_1 is least. Such a local heave is sometimes referred to as a *blow*.

HISTORICAL REVIEW OF DRAINAGE TECHNIQUES

The first attempts to replace the method of pumping from shallow pits by less hazardous procedures were made between 1870 and 1890 in England and Germany. The shallow sumps were replaced by filter wells with a diameter of 3 or 4 ft. Toward the end of the century it was realized that the efficiency of the new procedure could be improved by reducing the spacing between wells. This fact led to methods of drainage by pumping from rows of wells. The development of these methods took place along different lines in Europe and in the United States.

In Europe it became customary to provide each well with a casing
8 in. in diameter and to pump the water out of the casing through a
6-in. suction tube. The wells were spaced from 20 to 40 ft. The procedure
is referred to as the *Siemens method*, because it was developed by the
Siemens Bau Union in Berlin. Theories were established for computing
the depth to which the wells should be drilled on a given job and for
estimating the quantity of water that would have to be pumped at a
given average coefficient of permeability of the subsoil.[47.2]

In the United States the use of filter wells did not receive serious
attention until about 1920 when the well-point method was introduced.
In contrast to the Siemens method, which consists of pumping from
large-diameter wells spaced at tens of feet, the well-point system consists of drawing the water from wells with a diameter of about 2 in.,
spaced at 3 to 6 ft.

In both the Siemens and the well-point methods the upper ends of the
wells are connected by a horizontal *header pipe* that leads to the pump.
The header pipe is commonly installed on a berm located close to the
original water table. Because of the limited height to which water can be
lifted in a suction tube, the water table cannot be lowered more than
about 20 ft below its original position. Hence, if a project calls for draining the soil to a depth of more than 16 or 18 ft, either the water table
must be lowered by stages, or else the pumping must be done from wells
by means of deep-well pumps that can lift water from any depth below
the mouth of the well.

Soon after the methods of drainage by pumping from batteries of
wells came into general use, it was found that they were ineffective unless the soil had at least medium permeability. As the effective grain
size D_{10} decreased below about 0.1 mm, the time required for draining
the site of an excavation increased rapidly, and, if D_{10} was less than 0.05
mm, pumping from wells did not accomplish its purpose. To prevent the
rise of the bottom of excavations in cohesionless soils with effective size
smaller than 0.05 mm, several different methods were devised.

Starting about 1930, attempts were made in Germany to solidify the
soil located below the bottoms of proposed excavations by the successive
injection of two different chemicals that react in the voids of the soil and
form an insoluble gel. This procedure, known as the *Joosten method*, is
very expensive, and, if the soil contains layers with low permeability, it
is usually ineffective. As a consequence, its practical usefulness in connection with excavations is very limited. In the United States it was
observed that fine-grained soils such as coarse silt could be consolidated
by maintaining a vacuum in the riser pipes of well points. This observation led to the development between 1925 and 1930 of the *vacuum*

method. Finally, in about 1934, attempts were made to consolidate fine-grained soils by the electro-osmotic process. This procedure is called the *electro-osmotic method*.

The following paragraphs contain brief discussions of the principal methods of drainage and of the conditions for their success. The effects of drainage on adjoining property are discussed in Article 61.

Siemens Method

The well casings commonly have a diameter of 8 in. For a length of 15 to 30 ft, measured from their lower ends, they are perforated and surrounded by a brass mesh that acts as a strainer. The best results are obtained if the width of the mesh openings lies between the grain diameters D_{60} and D_{75} of the surrounding soil (see definitions in Article 5). The spacing between wells ranges from 40 ft for very permeable soils to 20 ft for the least permeable soils that can be drained effectively.

Well-Point Method

The term *well point* refers to the lower perforated end of a 2-in. or $2\frac{1}{2}$-in. pipe, commonly 40 in. long, that serves the double purpose of well casing and suction tube. The perforations are covered by a wire mesh. The well points are jetted into the ground at a spacing of 3 to 6 ft.[47.3]

If a series of well points is located beneath a continuous stratum with relatively low permeability, the soil above this stratum is likely to remain undrained. To avoid such an incident and to improve the efficiency of well points in soils of low permeability the following procedure is commonly used. After a well point is jetted into the ground, the pressure in the jetting water is increased, whereupon the soil surrounding the riser pipe is scoured out, and a cylindrical hole is formed. During this process all the fine particles of the soil that formerly occupied the scoured space are washed out of the ground, but the coarser particles that remain and accumulate in the lower part of the hole form a cylindrical filter. If the wash water fails to produce a scouring effect, the hole is made by mechanical means, and the filter is constructed by shoveling sand into the hole.

Drainage of a narrow cut can usually be accomplished by pumping from a single row of well points located on one side of the cut, provided the depth of the cut is considerably less than the depth to which the water table can be lowered by the well points. Otherwise, two rows of well points are required, one on each side of the cut. The cost of pumping is usually small compared to that of transporting and installing the well points, unless the soil contains very permeable layers. If the exploratory borings indicate the presence of exceptionally permeable layers, a pumping test should be made for the purpose of estimating the capacity of the pumps that will be required. In all other instances it is justifiable to select the pumping equipment on the basis of empirical rules. Commonly, one 6-in. self-priming pump is installed for every 500 or 600 ft of the length of the row of well points. If the height to which the water has to be lifted above the level of the header pipe is not excessive, a 20-hp motor is sufficient. The drainage requires between about 2 and 6 days.[47.4]

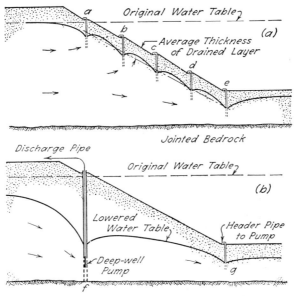

FIG. 142. Drainage of deep cut (a) by multiple-stage setup of well points and (b) by means of deep-well pumps.

MULTIPLE-STAGE SETUP AND DEEP-WELL DRAINAGE

Figure 142 is a section through an open cut with a depth of 50 ft below the original water table. By means of the uppermost set of well points a, the water table can be lowered only to the level of point b, at a depth of less than 20 ft below a. In order to carry the excavation to a lower level, a second row of well points interconnected by a header pipe must be installed several feet above the level of point b, and so on. Such an arrangement is known as a *multiple-stage setup*. One row of well points is required for about every 15 ft of the depth, and an additional row may be needed along the toe of the slope.

Regardless of the number of stages, the average thickness of the inclined layer of soil that is drained cannot be increased to more than about 15 ft, Figure 142a. Beneath this layer the soil is acted on by the seepage pressure of the percolating water. If the depth of the cut is many times greater than 15 ft, the drained layer is only skin deep compared to the thickness of the mass of soil adjoining the slope. The seepage pressures acting within this mass may compromise the stability of the slopes. To avoid this risk the flow of seepage must be intercepted before it enters the space located beneath the slopes. This can be done by pumping from a series of deep wells *f*, Figure 142b, located near the upper edge of the slope. The diameter of these wells must be large enough to permit the installation of deep-well pumps within the casings. The greatest efficiency can be obtained by the use of electrically operated multistage centrifugal pumps mounted on vertical shafts. To prevent sloughing of the toes of the slopes, the small quantity of water that flows through the gaps between the wells is removed through a row of well points *g*.

If the soil profile is fairly uniform, the spacing between the deep wells should be determined on the basis of a theoretical study of the flow of water toward the cut. Such an investigation is economically justified, because deep-well pumps are very expensive. The success of drainage by pumping from deep wells depends primarily on the efficacy of the measures taken to prevent the strainers from becoming clogged with fine particles.

Bleeder Wells

Since pumping from well points or filter wells lowers the water table to elevations everywhere below the slope or subgrade, the risk of slumps is eliminated. This is an important advantage over the method of pumping from open sumps. However, as previously explained, if the lower ends of the well points or filter wells are located above a relatively impervious stratum, such as *ab* in Figure 141, a heave or a blow may occur in spite of the drainage achieved by pumping from the wells. To prevent such accidents outlets must be provided for the water located below the obstructing layer. These outlets are known as *bleeder wells*. The simplest method for constructing bleeder wells is to jet well points into the ground, to wash an annular space around the riser pipe, and to fill this space with coarse sand.

The saturated unit weight γ of most soils is roughly equal to twice the unit weight γ_w of water. Hence, as a rule, the condition for a heave or blow,

$$\gamma h_1 \gtreqless \gamma_w h$$

is not satisfied unless *h*, Figure 141, is greater than $2h_1$. However, in some

performed on spoon samples from the exploratory borings. On large jobs pumping tests may be appropriate.

To determine whether or not bleeder wells are required, the exploratory borings should be drilled to a depth below subgrade equal at least to the vertical distance between the original water table and the subgrade level. As often as a spoon sample is taken, the water should be allowed to rise in the casing, and the elevation to which it rises should appear in the boring record.

Excavations in soils with high permeability (k greater than 0.1 cm per sec) or in very dense mixed-grained soils of medium permeability (k between 10^{-1} and 10^{-3} cm per sec) can as a rule be drained without undue risk by pumping from open sumps.

Under favorable conditions uniform soils of medium permeability can also be drained without mishap by pumping from sumps. However, this procedure involves the possibility of the formation of boils on the bottom of the excavation, associated with underground erosion and subsidence of the area surrounding the excavation. To avoid this risk it is preferable to drain soils of medium permeability by pumping from well points or filter wells. The drainage of the soil prior to excavation requires 2 to 6 days.

The greatest depth to which the water table can be lowered by drawing the water from one set of wells or well points is about 18 ft. If the bottom of the proposed excavation is located at a greater depth, a multiple-stage setup is required. Two or more header pipes must be installed at a vertical spacing of 15 ft. If the depth of the excavation exceeds 50 or 60 ft, it is preferable to drain the soil adjoining the site by means of deep-well pumps operating within the casings of large-diameter wells.

Uniform soils of low permeability (k between 10^{-3} and 10^{-5} cm per sec) cannot be drained by pumping either from sumps or from wells. Such soils can be stabilized most successfully by the vacuum method. The quantity of water that can be drawn out is very small, but, if the pumping is kept up for a period of several weeks, the soil may become so stiff that the sides of excavations up to 15 ft deep can be established at a slope angle of 60° to 70° without risk of failure.

Fine silts and uniform silty soils with a coefficient of permeability between about 10^{-5} and 10^{-7} cm per sec may be so soft that they will rise in the bottom of an excavation having even a moderate depth. Yet, they cannot be drained by any existing method at reasonable expense. Hence, excavations in soft soils of this category must be made by dredging or by the compressed-air method. Fortunately, soils of this category are seldom encountered.

Soils with a coefficient of permeability less than about 10^{-7} cm per sec are with few exceptions very cohesive. They cannot be drained by any practicable means, but drainage is seldom necessary, because the shearing strength is normally great enough to maintain the stability of the bottom of an open excavation of moderate depth. The depth to which an excavation can be made in such a soil without the risk of a rise of the bottom can be increased only by reducing the side slopes, or, if the sides of the excavation are vertical, by increasing the depth of penetration of the sheet piles that constitute part of the lateral support (see Article 48).

REFERENCES

47.1. R. L. Harris, A New Process for Dealing with Quicksand, *Eng. News*, Vol 27 (1892), pp 420–421. Detailed description of boils that developed during the excavation of open cuts in Providence, R. I. The method used for preventing the rise of the soil on the bottom of the excavation has been superseded by the vacuum method.

47.2. W. Kyrieleis and W. Sichardt, *Groundwater Lowering for Foundation Operations* (in German), second edition, Julius Springer, Berlin, 1930. Detailed account of the theory and practice of the Siemens method of drainage.

47.3. *Working in the Dry with the Moretrench Wellpoint System*, commercial publication, Moretrench Co., Rockaway, N. J.

47.4. E. A. Prentis and L. White, *Underpinning*, Columbia University Press, New York, 1931. Description of permeable lining for walls of open cuts, pages 60 and 61; examples of drainage of open excavations, pages 80–90.

47.5. L. Casagrande, *The Application of Electro-osmosis to Practical Problems in Foundations and Earthworks. Report on the Present Position*, H. M. Stationery Office Publication, London, 1947.

ART. 48. LATERAL SUPPORTS IN OPEN CUTS

Introduction

Open cuts may be intended to remain open permanently, like those for highways or railways, or they may be only temporary, to be backfilled after they have served their purpose. The sides of permanent earth cuts are commonly inclined at slopes not steeper than $1\frac{1}{2}$ to 1, Article 49, or else they are supported by retaining walls, Article 46. On the other hand, the sides of temporary cuts are made as steep as the soil conditions permit without risk of slope failure, Figures 144 and 145, or they are made vertical and are braced against each other. The choice depends on the relative costs and the restrictions imposed by the local conditions on the width of the cut.

This article deals with the design of the bracing in temporary cuts with vertical sides. If the bottom of a cut is to be located below the water table, the soil adjoining the cut is drained before or during excavation. Therefore, the design of the bracing can usually be made without considering the position of the water table.

The data needed as a basis for adequate design of the system of bracing depend primarily on the depth of the cut. Therefore, it is convenient to distinguish between *shallow cuts* with a depth less than about 20 ft and *deep cuts* with a greater depth. The bracing of shallow cuts such as trenches for the installation of sewers or water mains is more or less standardized. The customary systems can be used safely under very different soil conditions. Since refinements in the design of such systems would be uneconomical, only a general soil reconnaissance is needed in advance of construction, and no computations of earth pressure are required. On the other hand, in the design of the bracing of deep cuts such as those for subways, the dimensions of the cut and the character of the adjoining soil should be considered, because the savings that can be realized from such a procedure are likely to be very much greater than the cost of obtaining the data for design. In order to obtain adequate information concerning the character of the soil, tube-sample borings or penetration tests may be needed in addition to the standard exploratory borings.

In the past the design of the bracing of deep cuts was usually based on the assumption that the earth pressure increased like a hydrostatic pressure in simple proportion to the depth below the surface. However, both theory, Article 32, and experience have shown that this assumption is rarely justified. Hence, the discussion of deep cuts in the second part of this article includes the methods for designing bracing on the basis of the real pressure distribution.

Bracing of Shallow Cuts

In cohesive soils, cuts with vertical sides can theoretically be made to a depth H_c, equation 24.8, without bracing. The values of H_c for clays of various consistencies are approximately as follows:

	Very Soft	Soft	Medium
H_c (ft)	<5	5–10	10–18

Stiff and very stiff clays are likely to be jointed or fissured, and, as a consequence, the value of H_c may be as low as 10 ft. The value of H_c for cohesive sand depends on the degree of cohesion; it commonly lies between 10 and 15 ft, but it may be considerably greater.

In reality, if a cut with entirely unsupported vertical sides is made in cohesive soil, tension cracks are likely to appear on the surface of the ground adjoining the cut a few hours or days after excavation. The presence of such cracks considerably reduces the critical height (see Article 31), and sooner or later the sides cave in. To prevent such accidents the upper edges of narrow cuts are braced against each other, as shown in Figure 146*a*. The horizontal cross-members are usually referred to as *struts* or *braces*. They may consist of timbers, or of extensible metal supports known as *trench braces*. They are tightened by wedges or screws and support horizontal timbers that usually consist of 3-in. planks. The braces are commonly spaced at about 8 ft, and the load they carry remains very small, unless the cut is located in stiff swelling clay.

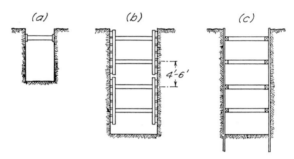

Fig. 146.   Diagrams illustrating different methods for constructing shallow open cuts.   (*a*) Single row of struts; (*b*) lagging; (*c*) sheeting.

If the depth of a narrow cut exceeds about $\frac{1}{2}H_c$, struts are usually inserted as excavation proceeds. They are wedged against short vertical timbers known as *soldier beams* that bear against horizontal boards known as *lagging* (see Figure 146*b*). It is usually unnecessary to fit the lagging boards tightly together; if space is left between them, they constitute *open lagging*. An alternative procedure is to wedge the struts against horizontal timbers known as *wales* that support vertical boards known as *sheeting*. The lowest part of the sides, with a height of about $\frac{1}{2}H_c$, can be left unsupported in order to furnish adequate working space, provided the soil does not have a tendency to slake or ravel. If it does, the sheets are carried down to the bottom of the excavation, but no struts are required to hold them in place.

In perfectly cohesionless sand or gravel only vertical sheeting can be used. One row of sheeting is usually driven on each side of the cut, and wales and struts are inserted as excavation proceeds. The sheets are commonly driven a few feet at a time, but their lower ends are always kept several feet below excavation level, Figure 146*c*.

The dimensions of the bracing are fairly well standardized, regardless of the type of soil. Struts are spaced at about 8 ft horizontally and 4 to 6 ft vertically. Metal trench braces are available for cuts up to 5 ft in width. For narrow cuts wooden struts are usually 4 by 6 in. The dimensions increase to about 8 by 8 in. for cuts 12 ft wide. Sheeting or lagging usually consists of planks 6 to 10 in. wide. Bracing of these dimensions can be used safely in cohesionless sand to a depth of about 30 ft and in soft clay to a depth of about 10 ft in excess of $\frac{1}{2}H_c$.

Bracing of Deep Cuts

General considerations in design of bracing. The most common methods for supporting the sides of deep cuts are illustrated in Figure

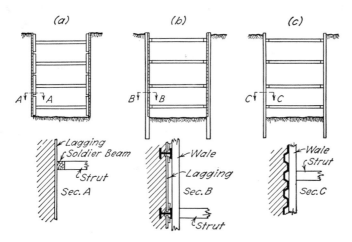

Fig. 147.   Diagrams illustrating different methods for constructing deep open cuts. (a) Use of lagging and soldier beams; (b) use of H-piles, lagging and wales; (c) use of sheet piles and wales.

147. When an open cut is excavated, the struts are inserted as the depth of the excavation increases. In Article 32 it is shown that this procedure is accompanied by an inward movement of the soil on each side of the cut. At the ground surface the movement is restricted to a very small amount, because the uppermost row of struts is inserted before the state of stress in the soil is appreciably altered by excavation. However, the movement that precedes the insertion of struts at lower levels increases as the depth of excavation increases. According to Article 32, this type of yielding is associated with a roughly parabolic distribution of pressure, and the maximum intensity of pressure occurs near mid-height of the cut, whereas the lateral pressure exerted against a retaining wall by a backfill with a horizontal surface increases like a hydrostatic pressure in simple proportion to the depth below the surface.

Another fundamental difference between a retaining wall and the bracing in a cut is the manner in which these two types of support fail. A retaining wall constitutes a structural unit, and it fails as a unit. Local irregularities in the magnitude of the backfill pressure are of little consequence. However, any strut in an open cut can fail as an individual. Since the failure of one strut involves an increase of the load on its neighbors, it may initiate a progressive failure of the entire system of bracing.

Finally, it should be borne in mind that the shearing resistance of the soil adjacent to a vertical face does not become fully active until the face has yielded through a certain distance (see Article 23). Every retaining wall can yield through several times this distance without being damaged, but a strut may fail by buckling before the shearing resistance of the supported soil becomes fully active.

It is impracticable to find out by laboratory tests or any other indirect means whether or not the process of excavating and bracing a cut is actually associated with enough movement to reduce the total lateral earth pressure to the active value. Furthermore, at a given total pressure on the bracing system, the loads carried by the individual struts can be very different, because they depend on accidental factors such as the force with which the wedges are driven, the local variations in the adjoining soil, and the time which elapses between excavation and insertion of a strut at a given point. In view of these facts, no procedure for designing the bracing in cuts should be trusted until its reliability has been demonstrated by the results of measurements in full-sized cuts. So far, measurements of this kind have been made only in deep cuts in dense sand and in soft and medium glacial clay.

Deep cuts excavated in sand. Strut-load measurements were made during the construction of a subway in Berlin, for which an open cut was excavated to a depth of 38 ft in fine, dense, fairly uniform sand. Before and during excavation, the ground-water level was lowered to a considerable depth below final grade by the Siemens method, Article 47. Hence, during construction the cut was located above the water table. The cut was braced as shown in Figure 147b. The struts were arranged in vertical planes spaced uniformly along the length of the cut, and the pressure on the struts was measured in ten of these planes.[48.1] The distribution of pressure on four sets of struts is shown in Figure 148a. The curves obtained for the other sets lie within the area occupied by the curves shown in the figure.

Although the sand at the site of this open cut was fairly uniform, the shape of the curves representing the pressure distribution varied considerably from the statistical average. The variations were probably caused to some extent by local differences in the soil properties and to a greater extent by differences in the details of construction procedure at different locations. Yet, all the curves were roughly parabolic, and the distance from the bottom of the cut to the center of pressure ranged between the rather narrow limits of $0.53H$ and $0.60H$. Most of the values ranged between $0.53H$ and $0.55H$.

According to Article 32, the total earth pressure against a vertical support is somewhat greater than the Coulomb value if the center of pressure is located above the lower third-point of the support. If the

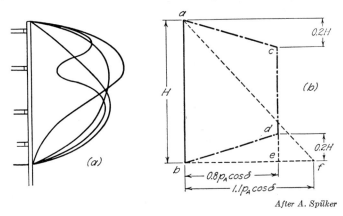

FIG. 148. (a) Results of measurement of lateral earth pressure against bracing of open cut in dense sand in Berlin; (b) diagram showing trapezoidal distribution of earth pressure to be assumed for design of struts in open cuts in sand.

distance from the bottom of the support to the point of application of the resultant pressure is about $0.55H$, as found in the open cut in Berlin, the total earth pressure is about 10 per cent greater than the Coulomb value. If the distribution of the pressure were hydrostatic, the total earth pressure against the bracing of the open cut would correspond to the area of the triangle abf, Figure 148b, in which the base bf is equal to 1.1 times the intensity p_A cos δ of the horizontal component of the Coulomb pressure at the bottom of the cut. The factor 1.1 represents the ratio between the total earth pressure on the sides of the cut and the corresponding Coulomb value.

However, the real distribution of pressure at a given vertical section may resemble any of the different curves in Figure 148a. It changes from place to place. Since each strut should be designed for the maximum pressure that may act on it, the greatest value that a strut load can assume is determined by the envelope of all the curves obtained by plotting the measured strut loads. This envelope is approximately represented by the trapezoid *acdb*. The maximum intensity of pressure corresponding to the fictitious trapezoidal distribution is only 0.8 of the maximum Coulomb value, but the area of the trapezoid exceeds that of the triangle by about 20 per cent. This excess provides for the scattering

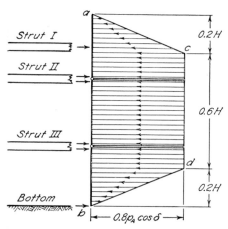

from the average of the individual strut loads at a given level and eliminates the danger of progressive failure of the strut system.

In order to estimate the loads for which the struts in a cut in dense sand should be designed, the following procedure can be used. A scale drawing, Figure 149, is prepared that shows a section through the vertical H-piles or sheet piles. At the elevation of

Fig. 149.   Diagram illustrating assumptions made in calculating loads for design of struts in open cut in sand.

each strut except the uppermost, the piles are assumed to be hinged, and at the bottom of the cut they are assumed to bear against a knife edge. The vertical piles are acted on by the horizontal load represented by the trapezoidal area *acdb*, Figure 149. The maximum intensity of the horizontal load, according to this figure, is

$$0.8p_A \cos \delta = 0.8\gamma H \left[P_A \frac{\cos \delta}{\frac{1}{2}\gamma H^2} \right]$$

The quantity in brackets may be taken directly from the charts, Figure 67. Each portion of the vertical pile between hinges acts as a simply supported beam carrying its own portion of the total load (see Figure 149). The reactions caused by the loading are computed according to the principles of statics. To obtain the strut loads, the total reaction at the level of each strut is multiplied by the horizontal spacing between struts. The design of each strut should be based on a factor of safety of 2 with respect to buckling.

Since the construction procedure used in Berlin did not differ in any essential respect from that commonly used in excavating and bracing open cuts in sand, the design procedure illustrated by Figure 149 may be used with confidence in connection with open cuts in dense sand in any other locality. On the other hand, no field data are yet available regarding the pressure exerted by loose sand. Therefore, it is not known whether the pressure at the bottom of the cut is reduced as effectively in loose as in dense sand. Because of this uncertainty, computations concerning the pressure of loose sand should be based on the pressure area *aceb* rather than *acdb*, Figure 148*b*. This rule should be followed until reliable measurements are available.

Conditions seldom warrant the determination of ϕ and δ by laboratory tests. Sufficiently accurate values of ϕ can be estimated on the basis of Table 7, page 82. The relative density of the sand can be ascertained by means of subsurface soundings, Article 44. For bracing of the type shown in Figure 147*a*, δ is equal to $0°$. For the types shown in Figures 147*b* and *c*, the value of δ is greater than zero, but it is not likely to exceed $20°$. The unit weight γ of the sand should be measured in the same manner as that of the sand backfill of a retaining wall, Article 46.

If the water table is lowered by pumping from open sumps in the cut, ample allowance should be made for seepage pressures against the lower part of the bracing. Drainage through the spaces between lagging boards is not sufficient to eliminate seepage pressures. The effect of this type of drainage is similar to that of the vertical drainage layer behind the retaining wall shown in Figure 139*a*.

Deep cuts excavated in clay. According to Article 15, the average shearing resistance s of the clay along a potential surface of sliding is roughly equal to one-half the average unconfined compressive strength q_u of 2-in. tube samples of the clay. Hence, the lateral pressure exerted by a mass of clay can be computed on the simplifying assumption that the clay is an ideal plastic material for which $\phi = 0°$ and $s = q_u/2$. If part of the mass of soil consists of sand, the average shearing resistance of the sand is estimated, and the sand stratum is replaced in the soil profile by a fictitious clay stratum having a shearing resistance $s = q_u/2$. The average shearing strength of the entire mass of soil adjacent to the cut is equal to the weighted average of the values of s for the individual layers.

According to Rankine's earth-pressure theory, Article 24, the active earth pressure at depth z below the horizontal surface of a semi-infinite mass of plastic material with a cohesion $c = s = q_u/2$, and an angle of internal friction $\phi = 0°$, is

$$p_A = \gamma z - q_u \qquad (48.1)$$

and the total pressure on a vertical plane with height H is

$$p_A = \int_0^H (\gamma z - q_u)dz = \frac{1}{2}\gamma H^2\left(1 - \frac{2q_u}{\gamma H}\right) \qquad (48.2)$$

Figure 150*a* represents a vertical section through one side of a deep cut in medium and soft clay in Chicago, Ill. In Figure 150b, the ordinates represent the depth below the ground surface, and the abscissas the corresponding values of the unconfined compressive strength q_u of the clay. The weighted average of the values of q_u for the clay and the super-imposed sand is 2100 lb per sq ft. By introducing this value into equation 48.1 and plotting the values of p_A as abscissas against the depth z the dash line in Figure 150a was obtained. It indicates the distribution of the active pressure against the bracing in the cut on the assumption that the adjoining clay is in an active Rankine state.

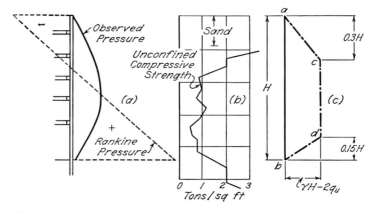

Fig. 150.   (a) Results of measurement of lateral earth pressure against bracing of open cut in medium clay in Chicago; (b) variation in unconfined compressive strength of clay adjacent to cut; (c) fictitious distribution of pressure used as a basis for design of struts in open cuts in soft and medium clay.

The data required for computing the real magnitude and distribution of the pressure were obtained by measuring the loads carried by the individual struts. The results of the computations are represented by the plain curve in Figure 150a. The shape of this curve leaves no doubt that the earth pressure against the bracing of this cut conformed not with Rankine's earth-pressure theory, but with the theory presented in Article 32. The results of similar measurements on several other cuts in soft and medium clays in Chicago led to the same conclusion.[48.2]

The vertical distance H_1 from the bottom of the cuts to the center of pressure was found to range between $0.42H$ and $0.56H$, with an average value of $0.45H$. For this range in the values of H_1, the theory given in Article 32 leads to the following conclusions. If the resultant of the earth pressure and the adhesion on the bracing acts in a horizontal direction, the real pressure should exceed the Rankine value, equation 48.2, by about 50 per cent. As the inclination of the resultant increases, the lateral pressure decreases, and, if the inclination of the resultant force is 20°, the two values of pressure should be approximately equal. Since the bracing of all the Chicago cuts was of the types shown in Figures 147b and c, the sheeting was capable of sustaining a vertical load, and it was estimated that the resultant force could develop a vertical component corresponding to an inclination of the resultant of 20°. Hence, the measured strut loads should have been approximately equal to the total pressure determined by equation 48.2.

The preceding conclusion was confirmed by the pressure measurements in all those cuts in which the bracing was carefully constructed and tightly prestressed or wedged. The greatest lateral yield of the clay toward the cut did not exceed 0.25 per cent of the depth of the cut, and, as a consequence, the settlement of the adjacent ground surface was insignificant. On the other hand, a conspicuous settlement of the ground surface adjacent to one cut indicated an excessive yield of the clay, and the pressure against the bracing considerably exceeded the value that would be expected on the basis of equation 48.2.

These observations indicated that even the small amount of yielding associated with the most workmanlike procedure for installing the bracing was sufficient to develop the full shearing resistance of the clay encountered in the cuts in Chicago. Any yield greater than this amount was detrimental in every respect. In order to prevent excessive yield, it was found advisable to prestress the struts by driving wedges between the wales and the piles or, preferably, by jacking the opposite wales apart while the struts were inserted.

The observations in Chicago were made in cuts excavated in clays for which the liquid limit varied between 28 and 52 per cent, with an average of about 36 per cent. The points representing the clays are all located above line A in the plasticity chart, Figure 9. Therefore, the materials belong in the class of inorganic clays of medium plasticity. The uppermost 3 to 6 ft of the clay stratum were precompressed by desiccation, whereas the underlying strata were normally or almost normally loaded. The ratio between the critical height H_c of the clay and the depth H of the cuts ranged from about 0.45 to 0.8. These data constitute the known range of the validity of conclusions that may be drawn from the observations.

Based on the observations on the clay cuts in the Chicago area, the following procedure has been developed for estimating the loads on individual struts in cuts in similar clays. The first requirement is to obtain reliable information concerning the unconfined compressive strength of the clay. Two-inch tube-sample borings should be located close to the center line of the proposed cut at a spacing not exceeding

100 ft. After the compressive strength values have been obtained, the design should be based on the lowest average value of q_u obtained from any one of the borings.

The method for determining the design loads for the individual struts is similar to that described in connection with cuts in dense sand. The calculations are based on the trapezoid *abdc*, Figure 150c, which contains all the curves representing the measured pressures against the cuts in Chicago. The width of the trapezoid is equal to the quantity,

$$\gamma H - 2q_u$$

The total pressure represented by the area *abdc*, Figure 150c, exceeds the total pressure that acts on any individual set of struts by about 50 per cent. As explained in the discussion of deep cuts in sand, the excess provides for the scattering from the average of the individual strut loads at a given level. The factor of safety of the struts with respect to buckling should not be less than 2.

Experience has shown that the reduction of the bending moments in the wales due to arching of the clay between the vertical H-piles or soldier beams is too small to deserve consideration. Therefore, the maximum bending moment in each wale should be computed on the assumption that the load transferred from the sheeting to the wale is uniformly distributed in the horizontal direction.

If a clay is so soft that the value H_c/H is close to zero, the lateral pressure may increase almost in simple proportion to the depth. In soft organic clays the yield associated with the processes of excavation and bracing may not be sufficient to develop the full shearing resistance of the clay. In heavily precompressed clays the tendency of the clay to expand may gradually increase the lateral pressure to several times the value that would be expected on the basis of equation 48.2. Because of these still unexplored possibilities, design rules of general validity for open cuts in clays cannot be worked out until observations similar to those made in Chicago have been repeated in cuts in very different types of clay.

If a cut is excavated in soft clay, the bottom may heave because of the inability of the clay to sustain the weight of the overburden on either side. The factor of safety with respect to heave can be estimated with reasonable accuracy by means of the theory given in Article 32. If the theoretical factor of safety is inadequate, the heave can usually be prevented by sheet piling driven to a sufficient depth below the bottom. The necessary depth of penetration can be computed. If the use of sheet piles is impracticable, the cut can be excavated only by dredging.

SUMMARY OF PROCEDURES AND PROBLEMS

The excavation and bracing of cuts with a depth of less than about 20 ft merely require conscientious adherence to existing empirical rules. The earth pressure against the bracing of such cuts is a factor of secondary importance, because it is more economical to use one of the standard systems of bracing at the price of some excess material than to adapt the bracing to local soil conditions.

On the other hand, the bracing of deep and wide cuts accounts for a considerable part of the total cost. Furthermore, substantial savings can often be realized by various departures from the standard methods of bracing, such as providing for a large unobstructed working space between the bottom of the cut and the lowest row of struts. In order to comply with the requirements of both safety and economy, it is necessary to make a thorough soil survey and to prepare the plans on the basis of the results of earth-pressure computations.

Experience has shown, in agreement with theory, that the classical earth-pressure theories are inapplicable to open-cut problems. The earth pressure exerted by dense or fairly dense sand and by normally loaded or partly desiccated inorganic moderately plastic clay can be computed by means of the procedures described under the preceding subheadings. The application of theory to the design of the bracing systems for cuts in other types of soil should be practiced with caution until the reliability of the results is demonstrated by field measurements.

Published records concerning experience in open cut construction are very scarce, and the value of most of them is impaired by the absence of adequate descriptions of the soil in which the cuts were made.

REFERENCES

48.1. K. TERZAGHI, General Wedge Theory of Earth Pressure, *Trans. ASCE*, Vol 106 (1941), pp 68–97. Methods and results of earth-pressure measurements in open cut in sand in Berlin.

48.2. R. B. PECK, Earth Pressure Measurements in Open Cuts, Chicago Subway, *Trans. ASCE*, Vol 108 (1943), pp 1008–1036. Contains results of earth-pressure measurements on several open cuts in soft and medium clays.

48.3. R. B. PECK, The Measurement of Earth Pressures on the Chicago Subway, *ASTM Bull.*, Aug. 1941, pp 25–30. Description of techniques for measuring strut loads.

48.4. J. C. MEEM, The Bracing of Trenches and Tunnels, with Practical Formulas for Earth Pressures, *Trans. ASCE*, Vol 60 (1908), pp 1–23, discussions pp 24–100. The paper contains interesting records of observations in trenches in very different soils. The theoretical parts of the paper and the discussions can claim only historical interest. The soil data are inadequate.

⟨Art. 49.⟩ STABILITY OF HILLSIDES AND SLOPES IN OPEN CUTS

Causes and General Characteristics of Slope Failures

Every mass of soil located beneath a sloping ground surface or beneath the sloping sides of an open cut has a tendency to move downward and outward under the influence of gravity. If this tendency is counteracted by the shearing resistance of the soil, the slope is stable. Otherwise a slide occurs. The material involved in a slide may consist of naturally deposited soil, of man-made fill, or of a combination of the two. In this article only slides in natural soil are considered. The other types are discussed subsequently.

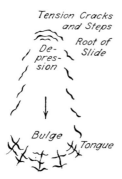

Fig. 151. Plan of typical slide in cohesive material.

Slides in natural soil may be caused by such external disturbances as undercutting the foot of an existing slope or digging an excavation with unsupported sides. On the other hand, they may also occur without external provocation on slopes that have been stable for many years. Failures of this nature are caused either by a temporary increase in porewater pressure or by a progressive deterioration of the strength of the soil.

In spite of the variety of conditions that may cause a slide, almost every slide exhibits the general characteristics illustrated by Figure 151. The failure is preceded by the formation of tension cracks on the upper part of the slope or beyond its crest. During the slide the upper part of the slide area, known as the *root*, subsides, whereas the lower part, known as the *tongue*, bulges. Hence, if the original surface of the slope is a plane, the profile of the ground surface along the axis of the slide becomes distorted into an S-shaped curve (see Figure 78). The shape of the tongue depends to a certain extent on the type of sliding material. Homogeneous clay with a low degree of sensitivity to disturbance is likely to bulge, as shown in Figure 151. On the other hand, clay with a very sensitive structure or clay with sand pockets is likely to flow like a liquid.

Even on uniform slopes of great length and approximately uniform height, slides seldom occur at more than a few places, separated from each other by considerable distances. For example, the well-known slides in the Panama Canal appear in plan as isolated scars separated by long stretches of intact slope. Slides in long railroad cuts of fairly uniform cross section exhibit similar characteristics.

One important class of slides, however, provides an exception to the general rule that slides do not occur over a broad front. If the geological conditions are such that the major part of the surface of sliding is located within a horizontal layer of coarse silt or sand that separates two layers of clay, the width of the slide measured parallel to the crest of the slope is likely to be very much greater than the length of the slide. Slides of this type are commonly caused by an excess pore-water pressure in the sand or silt layer. In contrast to slides of the other types, they are not preceded by readily detectible symptoms of impending danger, and the failure occurs almost suddenly.

Engineering Problems Involving the Stability of Slopes

Most of the problems involving the stability of slopes are associated with the design and construction of unbraced cuts for highways, railways, and canals. The necessity for excavating deep cuts did not arise until early in the 19th century, when the first railways were built. Since that time, however, countless cuts with increasingly greater depth and length have been excavated.

Experience has shown that slopes of $1\frac{1}{2}$ (horizontal) to 1 (vertical) are commonly stable. As a matter of fact, the sides of most railway and highway cuts less than 20 ft deep rise at that slope, as do the sides of many deeper perfectly stable cuts. Therefore, a slope of $1\frac{1}{2}$ to 1 can be considered the standard for highway and railway construction. The standard slopes for flooded cuts such as those for canals range between 2:1 and 3:1. Steeper than standard slopes should be established only on rock, on dense sandy soil interspersed with boulders, and on true loess.

Slopes on rock are beyond the scope of this book. On dense mixtures of sand and gravel with boulders slopes of 1:1 have been permanently stable. In arid climates real loess must be given a vertical slope, because inclined slopes cannot be adequately protected against rapid erosion. The foot of the vertical faces requires careful protection against temporary saturation during rainstorms. In spite of this precaution, slices inevitably break down from time to time, again leaving vertical faces that remain stable for years. To prevent blocking of traffic by the debris it is customary to make cuts in loess with a width greater than that called for by the traffic requirements. Submerged slopes in typical loess are likely to constitute a serious problem. They are discussed subsequently.

Preliminary estimates of the quantity of excavation required for establishing a new line of transportation are commonly based on the assumption that all the cuts in earth will be provided with standard slopes. However, experience has shown that the standard slopes are stable only if the cuts are made in favorable ground. The term *favorable ground* indicates cohesionless or cohesive sandy or gravelly soil in a moist or dry state. In soft clay or in stiff fissured clay the excavation of even a very shallow cut with standard slopes may cause the soil to move toward the cut, and the movement may spread to a distance from the cut equal to many times the depth. Clay soils containing layers or pockets of water-bearing sand may react to a disturbance of their equilibrium in a similar manner. Deposits with properties of this type constitute *troublesome ground*.

Experienced engineers always locate new lines of transportation with a view of avoiding cuts in troublesome ground as far as conditions permit. If a project requires long cuts in potentially troublesome soil, estimates are likely to show that the project is uneconomical, unless the margin of safety is reduced to considerably less than the margin of error in stability computations. As a consequence, in cuts through troublesome soil local slides are commonly and justly considered inevitable. At the same time sound engineering requires that the slides should not involve loss of life or serious damage to property. This requirement can be satisfied only by means of extensive and conscientiously executed field observations during and after construction. Such observations and no other means make it possible to detect the symptoms of impending slides and to take appropriate measures for avoiding fatal consequences.

The methods for dealing with unstable slopes depend primarily on the nature of the soils involved. Hence, for practical purposes it is most suitable to classify slides in accordance with the types of soil in which they occur. The most common types of troublesome soils and soil formations are accumulations of detritus derived from shales or schists, very loose water-bearing sand, homogeneous soft clay, stiff fissured clay, clay with sand or silt partings, and bodies of cohesive soil containing layers or pockets of water-bearing sand or silt. In the following text the causes of slides are described, and present practice in dealing with the engineering aspects of the problems are summarized. Because of the complexity of the subject, the information serves merely as an introduction to a study of the stability of slopes in natural soil strata.

Slopes on Detritus

The term *detritus* refers to a loose accumulation of relatively sound pieces of rock intermingled with completely weathered ones. Detritus may constitute a blanket covering a gentle rock slope to a thickness of up to about 20 ft, or it may occur as a talus at the foot of a steep rock cliff.

In a dry or permanently drained state detritus of any kind is likely to be so stable that standard slopes can be maintained without any difficulty. Slopes of 1:1 are not uncommon, and their stability is not necessarily impaired by occasional wet spells. However, there are notable exceptions to this statement. Detritus derived from some types of rock is so profoundly affected by saturation that it starts to flow even on gentle slopes as soon as the degree of saturation has reached a certain value.

In parts of West Virginia, southern Pennsylvania, and eastern Ohio periodic flows of this nature occur, without external provocation, on

From G. E. Ladd

Fig. 152.   Photograph of detritus slide on gentle slope, near Barboursville, W. Va.

slopes as gentle as 10°. As a matter of fact, much of the surface topography in these regions owes its origin to such slides.[49.1] Figure 152 shows a photograph of a detritus slide near Barboursville, W. Va. Figure 153 is a profile of a double slide in the same locality.

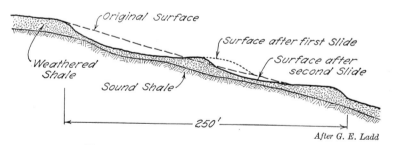

After G. E. Ladd

Fig. 153.   Profile of double slide in detritus.

The character of these flows indicates that they are caused by a temporary transfer of the weight of the sliding mass from the points of contact between the solid constituents to the pore water. This process is analogous to the liquefaction of loose water-bearing sand (see Article 17). However, the structure of detritus, unlike that of loose sand, is not sensitive to shock, and the weight transfer is due to a different cause.

Experience has shown that detritus slides on gentle slopes occur only in material composed of weak, brittle, partly decomposed fragments of laminated shale or of various schists. They are especially common in detritus containing fragments of chlorite-, mica-, and talc-schists. During each dry season, these fragments disintegrate to a certain extent. Under the increased load due to saturation in the following wet season some of the fragments fail and transfer their load to the water.

The most effective means for preventing detritus slides on gentle slopes is adequate drainage. However, since the layer of detritus is commonly shallow (see Figure 153), slow detritus flows can also be stopped by driving piles through the moving material into its firm base. Usually several rows are driven, at right angles to the direction of the flow.[49.1]

Slides on steep talus occur most commonly when snow is melting and less often during heavy rainstorms. The nature of the fragments does not seem to be significant. After a slide starts, the saturated material rushes in a swift torrent down the valley, transporting rock fragments up to several cubic yards in size, removing bridges in its path, and spreading at the mouth of the valley like a fan. These slides, known as *mud spates* or *mud rock flows*, are common in high mountain chains in every part of the world. On the western slope of the Wasatch Mountains in Utah every canyon contains the remnants of at least one mud rock flow.[49.2] Since slides of this type occur irrespective of the relative density or petrographic character of the detritus, and only on steep slopes, it is probable that they are caused exclusively by the seepage pressure of percolating water.

In the Alps it has been observed that mud rock flows are commonly preceded by the drying up of springs emerging from the root area of the flows. This phenomenon indicates a temporary increase in the pore space of the talus material prior to the shear, similar to the increase of the void ratio of a test specimen of dense sand before failure by shear (see Article 15).

Since no slide in detritus can take place without an abundance of water, the danger of such slides can be eliminated by preventing temporary saturation. This can be accomplished by installing a deep drain along the upper boundary of the area to be protected and by covering the surface of the area with a layer of relatively impermeable soil. In many instances the drain alone will have the desired effect.

STABILITY OF SLOPES AND CUTS IN SAND

Sand of any kind, permanently located above the water table, can be considered stable ground in which cuts with standard slopes can be made safely. Dense and medium sands located below the water table are equally stable. Slides can occur only in loose saturated sand. They are caused by spontaneous liquefaction, Article 17. The disturbance required to release a sand slide can be produced either by a shock or by a rapid change in the position of the water table. Once the movement has started, the sand flows as if it were a liquid and does not stop until the slope angle becomes smaller than 10°.

In some localities slides of this nature constitute a recurrent phenomenon. The sand slides along the coast of the island of Zeeland in Holland belong in this category.[49.3] The coast is located on a thick stratum of fine quartz sand that consists of rounded grains. The slope of

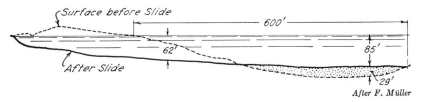

After F. Müller

FIG. 154.   Section through flow slide in sand at coast of Zeeland.

the beach is only about 15°. Yet, once every few decades after exceptionally high spring tides, the structure of the sand breaks down beneath a short section of the coastal belt. The sand flows out and spreads with great speed in a fan-shaped sheet over the bottom of the adjacent body of water. The tongue of the slide is always very much broader than the root. Figure 154 shows a section through one such slide. The final slope of the ground surface was less than 5°. A slide that occurred at Borssele in 1874 involved nearly 2,000,000 cu yd.

Since flow slides in sand occur only if the sand is very loose, the tendency toward sliding can be reduced by increasing the density of the sand. This can be accomplished by several different means, such as pile driving or exploding small charges of blasting powder at many points in the interior of the mass (see Article 50).

STABILITY OF CUTS IN LOESS

Real loess is a cohesive wind-laid soil with an effective grain size between about 0.02 and 0.006 mm and a low uniformity coefficient. It consists chiefly of angular and subangular quartz grains that are slightly cemented together. Furthermore, it always contains an intricate network of more or less vertical root holes. The cohesion of the loess is due to thin films of slightly soluble cementing material that cover the walls of the root holes. Since the root holes are predominantly vertical, the loess has a tendency to break by splitting along vertical surfaces, and its permeability in a vertical direction is very great compared to that in a horizontal direction. Its porosity may be as great as 52 per cent.

When loess is permanently located above the water table, it is a very stable soil except for the fact that it is readily attacked by erosion. On the other hand, permanently submerged loess is likely to be very unstable because of its high porosity and because of the leaching effects of submergence. Leaching removes the cementing substance and transforms the loess into an almost cohesionless material that is not stable unless its porosity is less than about 47 per cent.[49.4]

The effect of submergence is illustrated by the results of a large-scale experiment performed on a plateau of loess in Soviet Turkestan. The loess has an average porosity of 50 per cent. In dry cuts it stands with unsupported vertical faces for a height of more than 50 ft. The experiment was made to find out whether the material would remain stable if an unlined canal were excavated across the plateau and filled with water for irrigation. An open pit, 160 by 60 ft in plan, was dug 10 ft deep with sides sloping at 1.5 to 1. The pit was then filled with water, and the water level kept constant by replacing the seepage losses. After a few days the slopes started to slough, and the bottom began to subside. This process continued at a decreasing rate for a period of about 6 weeks. At the end of this period the surface surrounding the excavation had cracked and subsided within a distance of about 20 ft from the original edge of the pit, and the bottom had subsided about $2\frac{1}{2}$ ft. Within the area of subsidence and sloughing the loess was so soft that it was not possible to walk on it.

It is conceivable, but not certain, that the strength of the loess beside and beneath such a canal could be preserved by treating the wetted perimeter of the canal with a bituminous material.

SLIDES IN FAIRLY HOMOGENEOUS SOFT CLAY

If the sides of a cut in a thick layer of soft clay rise at the standard slope of 1.5:1, a slide is likely to occur before the cut reaches a depth of 10 ft. The movement has the character of a base failure (see Article 31 and Figure 79*b*) associated with a rise of the bottom of the cut. If the clay stratum is buried beneath stable sediments, or if it has a stiff crust, the heave occurs when the bottom of the cut approaches the surface of the soft material.

On the other hand, if the soft clay is underlain by bedrock or a layer of stiff clay at a short distance below the bottom of the cut, failure occurs along a toe or slope circle tangent to the surface of the stiff stratum, because the bottom cannot heave (see Article 31).

If a mass of soft clay has an irregular shape, the location of the surface of sliding is likely to be determined by that shape. Figure 155 illustrates this statement. It represents a section through a slide that occurred during the construction of the Södertalje canal in Sweden. If the soft clay had extended to a considerable depth, base failure would have occurred approximately along a mid-point circle. However, the presence of the gravel below the soft clay excluded the possibility of a base failure, and the slide occurred along a toe circle. The movement was so rapid that several workmen were killed.[49.5]

Experience has shown that the average shearing resistance along a surface of sliding in homogeneous clay is roughly equal to one-half the unconfined compressive strength of the clay (see references 49.6 and 49.7; also Article 15). Therefore, the factor of safety of the slopes of proposed cuts in such clay with respect to sliding can be estimated in advance of construction by the method described in Article 31. However, it should be emphasized that discontinuities in the clay, consisting of sand or silt partings, may invalidate the results of the computation. The reason is explained in the paragraphs dealing with nonhomogeneous clay.

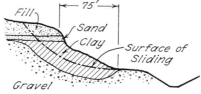

After Swedish Geotechnical Commission

Fig. 155.   Section through toe-circle slide in soft clay on Södertalje canal in Sweden.

CLAY FLOWS

After a slope on soft clay fails, the movement commonly stops as soon as the tongue of the slide, Figure 151, has advanced to a moderate distance from its original position. There is, however, one notable exception to this rule. If the sensitivity of the clay is very high, Article 8, the breakdown of the structure caused by remolding transforms the clay into a thick slurry. During a slide in such a clay the moving mass breaks up into chunks that are lubricated by the remolded portion of the clay. The mixture of chunks and matrix is so mobile that it may flow like a stream for hundreds or even thousands of feet on an almost horizontal surface. Movements of this kind are referred to as clay flows, although their origin may be the same as that of ordinary clay slides.

Typical clay flows have occurred from time to time, without artificial cause, along the banks of the northern tributaries of the St. Lawrence River in Quebec. The block diagram, Figure 156, shows the principal features of such a flow. During the flow a roughly rectangular area having a length of 1700 ft parallel to the river and 3000 ft perpendicular to the river subsided from 15 to 30 ft. Within several hours 3,500,000 cu yd of the underlying silty clay moved into the river channel through a gap 200 ft wide. The channel was blocked for over 2 miles, and the upstream water level was raised 25 ft.[49.2]

Similar flows have occurred in other parts of Canada, in the state of Maine, and in the Scandinavian countries.[49.2, 49.8] The index properties of the soils which flow in this manner are not yet reliably known. The few data which are available indicate that the soils are either very fine rock flours or very silty clays of glacial origin with a natural water con-

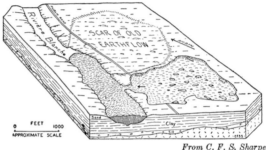

From C. F. S. Sharpe

Fig. 156.   Block diagram showing principal features of slide in very silty clay near St. Thuribe, Quebec.

tent high above the liquid limit. In the plasticity chart, Figure 9, they are represented by points in the region reserved for inorganic clays of low plasticity. The excessive water content, which seems to constitute a prerequisite, indicates a very high degree of sensitivity and possibly a well-developed skeleton structure.

The records of the slides suggest that the soil movements are preceded by extensive subterranean erosion starting from springs at the foot of the slope (see Article 59). If the springs are submerged, the erosion may not be noticed. However, since the width of an eroded tunnel increases with increasing distance from the point of discharge (see Article 59), it is conceivable that at some distance from the outlet the width may become so great that the roof will collapse. Because of its high sensitivity, the falling clay would liquefy, whereupon it could escape by flowing through the intact part of the tunnel. The stream of semiliquid clay would cause further erosion, leading to the collapse of the roof of the discharge section of the tunnel. If this hypothesis is confirmed by future more specific observations, it should be possible to prevent such slides by covering the ground surface near the toe of the slope by an inverted filter.

SLIDES IN STIFF CLAY

Almost every stiff clay is weakened by a network of hair cracks or slickensides. If the surfaces of weakness subdivide the clay into small fragments 1 in. or less in size, a slope may become unstable during construction or shortly thereafter. On the other hand, if the spacing of the joints is greater, failure may not occur until many years after the cut is made.

Slides in clay with closely spaced joints occur as soon as the shearing stresses exceed the average shearing resistance of the fissured clay. Several slides of this type took place in a long railway cut at Rosengarten, near Frankfurt in Germany. The slope of the sides was 3:1.

FIG. 157. Section through fissured stiff clay mass. (a) Old fissures closed before relief of stress by excavation; (b) relief of stress causes fissures to open, whereupon circulating water softens clay adjoining the walls.

The greatest depth of the cut was 100 ft, and the average shearing stresses along the surfaces of sliding adjoining the deepest part of the cut were roughly 10 tons per sq ft. The clay was very stiff, but large specimens broke readily into small angular pieces with shiny surfaces. Slides started immediately after construction, and continued for 15 years.[49.9]

Attempts to determine the shearing resistance of such clays in advance of construction have not yet been made. However, it is conceivable that an empirical relation could be established between the results of triaxial compression tests on large undisturbed samples of the clay and the average shearing resistance of the clay in the field. So far no remedy other than reducing the slope angle is available. Attempts to prevent or to stop the movements by drainage or the injection of cement grout have been unsuccessful.

If the spacing of the joints in a clay is greater than several inches, slopes may remain stable for many years or even decades after the cut is made. The lapse of time between the excavation of the cut and the failure of the slope indicates a gradual loss of the strength of the soil. Present conceptions regarding the mechanics of the process of softening are illustrated by Figure 157. Before excavation, the clay is very rigid, and the fissures are completely closed. The reduction of stress during excavation causes an expansion of the clay, and some of the fissures open. Water then enters and softens the clay adjoining these fissures. Unequal swelling produces new fissures until the larger chunks disintegrate, and the mass is transformed into a soft matrix containing hard cores. A slide occurs as soon as the shearing resistance of the weakened clay becomes too small to counteract the forces of gravity. Most slides of this type occur along toe circles involving a relatively shallow body of soil, because the shearing resistance of the clay increases rapidly with increasing distance below the exposed surface. The water seems to cause only the deterioration of the clay structure; seepage pressures appear to be of no consequence.

Figure 158 shows a slide in very stiff fissured clay beside a railroad cut having side slopes of 2.5:1. The height of the slope was 60 ft. The

Fig. 158.   Photograph of slide in very stiff fissured clay.

characteristic S-shape of the slope after failure is apparent. Failure occurred about 80 years after the cut was excavated. No springs or other indications of percolating water were present.

A study of the records of several delayed slides in stiff clays with widely spaced joints has shown that the average shearing resistance of the clay decreases from a high initial value at the time of excavation to values between 0.20 and 0.35 ton per sq ft at the time of the slide. Since the process of deterioration may require many decades, it would be uneconomical to select the slope angle for the sides of cuts in such clays on the basis of the ultimate value of the shearing resistance. However, it is desirable to delay the deterioration as much as possible by draining the strip of land adjoining the upper edge of the cut for a width equal to the depth of the cut and by treating the ground surface of the cut area to reduce its permeability. Should local slides occur at a later date, they can be remedied by local repairs. If delayed slides would endanger life or cause excessive property damage, the slope should be provided with reference points, and periodic observations should be made, inasmuch as slides of this type are always preceded by deformations that increase at an accelerated rate as a state of failure is approached. When the movement becomes alarming, the slopes in the danger section should be flattened.

Hard core drains have also been successfully used to prevent movements at danger sections. These drains consist of ribs of dry masonry installed in trenches running up and down the slope at a spacing of about 15 or 20 ft. The trenches are excavated to a depth somewhat greater than that to which the clay has been softened. A concrete footwall supports the lower ends of all of the ribs. The beneficial effect of this type of construction is commonly ascribed to the action of the ribs as drains, but it is more likely that the principal function of the ribs is to transfer part of the weight of the unstable mass of clay through side friction to the footwall.

Stability of Slopes on Clay Containing Layers or Pockets of Water-Bearing Sand

In the preceding text we have considered only the stability of more or less homogeneous soils. The most important nonhomogeneous soil formations are stratified deposits consisting of layers of sand and clay and masses of cohesive soil containing irregular lenses or pockets of sand or silt.

In a sequence of layers of clay and sand or coarse silt, at least some of the latter are commonly water-bearing during part or all of the year. If a cut is excavated in such a soil, water seeps out of the slopes at various points or along various lines. Therefore, such cuts are commonly referred to as *wet cuts*. They require special attention, particularly if the strata dip toward the slope. The springs that issue along the base of the sand outcrops are likely to cause sloughing, and frost action may also lead to deterioration. Therefore, it is common practice to intercept the veins of water by means of drains that follow the base of the water-bearing layers at a depth of at least 5 ft measured at right angles to the slope. If the clay strata are soft or fissured, they may constitute an additional source of structural weakness. Hence, if the cut is deep, a stability investigation should be made to learn whether or not it is advisable to adhere to the standard slope.

Masses of cohesive soil containing irregular lenses or pockets of cohesionless soil are common in regions of former glaciation where the sediments were deposited by melting ice and then deformed by the push of temporarily advancing ice sheets. They have also been encountered at the site of old landslides that took place in stratified masses of sand and clay.

The sand pockets within the clay serve as water reservoirs. During wet weather they become the seat of considerable hydrostatic pressure that tends to cause the outward movement of the masses in which they are located. As the soil masses move outward, they disintegrate into a mixture of saturated silt, sand, and chunks of clay that flows like a glacier or like a thick viscous liquid.

Since the source of instability is the pressure of the water trapped in the sand pockets, stabilization can be accomplished by means of drainage galleries. However, the geological profile is likely to be very irregular, and the spacing of drains should not be decided on until the soil and hydraulic conditions have been thoroughly investigated by boring, testing, and periodic surveys of the water table. The latter require the installation of observation wells at strategic points. Once drainage has been accomplished, the terrain may become so stable that the cut can be made with standard slopes.

SUDDEN SPREADING OF CLAY SLOPES

Experience has shown that failures of clay slopes by sudden spreading tend to occur in cycles with periods of maximum frequency at more or less regular intervals. It is characteristic of this type of failure that a gentle clay slope, which may have been stable for decades or centuries, moves out suddenly along a broad front. At the same time the terrain in front of the slide heaves for a considerable distance from the toe. On investigation, it has invariably been found that the spreading occurred at a considerable distance beneath the toe, along the boundary between the clay and an underlying water-bearing stratum or seam of sand or silt. The probable causes of these sudden and frequently catastrophic slope failures are illustrated by Figure 159a.

Figure 159a represents a section through a valley located above a thick stratum of soft clay that gradually merges toward the left into sand. The clay, which has an average cohesion c, contains thin horizontal layers of fine sand or coarse silt, such as the layer $S-S$. The pore water in $S-S$ communicates with the water in the large body of sand on the left side of the diagram. The plain lines Ad and Be, respectively, represent the water table in the sand during a dry and an exceptionally wet season. The dash lines Ab and Bg represent the corresponding piezometric levels for the pore water in $S-S$.

A cut ab has been excavated in the clay to a depth H. Every horizontal section beneath the cut, including that through $S-S$, is acted on by shearing stresses, because the overlying clay tends to settle vertically and to spread horizontally under the influence of its own weight. If the pore-water pressure in the layer $S-S$ is low, corresponding to the piezometric line Ab, the shearing resistance along S–S is likely to be considerably greater than the sum of the shearing stresses. When this is true, the stability of the slope depends only on the cohesion c of the clay. For any slope angle less than 53° the critical height H_c of the slope is

$$H_c = 5.52 \frac{c}{\gamma} \qquad (49.1)$$

where γ is the unit weight of the clay (see Article 31). If a firm base underlies the clay stratum at a shallow depth below the bottom of the

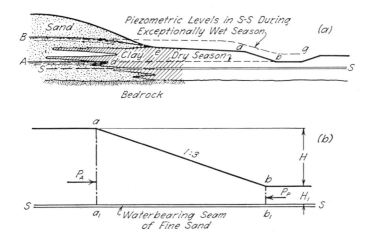

Fig. 159.   (a) Geological conditions involving danger of slope failure by spreading; (b) diagram of forces which act on soil beneath slope ab.

excavation, corresponding to a low value of the depth factor n_D, Figure 80, the critical height is even greater, and it increases with decreasing slope angles up to values of $9c/\gamma$ for slopes of 20°, as shown in the same figure.

However, because of a protracted wet spell or the melting of snow on the surface of the ground above the large body of sand, the piezometric levels for the stratum S–S may rise to the position indicated by the line Bg. During the rise the total load on S–S, p per unit of area, remains unchanged, but the pore-water pressure u_w increases. Since the layer S–S consists of almost cohesionless soil, its shearing resistance is determined by the equation,

$$s = (p - u_w)\tan \phi \qquad (15.3)$$

Hence, the increase of the piezometric levels for this layer corresponds to a decrease of the shearing resistance on any horizontal section through the layer. As soon as the average shearing resistance decreases to the value of the average shearing stress, the slope above S–S fails by spreading, in spite of the fact that it may still possess an adequate factor of safety against sliding along any curved surface located above or cutting across S–S.

The critical height of the slope above S–S can never be less than the value obtained on the assumption that the pore-water pressure u_w is equal to p, equation 15.3, whereupon the shearing resistance along S–S becomes zero. The implications of this condition are illustrated by Figure 159b which represents a vertical section through the slope ab to a larger scale. According to equation 24.9, the active earth pressure on the vertical section aa_1 is

$$P_A = \frac{1}{2}\gamma(H + H_1)^2 - 2c(H + H_1)$$

and, according to equation 24.16, the passive earth pressure on bb_1 is

$$P_P = \frac{1}{2}\gamma H_1{}^2 + 2cH_1$$

If the shearing resistance on a_1b_1 is zero, the slope will be on the verge of failure when $P_A = P_P$, whence

$$H = H_c = 4\frac{c}{\gamma} \tag{49.2}$$

This value is approximately equal to $3.85c/\gamma$ which, according to Figure 80, is the critical height of a vertical slope. Hence, if the pore-water pressure is great enough to eliminate the friction in the seam S–S, it reduces the critical height of the slope located above the seam to slightly more than the critical height of a vertical slope, regardless of what the actual slope angle may be. For gentle slopes, this effect of the pore-water pressure may involve a reduction of the critical height by almost 50 per cent.

During exceptionally wet years or during the melting of an exceptionally thick snow cover, the water table rises everywhere. As a consequence, the shearing resistance of every water-bearing seam decreases, and slopes may fail that were previously always stable. In 1915 a slide occurred on a very gentle slope about 40 ft high, within the boundaries of the Knickerbocker Portland Cement Company on Claverack Creek near Hudson, N. Y. The slope was located on varved clay consisting of alternate layers of clay and silt, each about $\frac{1}{2}$ in. thick. Suddenly, without any visible provocation, the slope moved out over a length of 1200 ft, and the surface of the flat in front of the toe heaved for a distance of about 300 ft. Over a length of about 600 ft, the creek bottom was lifted above the level of the surrounding ground, and the heave occurred so rapidly that fish remained stranded on the gentle ridge that occupied the former site of the creek. The powerhouse located on the premises was wrecked, and the occupants perished. This slide was only one of many that have occurred in the varved clays of the Hudson River valley since

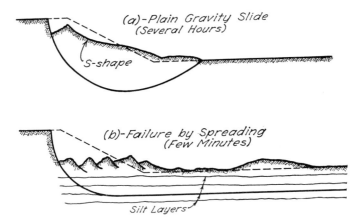

FIG. 160.   Cross section through typical slide in varved clay (*a*) if pore-water pressure in silt layers is inconsequential; (*b*) if pore-water pressure in silt layers is almost equal to overburden pressure.

its settlement.[49.10] The history of the valley indicates quite clearly that the slides occurred most frequently at intervals of roughly 20 or 25 years, corresponding to years of maximum rainfall.

The difference between plain gravity slides due to inadequate cohesion of the clay and slides due to spreading of the clay strata is illustrated by Figures 160*a* and *b*. In contrast to slides of type *a*, those of type *b* occur almost suddenly. It is probable that they are not even preceded by measurable deformations of the mass of soil that ultimately fails, because the seat of weakness is located not within the clay but only at the boundary between the clay and its base. Furthermore, the critical height for slopes on homogeneous clay depends only on the slope angle and the average cohesion *c*, whereas the critical height for slopes on clay located above water-bearing seams or strata of cohesionless soil depends to a large extent on the pore-water pressure u_w in the seams. As the pore-water pressure increases, the critical height decreases and approaches the value H_c, equation 49.2, regardless of what the slope angle may be. Hence, if the height of a slope on a clay with water-bearing seams of sand or silt is greater than H_c, no reliable opinion can be formed concerning the factor of safety of the slope with respect to sliding unless the pore-water pressure u_w is known.

A rough estimate of the maximum possible value of the pore-water pressure in the water-bearing seams can be made on the basis of the general geology and physiography of the region in which the slope is located. However, the real value of the pore-water pressure can be computed neither by theory nor on the basis of laboratory tests. It can be determined only in the field, by means of pressure-gage observations. Hence, if the prerequisites for a slide of type b, Figure 160, may conceivably exist, the engineer must judge what the practical consequences of such a slide would be. If it could do no more than block traffic, the engineer might be justified in proceeding with construction without special precautions, in full knowledge that a slide might occur a few years or decades after construction. On the other hand, if a slide could cause loss of life or serious damage to valuable property, the installation and periodic observation of pore-water pressure gages are imperative. Whenever a stability computation based on the results of the gage readings indicates that the safety margin for the slope is narrow, sound engineering requires that the danger be eliminated by the installation of drains to keep the pore-water pressure in the water-bearing constituents of the subsoil within safe limits.

Summary of Problems and Procedures

In selecting the route for a highway or railway, or the site for a project that requires the excavation of open cuts, the degree of engineering skill required depends to a considerable extent on the nature of the terrain. The layout and the construction of open cuts in favorable ground is fairly well standardized, but, if the project involves troublesome ground, the engineer must possess the highest qualifications. This is due partly to the infinite variety of combined soil and hydraulic conditions that may lead to slides and partly to the fact that economic considerations commonly require a radical departure from the customary standards of safety. The engineer in charge of location must be capable of identifying favorable, troublesome, and very troublesome ground on the basis of surface indications and occasional exploratory borings. He must also be able to visualize the worst construction difficulties that may arise at the various possible sites, and to evaluate the corresponding expenditures and delays.

If troublesome ground cannot be avoided, the engineer must successively perform the following tasks:

(a) Locate the most critical sites and explore them by sampling and testing.

(*b*) Select the slope angles on the basis of a reasonable compromise between the requirements of economy and safety.

(*c*) Design drainage systems, if they are needed.

(*d*) Prepare the program of observations that must be made during construction to remove the uncertainties in the knowledge of the site and to eliminate the risk of accidents.

(*e*) Stabilize those slopes that begin to move out, at a minimum of expense and delay.

The preceding sections of this article have made it plain that no hard and fast rules can be established for performing any one of these tasks. The theory of the stability of slopes, Article 31, can be used to advantage only in those rare instances when a cut is to be made in a fairly homogeneous mass of soft or medium clay. When dealing with other soils or with combinations of soils the engineer must depend entirely on his capacity to recognize the factors that determine the stability of the soil deposit under consideration, on his ability to visualize the implications of the uncertainties that will still exist while the project is in the design stage, and on his ingenuity in devising means for eliminating these uncertainties as construction proceeds.

The development of these vital attributes requires a working knowledge of geology and a thorough acquaintance with the laws that govern the interaction between water and the different types of soil. These laws are set forth in Part A of this book. They must be supplemented by a broad knowledge of construction experience dealing with excavations and slides. Personal experience can supply only part of this knowledge; equally important is the experience summarized in published case histories.

Records of precedents are useful in predicting the behavior of a given mass of soil on the basis of experience with soils possessing similar significant properties. The practical value of older records of this type is seriously impaired by the complete absence of reliable information on the type and the state of the soils involved in the construction operations and on the hydraulic conditions responsible for the observed events. Nevertheless, at present these records still constitute the only source of information, because adequate records have rarely been made.

REFERENCES

49.1. G. E. Ladd, Landslides, Subsidences and Rock-Falls, *Proc. Am. Rwy. Eng. Assoc.*, Vol 36 (1935), pp 1091–1162. Instructive review of slide records up to 1934 and of slide remedies, with extensive bibliography. The suggested classification of soil movements appears to be too complex for engineering purposes, and the statements regarding the physical causes of some of the described phenomena are debatable.

49.2. C. F. S. Sharpe, *Landslides and Related Phenomena*, New York, Columbia University Press, 1938. Classification and review of landslides as geological phenomena. Extensive bibliography.

49.3. Fr. Müller, *The Sand Slides of Zeeland Province* (in German), Ernst and Son, Berlin, 1898. Detailed description of sand flows, including results of mechanical analysis.

49.4. A. Scheidig, *Loess* (in German), Th. Steinkopff, Dresden, 1934. Monograph on loess and its relation to civil engineering.

49.5. Reference 44.6.

49.6. K. Terzaghi, Stability of Slopes of Natural Clay, *Proc. Intern. Conf. Soil Mech.*, Cambridge, Mass., (1936), Vol. I, pp 161–165. Numerical data regarding the average shearing resistance of various clays in the field.

49.7. A. W. Skempton, A Slip in the West Bank of the Eau Brink Cut, *J. Inst. Civil Engrs. (London)*, Vol 24 (1945), pp 267–286; discussions, pp 535–553. The slide occurred on the slope of an old permanently flooded cut. The paper illustrates the uncertainties involved in evaluating the shearing resistance of clay in the field.

49.8. E. A. Hodgson, The Marine Clays of Eastern Canada and their Relation to Earthquake Hazards, *J. Royal Astron. Soc. Can.*, Vol 21 (1927), pp 257–264. Descriptive records of flow slides in silty clay.

49.9. V. Pollack, Concerning Slides in Soils of Glacial Origin and the Need for a Classification of Soils (in German), *Jahrb. geol. Reichsanstalt*, Wien, Vol 67 (1917), Heft. 3 and 4. Record of slides in stiff fissured clay in Rosengarten, Germany.

49.10. D. H. Newland, Landslides in Unconsolidated Sediments, *N. Y. State Museum Bull.* 187, Albany, 1916. Descriptive records of slope failures by spreading.

49.11. A. H. Toms, Folkestone Warren Landslips: Research carried out in 1939 by the Southern Railway Company, *Inst. Civil Eng. (London)*, Rwy. Eng. Div., Railway Paper No. 19. Record of thorough and expert investigation of the characteristics and causes of a large slide in stiff clay, supplemented by soil test results.

ART. 50. COMPACTION OF SOILS

Purposes and Methods of Soil Compaction

The preceding article dealt with the stability of soil masses in their natural state. By excavating such soil masses and redepositing them without special care, the average porosity, permeability, and compressibility of the soil are increased, and the capacity to resist internal scour by water veins is greatly reduced. Therefore, even in ancient times it was customary to compact fills to be used as dams or levees. On the other hand, no special efforts were made to compact highway embankments, because the road surfaces were flexible enough to remain unharmed by the settlement of the fill. Until very recently railroad fills were also built up by loose dumping and allowed to settle under their own weight for several years before placement of high-quality ballast.

The settlement of uncompacted fills did not result in any serious inconveniences until the beginning of the 20th century, when the rapid development of the automobile created an increasing demand for hard-surfaced roads. It soon became apparent that concrete roads on un-

tain the water content within 2 or 3 per cent of the optimum. However, for uniform slightly cohesive nonplastic soils a closer approach to the optimum water content may be required.

The unit weight and the water content of the soil are checked in the field by routine sampling and testing.[50.4, 50.6] To determine the unit weight, a hole having a volume of at least 1/20 cu ft is excavated in the compacted soil, and the excavated material is carefully recovered and weighed before any moisture is lost by evaporation. The volume of the excavated material is commonly measured by filling the hole with dry sand in a loose state, after the unit weight of the sand in this state has been established. The sand is poured from a container that is weighed before and after the hole is filled. An approximate value of the water content can be obtained quickly by determining the loss of weight due to drying the sample in a pan resting on a hot plate. However, after a moderate amount of experience on a given job, an inspector can estimate the water content quite accurately from the appearance and texture of the material. Under some conditions, the water content can be determined expediently by means of a small-scale penetration device known as the *plasticity needle*.[50.5] If the material to be used for a fill is quite variable in character, or if the job is located in a region subject to frequent rainy spells, compliance with the moisture-content requirements may considerably increase the cost of constructing the fill.

The water content at which a soil is compacted has an effect on all the physical properties of the compacted soil, including the permeability. Experience indicates that an increase in initial water content from a value somewhat below the optimum to a value somewhat above is likely to cause a large decrease in the coefficient of permeability. The decrease seems to increase with increasing clay content of the soil. In connection with the core material for Mud Mountain Dam, which contained as much as 3 per cent of clay with a high montmorillonite content, it was found that an increase in the water content from 2 per cent below optimum to 2 per cent above decreased the coefficient of permeability about 10,000 times.[50.7] An influence of this magnitude is probably a rare exception, but even much less important effects deserve consideration.

COMPACTION OF CLAY

If the natural water content of a clay located in a borrow-pit area is not close to the optimum water content, it may be very difficult to change it to the optimum value. This is particularly true if the water content is too high. Therefore, the contractor may be compelled to use the clay in approximately the state in which it is encountered.

Excavating machinery removes the clay from a borrow pit in chunks.

An individual chunk of clay cannot be compacted by any of the pro-cedures previously mentioned, because neither vibration nor pressure of short duration produces more than an insignificant change in the water content. However, use of a sheepsfoot roller is effective in reducing the size of the open spaces between the chunks. The best results are ob-tained if the water content is slightly greater than the plastic limit. If it is considerably greater, the clay tends to stick to the roller, or the roller tends to sink into the ground. If it is considerably less, the chunks do not yield, and the spaces remain open.

The use of fairly stiff clay for the construction of an embankment may involve the danger of subsequent expansion by swelling in contact with water. If the expansion is unequal, fissures are likely to form, whereupon the structure of the clay may disintegrate and the slopes may start to slough. Heavily precompressed clays and clays with high values for the swelling index, Article 13, should, at the present state of knowledge, be regarded with suspicion as material for the construction of embank-ments. If C_s, equation 13.5a, exceeds about 0.07, the clay is likely to swell excessively.

The swelling characteristics of a fill composed of rolled chunks of a precompressed clay can also be investigated by preparing samples representative of the clay in its initial state in the fill. Each sample is introduced into a consolidation ring and subjected to a pressure equal to that which will act on the clay at some point in the fill. Water is then admitted to the porous stones that cover the top and bottom of the sample, and the increase in volume is measured. The suitability of the material is judged by its tendency to swell.

The performance of swelling tests and the interpretation of the results require considerable experience, and the conclusions cannot be accepted without reservation. For instance, several successful dams over 100 ft high have been constructed of clay for which $C_s = 0.09$. Hence, no rules of general validity can as yet be stated.

In Great Britain and the British Dominions, earth dams have been constructed with rather permeable outer parts and plastic clay cores of such consistency that the clay can be handled and packed into place with a spade. To permit spading the water content of the clay is maintained at a value about halfway between the liquid and plastic limits. If the clay in the borrow pits has a smaller water content, it is mixed with water while being fed through pug mills. This procedure is common practice for treating the clays used for the cores in the storage dams of the municipal water system of the city of London. The impervious sections constructed in this manner are known as *clay-puddle cores*. The term clay puddle used in this sense should not be confused with the meaning of the same term in the United States, where it refers to clay thrown into water and soaked until it is much too soft to be spaded.

COMPACTION OF NATURAL MASSES OF SOIL AND OF EXISTING FILLS

Natural strata and existing fills cannot be compacted in layers. This fact excludes the application of most of the methods previously described, because in order to be effective the compacting agent must act in the interior of the soil mass. The method most suitable for a given job must be selected in accordance with the nature of the soil.

Cohesionless sand can be compacted most effectively by vibration. The simplest method for producing vibrations at considerable depth is to drive piles. When piles are driven into loose sand, the ground surface between the piles commonly subsides in spite of the displacement of the sand by the piles. In one instance, after cast-in-place concrete piles 45 ft long were driven at 3-ft centers into fine sand below the water table, the ground surface subsided as much as 3 ft, although the volume of the piles was equivalent to a 1-ft layer. The pile driving reduced the porosity of the sand from about 44 to about 38 per cent.

On another project, piles were driven to compact a layer of sand extending to a depth of 50 ft below the water table. Steel shells, subsequently recovered, were partly filled with a mixture of sand, gravel, and tufa, and then driven into the ground. During the driving, the surface settled about 1.5 ft, and the average porosity of the sand decreased from 42 to 35 per cent. An independent check on the degree of compaction was made by measuring the rate of propagation of elastic waves. Because of the compaction, this rate increased from about 1000 ft per sec, a common value for loose sand, to about 4000 ft per sec, corresponding to soft sandstone. Since pile driving is not effective in compacting the uppermost layers, the top 6 ft of sand on this project were compacted by the 24-ton vibrator previously described.

On the same job, a second method was used, known as the *vibroflotation process*. The tool that produces the compaction consists of a vibrator combined with a device for forcing water into the surrounding sand. The vibrator is first jetted into the sand to the depth within which the sand stratum is to be compacted and then is gradually lifted out again. The compaction is produced during the upward trip by the vibrations combined with the action of the water jets.[50.8] The operation compacts the sand within a cylindrical space having a diameter of 8 to 10 ft at moderate expense. However, the method is most successful in clean sand. If the sand contains an admixture of silt or clay, the results are likely to be disappointing.

Satisfactory compaction of thick strata of very loose sand has also been accomplished by detonating small charges of dynamite at many points in the interior of the strata. In one such stratum, extending from the ground surface to a depth ranging between 15 and 30 ft, 8-lb charges of 60 per cent dynamite were fired at a depth of 15 ft. The vibrations produced by the blasts reduced the porosity of the sand from its original value of 50 per cent to 43 per cent. The prerequisites for successful application of this method are the same as those for the vibroflotation process.[50.9]

Sandy soils with some cohesion and existing cohesive fills can also be compacted by pile driving. However, the compaction of such soils is caused not by the vibrations associated with the driving, but by static pressure which decreases the size of the void spaces. If the soil is located above the water table and the voids are largely filled with air, the compacting effect of pile driving is commonly very satisfactory. However, if the soil is located below the water table, this effect decreases rapidly with decreasing permeability of the soil. In order to facilitate removal of the water, gravel drains may be installed. Thus, for instance, the following prodecure was successfully used to compact a loose marl fill placed within the cells of a sheet-pile cofferdam. Steel pipes with a diameter of 12 in. were driven into the fill. The lower end of each pipe was closed with a loosely attached steel disk that remained in the ground when the pipe was pulled. After a pipe had been driven to the base of the marl, it was filled with a mixture of gravel and sand and was provided with an airtight cap. The pipe was then removed by pumping air into it under a pressure of 20 to 30 lb per sq in. The air pressure held the soft soil in place and prevented it from squeezing in while the gravel was falling out of the pipe into the hole. Vertical columns of sand or gravel installed in the soil by this or a similar process are known as *sand piles*. The consolidation of the surrounding soil can be accelerated by pumping or bailing the water from the sand piles.[50.10]

Soft silt below the water table is transformed by pile driving into a semiliquid state. Hence, instead of compacting the soil, the process of pile driving weakens the soil at least temporarily. If the compaction of such strata is practicable at all, it can be accomplished only by some process of drainage, Article 47. This statement also applies to strata of soft clay. In one case the drainage was effected by pumping hot dry air into a system of galleries.[50.11] In others water was pumped out of water-bearing sand strata contained in the clay. When such strata are present, the rate of consolidation and the final void ratio can be estimated by means of the theory of consolidation and the results of consolidation tests. The curves in Figure 108 may be used for estimating the rate.

REFERENCES

50.1. W. Loos, Comparative Studies of the Effectiveness of Different Methods for Compacting Cohesionless Soils, *Proc. Intern. Conf. Soil Mech.*, Cambridge, Mass. (1936), Vol III, pp 174–179. Tests showing relative ineffectiveness of watering.

50.2. *Compaction Tests and Critical Density Investigation of Cohesionless Materials for Franklin Falls Dam*, Appendix BI, Embankment Compaction Tests on Cohesionless Material, Corps of Engineers, U. S. Army, Boston, 1938.

50.3. O. J. Porter, The Use of Heavy Equipment for Obtaining Maximum Compaction of Soils, *Tech. Bull.* 109 (1946), Am. Road Builders Assoc.

50.4. L. W. Hamilton et al, Compaction of Earth Embankments, *Proc. Highway Research Board*, Vol 18 (1938), Part 2, pp 142–181.

50.5. R. R. Proctor, Four Articles on the Design and Construction of Rolled-Earth Dams, *Eng. News-Record*, Vol 111 (1933), pp 245–248, 286–289, 348–351, 372–376. Contains original description of Proctor method.

50.6. H. F. Peckworth, Field Control of Compacted Earth Fill, *Civil Eng.*, Vol 9 (1939), pp 221–226.

50.7. A. S. Cary et al, Permeability of Mud Mountain Core Material, *Trans. ASCE*, Vol 108 (1943), pp 719–728, discussions pp 729–737. Tests showing large increase of permeability of compacted fill material if water content drops below optimum.

50.8. S. Steuermann, A New Soil Compacting Device, *Eng. News-Record*, Vol 123 (1939), pp 87–88. (See also *Report on Soil Compaction by Vibroflotation*, issued by Parsons, Brinckerhoff, Hogan, and McDonald, Engineers, New York, 1945.)

50.9. A. K. B. Lyman, Compaction of Cohesionless Foundation Soils by Explosives, *Trans. ASCE*, Vol 107 (1942), pp 1330–1348.

50.10. M. M. Fitz Hugh et al, Shipways with Cellular Walls on a Marl Foundation, *Proc. ASCE*, Nov. 1945, pp 1327–1353. Description of sand piles, pp 1336–1339.

50.11. R. A. Hill, Clay Stratum Dried Out to Prevent Landslips, *Civil Eng.*, Vol 4 (1934), pp 403–407.

ART. 51. DESIGN OF FILLS, DIKES, AND EARTH DAMS

Principal Types of Earth Embankments

Earth embankments can be divided into four large groups: railway fills, highway fills, levees, and earth dams. The embankments in each group are similar not only in the purpose they serve, but also in the factors that should be considered when the side slopes are selected. In the following discussion of the choice of slopes it is assumed that the embankments rest on stable subsoil. The conditions for the stability of the base and the effect of unfavorable subsoil conditions on the stability of the embankments are discussed in Article 52.

Railway Fills

In the past, railway fills were usually constructed by dumping the borrow material over the end of the completed portion of the fill. Such fills were considered satisfactory if they were permanently stable. Since artificial compaction was not used, hard ballast was not placed beneath the track until the fills had "seasoned" for several years. During this period the fills settled under their own weight. The settlement amounted to about 3 per cent of the height of rock fills, 4 per cent of the height of fills of sandy materials, and about 8 per cent of the height of fills with a considerable clay content. To prevent the development of sags in the track between the ends of a fill, the crest was customarily established at a distance above theoretical grade equal to the expected settlement.

The standard slope of railway fills constructed in this manner is 1.5 (horizontal) to 1 (vertical). However, if a fill with a height greater than 10 or 15 ft contains a high percentage of clay, it is likely to fail either during construction or after a few wet seasons. Therefore, it has become the practice to reduce the slope angle of such fills from 1.5:1 at the crest to about 3:1 at the base. The decision whether the character of the clay requires flattening of the slopes is commonly left to the engineer in charge of construction. No more refined procedure is justified, because the shearing resistance of an uncompacted clay fill depends not only on the properties of the fill material but also on the method of placing and on the weather conditions during construction. However, even the most experienced engineer occasionally misjudges the character of a soil, and, as a consequence, a section of the fill may fail. The slope is then repaired, and its stability increased either by constructing a low fill along the toe that moved out or by means of a dry masonry footwall, possibly supplemented by hard core drains.

During the 1930's the practice of constructing fills by loose dumping was largely abandoned by railroads in the United States because of the rapid development of offtrack earth-moving equipment similar to that used for the construction of dams and highway fills. It has become customary to spread fill material in layers about 1 ft thick, by means of bulldozers or tractor-drawn scrapers. Because of the compacting effect of the construction equipment, the settlement of the fills is considerably reduced. The standard slope of 1.5:1, however, remains unchanged. In the construction of some new fills on lines operating high-speed trains, water-content control and rolling have been used. This is done primarily to make fills ready for normal service immediately after construction and must be considered an exceptional procedure.

Regardless of the method of construction, if the available fill material consists of both sandy soils and clay, it is considered good practice to avoid mixing the two soils so far as is possible. Part of the sandy soil is reserved for constructing the upper part of the fill, and the remainder either for the outer parts or for the lowest portions of the highest fill sections.

If the top of a clay fill becomes damp, the clay may squeeze under the influence of traffic into the voids of the ballast. The track then settles. The crest of the fill assumes the shape of a shallow trough in which water collects and further softens the subgrade. The cost of maintenance increases as the process continues. On new fills more favorable conditions for track support can be established by compacting the upper few feet of the fill and giving the clay surface a pronounced crown. On existing fills the progressive deterioration of the roadbed can sometimes be arrested by injecting cement grout into the lower part of the ballast section. The grout fills the voids and keeps the clay out of the ballast.[51.1]

Highway Fills

The standard slope for highway embankments varies in different parts of the United States between 1.5:1 and 1.75:1. Whereas moderate settlement of railroad fills is of no great consequence, because the track can readily be raised by tamping additional ballast under the ties, warping of the base of highway pavements may cause failure of the road surface or, at best, unsatisfactory riding characteristics. Therefore, modern highway embankments are always carefully compacted, and the moisture content of the fill material is rigidly controlled during construction (see Article 50). The behavior of fills compacted in this manner depends primarily on the physical properties of the fill material. As a consequence, reliable decisions as to the suitability of a given soil for constructing an embankment can be made on the basis of the results of routine laboratory tests on representative samples of the material in the borrow pit.

During the last 25 years efforts were made, first by the Bureau of Public Roads and later also by the various state highway departments, to correlate the behavior of compacted embankments with the index properties of the fill material. These efforts have led to the generally accepted practice of judging the quality of the soil on the basis of its maximum compacted dry density and its Atterberg-limit values.[51.2] Before it is decided whether a given soil is suitable for constructing a proposed fill, representative samples are submitted to a Proctor test or the locally practiced equivalent (see Article 50). General directions for interpreting the test results have been published by the American Association of State Highway Officials,[51.3] but the details of interpretation vary from state to state. Table 16 is a typical example of the specifications of a state highway department.

It is obvious that rules like those contained in Table 16 should not be considered final. They represent merely one stage of progress toward the elimination of guesswork in the selection of fill material, and they will undoubtedly be modified as experience increases. In particular, the specifications regarding the use of clay soils appear to leave a considerable margin for improvement. For example, it is specified in Table 16 that clay soils having a liquid limit greater than 65 should not be used in the construction of fills. Yet, in some localities, storage dams as high as

TABLE 16

Embankment Soil Compaction Requirements

Abstract of 1946 Construction and Material Specifications
of the Department of Highways, State of Ohio

Condition I Fills 10 ft or less in height, and not subject to extensive floods		Condition II Fills exceeding 10 ft in height, or subject to long periods of flooding	
Maximum Laboratory Dry Weight* (lb per cu ft)	Minimum Field Compaction Requirements (Per Cent of Laboratory Maximum Dry Weight)	Maximum Laboratory Dry Weight* (lb per cu ft)	Minimum Field Compaction Requirements (Per Cent of Laboratory Maximum Dry Weight)
89.9 and less	†	94.9 and less	‡
90.0–102.9	100	95.0–102.9	102
103.0–109.9	98	103.0–109.9	100
110.0–119.9	95	110.0–119.9	98
120.0 and more	90	120.0 and more	95

* Maximum laboratory dry weight is determined by standard Proctor test, as described in Article 50.

† Soils having maximum dry weights of less than 90.0 lb per cu ft will be considered unsatisfactory and shall not be used in embankment.

‡ Soils having maximum dry weights of less than 95.0 lb per cu ft will be considered unsatisfactory and shall not be used in embankment under condition II requirements or in the top 8-in. layer of embankment which will make up the subgrade for a pavement or subbase under condition I requirements.

Soil, in addition to the above requirements, shall have a liquid limit not to exceed 65, and the minimum plasticity index number of soil with liquid limits between 35 and 65 shall not be less than that determined by the formula 0.6 liquid limit minus 9.0.

100 ft with slopes as steep as 2.5:1 have been successfully built of clay with a considerably higher liquid limit. Other equally satisfactory storage dams consist of clay with a maximum laboratory dry density much less than the minimum value of 95 lb per cu ft stipulated in Table 16. As a rule, if the existing specifications would require the rejection of more than about 100,000 cu yd of clay in favor of a more expensive substitute, economic considerations would probably justify thorough soil studies and stability computations to determine whether

the rejection of the cheaper construction material could be avoided. In addition to serving their immediate purpose, the results of investigations of this kind, combined with the records of observations during and after construction, constitute the one reliable basis for revision of existing specifications.

LEVEES OR DIKES

Levees serve to protect lowlands against periodic inundation by high water, storm floods, or high tides. They differ from earth storage dams in three principal respects: Their inner slopes are submerged during only a few days or weeks per year; their location is determined by flood-protection requirements regardless of whether or not the foundation conditions are favorable; and the fill material must be derived from shallow borrow pits located near the site of the levees. These conditions introduce a considerable element of uncertainty into the design of such structures. Nevertheless, the necessity for levees existed in some regions during the earliest days of human civilization, and as a consequence the art of levee construction was developed in these regions to a high degree of perfection.

If the soil conditions in the borrow-pit area change from place to place, the cross section of a levee is customarily chosen in accordance with the requirements of the most unsuitable materials that will have to be used. Consideration is also given to the degree of freedom permitted the contractor in choosing the time and method of construction. In some levee districts the method of placing the soil is rigidly controlled, whereas in others the contractor is free to choose between widely different methods of construction. The influence of the method of construction on the cost of a levee depends chiefly on the ratio between the cost of hand and machine labor. Since this ratio is very different in different countries, efforts to build satisfactory levees at minimum expense have led to different rules in different parts of the world.

In countries such as Germany and Holland, where hand labor is cheap, levees are carefully compacted and built with steep slopes. On the other hand, in the Mississippi valley and various other parts of the United States, no efforts are made to compact levees, because in the United States uncompacted levees with gentle slopes are commonly cheaper than carefully compacted ones with much smaller cross sections.[51.4] In Europe and Asia many levees of clay have been constructed with side slopes of 2:1, whereas clay levees along the Mississippi River are commonly given an inner slope of 3:1 and an outer slope of 6:1. Both types of construction grew out of a slow process of trial and error, and both serve their purpose equally well under the conditions that prevail in the regions where they originated.

In regions where levee systems are already in existence, soil mechanics can be used to advantage only for correlating construction and maintenance experience with the index properties of the soils that serve as the construction materials. The information obtained in this manner leads to the elimination of guesswork in classifying the soils encountered in new borrow-pit areas.

The use of theoretical methods in the design of levees on stable subsoil can hardly be justified unless a levee is to be located in a region where no levees have previously been built. Under such circumstances the method of trial and error is too slow and expensive, and experience based on existing levee systems can hardly be used as a guide, because very few of the available construction records contain adequate data concerning the properties of the construction materials. Therefore, the designer is compelled to use the methods practiced in connection with the design of earth dams.

The influence of the subsoil conditions on the stability of levees and other earth embankments is discussed in Article 52.

Earth Dams for Storage Purposes

If a storage dam fails while the reservoir is full, loss of life and serious damage to property may ensue. Therefore, sound engineering requires that storage dams be designed in such a manner that there can be no possibility of a failure. Because of the great variety of subsoil conditions that may have an adverse influence on the stability of an earth dam and of the diversity of soils that may be available for building the dam, the design of every new earth dam constitutes a problem that calls for individual treatment. No standard slopes for earth dams can be established.

The design must satisfy the requirements that the dam should be stable, that the loss of water through the body of the dam should be compatible with the purpose of the dam, and that the soil or soils required for building the dam should be available within a reasonable distance. This last condition imposes severe restrictions on the choice of the construction material for the dam. Fortunately, almost any soil or combination of soils can be used for constructing a satisfactory earth dam. Consequently, the problem of the designer is to utilize the available materials to best advantage.[51.5]

Homogeneous earth dams can be made only of soils that are stable and yet not too permeable. The soils that may or do satisfy both conditions can be divided into three large groups: well-graded coarse-grained soils with a sufficient amount of fine material to reduce the permeability to a tolerable value, silts, and certain types of clay. Neither clean sand or gravel nor soft clay is included in these three groups. However, if the borrow pits contain both clean sand and soft clay, the clay can be used for constructing a practically impermeable core that intercepts the seepage through the dam and the sand deposited on both sides of the core to provide the required stability. If no relatively impermeable soils can be obtained at a reasonable cost, the seepage must be prevented by a core wall of reinforced concrete or some other manufactured construction material.

Irrespective of the nature of the available fill materials, the soils to be used in the dam must be carefully selected, and erratic variations within the dam must be avoided as much as possible under the local conditions.

TABLE 17

Side Slopes for Preliminary Design of Earth Dam

Type of Dam	Upstream Slope	Downstream Slope
Homogeneous well-graded material	2.5:1	2:1
Homogeneous coarse silt	3:1	2.5:1
Homogeneous silty clay or clay; height less than about 50 ft	2.5:1	2:1
Homogeneous silty clay or clay; height more than about 50 ft	3:1	2.5:1
Sand or sand and gravel, with clay core	3:1	2.5:1
Sand or sand and gravel, with reinforced-concrete core wall	2.5:1	2:1

To accomplish these ends suitable acceptance tests are specified for the borrow material, and the method for compacting the soil is prescribed as rigorously as for highway embankments. The design of a dam to be built in this manner is a legitimate field for the extensive use of experimental and theoretical methods. If no such investigations are made, the absence of reliable information concerning the degree of stability of the proposed structure must be compensated by very liberal dimensions involving the likelihood of using much more material in the dam than safety requires. Therefore, in connection with earth dams for storage purposes, thorough soil investigations are always economically justified.

The preceding paragraph indicates that stability computations are a necessary step in the design of an earth dam. Before such a computation can be made, the dimensions of the structure must be tentatively selected.[51.6] As a first approximation, subject to verification or modification on the basis of the stability computation, the side slopes given in Table 17 may be assumed.

The fundamental principles of stability computations have been set forth in Article 42. In that article it was emphasized that the computations require experience, judgment, and a thorough acquaintance with the theoretical principles involved. The computations should be based on the most unfavorable results of the tests made on the materials from the borrow pit and not on the average values. The theoretical factor of safety with respect to slope failures should never be less than 1.3 and should preferably be 1.5.

Glacial tills ideal for the construction of homogeneous earth dams are available at many sites in Canada and the United States north of the 42d parallel. Both the original and the slightly modified till are likely to

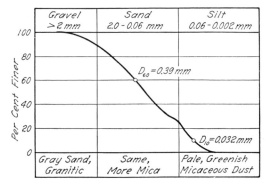

Fig. 162.   Grain-size curve of glacial till particularly suitable for construction of homogeneous earth dam.

satisfy the most exacting requirements. Although the material contains almost no clay, its permeability is of the order of 10^{-6} cm per sec, a value low enough to obviate the necessity for constructing a core wall. By means of sheepsfoot rollers and heavy hauling equipment it can be compacted to a dry weight of more than 120 lb per cu ft, and in this compacted state its angle of internal friction is at least 38°. Figure 162 shows a typical grain-size curve.

If the available construction material consists chiefly of coarse silt, adequate water-content control is very difficult. At the same time it is very important, because even a small deviation of the dry density of the compacted fill material from the maximum value is associated with a marked tendency of the material to slough during a drawdown.

The most difficult design problems arise in connection with dams to be constructed entirely of silty clay or clay. In addition to the required stability analyses, independent investigations must be made to determine whether the gradual swelling of the outer parts of the clay fill may cause the opening of cracks that would be followed sooner or later by sloughing. No specific rules can be given for making these investigations.

Nevertheless, excessive swelling capacity may render the clay unsuitable for constructing the dam. If the swelling capacity is moderate, sloughing can be prevented by covering the upstream slope with a gravel blanket several feet thick. Further uncertainties in design arise from the lack of reliable information concerning the influence of progressive failure on the average shearing resistance along the potential surfaces of sliding in rolled clay fills. Finally, if the water content of the clay in the borrow pits is considerably higher than the optimum value, water-content control during construction is likely to be a serious problem.

Since our knowledge of the conditions for the stability of clay embankments is still incomplete, and since, in addition, failures of clay embankments are by no means unusual, a theoretical factor of safety of 1.5 should be regarded as the minimum requirement.

Whatever the construction material for a homogeneous earth dam may be, the softening of the fill material at the downstream toe must be prevented by the construction of a toe filter, such as that shown in Figure 102. The filter must be large enough to prevent the line of seepage from intersecting the downstream slope. The necessity for providing toe filters had already been recognized by a few experienced engineers more than half a century ago, but the practice of installing them did not become generally accepted until soil mechanics demonstrated on a rational basis the decisive influence of such filters on the stability of the downstream slope. Today the toe filter is usually considered an essential part of the design.

Hydraulic-Fill Dams

If the available material is a well-graded mixture containing all the grain-size fractions from gravel, stones, and very coarse sand to fine silt or clay, an earth dam can be constructed advantageously by the hydraulic process. In this process, the borrow pits are opened up well above the level of the crest of the dam. Material is excavated by powerful jets of water under a pressure of 100 to 150 lb per sq in. at the nozzle and is washed through flumes or pipe lines to the site. At the dam the flumes are mounted on trestles, or else they are established along the outer edges of the fill that has already been placed, as shown in Figure 163. In either event the flumes must be shifted toward the center line and raised as the dam grows higher. The mixture of soil and water is deposited in two ridges parallel to the axis of the dam, one near the upstream edge of the finished portion of the dam, and the other near the downstream edge. The coarsest materials settle near the outer slopes, whereas the finer particles are washed into the core pool near the axis of the dam and settle. The finest particles are wasted through an overflow pipe with its upper end located at core-pool level. Hence, the constituents of a dam built according to this procedure range from very coarse materials at the slopes to fines in the core. The outer portions provide stability, whereas the core is relatively impermeable and prevents seepage loss through the dam. The percentage of fines in the core can be controlled to a certain extent by adjusting the level of the core pool.

Confidence in the reliability of this economical method of dam construction has been somewhat shaken by rather frequent failures. Some failures have been caused by incorrect evaluation of stability conditions, and others by inadequate control of the width of the core. If

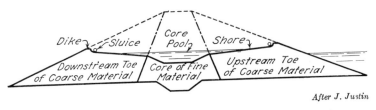

After J. Justin

Fig. 163.   Diagram illustrating construction of hydraulic-fill dam.

the outer portions consist of sand with little coarse material, the danger of a flow slide like those in loose natural sand slopes, Article 49, should be considered.

During and immediately after construction the core is in a semiliquid state, and its outward pressure tends to dislodge the coarse-grained shell. It is customary to specify that the shell should be able to sustain the lateral pressure exerted by the core material, on the assumption that the core is a heavy liquid with a unit weight equal to that of the core material. The theoretical factor of safety against failure of the shell, based on this assumption, should be unity. In reality, even immediately after construction, the factor of safety of a dam designed on this basis is somewhat greater than unity, because during construction the core acquires some strength. The effect of this gain in strength may be interpreted as a decrease of the unit weight of the equivalent fluid that is assumed to constitute the core. As time goes on, this unit weight continues to decrease, until finally it becomes practically constant. The unit weight of the real core material is commonly about 110 lb per cu ft. Pressure-cell observations in various hydraulic-fill dams indicated the ultimate values for the equivalent fluid weight shown in Table 18. In all instances, the pressure-cell readings were very erratic. Hence, they indicate merely that the equivalent fluid weight is considerably smaller than the unit weight of the core material. The real value of the ratio between the two unit weights is not yet known. Likewise, it is not even known whether the equivalent unit weight is independent of the depth below the crest of the dam.

Attempts have been made to compute the rate and degree of consolidation of the cores of hydraulic-fill dams on the basis of the theory of consolidation, Article 41, and the results of consolidation tests on representative samples of the core material.[51.7] According to the results of these computations, the settlement of the crest of a hydraulic-fill dam with a silty-clay core should increase for many years, and, if the height of the dam exceeds about 100 ft, the ultimate settlement of the crest should be at least several feet. Furthermore, the final water content of the core should decrease appreciably with increasing depth below the crest. In

TABLE 18

EQUIVALENT FLUID WEIGHT OF CORE MATERIAL OF VARIOUS
HYDRAULIC-FILL DAMS

Name of Dam	German-town	Taylors-ville	Kingsley	Fort Peck
Percentage of clay (< 0.002 mm)	15	20	2	12
Equivalent fluid weight (lb per cu ft)	58	47	45	71
Effective grain size (mm)	< 0.001	< 0.001	0.01	0.001

contrast to these theoretical conclusions, the settlement of the crests of hydraulic-fill dams with clay cores is commonly very small, and it ceases to increase perceptibly within 1 or 2 years after construction. In addition, the few records that have been obtained up to the present time indicate that the water content of the core material is practically independent of the depth below the crest of the dam.

These observations suggest that extrapolation from the results of consolidation tests to the processes that occur in the aging core of a hydraulic-fill dam are not justified. The principal reason for the discrepancies between theory and actuality seems to be the thixotropic hardening of the core material, possibly combined with the skeleton structure developed during sedimentation (see Article 17). Similar considerations indicate that the relations between the grain-size characteristics and the stability of the core material are much less simple than they appeared to be in the early days of hydraulic-fill construction. According to the early concepts, the stability of the core material should increase with increasing effective grain size, and the ideal core material should not contain any clay at all.[51.8] Yet, the data in Table 18 indicate that the equivalent fluid weight of the core material in the Kingsley Dam with a clay content of 2 per cent is not appreciably less than that of the Taylorville Dam with a clay content of 20 per cent.

According to these and various other observations, it appears that the grain-size characteristics of the core material are not so important as they were once believed to be. The foremost requirements for successful construction of a hydraulic-fill dam are the use of a heavy shell material and rigid control of the width of the core during construction.

SUMMARY OF DESIGN METHODS

The standard slope for railway fills is 1.5:1, and relatively few slopes deviate from this value. Railway fills were formerly constructed by such methods as end dumping, in which no efforts were made to compact the soil. More recently, many fills have been built up in layers and compacted to a certain extent by the action of the construction equipment. Modern highway fills, on the other hand, are commonly constructed in accordance with detailed specifications regarding water-content control and method of compaction. The standard slope varies from 1.5:1 to 1.75:1. In connection with either type of fill the principal function of the engineer is to decide what materials are unsuitable for use as fill material.

In the field of railroad construction this decision is generally left to the engineer in charge of construction. If a fill fails, it is repaired. In highway engineering embankment materials are rejected unless they comply with more or less rigid standards. Adherence to these standards practically eliminates the risk of slope failures, but it leads to the unconditional rejection of some clay soils that may actually be suitable. If the existing standards would require the rejection of a large amount of clay that is much cheaper than the cheapest substitute that would be acceptable according to the standards, it is economically justifiable to investigate, by laboratory tests and stability computations, whether the clay can be used with safety.

In the design of levees, various factors must be considered besides those revealed by the results of laboratory tests. The construction material has to be taken out of shallow borrow pits located near the levee, regardless of whether the soil profile is uniform or erratic. Since it is rarely practicable to separate the permeable from the less permeable soils, the permeability profile of the levee is likely to depend on mere chance. Furthermore, on many levee systems it has been found economical to make no effort to compact the fill material, to give the contractor full freedom in choosing the method of construction, and to compensate for the deficiencies in the quality of the finished product by providing the levees with very gentle slopes. The design of levees built in this manner is governed chiefly by experience. Extensive soil investigations and stability computations are warranted only if a levee is to be constructed in a region where none has yet been built, or if the levee is to protect an exceptionally densely populated area. Under these conditions the cross sections of levees in other districts can hardly be used as a guide in design, because very few records of older levees contain the data required for reliable soil identification.

In the design of earth dams for storage purposes, both safety and economy call for thorough soil studies combined with stability computations for several tentative cross sections. The soil tests should include all the identification tests listed in Table 5, page 38, as well as compaction and triaxial compression tests on representative samples of the fill material. If part or all of the dam is to be made of clay, consolidation and swelling tests are also required. The interpretation of the results of these tests demands broad experience and mature judgment.

REFERENCES

51.1. First Progress Report of the Investigation of Methods of Roadbed Stabilization, *Proc. Am. Rwy. Eng. Assoc.*, Vol 47 (1946), pp 324–353.

51.2. K. B. Woods and R. R. Litehiser, Soil Mechanics Applied to Highway Engineering in Ohio, *Bull.* No. 99, *Ohio State Eng. Exp. Sta.*, Columbus, Ohio (1938).

51.3. *Standard Specifications for Highway Materials and Methods of Sampling and Testing*, fourth edition (1942), Am. Assoc. of State Highway Officials, Part I, pp 33–34, designation M 57–42.

51.4. S. J. Buchanan, Levees in the Lower Mississippi Valley, *Trans. ASCE*, Vol 103 (1938), Paper 2008, pp 1378–1395, discussions, pp 1449–1502.

51.5. C. H. Lee, Selection of Materials for Rolled-Fill Earth Dams, *Trans. ASCE*, Vol 103 (1938), Paper 1980, pp 1–61. The importance of the grain-size characteristics of the fill materials appears to be somewhat overemphasized. The discussions reveal some of the controversial aspects of the subject.

51.6. William P. Creager et al, *Engineering for Dams*, John Wiley & Sons, New York, 1945, Vol III, Chap 17, Earth Dams–General Principles of Design, and Chap 19, Details of Earth Dams.

51.7. G. Gilboy, Mechanics of Hydraulic-Fill Dams, *J. Boston Soc. Civil Engrs.*, Vol 21 (1934), pp 185–203. The conclusions regarding the rate of consolidation of the core are not confirmed by experience.

51.8. A. Hazen, Hydraulic-Fill Dams, *Trans. ASCE*, Vol 83 (1920), Paper No. 1458, pp 1713–1821. Both paper and discussion contain a wealth of information on hydraulic-fill dams. In the paper the effect of grain-size characteristics on the significant properties of the core seems to be overstressed. Special attention is called to the discussion by A. E. Morgan, pages 1780–1785.

51.9. L. I. Hewes, *American Highway Practice*, John Wiley & Sons, New York, 1942, Vol I, pp 171–194. Review of present practice in design and construction of highway fills.

51.10. T. T. Knappen and R. R. Philippe, Practical Soil Mechanics at Muskingum, *Eng. News-Record*, Vol 116 (1936), pp 453–455, 532–535, 595–598, 666–669. Deals with the earth dams of the Muskingum flood-control works, constructed of very different soils. Description of sampling, soil classification, settlement forecast and water-content control. The practical value of the model tests is questionable.

51.11. P. Baumann, Design and Construction of San Gabriel Dam No. 1, *Trans. ASCE*, Vol 107 (1942), Paper 2168, pp 1595–1634, discussions pp 1635–1651. Description of design and construction, including summary of results of soil investigations. Method for determining the shearing characteristics of the fill material is somewhat controversial.

51.12. L. J. G. Van Es, Investigations on the Suitability of Soil Types for the Construction of Dams with the Aid of the Consistency Values of Atterberg (in German), 1 *Congr. Grands Barrages* (Stockholm 1933), Vol III, Rapport 21, pp 125–131. This paper illustrates strikingly the influence of factors other than the grain-size characteristics on the stability of clay dams. However, the findings related in the paper cannot be generalized.

ART. 52. STABILITY OF BASE OF EMBANKMENTS

Types of Base Failure

Whenever possible, embankments and earth dams are constructed on firm relatively incompressible subsoils. However, in many regions railway or highway embankments must be built on broad swampy flats or buried valleys filled with soft silt or clay. Levees must be constructed near the flood channels, irrespective of subsoil conditions. Even earth dams must occasionally be located at sites underlain by undesirable materials. In all these instances the design of the embankment must be adapted not only to the character of the available fill material, but also to the subsoil conditions.

Base failures may occur in several different ways. The fill may sink bodily into the supporting soil. Such an accident is referred to as *failure by sinking*. On the other hand, the fill together with the layer of soil on which it rests may spread on an underlying stratum of exceptionally soft clay or on partings of sand or silt containing water under pressure (see Article 49 and Figure 160b). This is known as *failure by spreading*. If the embankment retains a body of water, it may also fail by *piping*, as a consequence of backward erosion from springs that emerge from the ground near the toe of the fill. Finally, base failures may occur beneath fills located above strata of very loose sand because of spontaneous liquefaction of the sand. However, this type of failure is very rare, and it can be avoided by compacting the sand by one of the methods described in Article 50. Failure by piping is discussed independently in Article 59. Hence, the present article deals only with base failures by sinking or spreading.

Methods for Investigating Stability

The design of a fill to be constructed above clay strata should always be preceded by a thorough soil exploration involving boring, sampling, and testing. The results of the exploration inform the designer about the soil profile and the physical properties of the subsoil. The next step is to compute the factor of safety of the fill with respect to a failure of its base. The computation should be made according to the average stress method, Article 31. Under normal conditions, the foundation conditions are not considered satisfactory unless the factor of safety with respect to a base failure during or immediately after construction is at least equal to 1.5.

The conditions for the stability of the base of fills and the methods for preventing base failures are discussed in the following sequence: fills on very soft or marshy ground, fills on thick strata of fairly homogeneous soft clay, fills on stratified ground containing fairly homogeneous layers of soft clay, and fills on clay containing sand or silt partings. Subsoil conditions of the first two types are likely to be associated with failures by sinking, and those of the last two with failures by spreading.

Fills on Very Soft Organic Silt or Clay

Natural deposits of this type are common in regions formerly occupied by shallow lakes or lagoons. The fringes of such shallow deposits are likely to support growths of peat moss or other types of marsh vegetation. The silt or clay brought into the lakes in suspension intermingles with the decayed organic constituents washed in from the fringes. Hence, the fine-grained sediments in such bodies of water are likely to have a high organic content. The natural void ratio of the sediments is very commonly greater than 2. The deposits may contain layers of peat or be buried beneath a bed of peat.

If the surface of such a deposit has never before carried an overburden, the subsoil is likely to be unable to sustain the weight of a fill more than a few feet in height. In many regions soft marshy ground is covered with a mat several feet thick that is stiffer than the deeper layers and is effectively reinforced by a dense network of roots. The mat acts like a raft and may be able to carry, at least temporarily, the weight of a fill several feet high. However, fills on such foundations continue to settle excessively for many years or decades, and maintenance records show that they may even suddenly break through the mat long after construction. Hence, if a fill is to be permanent, the continuity of the mat should be destroyed before the fill is placed, to facilitate the penetration of the fill material into the softer layers.

Inasmuch as the cost and the relative merits of the various methods for constructing fills across marshy flats depend on the depth of the soft stratum, construction should be preceded by the preparation of a contour map of the firm bottom. If the thickness of the soft stratum does not exceed 5 or 6 ft, it may be economical to excavate the soft material. If the thickness is greater, it is usually preferable to permit the sinking fill to displace the soft material. This procedure is known as the *displacement method*.

To accelerate the penetration of the fill material and to shorten the subsequent period of settlement, the fill may be built up to a height of 15 or 20 ft above final grade, and the excess material removed later. As an alternative the penetration of the fill material may be facilitated by blasting the soft subsoil. During the last few decades the blasting method has been brought to a high state of perfection, and, if the posi-

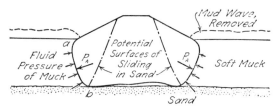

Fig. 164.   Diagram showing forces that act on soil adjoining buried part of a fill constructed by the displacement method.

tion of the bottom of the soft stratum is known, the quantity of material required for constructing the fill can be estimated fairly accurately in advance of construction.[52.1]

The conditions for the equilibrium of a fill with its base established by displacement are illustrated by Figure 164. The contact face *ab* is acted on by the active earth pressure exerted by the fill material. The displacement of *ab* toward the left is resisted by the sum of the liquid pressure of the soft material and the force required to overcome its cohesion. If the penetration of the fill is aided by a temporary surcharge or by blasting, the force that produces the corresponding displacement is very much greater than the force that acts on *ab* after construction. Furthermore, after the fill is completed, the soft material regains a part of the strength lost during the process of displacement (see Article 4). Therefore, if the fill has a cross section similar to that shown in Figure 164, the progressive settlement of its crest is likely to become inconsequential shortly after construction.

An outstanding example of the successful application of the displacement method is the Kiel canal, built during the years 1887–1895. For a distance of about 12 miles the canal had to be established on a layer of peat and very soft organic clay with a thickness up to 30 ft. In some sections the soil was so soft that a man could not walk on it. The method of building the canal in these sections is illustrated by Figure 165. On the inner side of the center line of each of the future dikes sand fills were constructed as indicated by the dash line. These fills displaced the soft material over a broad belt almost down to firm ground. They served as a base for the dikes and formed the uppermost part of the slopes of the finished canal. To reduce the danger of slides during construction,

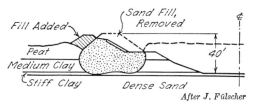

After J. Fülscher

FIG. 165.   Typical cross section of Kiel Canal.

excavation was not started until 6 months after the fill was placed. Nevertheless, slides did occur at a few points.

One of the slides is illustrated in Figure 166. This figure represents four successive stages in the excavation of the canal. The second stage *b* was

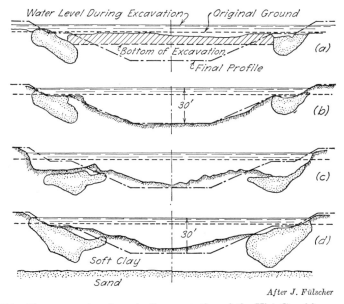

After J. Fülscher

FIG. 166.   Four successive stages in the excavation of the Kiel Canal in exception-ally soft ground.

followed by slides, stage *c*, during which the sand fills moved toward the center line of the canal. In order to finish construction, it was necessary to dump still more sand (stage *d*), whereupon the excavation was completed without further mishap.[52.2]

In connection with the construction of railway and highway fills, the displacement method has been reduced to a routine procedure. It has even been proposed as a means for constructing a rock-fill dam with a height of about 100 ft, across Cobsock Bay on the Passamaquoddy project in Maine.[52.3]

Soft strata with relatively high average permeability in horizontal directions can be made suitable for supporting the weight of super-imposed fills by drainage during construction. The drainage is accomplished by filter wells that discharge the water into collector drains located at the base of the fills. The filter wells used for this purpose by the California Division of Highways have a diameter of about 2 ft and are spaced at 10 to 20 ft.[52.4] Theory shows that the effectiveness of the drains can be considerably increased by reducing the spacing. To meet this requirement, the Swedish Department of Public Works has developed a method that permits the installation of cardboard drains in very soft clay at a spacing of 3 or 4 ft in either direction, with great speed and at very low cost.

FILLS ON SOFT HOMOGENEOUS CLAY

In the following discussion, it is assumed that the surface of the clay is very close to the base of the fill, that the thickness of the clay stratum is at least half as great as the base width of the fill, and that the stratum is fairly homogeneous.

The failure of a fill on such a base has the general character of a base failure along a mid-point circle, Article 31. However, the uppermost part of the surface of sliding is located within the artificial fill, and the shearing resistance per unit of area along this part is different from that along the lower part. The first step in making a stability computation is to ascertain the average shearing resistance s along the lower part, on the basis of a compressive strength survey of the clay stratum. The value of ϕ is assumed to be zero (see Article 15), and s to be equal to one-half the average unconfined compressive strength. The second step is to determine the average shearing resistance s_2 along the part of the surface of sliding located within the fill. This shearing resistance may consist of cohesion and friction or of friction alone. In the stability analysis the real fill is replaced by an ideal clay ($\phi = 0°$) that has a cohesion equal to s_2. As a first approximation it is assumed that failure occurs along a mid-point circle; however, the real critical circle must be determined by trial and error.

It is commonly required that the factor of safety with respect to a base failure should be at least 1.5. Considering the unavoidable errors in estimating the average shearing resistance of the clay, this factor is very low. Nevertheless, in order to satisfy the requirement, high fills on soft clay must be provided with very gentle slopes. Hence, if a high fill is also very long, it may be economical to reduce the factor of safety still further, to 1.2 or 1.1, and to rely on the results of observations during construction to detect impending slides and to prevent the slides by local modifications in the design.

The failure of the base of an embankment on clay is commonly preceded by the gradual heave of broad belts located one on each side of the fill. The rate of heave increases as failure is approached. If the heave is detected in its initial state by means of periodic levels on reference points located within the areas of potential heave, the failure can be prevented by covering these areas with a thick layer of fill.

Slides caused by the failure of a soft clay base generally occur during or immediately after construction, because thereafter the strength of the base gradually increases on account of consolidation. If a slide has already occurred, it is usually possible to ascertain the position of the surface of sliding by means of test shafts and to compute the average shearing resistance of the clay with considerable accuracy. The value thus obtained serves as a basis for redesign. Figure 167 illustrates the procedure. It shows a section through a highway fill of well-compacted gravel placed on a deposit of organic silty clay.[52.5] Failure occurred when the top of the fill was 8 ft below finished grade. A mass of soil, having an effective weight W (see Article 12), failed by rotating about point O. The driving moment was Wl. To complete the fill a gravel counterweight W_1 was added with its line of action at a horizontal distance l_1 from O. The counterweight was given dimensions such that its moment W_1l_1 plus that due to the shearing resistance along the surface of sliding exceeded the driving moment of the completed fill by 50 per cent. The right side of Figure 167 shows a section through the finished fill. The upper 8 ft were made of rolled cinders to keep the weight of the fill as small as possible. After construction of the counterweight there was no movement other than a slight subsidence due to consolidation of the base.

After a fill has been successfully constructed on the surface of a homogeneous mass of clay, its base gradually settles on account of the consolidation of the underlying clay. The magnitude of the settlement can become very great.[52.6] It should be estimated by means of the procedure outlined in Article 36, and the crest of the fill established a corresponding distance above final grade. As consolidation progresses, the bearing capacity of the fill increases.

Observations on rock fills serving as bases for breakwaters suggest that the settlement of such fills depends not only on the properties of the underlying clay but also to a large extent on the method of construction. In the last century the fills were made by dumping large rocks into the water. This procedure completely destroyed the structure of the uppermost layer of clay and caused great local stress concentrations in the

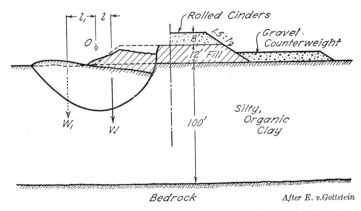

After E. v.Gottstein

Fig. 167. Section through gravel fill on deposit of uniform soft clay. Left side shows principal features of failure during construction; right side shows reconstructed fill stabilized by means of gravel counterweight.

underlying material. The settlement of these fills was very large. The older part of the breakwater in the harbor of Spezia, Italy, is an example. Figure 168a is a section through the fill. The depth of water was 33 ft, and the water content of the soft clay was close to 100 per cent. The

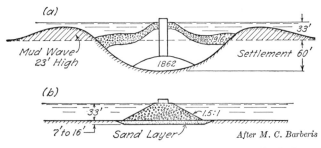

After M. C. Barberis

Fig. 168. Rock fill breakwater on soft clay in harbor of Spezia, Italy, constructed by dumping rock (a) directly onto clay; (b) onto sand layer which was previously deposited in shallow dredged cut.

results of load tests indicated that the deeper layers had an unconfined compressive strength of about 0.5 ton per sq ft. Construction was started in 1862. To maintain the crest of the fill at approximately constant elevation in spite of the rapid settlement, it was necessary to add new material to the fill. This in turn accelerated the settlement. During a period of 50 years the material that had to be added was equivalent to a layer 60 ft thick. As subsidence increased, the base of the fill assumed the shape shown in Figure 168a.

In 1912 construction of a new section of the breakwater was started. To prevent excessive settlement of the new section, the mud was removed by dredging to a depth between 7 and 16 ft below its original surface and replaced by sand with a grain size between 0.2 and 0.4 mm, Figure 168b. Hence, when the fill was constructed, the rocks came to rest on the sand instead of penetrating into the clay, and no local stress concentrations were established in the clay. Probably as a result of this condition, the settlement of the new fill was insignificant compared to that of the old one. At the end of the construction period the settlement was 1.7 ft; 9 years later it had reached only 2.7 ft. Similar procedures were successfully used in constructing breakwaters in the harbors of Valparaiso, Chile, and Kobe, Japan.[52.7]

VARIETIES OF FAILURE BY SPREADING

Failures by spreading have been observed only in connection with fills located above stratified deposits that contain layers of soft clay. Such fills are commonly safe with respect to sinking, but they may fail by spreading.

During the last 20 years half a dozen major and several minor dam failures have occurred in this manner. Hence, the stability of fills above clay strata deserves special attention. Outstanding failures due to spreading are those of Lafayette Dam in California in 1928,[52.8] Marshall Creek dam in Kansas in 1937,[52.9] and the Hartford flood-protection dike in Connecticut in 1941.[52.10]

A study of the records reveals two different types of failure by spreading. One type is distinguished by a relatively slow subsidence of the crest of the fill. The slope, if originally plane, assumes a gentle S-shape, as shown in Figure 160a, and the heave of the ground surface extends only a short distance beyond the foot of the slope. The failure of Chingford Dam near London, England,[52.11] and of Lafayette Dam are instructive examples of this type. Failures of the other type occur very rapidly, and the heave extends to a great distance from the foot of the slope. During the failure of Lafayette Dam, which was 120 ft high, the crest subsided 15 ft in about 3 days, over a length of about 500 ft. The toe moved out about 20 ft, and the heave was confined to a short distance from the foot of the slope. On the other hand, the Hartford dike, only 30 ft high, failed in less than 1 min. The crest subsided 15 ft over a length of more than 1000 ft. A row of sheet piles at the foot of the slope moved laterally for 60 ft, and the heave extended about 150 ft from the foot.

Analysis of case records and study of the causes of failure have demonstrated that the catastrophic rapid type of failure cannot and does not occur unless the clay stratum contains continuous layers of coarse silt or sand. Therefore, the details of stratification of the clay layer are of decisive importance, and a distinction must be made be-

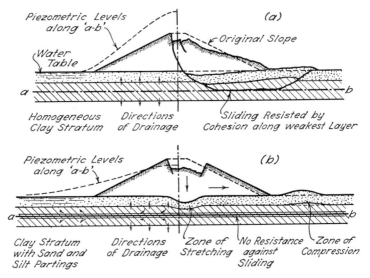

Fig. 169. Type of failure of base of fill containing thin clay stratum if (*a*) clay stratum contains no horizontal pervious partings, and (*b*) clay stratum contains pervious sand or silt parting.

tween clay strata with and without highly permeable partings. In the following discussion we shall first examine the causes of failure in each of the two types of clay strata and subsequently consider methods for improving the stability of fills located above such strata.

Spreading of Fills above Fairly Homogeneous Layers of Soft Clay

The clay stratum below the fill shown in Figure 169a is assumed to be perfectly homogeneous. Shortly after filling starts, the clay begins to consolidate and the stratum becomes stiffer near its upper and lower boundaries. Near mid-height, however, the weight of the fill is still carried by excess hydrostatic pressure, indicated by the piezometric levels shown on the left side of the figure. In this part of the stratum the shearing resistance of the clay remains equal to its initial value. Hence, if failure occurs, the surface of sliding follows some layer of minimum shearing resistance located near midheight of the clay stratum. In order to estimate the value of the minimum shearing resistance, a compressive strength survey must be made (see Article 45). Since the compressive strength of the clay is likely to vary in both the horizontal and vertical directions, the selection of an appropriate value for the cohesion requires experience, mature judgment, and a thorough investigation of the character of the stratification of the clay bed. It is also essential to make sure that the clay actually does not contain any continuous seams of sand or silt.

After the appropriate value for the shearing resistance has been selected, the factor of safety with respect to sliding can be evaluated by the method described in Article 31 in connection with composite surfaces of sliding. Since there is an appreciable resistance along the horizontal portion of the surface of sliding, the slope assumes the characteristic S-shape shown in Figure 169a.

Spreading of Fills above Clay Strata with Sand or Silt Partings

If the clay contains fairly continuous seams of sand or silt, the excess water from the central part of the stratum drains not only vertically through the top and bottom of the stratum, but also horizontally through the highly permeable seams as shown in Figure 169b. Therefore, the seams become the seat of high excess hydrostatic pressure. In several instances the existence of hydraulic conditions of the type shown by the piezometric levels in Figure 169b has been demonstrated by pressure-gage observations in the field.[52.12] The difference between the excess pore-water pressure and the weight of the overlying soil and fill is greatest near the toes of the slopes. In these regions the shearing resistance of the cohesionless seams is likely to be reduced to zero, and the only resistance to the spreading of the fill is offered by the passive pressure of the earth located above and beyond the surface of sliding. If this pressure is exceeded, the outer parts of the fill move bodily away from the center, and the central part subsides leaving a troughlike depression, as indicated in Figure 169b. Since soil conditions are never exactly symmetrical with respect to the center line of the fill, failure occurs on one side only, but it is hardly possible to predict on which side. The trough-like subsidence characteristic of this type of failure has been observed repeatedly.

The factor of safety against sliding depends on the distribution of the excess hydrostatic pressure within the pervious seams, which in turn depends on unknown local variations in the permeability and on other unknown geologic details. The practical implications of these uncertainties are illustrated by Figure 170. Test borings were made along the center line of the proposed fill shown in the figure. Since no pervious seams were encountered in any of the holes, the designers assumed that during construction the hydrostatic conditions would be as indicated by the dotted piezometric line. These conditions are normal and do not compromise the stability of the base of a fill. In reality, the clay contained a seam of fine sand located beneath the right-hand section of the dam. Since hydrostatic pressures are freely transmitted through such seams, the real pressure conditions assumed the character indicated by the dash line, and the fill failed, as shown in Figure 169b.

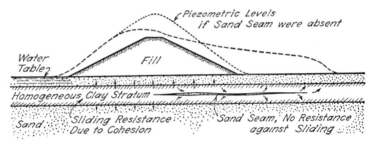

Fig. 170.   Diagram showing effect on hydrostatic pressure conditions of pervious seam in clay stratum below fill.

Hence, if the geology of the stratum indicates that the clay may contain highly permeable seams, the risk of failure can be avoided only by providing the fill with very flat slopes, at the cost of excessive yardage, or else by using one of the construction expedients described in the following paragraphs.

Means for Increasing Stability of Fills above Thin Strata of Soft Clay

If the bottom of the soft clay stratum is located at a depth less than 5 or 6 ft below the ground surface, it is advisable to remove the clay over the full width of the base of the fill. Otherwise, the designer may choose between two alternatives. He may specify that the fill be constructed more slowly than the rate of consolidation of the clay at mid-height of the stratum, or he may make provisions to accelerate the process of consolidation by means of filter wells. Each of these methods deserves consideration, regardless of whether or not the clay strata contain thin permeable seams.

To use the first procedure, the designer must know the rate of consolidation of the inner part of the stratum. Computation alone should not be relied on, because the result may be invalidated by some unnoticed geological detail such as the presence of highly colloidal seams. It should be used only to make a preliminary estimate of the maximum rate at which the fill can be constructed. To eliminate the risk of failure, the progress of consolidation must be observed in the field during construction by means of pore-water pressure gages, and the rate of construction must be adapted to the findings. This is a decided disadvantage, because it does not eliminate the possibility that construction may be intolerably delayed.

If the results of computation show that the normal process of consolidation is too slow to be utilized as a means for strengthening the base of the fill, acceleration of the process by means of vertical filter wells should be considered. The procedure has already been described.

SUMMARY

On very soft ground high fills can be established by one of two methods. The first consists of displacing the soft ground by the weight of the fill. To avoid excessive settlement after construction, the fill should be built up to a height of 15 or 20 ft above final grade, and the excess material removed after the fill has subsided. The second method consists of accelerating consolidation by means of filter wells extending to the bottom of the stratum. The wells discharge the water into drainage conduits located at the base of the fill. To determine the most economical procedure, it is necessary to prepare a contour map of the firm base of the soft layer. Wherever the depth of the layer is less than 5 or 6 ft, it may be advantageous to remove the soft soil by excavation.

The design of fills to be built above thick beds of soft clay should be preceded by a stability computation. The computation should be made by means of the average stress method. Under normal conditions a factor of safety of 1.5 with respect to sinking should be specified. However, if the fill is very long, it may be more economical to base the design on a factor of safety of 1.2 or 1.1, to locate the weakest spots in the subsoil by means of heave observations during construction, and to cover the heave areas by a counterweight consisting of a thick layer of fill.

Special vigilance is required if a fill is to be built on stratified soil containing layers of soft clay. A number of catastrophic accidents have occurred, because the stability of subsoils of this type has been overestimated. If the clay strata contain no sand or silt partings, the resistance against spreading depends on the average shearing resistance of the weakest layers in the subsoil. Since exceptionally weak layers are not necessarily continuous, their presence may escape the attention of even a conscientious investigator. If the clay contains sand or silt partings, the resistance against spreading depends chiefly on the pore-water pressure in the partings. This pressure changes during construction, and an accurate forecast of its magnitude is impracticable. Only two reliable safeguards are known against failure due to spreading along such a parting. These are the periodic measurement of the pore-water pressure during construction for the purpose of detecting impending danger and the elimination of the pressure by adequate drainage provisions.

REFERENCES

52.1. *Blasters' Handbook*, E. I. DuPont de Nemours and Company, Inc., Wilmington, Del., 1942, pp 234–239. Use of explosives to accelerate settlement of fills on soft ground.

52.2. J. Fülscher, *Construction of the Kaiser Wilhelm Canals* (in German), Wilh. Ernst. u. Sohn, Berlin, 1898. Design and construction of dikes by displacement.

52.3. B. K. Hough, Jr., Stability of Embankment Foundations, *Trans. ASCE*, Vol 103 (1938), pp 1414–1431; discussions, pp 1450–1502. Model tests and stability computations for proposed rock-fill dam to be built by displacement method on the Passamaquoddy Tidal Power Project.

52.4. O. J. Porter, Studies of Fill Construction over Mud Flats including a Description of Experimental Construction Using Vertical Sand Drains to Hasten Stabilization, *Proc. Intern. Conf. Soil Mech.*, Cambridge, Mass. (1936), Vol I, pp 229–235.

52.5. E. v. Gottstein, Two Examples Concerning Underground Sliding Caused by Construction of Embankments and Static Investigations on the Effectiveness of Measures Provided to Assure Their Stability, *Proc. Intern. Conf. Soil Mech.*, Cambridge, Mass. (1936), Vol III, pp 122–128. The assumptions regarding the angle of internal friction of the clay strata in which the breaks occurred are arbitrary and rather superfluous.

52.6. Subsidence of Earth Fills as a Factor in Valuation, *Eng. News-Record*, Vol 86, pp 434–436. Boring records showing the displacement of soft soil by railway fills.

52.7. M. C. Barberis, Recent Examples of Foundations of Quay Walls Resting on Poor Subsoil, Studies, Results Obtained, *XVI Intern. Congr. Navigation*, Brussels, 1935, second section, Ocean Navigation, third communication. The theoretical interpretation of the observed performance of the breakwater is somewhat controversial. This is partly due to arbitrary assumption regarding the coefficient of internal friction of the harbor mud.

52.8. Reconstruction of Lafayette Dam Advised, *Eng. News-Record*, Vol 102 (1929), pp 190–192. Failure by spreading.

52.9. Foundation of Earth Dam Fails, *Eng. News-Record*, Vol 119 (1937), p 532. Failure of Marshall Creek Dam, Kan., by spreading.

52.10. Foundation Failure Causes Slump in Big Dike at Hartford, Conn., *Eng. News-Record*, Vol 127 (1941), p 142. Failure by rapid spreading.

52.11. L. F. Cooling and H. Q. Golder, The Analysis of the Failure of an Earth Dam during Construction, *J. Inst. Civil Engrs. (London)*, Paper 5324, No. 1, Nov. 1942, pp 38–55; discussions pp 289–304. Failure due to spreading.

52.12. K. E. Fields and W. L. Wells, Pendleton Levee Failure, *Trans. ASCE*, Vol 109 (1944), pp 1400–1413; discussions, pp 1414–1429.

See also Ref. 51.9, pp 180–182, review of American practice in constructing highway embankments on very soft ground; Ref. 51.4, brief discussion of foundation of levees on unfavorable ground.

Chapter IX

FOUNDATIONS

ART. 53. FOUNDATIONS FOR STRUCTURES

Types of Foundations

The *foundation* is that part of a structure which serves exclusively to transmit the weight of the structure onto the natural ground.

If a stratum of soil suitable for sustaining a structure is located at a relatively shallow depth, the structure may be supported directly on it by a *spread foundation*. However, if the upper strata are too weak, the loads are transferred to more suitable material at greater depth by means of *piles* or *piers*. Spread foundations are of two types. If a single slab covers the supporting stratum beneath the entire area of the super-structure, the foundation is known as a *mat* or *raft*. If various parts of the structure are supported individually, the individual supports are known as *spread footings*, and the foundation is called a *footing foundation*. A footing that supports a single column is called an *individual footing;* one that supports a group of columns is a *combined footing*, and one that supports a wall is a *continuous footing*.

The *depth of foundation* D_f is the vertical distance between the base of the footing or pier and the ground surface, unless the base is located beneath a basement or, if the structure is a bridge, beneath the surface of the river. In these instances the depth of foundation is referred to the level of the basement floor or to that of the river bed. The principal difference between footings and piers lies in the value of the ratio D_f/B, where B is the width of the base. For footings D_f/B commonly ranges between 0.25 and 1, whereas for piers it is usually greater than 5 and may be as great as 20. However, monolithic supports for bridges are commonly called piers, irrespective of the value of D_f/B. Depending on this value, bridge piers are designed according to the same principles as those governing the design of footings or piers for buildings.

Minimum Depth of Building Foundations

The conditions that determine the minimum depth of building foundations are illustrated by Figure 171, which represents a cross section

407

through part of a building. The outer portion of the structure does not have a basement, but the inner part does.

The first requirement is that the base of every part of the foundation should be located below the depth to which the soil is subject to seasonal volume changes caused by alternate wetting and drying. This depth usually does not exceed 4 ft, but there are notable exceptions to this statement. One of them was mentioned in Article 21 in connection with the seasonal swelling and shrinking of certain clays in central Texas. Although these clays are stiff enough to sustain a load of 2 or 3 tons per sq ft without perceptible settlement, the seasonal volume changes make

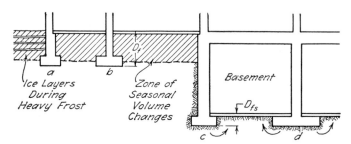

Fig. 171.   Simplified section through footing foundation of building with basement beneath its central part.

it necessary to provide even light structures with pier foundations that extend to a depth of more than 20 ft.[53.1] Similar seasonal volume changes extending to great depth have been observed in some parts of Burma.[53.2] Withdrawal of water from the ground by the root systems of large trees located close to buildings has also been responsible for important and detrimental differential settlement.

The base of each part of the foundation should also be located below the depth to which the structure of the soil is significantly weakened by root holes or cavities produced by burrowing animals or worms. The lower boundary of the weakened zone can be discerned readily on the walls of test pits.

In regions with a cool humid climate the foundations of the outside columns or walls should be located below the level to which frost may cause a perceptible heave, Article 21. In the northeastern part of the United States this depth may be as great as 5 ft. Hence, outside walls or columns may require deeper foundations than interior columns.

Basement floors are commonly located well below the minimum depth required for footings of buildings without basements. Hence, under normal conditions the minimum depth of foundations located within the boundaries of a basement, c and d in Figure 171, is governed solely by structural requirements. Exceptions to this statement need be considered only if conditions may arise that could subsequently affect the integrity of the soil beneath the footings. In one instance large unequal settlement of a building resting on medium clay was caused by the gradual desiccation of the clay surrounding a deep boiler room. On account of the low humidity and high temperature of the air in the boiler room, the water in the clay evaporated through the concrete walls of the room. In another instance the footings of a building on fine sand settled because of the leakage of water through open joints in a defective sewer located beneath the base level of the footings. The water washed sand into the sewer, and settlement occurred because of the loss of ground. Hence, before the minimum depth of foundation for a building with a basement is decided upon, the possibilities for subsequent artificial changes in the conditions of soil support should be considered.

Minimum Depth of Bridge Foundations

Whenever the water level in a river rises, the soil that constitutes the river bed starts to move throughout the greater part of the length and width of the river, and the bottom of the river goes down. This process is known as *scour*. The minimum depth for the foundation of a bridge pier is determined by the condition that the base of the foundation should be several feet below the level to which the river may scour during high water.

In those sections of a river where flood water is prevented by high banks or dikes from spreading over a wide area, scour can be very deep, even in a channel unobstructed by bridge piers. Figure 172 illustrates this possibility. Figure 172a is a section through the Colorado river near Yuma, Ariz. The river bed consists of fine silty sand and silt. As the river level rose 14 ft, the level of the bottom of the river channel went down as much as 36 ft. Figure 172b is a section through a mountain stream confined between the abutments of a bridge. The river bed consists of coarse sand and gravel with a high percentage of large cobblestones. A rise of the river level of 3.3 ft was associated with a scour ranging between 2 and 12.5 ft.

Obstruction of the flow by bridge piers increases the amount of scour, particularly in the proximity of the piers. The influence of the shape of the piers on the topography of the depression formed by the scour is illustrated in Figure 173. The information is based on the results of model tests.

Scour does not always receive the attention it deserves, and, as a consequence, failure of bridge piers due to this cause is not uncommon. Failure may occur even under conditions that seem to exclude the risk of scour. In a torrential river in Colorado the base of a bridge pier was established at a depth of 10 ft below the bottom of the river channel. At that depth the river bed contained boulders of a size up to 8 cu ft, so tightly wedged that further excavation would have been impracticable

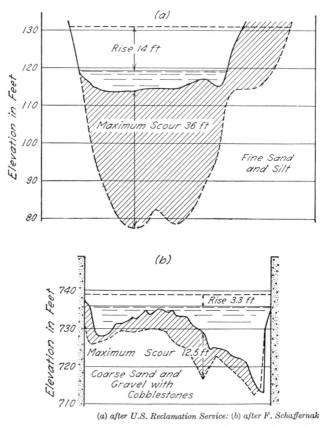

(a) after U.S. Reclamation Service: (b) after F. Schaffernak

Fig. 172. Scour due to high water (a) in unobstructed river bed of Colorado River near Yuma, Ariz., and (b) between abutments of bridge over Drau River in eastern Alps. Horizontal scale 10 times vertical scale.

without blasting. Therefore, the base of the pier was established at that depth. Yet, the first high water after construction caused the pier to fail.

Near the east coast of the United States, a bridge pier was founded 2 ft below the surface of a stratum of gravel 7 ft thick. The gravel was covered with 8 ft of soft mud. During exceptionally high water the pier settled appreciably. After the water level dropped the gravel was still buried beneath mud. From the records of the failure, it appeared likely that the settlement was due to scour in the gravel, preceded by complete removal of the overlying mud layer. While the high water was receding, a new layer of mud was deposited.

In those parts of a river where the high water has an opportunity to spread over a wide area, the scour may be imperceptible. Locally, the river bed may even be raised. However, bridges are commonly located at points where these conditions are not satisfied. Furthermore, at any given cross section of the river the point of deepest scour may shift from year to year in an unpredictable manner.

Since reliable scour forecasts require mature and varied experience in the hydraulics of rivers, they can be made only by specialists in this

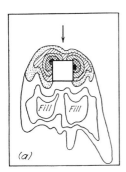 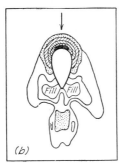 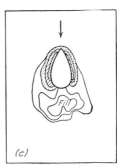

After Th. Rehbock

FIG. 173.   Results of hydraulic model tests for investigating effect of shape of bridge piers on scour.

field. On account of the inevitable uncertainties involved in the forecasts, a large margin of safety is required. If no scour investigation has been made by a river specialist, and if, in addition, the depth to bedrock or a scourproof stratum is very great, it is advisable to establish the base of the foundation at a depth below the bottom of the low-water channel equal to not less than four times the greatest known rise of the river level.

ALLOWABLE PRESSURE ON THE SUBSOIL

Every foundation should satisfy two independent conditions. First, the factor of safety of the foundation with respect to breaking into the ground should not be less than 3, which is the minimum factor of safety customarily specified for the design of the superstructure. Second, the deformation of the base of the structure due to unequal settlement should not be great enough to damage the structure.

There is no definite relation between the factor of safety with respect to breaking into the ground and the settlement. Therefore, both factors require independent consideration. Since the theoretical methods for evaluating the factor of safety of foundations with respect to breaking into the ground, Article 29, are simple and fairly reliable, they can be used without essential modification in connection with the design of foundations. On the other hand, the methods for evaluating the magnitude and distribution of the settlement are cumbersome and in many instances very unreliable. This fact determines the procedure for estimating the allowable soil pressure whenever the design must be based on settlement considerations.

Since all substances including soil and rock are compressible, every foundation settles. If the base of a structure remains plane while settlement proceeds, the magnitude of the settlement may be more or less irrelevant. However, if the base becomes warped during the settlement, the structure may be damaged. For this reason, the distribution of the settlement over the base of the structure is far more important than the maximum value. At the same time, it is also far more difficult to evaluate.

According to Article 36, the magnitude and the distribution of the settlement of a loaded area depend on the physical properties of the soil located beneath the area, on the size of the area, on the depth of foundation, and on the position of the water table. If a building rests on footings, the estimate of the settlement is further complicated by the fact that the soil conditions prevailing under the different footings are likely to be different, Article 45. An accurate evaluation of the effect of all these factors on the settlement is impracticable. Therefore, under normal conditions the designer is compelled to estimate the settlement on the basis of simple semiempirical rules. The theory of settlement, Article 36, serves merely as a basis for a rational interpretation of the results of soil and load tests and for determining the limits of validity of the semiempirical rules. Refined settlement computations are justified only if the subsoil contains strata of soft clay located below the base of the foundation or the points of the piles, Articles 54 to 56.

Semiempirical rules for determining settlement are based on observed relations between the results of simple field tests such as penetration tests, the load per unit of area, and the behavior of existing structures. Every relation of this type is a statistical one involving more or less important scattering from the average. Experience shows that a relation developed within a geologically well-defined region always involves less scattering than the corresponding relation for all deposits of a given kind, irrespective of their geological origin and environment. In this book only relations of the latter type can be considered. On account of the great scattering they represent a very conservative basis for design. Therefore, whenever extensive construction operations are carried out within a limited area, such as that occupied by a large city, the rules given in the following articles should be checked against local experience. If they are found to be too conservative for this particular region, they should be modified accordingly.

For example, according to one of the general relations discussed in the next article, a sand having an N-value of 25 as determined by the standard penetration test (page 265) is of medium density, and, if the groundwater level is near footing level, it should be assigned an allowable soil pressure beneath a large footing of about 2400 lb per sq ft. Yet local investigations have demonstrated that the sand deposit at the south end of Lake Michigan near the Illinois–Indiana border, which has an N-value of 25, is actually a dense sand that can safely be subjected to a load of 3200 lb per sq ft beneath large footings.

Until local rules are established, the requirements of safety call for design on the basis of the more conservative general rules. Because of the additional expense involved in this procedure, the accumulation of the observational data needed for establishing local rules is a very good investment and should be encouraged. Only in this manner can the engineer exploit the desirable characteristics of the principal local soil types to the fullest extent.

The following articles deal with the methods for adapting the four principal types of foundations to the subsoil conditions.

REFERENCES

53.1. See 21.2. Effect of periodic desiccation and saturation of the soil to great depth on foundation conditions in central Texas.

53.2. See 21.3. As before, in Burma.

53.3. Lorenz G. Straub, Mechanics of Rivers, in *Physics of the Earth—Part IX, Hydrology*, edited by O. E. Meinzer, McGraw-Hill Book Company, first edition, New York, 1942, pp 614–636. General discussions of seasonal changes in river beds.

53.4. K. Terzaghi, Failure of Bridge Piers Due to Scour, *Proc. Intern. Conf. Soil Mech.*, Cambridge, Mass. (1936), Vol II, p 264. Discussion by Irving B. Crosby, Vol III, p 238.

53.5. E. C. Murphy, Changes in Bed and Discharge Capacity of the Colorado River at Yuma, Ariz., *Eng. News*, Vol 60 (1908), p 344.

ART. 54. FOOTING FOUNDATIONS

Origin and Shortcomings of Conventional Design Methods

The most important step in the design of a footing foundation is the evaluation of the greatest pressure that can be applied to the soil beneath the footings without causing either failure of the loaded soil or excessive settlement. The current methods for choosing this pressure originated many years ago. They are expedient, but they contain many shortcomings.

Before the 19th century the framework of most large buildings consisted of strong but somewhat flexible main walls interconnected by massive but equally flexible partition walls intersecting each other at right angles. Since such buildings could stand large settlements without damage, their builders gave little consideration to foundations other than to increase the wall thickness at the base. If the ground was obviously too soft to support the loads, the walls were established on piles. When exceptional structures were built with large domes, vaults, or heavy individual columns, the designers tended to underdimension the foundations because they had neither rules nor experience to guide them. As a consequence, many important buildings either collapsed or were disfigured by subsequent reinforcements.

The development of highly competitive industry during the 19th century led to a demand for large but inexpensive buildings. The types that developed were more sensitive to differential settlement than their predecessors. Furthermore, many of the most desirable sites for industrial buildings were located in regions that had previously been avoided because of notoriously bad soil conditions. Hence, designers found themselves in need of a reliable procedure, applicable under all soil conditions, for proportioning the footings of a given building in such a manner that they would all experience nearly the same settlement.

To satisfy this need the concept of an "allowable soil pressure" was developed during the 1870's in several different countries. The concept was based on the obvious fact that, under fairly similar soil conditions, footings transmitting pressures of high intensity to the subsoil generally settled more than those transmitting pressures of low intensity. With this fact in mind designers began to observe the condition of buildings supported by footings that exerted various pressures against the subsoil. The pressures beneath the footings of all those buildings that showed signs of damage due to settlement were considered too great for the given soil conditions. The maximum pressure not associated with structural damage was considered a satisfactory basis for design and was accepted as the *allowable soil pressure* or *allowable bearing value*. The values obtained for each type of soil in a given locality by this purely empirical procedure were assembled into a table of allowable soil pressures that was subsequently incorporated into the building code governing construction in that locality. Excerpts from the building codes of several American cities are given in Table 19.

Although most existing building codes contain tables of allowable soil pressures. they do not offer any hint regarding the origin of the values, or any explanation of the meaning of the term "allowable soil pressure." These omissions have fostered the belief that the settlement of a building will be uniform and of no consequence if the pressure on the soil beneath each footing is equal to the allowable soil pressure.The size of the loaded area and the type of building are believed to be immaterial. Some engineers are even under the delusion that a building with footings that exert the allowable soil pressure will not settle at all.

Many foundations designed on the basis of the allowable-soil-pressure tables have been entirely satisfactory, but from time to time the results have been disappointing, and structures have settled excessively. Since

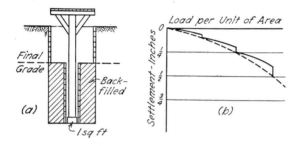

FIG. 174.   (a) Test arrangement for determining relation between load per unit of area and settlement of test plate, as basis for selecting allowable soil pressure; (b) one of several customary methods for plotting results of load test.

engineers believed that footings would not settle noticeably if the allowable pressure was not exceeded, they attributed the failures to faulty classification of the soil. They assumed that the wrong allowable pressures had been selected because the terms used to describe the soil in the field and in the building codes did not have the same meaning. In order to avoid this difficulty, it gradually became customary to select the allowable soil pressure on the basis of the results of load tests.

A load test is made by increasing the load on a bearing plate by small increments and measuring the corresponding settlements. The bearing plate rests on the bottom of a pit at the level of the base of the footings. Depending on the preference of the engineer who makes the test, the plate may be surrounded by a box and the pit backfilled to final grade (see Figure 174a), or the pit may be made so large that the plate rests in the middle of a level area. The test results are represented by load-settlement curves similar to the one shown in Figure 174b. In the following paragraphs two of the most common methods for performing the tests and interpreting the results are described.

The first method consists of loading a square or circular bearing block

TABLE 19

SOIL PRESSURES ALLOWED BY VARIOUS BUILDING CODES

Character of Foundation Bed, Loads in tons per sq ft	Akron, 1920	Atlanta, 1911	Boston, 1926	Chicago, 1924	Cleveland, 1927	Denver, 1927	Louisville, 1923	Minneapolis, 1911	Newark, 1924	New York, 1922	Pacific Coast, 1928	Philadelphia, 1929	Portland, Oreg., 1924	Richmond, 1908–12	St. Louis, 1917	St. Paul, 1910	Jacksonville, 1922	Prop. N. Y. Code, 1929
1 Quicksand or alluvial soil	½				½						½							
2 Adobe	1	1			2			1	1	1	1	1	1	1			1	1
3 Soft or wet clay, at least 15′ thick																		
4 Soft clay, sand, loam, or silt	1½			1¾	1½											1		
5 Soft clay and wet sand		2		1½				2	2	2	2		2	2		2	2	2
6 Sand and clay mixed or in layers									2	2								2
7 Firm clay									2	2								
8 Wet sand	2				2													
9 Dry clay and sand	2				2							2				3		2
10 Fine wet sand																		
11 Soft clay held against displacement			2										3				3	
12 Clay in thick beds, mod. dry				2¼		2–4												
13 Dry solid clay																		
14 Loam, clay or fine sand, firm and dry				2½			2½								2½			
15 Clean sand								3										
16 Firm dry loam	2½	2–3				1–2												
17 Firm dry sand	3	2–3			3	2–4			3	3							3	3
18 Quicksand when drained																		

No.	Material													
19	Hard clay	3–4					3		4		4			4
20	Fine-grained wet sand		3	3				3						4
21	Moderately dry sand													
22	Moderately dry sand and clay						3	4						
23	Clay or fine sand, firm and dry	3–4			4–6	4	4	4	4	4	4			4
24	Very firm coarse sand	3–4				6		4	4	4	4			4
25	Gravel					4		6				3	4	6
26	Dry hard clay											4	4	
27	Clay in thick beds always dry	4			4–6	4		4	4	4				
28	Stratified stone and clay													4
29	Fine dry clay	2–3				4								
30	Plastic clay, mixed or unmixed with sand		4	4			4			4				
31	Fine-grained dry sand		4		8			6				4		
32	Compact coarse sand and gravel	5	5											
33	Gravel and coarse sand in thick beds		5					4		4				6
34	Wet or dry, med. or coarse sand													
35	Hard blue clay—sand mix													
36	Firm coarse sand and gravel		6			8–10		5						6
37	Gravel, compact sand, and hard yellow clay													
38	Gravel or coarse sand well cemented													
39	Hardpan	6											8	10
40	Hard shale, unexposed		10	6			6	8	10	10				
41	Shale and hardpan		5											
42	Disintegrated ledge rock					8	8	8	8				8	8
43	Soft rock	10	15	10		10–200	16	24	48	40	40			25
44	Medium rock	15	100											40
45	Rock													

Rock unit 20% of crushing strength

FROM KIDDER-PARKER: *Architects' and Builders' Handbook*, 1931.

of any dimensions chosen by the investigator. The allowable load q_a per unit of area is taken as some fraction, such as one half, of the average pressure on the block at the time of failure. This procedure is objectionable for several reasons. In the first place, if the load-settlement curve resembles C_2, Figure 72, there is no definite failure load. Second, the size of the loaded area, which is optional, may have a large influence on the ultimate bearing capacity per unit of area (see Article 29). Hence, by using this first procedure two different investigators can obtain very different values of q_a for the same soil.

The second method consists of loading a bearing block covering an area of 1 sq ft. The allowable load q_a is arbitrarily defined as one-half the load at which the settlement of the bearing block is 0.5 in. (In countries using the metric system the area of contact is customarily taken as 0.1 sq m or 1.08 sq ft, and the settlement as 1 cm or 0.4 in.) This procedure, although arbitrary, is preferable because two different investigators will at least obtain the same value of q_a for the same soil.

There are many other methods for performing load tests and many other rules for interpreting the results. Yet, whatever the method may be, the test results reflect the character only of the soil located within a depth of less than twice the width of the bearing plate, whereas the settlement of the footings depends on the properties of a much thicker soil stratum. As a consequence, if the character of the soil changes below a depth of about twice the width of the bearing plate, as it commonly does, the test results are certain to be misleading. Since it is also almost universal practice to select the allowable soil pressure without regard for the size of the footings, the type of superstructure, and other vital characteristics of the proposed foundation, it is not surprising that increasing recourse to load tests has not significantly reduced the frequency of faulty footing design. In fact, several complete foundation failures have occurred in spite of the conscientious performance of load tests. To reduce the risk of faulty design, the allowable soil pressure must be chosen in accordance not only with the results of load tests or their equivalent, but also with the character of the soil profile and of the foundation itself. Part of the necessary information can be obtained from the theories given in Articles 29, 35, and 36. The rest is derived from construction experience.

Because of the great variety of soils and combinations of soils encountered in practice, no single method for determining the allowable soil pressure can be developed that would be suitable under all circumstances. The procedure must always be adapted to the soil conditions revealed by the exploratory borings. In particular, the procedure depends on the *significant depth*. This term refers to the depth within which the load on the footing alters the state of stress in the soil enough to produce a perceptible contribution to the settlement.

The significant depth depends not only on the size of the footing and on the load it supports, but also to a high degree on the soil profile and the physical properties of the soils that constitute the individual strata. If the initial tangent modulus of the soil, Article 18, increases as the depth below a footing increases, the significant depth does not exceed the width B of the footing. On the other hand, if the soil beneath the footing becomes softer with depth, the significant depth may be equal to several times the width B.

In the following discussion, four principal types of soil conditions are considered:

(a) The footings are supported by sand or sand and gravel that do not contain any layers of soft clay or other highly compressible soil within the significant depth.

(b) The footings are supported by clay that is fairly homogeneous within the significant depth.

(c) The footings rest on soil with properties intermediate between those of sand and clay, such as silt, some types of fill, or loess. The soil is fairly homogeneous within the significant depth.

(d) The footings are supported by soil that contains one or more soft layers within the significant depth.

FOOTINGS ON HOMOGENEOUS SAND

Present conceptions regarding the allowable soil pressure on sand are exemplified by Table 20. As the first step in establishing a rational basis

TABLE 20

CUSTOMARY ALLOWABLE BEARING VALUES FOR SAND

Abstract from Table 19

Soil	q_a in tons/sq ft
1 Quicksand	0.5
8 Wet sand	2
14 Fine sand, firm and dry	2.5–3
18 Quicksand when drained	3
24 Very firm coarse sand	3–6
33 Gravel and coarse sand in thick beds	5–8

for selecting the allowable pressure, we shall examine the shortcomings of this table. The numerical values are likely to be inappropriate, because the soil classification is based on properties that are largely irrelevant, whereas significant properties are ignored. For example, the term quicksand (1) is not descriptive of a type of sand. It does not even indicate a sand that was necessarily in a loose state before construction started. This fact is illustrated by the ill-deserved reputation of a very fine uniform sand located beneath the water table near Lynn, Mass. Curve 2 in Figure 128a represents the results of a load test made on this sand after the water table was lowered by well points; it indicates that the sand is firm and dense. Yet, among the construction men in its locality it once had the reputation of a dangerous quicksand, because on former jobs, when more primitive methods of drainage were used, it became soft on the bottom of excavations and started to boil on slight provocation. Description 8 does not state whether the sand is above or below water table, although this factor is decisive. The grain size, mentioned in descriptions 14, 24, and 33, has no direct influence on the bearing capacity. The poorest of the sands represented in Figure 128a, indicated by curve 5, was clean, coarse, mixed-grained, and dry. The best one, represented by curve 1, was uniform, fine, and wet. In order to establish more reliable criteria for the design of footings on sand, the allowable soil pressure must be correlated not with irrelevant properties of the sand, but with properties and conditions that have a significant influence on the behavior of the sand under load. These conditions are the relative density of the sand and the position of the water table with reference to the base of the footings.

The relative density has a decisive influence on the angle of internal friction ϕ and the shape of the load-settlement curve. Depending on the relative density, the value of ϕ for a sand may vary over as wide a range as 34° to 46°, Article 15, and the load-settlement curve may have any shape intermediate between C_1 and C_2 in Figure 72. If standard penetration tests are made, the relative density can be judged by means of Table 10, page 294. More comprehensive data can be obtained expediently by making subsurface soundings.

The position of the water table with reference to the base of the footings has an influence on both the ultimate bearing capacity of the sand and the settlement. If the water table rises from beneath the seat of settlement toward the base of a footing, it reduces the effective unit weight of the soil located beneath the footing by roughly 50 per cent, Article 12. As a consequence the factor of safety of the footing with respect to breaking into the ground is reduced by the same percentage, Article 29, and the settlement is nearly doubled, Article 36.

Computations based on the theory presented in Article 29 lead to the following conclusions regarding the factor of safety G_s of footings designed on the basis of the customary allowable pressures on sand: If the base of a footing rests on loose sand at or below the water table, and if, in addition, the width B of the footing is less than about 6 ft, and the depth of foundation is less than B below the ground surface or basement floor, the value of G_s may be smaller than the required minimum of 3. In the rare instances when these conditions are simultaneously satisfied, a stability computation should be made to find out whether or not the safety requirement is met. In all other instances the factor of safety is greater and commonly much greater than 3. Hence, under normal conditions, the allowable soil pressure on sand is determined exclusively by settlement considerations.

The distribution of the settlement over the base of a building supported by footings with width B is determined chiefly by the variations in the compressibility of the layer of sand with thickness B located immediately below the footings (see Article 45). The practical importance of these variations is illustrated by Figure 175, which shows the settlement of several uniformly loaded continuous footings of constant width. The footings represented by curves b, c, and d rested on sand or gravel. If the subsoils had been uniform, each footing would have settled almost uniformly. The unequal settlement was due to local variations in the compressibility of the soil.

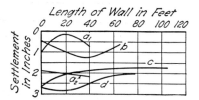

Fig. 175. Diagram showing settlements of long narrow continuous footings supporting brick walls.

A study of available settlement records leads to the conclusion that the differential settlement of uniformly loaded continuous footings and of equally loaded spread footings of approximately equal size is unlikely to exceed 50 per cent of the maximum settlement. However, in practice, the size of footings supporting the different columns of a building may be very different because the loads on the columns are likely to be different. This is a source of additional differential settlement.

According to the results of various theoretical investigations, the settlement of square footings exerting equal soil pressures on a homogeneous sand should increase with increasing width as shown by the plain curve in Figure 94. In accordance with this theoretical conclusion, the results of experiments and observations indicate that the settlement increases with the width B of the footing approximately as shown in Figure 176. The empirical data were derived from small-scale load tests on artificially compacted sand, from load tests on relatively homogeneous sand strata, and from settlement observations on buildings. In this figure, S_1 is the settlement of a loaded area 1 ft square under a given load q per unit of area, and S is the settlement at the same load per unit of area of a footing with a width B. The relation between S, S_1 and B is given approximately by the equation,

$$S = S_1\left(\frac{2B}{B + 1}\right)^2 \qquad (54.1)$$

in which S and S_1 are expressed in inches and B in feet. There is no significant difference between the settlements of square and continuous footings having the same width B, because the effect of stressing the sand to a greater depth below a continuous footing is compensated by the restraint that keeps the sand from being displaced in directions parallel to the footing. According to Figure 176, the settlement of a large footing, greater than about 20 ft square, exceeds that of a small footing 4 or 5 ft square by roughly 30 per cent, provided the soil pressures are equal. At a given width B of the footing, the settlement decreases to some extent

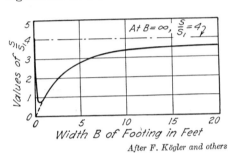

Width B of Footing in Feet

After F. Kögler and others

FIG. 176. Approximate relation between width B of footing on sand and the ratio S/S_1, wherein S represents the settlement of a footing with width B and S_1 the settlement of a footing 1 ft wide subject to the same load per unit of area.

with increasing values of the *depth ratio* D_f/B, wherein D_f is the depth of foundation, Article 53. Yet, even under extreme conditions involving a foundation on footings with very different sizes and depth ratios, Figure 171, the differential settlement is unlikely to exceed 75 per cent of the maximum settlement. Normally it is very much smaller.

Most ordinary structures, such as office buildings, apartment houses, or factories, can withstand a differential settlement between adjacent columns of three quarters of an inch. As indicated in the preceding paragraph, this settlement will not be exceeded if the soil pressure is selected such that the largest footing would settle 1 in. even if it rested on the most compressible part of the sand deposit. Therefore, the allowable soil pressure for the design of the footings of such structures can be assumed equal to the pressure that will cause the largest footing to settle 1 in. The following paragraphs contain a description of an approximate method for selecting the allowable soil pressure on sand in accordance with this assumption. If a differential settlement ΔS of more than $\frac{3}{4}$ in. can be tolerated, the allowable soil pressure can be multiplied by $4\Delta S/3$. However, in such instances it may be advisable to investigate whether the stability condition is satisfied.[54.1]

Allowable Pressure on Dry and on Moist Sand

The settlement of a footing on dry or moist sand depends primarily on the relative density of the sand and the width of the footing. The relative density can be judged adequately on the basis of the results of any of the sounding methods described in Article 44, provided the relation between relative density and penetration resistance has been determined previously by means of suitable calibration tests. Each of these methods furnishes continuous penetration records. However, up to the present time the only procedure commonly used in the United States is the standard penetration test (page 265). In contrast to the other subsurface soundings, it furnishes a penetration record with large gaps between the points of observation, and the calibration is very crude. Hence, it still leaves a wide margin for improvement. Nevertheless, the test results are a far more reliable basis for judging the allowable soil pressure than the soil-pressure tables or the results of a few conventional load tests.

In order to select the allowable soil pressure on the basis of the results of standard penetration tests, it is necessary to estimate very roughly the width B of the largest footings. Between the level of the base of the footings and a depth B below this level one standard penetration test should be performed for every $2\frac{1}{2}$ ft of depth. The average value of N for this depth indicates the relative density of the sand within the seat of settlement of the footing. If the tests in different drill holes furnish different values of N, the lowest value should be used for estimating the allowable soil pressure.

The value of the allowable soil pressure is then obtained by means of the chart, Figure 177, in which the curves represent the relation between the width B of a footing, in feet, and the soil pressure required to produce a settlement of the footing

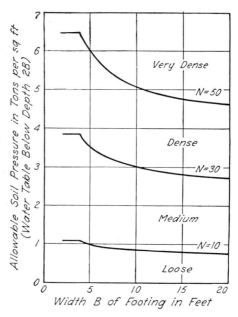

Fig. 177. Chart for estimating allowable soil pressure for footings on sand on the basis of results of standard penetration test.

of 1 in., provided the footing rests on a sand for which the number of blows N has the value inscribed on the curve. If N has a value other than those for which the curves are drawn, the allowable soil pressure is obtained by linear interpolation between curves.

The chart, Figure 177, was prepared on the basis of present knowledge concerning the relation between the number of blows N per foot of penetration of the sampling spoon, the results of surface loading tests, and equation 54.1. If B is the width of the largest footing supporting a structure, and if all of the footings are proportioned in accordance with the allowable soil pressure corresponding to B, the maximum settlement of the foundation should not exceed 1 in., and the differential settlement $\frac{3}{4}$ in.

If the subsoil consists of gravel or of sand containing large pieces of gravel, the number of blows on the sampler cannot be considered indicative of the degree of compactness of the soil. Yet, the bearing properties of such soils are as variable as those of sand. A well-packed mixture of sand and gravel is less compressible than a very dense sand, whereas the compressibility of a loose gravel may be as great as that of a sand of only medium density. In order to avoid overestimating the allowable soil pressure on gravel, several test pits should be excavated into the layers that will constitute the seat of settlement of the footings, and the degree of compactness of the exposed soil should be evaluated at least on the basis of its appearance, stability, and resistance to excavation. If the allowable soil pressure for the gravel is assumed equal to that of a sand with the same relative density, conservative values are obtained by means of the chart, Figure 177.

Even if very low soil pressures are used in design, footings on sand are likely to settle excessively if the sand is subject to high-frequency vibrations. The statement applies to saturated as well as to moist or dry sands. Foundations intended to support vibrating machinery must be designed on the basis of the theory of vibrations. They are beyond the scope of this book.

ALLOWABLE SOIL PRESSURE ON SATURATED SAND

If a saturated sand located beneath a footing is very loose, a shock of any kind may cause spontaneous liquefaction, Article 17, followed by a sinking of the footing. It has even been observed that a rapid change of the ground-water level in loose sand occasionally causes a large subsidence. Hence, if the sand is very loose (N equal to 5 or less), the footings should be supported by piles, or else the sand should be compacted, Article 50.

If the value of N for the sand in its natural state is greater than 5, or if the sand has been compacted, the allowable soil pressure q_a on the sand should be chosen such that the maximum settlement will not exceed 1 in. In order to determine q_a by means of the chart, Figure 177, the effect of submergence on settlement must be considered.

According to theory, the submergence of the sand located beneath the base of a footing should approximately double the settlement, provided the base is located at or near the surface of the sand, Article 36. Laboratory tests have confirmed this conclusion. If this fact is taken into consideration, the load per unit of area required to cause a footing on saturated sand to settle 1 in. can be estimated by means of the chart, Figure 177, in the following manner: If the depth ratio D_f/B for the footings is small, like that for the basement footings in Figure 171, the values obtained from the chart should be reduced 50 per cent. On the other hand, if the depth ratio is close to unity, two thirds of these values can be tolerated, because the effect on the settlement of the weight of the soil surrounding the footing partly compensates for that of the increase due to saturation. More refined methods for considering the effect of submergence would be out of proportion to the degree of accuracy of the data obtained by means of standard penetration tests.

The procedure outlined in the preceding paragraph calls for two qualifications. The first has already been stated on page 421, where the conditions are outlined that make a stability computation imperative. The computation can be made by means of equations 29.5 and 29.10. The values of the bearing-capacity factors contained in the equations can be obtained from the diagram, Figure 75. For loose sand with an N-value of 5 the dash curves should be used, and for dense sand with an N-value equal to 30 or more the full curves. The bearing-capacity factors for values of N between 5 and 30 can be estimated by linear interpolation between the two curves. If the investigation shows that the factor of safety of these footings is smaller than 3, either the size of the footings or the depth of foundation should be increased sufficiently to satisfy the safety requirement.

Second, if the saturated subsoil consists of very fine or silty sand, the effect of the low permeability of the soil on the value of N must be considered. If the void ratio of the soil is higher than the critical void ratio, the resistance against penetration of the sampling spoon is smaller than that of a more permeable soil of equal relative density. If the void ratio is below the critical value, the reverse is true (see Article 15). The value of N corresponding to the critical void ratio seems to be about 15. This statement is the basis for the following rule, which represents the present state of our experience: If the number of blows N is greater than 15, it should be assumed that the density of the soil is equal to that of a sand for which the number of blows is equal to $15 + \frac{1}{2}$ $(N - 15)$. Pending more reliable information, this rule should be adhered to unless reliable load tests have shown that higher pressures can safely be applied.

PREREQUISITES FOR THE SUCCESS OF LOAD TESTS ON SAND

The procedure for determining the allowable soil pressure on sand by means of the chart, Figure 177, eliminates much of the guesswork involved in the use of soil-pressure tables such as Table 20, because it furnishes values that are related to significant and not to irrelevant soil properties and conditions. In contrast to the conventional methods, it allows the designer to adapt the soil pressures at least in a crude way to the differential settlement that he feels can be tolerated, and the method lends itself to progressive improvement as knowledge and experience increase.

At present, more reliable data regarding the allowable soil pressure on sand can be obtained only by means of calibrated subsurface soundings, Article 44, or, at a very much greater sacrifice of time and money, by means of load tests.

Year after year in almost every country a great number of load tests are performed. Yet, most of them are worthless, if not misleading, because the results are unfit for rational interpretation. Therefore, the engineer should be familiar with the prerequisites for obtaining trustworthy results.

Each load test should be made on a bearing plate 1 ft square located at the bottom of a test pit at least 5 ft square. The bearing surface should be at the level of the base of the footing. The load should be applied in increments of 200 lb and increased to at least 1.5 times the estimated allowable soil pressure. The apparatus for measuring the settlement should permit direct readings to 0.01 in. Load tests that satisfy these conditions are referred to as *standard load tests*.

The results of each test should be represented graphically by a load-settlement curve. The load per unit of area at which the settlement of the largest footing would be equal to the predetermined allowable value can be estimated by means of the relation shown in Figure 176. If B_l is the width of the footing in feet and the design is to be based on a maximum settlement $S = 1$ in., the allowable soil pressure is equal to the load per unit of area at which the settlement of the bearing plate in inches is

$$S_1 = \left(\frac{B_l + 1}{2B_l}\right)^2 \qquad (54.2)$$

If load tests are made at different points of the same site, the results are usually more or less different. This is due to local variations of the relative density of the sand in horizontal directions. Similar variations in vertical directions are observed whenever penetration tests are made in drill holes, Figures 124 and 131. These omnipresent variations are a potential source of serious errors. If, for instance, a load test is made on a layer of dense sand 2 ft thick that rests on a stratum of loose sand, the test result will be the same as if the dense sand extended to a very great

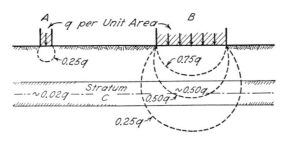

FIG. 178.   Section through stratified subgrade showing stress produced in stratum C by load q per unit of area transmitted to surface of ground by (A) bearing block one ft square; (B) full-sized footing.

depth. However, the full-sized footing will settle much more than would be anticipated on the basis of the load test. The reason is illustrated by Figure 178.

This figure represents a vertical section through a stratified subgrade. A is a bearing block covering an area 1 ft square, and B is a full-sized footing. The load on both A and B has the same intensity q. Beneath A and B are shown curves of equal vertical pressure in the subsoil. The pressures were computed by means of the chart, Figure 90. The load on A increases the average vertical pressure in stratum C beneath the loaded area by about $0.02q$, whereas the footing B increases it by $0.50q$. If stratum C is very compressible, the settlement of B may be very large. If C is hard, the settlement of B may be very small. Yet, the result of the load test is practically independent of the compressibility of C, because the increase of the pressure in stratum C due to the load on the bearing plate is negligible.

Because of the fact illustrated by Figure 178, it is necessary to make sure, by means of penetration tests, whether the variations in the density of the subsoil are purely erratic or whether the density of the subsoil within the significant depth for the proposed footings increases or decreases conspicuously and consistently in a downward direction. If the variation is entirely erratic, it is sufficient to make at least six load tests in different locations at the level of the base of the proposed footings. If the density varies consistently with depth, additional load tests must be made at one or two different levels within the significant depth. The allowable load should always be selected on the basis of the most unfavorable test results. Under no circumstances should the results of one or two load tests be relied on.

The preceding description of the technique for making load tests is based on the assumption that the water table is located at a considerable depth below the base of the footings. If it is located at or slightly above this level, the bearing plate should be established at the water table, on the bottom of a pit 5 ft square. On the other hand, if the water table is located at a considerable height above the level of the base of the footings, it must be lowered by pumping from well points or open sumps before the load tests are made. If well points are used, the pit need not be wider than 5 ft. The bearing plate should be located at the lowered water table. The allowable soil pressure can be computed by means of equation 54.2.

Even if the water table is located 3 or 4 ft below the base level of the footings, the load tests should be made at the water table. Otherwise the apparent cohesion imparted to the sand by the soil moisture may introduce an error on the unsafe side.

If the water level is lowered by pumping from open sumps, the test pit must be at least 10 ft wide. As soon as the excavation level arrives at the water table, a drainage ditch must be dug all the way around the floor of the pit. During further excavation the ditch must be maintained deep enough to prevent water from flowing up through the central part of the bottom. These requirements call for great care and close supervision. If they are not strictly satisfied, the results of the load tests can be very misleading, because the seepage pressure of water rising toward the bottom of the excavation may greatly increase the settlement.

In any event, the load-test method is very expensive and cumbersome because of the elaborate preparations and the great number of tests required. If the program is not expertly planned and executed, the results may be misleading. Therefore, use of the method should be considered only on very important jobs where the cost of the tests is a small fraction of the total expenditure.

ALLOWABLE PRESSURE ON CLAY

Customary values for the allowable soil pressure on clay are given in Table 21. This table, like Table 20 that applies to sands, is open to the criticism that the terminology is vague, and the soil properties on which it is based are irrelevant. A satisfactory procedure for design can be developed only by correlating the allowable soil pressures with well-defined mechanical properties of the clay.

The allowable soil pressure on clay, as well as that on sand, should satisfy the two requirements that the factor of safety against breaking into the ground should be adequate, and the settlement produced by the load should be within tolerable limits.

The factor of safety against the breaking of a footing into clay depends on the shearing resistance of the clay. As long as its water content is not appreciably altered by consolidation, the clay behaves in the field as if

TABLE 21

CUSTOMARY ALLOWABLE BEARING VALUES FOR CLAY

Abstract from Table 19

Soil	q_a in tons sq/ft
3 Soft or wet clay, at least 15 ft thick	1–2
4 Soft clay, sand, loam, or silt	1
5 Soft clay and wet sand	$1–1\frac{1}{2}$
11 Soft clay held against displacement	2
7 Firm clay	2
12 Clay in thick beds, moderately dry	2–4
13 Dry solid clay	$2\frac{1}{4}–3$
19 Hard clay	3–4
26 Dry hard clay	4
27 Clay in thick beds always dry	4–6

ϕ were equal to zero and as if the cohesion c were approximately equal to one-half the unconfined compressive strength q_u of fairly undisturbed samples (see Articles 15 and 17). Hence, according to equations 29.3 and 29.11, the ultimate bearing capacity q_d per unit of area of a continuous footing is

$$q_d = 5.70c = 2.85q_u \qquad 29.3$$

and of a circular or square footing is

$$q_{dr} = q_{ds} = 7.4c = 3.7q_u \qquad 29.11$$

The ultimate bearing capacity of a rectangular or oblong footing with width B and length L is roughly equal to

$$q_{do} = 2.85q_u \left(1 + 0.3\frac{B}{L}\right) \qquad (54.3)$$

Table 22 contains information concerning the ultimate bearing capacity of clays based on their unconfined compressive strength q_u. The values of q_d and q_{ds} were computed by means of equations 29.3 and 29.11.

For soft clays these values are only slightly greater than the customary allowable soil pressures given in Table 21. Therefore, it is not surprising that complete failures of footings on soft clay are by no means infrequent. In one instance, a footing 8 by 9 ft was constructed on a clay with an

TABLE 22

Proposed Allowable Bearing Values for Clay

N = number of blows per foot in standard penetration test
q_u = unconfined compressive strength in tons per square foot
q_d = ultimate bearing capacity of continuous footing in tons per square foot
q_{ds} = ultimate bearing capacity of square footing in tons per square foot
q_a = proposed normal allowable bearing value in tons per square foot $(G_s = 3)$
q_a' = proposed maximum tolerable bearing value in tons per square foot $(G_s = 2)$
G_s = factor of safety with respect to base failure

Description of Clay	N	q_u	q_d	q_{ds}	q_a		q_a'	
					Square $1.2q_u$	Continuous $0.9q_u$	Square $1.8q_u$	Continuous $1.3q_u$
Very soft*	Less than 2	Less than 0.25	Less than 0.71	Less than 0.92	Less than 0.30	Less than 0.22	Less than 0.45	Less than 0.32
Soft*	2 to 4	0.25 to 0.50	0.71 to 1.42	0.92 to 1.85	0.30 to 0.60	0.22 to 0.45	0.45 to 0.90	0.32 to 0.65
Medium	4 to 8	0.50 to 1.00	1.42 to 2.85	1.85 to 3.70	0.60 to 1.20	0.45 to 0.90	0.90 to 1.80	0.65 to 1.30
Stiff	8 to 15	1.00 to 2.00	2.85 to 5.70	3.70 to 7.40	1.20 to 2.40	0.90 to 1.80	1.80 to 3.60	1.30 to 2.60
Very stiff	15 to 30	2.00 to 4.00	5.70 to 11.40	7.40 to 14.80	2 40 to 4.80	1.80 to 3.60	3.60 to 7.20	2.60 to 5.20
Hard	Over 30	Over 4.00	Over 11.40	Over 14.80	Over 4.80	Over 3.60	Over 7.20	Over 5.20

* If clay is normally loaded, settlement can be important even under smallest allowable soil pressures.

average unconfined compressive strength of 700 lb per sq ft.[54.2] Hence, according to equation 54.3, the ultimate bearing capacity of the footing was 2590 lb per sq ft. At a load of 2500 lb per sq ft the footing actually subsided 10 in. within a few days.

Under normal conditions the factor of safety of footings on clay, like that of footings on sand, should not be smaller than 3. The corresponding pressures on the clay are given on the right-hand side of Table 22. If the loads for which a footing is designed are very unlikely to develop, the value of $G_s = 2$ can be tolerated. For example, this value would be appropriate if the design load for the footing of an office building included the maximum live load combined with maximum snow and wind load.

To compute the bearing capacity of a clay it is necessary to determine the average unconfined compressive strength of the clay below the proposed footings. This information can be obtained most readily by making test borings at the site of several footings and securing continuous 2-in. tube samples between the level of the base of the footings and a depth below the base equal to the width of the footing. The unconfined compressive strength q_u of the clay is then determined at 6-in. intervals in the vertical direction, either by means of laboratory tests or, on rush jobs, by means of a portable compression device in the field. The average value of q_u is computed for each of the borings, and the smallest of these average values is introduced into equation 54.3. The value of the ultimate bearing capacity is then calculated and divided by a factor of safety of 3.

This procedure is valid providing the subsoil does not contain within the significant depth a layer of clay softer than the clay defined by the value q_u on which the estimate of the allowable soil pressure is based. Hence, it cannot be used for computing the allowable soil pressure on a stiff clay crust that rests on softer clay.

If a foundation job is not important enough to justify experimental determination of the unconfined compressive strength of the clay, the ultimate bearing capacity can be roughly estimated on the basis of the standard penetration test described in Article 44. However, the relation between the number of blows N on the sampling spoon and the unconfined compressive strength involves a wide scattering from the average values of N given in Table 22. Therefore, it is advisable to supplement the penetration tests by determining the unconfined compressive strength q_u of the spoon samples.

Some stiff clays consist of small angular fragments separated from each other by hair cracks. The presence of the cracks makes it impracticable to determine the unconfined compressive strength of the clay, because the test specimens are likely to disintegrate while they are being prepared. Furthermore, the hair cracks invalidate equation 54.3, because they change the stress conditions for failure. The ultimate bearing capacity of such clays should be determined by the load-test method, described in the following paragraphs.

The allowable soil pressure q_a on a clay can be assumed equal to the value given in Table 22 under the heading $G_s = 3$, provided the soil conditions justify the assumption that the settlement of the foundation will be tolerable. Whether this requirement is satisfied depends primarily on whether the clay is normally loaded or precompressed.

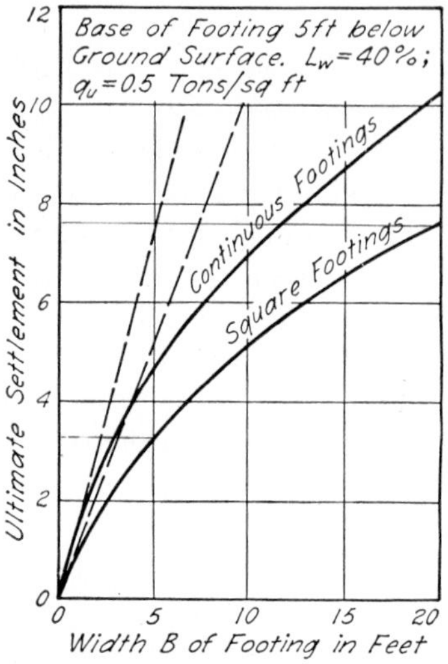

If the footings rest on normally loaded clay, the magnitude of both the total and the differential settlement can be very large. This can be demonstrated by computing the ultimate settlement of continuous footings of different widths resting on soft normally loaded clay. The results of such a computation are shown in Figure 179. The soil pressure on the base of the footings was taken as 1000 lb per sq ft. In addition, it was assumed that the depth of foundation was 5 ft, that within this depth the effective unit weight of the soil was 100 lb per cu ft, that the liquid limit of the clay was 40 per cent, and that the settlement of the footings was caused solely by consolidation. The compression index of the clay was estimated by means of equation 13.11, and the settlement by means of equation 13.8. The curve that represents the relation between the settlement and the width of the footing resembles the dash–dotted line in Figure 94. The trend of the curve indicates that the settlement of footings on clay, in contrast to that of footings on sand, increases in almost direct proportion to the width of the footings.

The graph is labeled: Base of Footing 5 ft below Ground Surface. $L_w = 40\%$; $q_u = 0.5$ Tons/sq ft. The vertical axis is "Ultimate Settlement in Inches" ranging 0 to 12, and the horizontal axis is "Width B of Footing in Feet" ranging 0 to 20. The curves are labeled "Continuous Footings" and "Square Footings."

FIG. 179. Approximate relation between width B and ultimate settlement of footing on normally loaded clay.

The diagram, Figure 179, shows that the settlement of continuous uniformly loaded footings of constant width on a uniform deposit of normally loaded clay can be very large and that the settlement of footings with different widths can be very different. Furthermore, the settlement of footings with the same width can also be very nonuniform, because the compressibility of natural clay strata may vary considerably in horizontal directions. As a matter of fact, in those parts of such cities as Istanbul or Mexico City that are underlain by normally loaded clays, the unequal settlement of the house fronts can be discerned with the naked eye. Fortunately, footing foundations on normally loaded clays are rare exceptions. In most localities even soft clays are precompressed to some extent, either by desiccation or temporary lowering of the water table. Medium and stiff clays beneath a shallow overburden are always precompressed. Since the allowable soil pressures rarely exceed the precompression pressure, the differential settlement of footing foundations on such clays designed on the basis of the conservative allowable soil pressures q_a corresponding to $G_s = 3$ in Table 22 rarely exceeds that of adequately designed footing foundations on sand. The maximum settlement, however, is likely to be greater.

In the few regions where structures must be built above normally or almost normally loaded clays differential settlements of several inches or even half a foot are commonly considered unavoidable. Attempts to reduce the settlement by reducing the allowable soil pressures to values smaller than those in Table 22 are ineffective and wasteful. Hence, the designer must choose between two alternatives. Either he designs the footings on the basis of the values given in Table 22 at the risk of large unequal settlements, or else he provides the structure with another type of foundation (raft, pile, or pier foundation). The characteristics of the alternative types of foundations are discussed in subsequent articles.

If it is doubtful whether or not the settlement of the proposed footings with width B will be excessive, load tests should be made at the level of the base of the footings, on bearing plates 2 ft square at the bottom of test pits 6 ft square. If the consistency of the clay varies considerably between this level and a depth B (square footings) or $2B$ (continuous footings), load tests must be made at two or three different levels within this depth. The number of load tests or sets of tests that are required depends primarily on the degree of homogeneity of the clay stratum and the number of footings. After the application of each load increment, the load should be kept constant until further settlement becomes imperceptible. If the tests are made in this manner, the measured settlement includes at least a considerable fraction of that part which is due to consolidation of the loaded soil.

In accordance with the relation represented by the dash–dotted line in Figure 94, it can be assumed that the settlement S of a footing with width B_l will very roughly be equal to the value,

$$S = S_0 \frac{B_l}{B_0} \qquad (54.4)$$

where S_0 is the settlement of the bearing plate under the design load per unit of area, and B_0 is the width of the bearing plate.

Some years ago a load test was made on stiff clay. The stiffness of the clay increased slightly with depth, and some layers contained a network of slickensided hair cracks. The bearing plate was 2 ft square. Under the design load of 3200 lb per sq ft the settlement was 0.04 in. The proposed foundation covered an area of 126 by 126 ft. According to equation 54.4, it should have settled:

$$S = 0.04 \times \frac{126}{2} = 2.6 \text{ in.}$$

Immediately after construction, the settlement ranged between 1.0 and 1.5 in. At present it ranges between 2.5 and 3.5 in., and it is still increasing slightly.

Allowable Pressure on Soil Intermediate between Sand and Clay

The most important soils intermediate in character between sand and clay are silt and loess. Preliminary information on the nature of a silt can be obtained by means of the standard penetration test. If the number of blows required to drive the sampler (see Article 44) is smaller than 10 per ft, the silt is loose. If it is greater than 10, the silt is medium or dense.

Loose silt is even less suitable for supporting footings than normally loaded soft clay. This fact is demonstrated by the results of settlement observations on nine structures resting on silt deposits in Germany. Although the soil pressure ranged between the relatively low values of 1.1 and 2.0 tons per sq ft, the settlement ranged between 8 and 40 in. A reduction of the soil pressure by 50 per cent would have greatly increased the cost of the foundations without reducing the settlements to tolerable amounts.

Medium or dense silts can be divided into two categories: those with the characteristics of a rock flour, and those that are plastic (see Article 2). The allowable pressure on silts of the rock-flour type can be determined by means of the rules for very fine sand, and that on plastic silts by the methods used for clay.

The second important soil intermediate in character between sand and clay is loess (see Article 2). It covers large areas in the central part of each of the five continents.

Because of the calcareous binder and the root holes typical of every true loess, the properties of loess are very different from those of other soils with similar grain-size characteristics. The bearing capacity of a normally loaded silt is commonly very low, whereas that of loess may be very high. If a stratum of true loess is located permanently above the water table, it may be capable of supporting footings at a soil pressure of 2 or 3 tons per sq ft without perceptible settlement.

Nevertheless, loess cannot always be trusted, because in some localities its bearing capacity changes considerably with the seasons. The changes are caused by variations in the strength of the cohesive bond due to changes in moisture content. Thus, for example, the foundation for a coal bin in central Russia was designed on the basis of the results of load tests made during the summer. The bin was also constructed in summertime. Before construction was finished the autumn rains began, whereupon the bin started to settle unequally and the walls cracked. In central Germany a boilerhouse was built on a stratum of loess located partly below water table. Here also the designers were deceived by the apparent strength of the soil. The footings were designed on the basis of a soil pressure of 1.2 tons per sq ft, but under very much smaller loads the settlement had already become excessive. Some of the footings had to be underpinned, whereas others were redesigned during construction for a soil pressure as low as 0.35 tons per sq ft.[54.3]

Because of the extraordinary variety of the physical properties of loess soils, no simple empirical rules comparable to those for sand or clay can be established for evaluating the allowable soil pressure. Hence, if a footing foundation is to be constructed on loess in a region where there are no precedents, the designer must resort to the load-test method combined with an investigation of the effect of moisture on the bearing capacity of the soil. In some instances he will learn that a footing foundation is impracticable in spite of the apparent solidity of the loess.

FOOTING FOUNDATIONS LOCATED ON FIRM SOIL ABOVE SOFT LAYERS

The values given for the settlements of footings designed in accordance with the rules discussed under the preceding subheadings are based on the assumption that the soil does not become softer with depth. If this condition is not satisfied, the values cease to be reliable. The reason for this fact is illustrated by Figure 180.

Figure 180 shows the stress conditions beneath a footing that rests on a firm stratum A located above a soft stratum B. If the upper boundary of the soft stratum is located close to the base of the footing, the footing may break through the firm layer into the soft deposit. Failures of this type are not uncommon. They can be avoided by giving the footing such dimensions that the pressure on the upper boundary of stratum B does not exceed the allowable bearing value for the soil in that stratum. The pressure at the boundary can be computed by the method described in Article 35. Less accurately, the total footing load can be assumed uniformly distributed over the base of a truncated pyramid whose sides slope from the edges of the footing to the upper surface of B at an angle of 60° with the horizontal.

If the upper boundary of the soft stratum B is located at a considerable depth below the base of the footings, failure by breaking into the ground cannot occur because stratum A acts like a thick raft that distributes the entire weight of the building almost uniformly over the surface of B. The flexural rigidity of this natural raft prevents the surface of B from heaving beyond the loaded area. Nevertheless, the settlement may be very large. For example, the weight of the building represented in Figure 181 is transmitted by continuous footings onto a

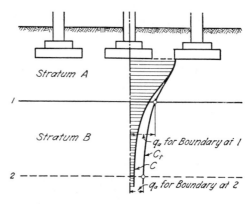

FIG. 180.   Diagram illustrating method of calculation to ascertain whether allowable soil pressure is exceeded for members of stratified clay subsoil. Curve C represents variation with depth of vertical pressure below single footing neglecting influence of adjacent footings. Curve C_t represents vertical pressure below same footing, considering influence of adjacent footings.

stratum of dense sand and gravel that rests, at a depth of 23 ft below the footings, on a layer of soft clay 50 ft thick. The footings were designed for a soil pressure of 2.5 tons per sq ft, a conservative value for dense sand and gravel. The greatest pressure on the surface of the clay due to the weight of the building was 1.1 tons per sq ft. During the construction period, which lasted 1 year, the footings settled between 1 and 4 in. During the following 40 years the maximum settlement increased to about 3 ft. Since the basement floor, which rested on the sand between the footings, neither cracked nor moved with respect to the footings, it is evident that the layer of sand and the footings settled together.

Ten years after construction the deterioration of the building was such that the owners decided to strengthen the foundation. In spite of the symptoms previously mentioned, it was not suspected that the seat of settlement was located below the sand. Hence, the "strengthening" was accomplished by increasing the width of the footings so that the intensity of the pressure exerted by the footings was reduced about 30 per cent. However, since the pressure on the clay remained unchanged, the expensive alterations did not have the slightest effect on the trend of the time-settlement curves shown in Figure 181c.

At a later date undisturbed samples were taken from the clay at some distance from the building. On the basis of the results of consolidation tests the average rate of settlement for the building as a whole was

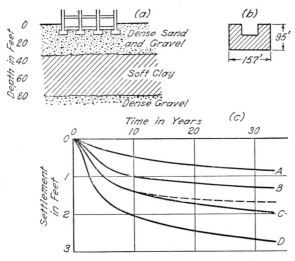

FIG. 181. (a) Cross section through foundation of structure supported by dense sand underlain by soft clay; (b) plan of structure; (c) observed time–settlement curves. Dash curve represents time–settlement relation computed from results of consolidation tests.

computed. The theoretical trend of the settlement, represented by the dash curve in Figure 181c, is very similar to the real one except for the secondary time effect which cannot yet be computed, Article 14. On account of the secondary time effect, the real settlement approaches a constant rate ranging for different parts of the structure from 0.12 to 0.32 in. per year, whereas the curve of computed settlement approaches a horizontal asymptote.

The observations illustrated by Figure 181 show very clearly that the settlement due to consolidation of soft layers located at a considerable depth below the footings is in reality practically independent of the pressure on the base of the footings. This is due to the fact that the firm stratum supporting the footings acts like a natural raft that distributes the load from the footings over the softer strata. Procedures for computing the settlements caused by the consolidation of the lower layers and methods for reducing them are discussed in connection with raft foundations, Article 55. After the foundations are laid out in such a manner that the settlement due to consolidation of the soft layers will be tolerable, the footings can be designed as if the soft strata did not exist. Hence, the presence of the soft strata may compel the designer to change the entire layout of the foundation, but it has no bearing on the allowable soil pressure for the footings.

SUMMARY OF RULES FOR SELECTING ALLOWABLE SOIL PRESSURE

(1) Except for narrow footings on loose saturated sand, the allowable bearing values for sand are governed only by settlement considerations, because it can be taken for granted that the factor of safety with respect to a base failure is adequate. The rules suggested for choosing these values satisfy the condition that the maximum settlement is unlikely to exceed 1 in. and the differential settlement $\frac{3}{4}$ in. On routine jobs the allowable soil pressure on dry and moist sand can be determined by means of the chart, Figure 177, on the basis of the results of standard penetration tests. If the water table is located close to or above the base of the footings, the depth ratio D_f/B must also be considered. If the depth ratio is very small, the values obtained from the chart must be reduced by 50 per cent; if it is close to unity, the values need be reduced only by one third. The most important sources of error in this procedure and the means for avoiding them have been discussed. On large jobs the load-test procedure may be used. However, it is expensive and cumbersome, and, if it is not expertly planned and executed, the results may be very misleading. If the sand is very loose and saturated, it should be compacted.

(2) The allowable bearing value for clay is usually determined by the condition that the factor of safety with respect to breaking into the ground should be at least 3. The relation between the average unconfined compressive strength q_u of a clay, the results of standard penetration tests, and the allowable soil pressure q_a are represented in Table 22. After the allowable soil pressure has been selected on the basis of this relation, it is necessary to find out whether the settlement will be tolerable. If the clay is normally loaded, the settlement is likely to be excessive, and a type of foundation other than a footing foundation may be indicated. On the other hand, if the clay is precompressed, the differential settlement is likely to be tolerable. In doubtful cases the load-test method should be used. The allowable soil pressure on stiff fissured clays can be determined only by this method.

(3) Loose saturated silt of any kind is unsuitable for supporting the weight of a foundation on footings. The allowable bearing value of

medium or dense silt of the rock-flour type can be determined by means of the rules proposed for sand. That of medium or stiff plastic silt can be determined by means of Table 22. No general rules can be established for ascertaining the allowable soil pressure for loess.

(4) If the area occupied by the footings exceeds half the total area covered by the building, it is commonly more economical to provide the building with a raft foundation.

Design of Footings

Steps in design. The first step in designing a footing is to compute the total effective load that will be transferred to the subsoil at the base of the footing. The second step is to determine the allowable bearing value for the soil. The area of the footing is then obtained by dividing the total effective load by the allowable bearing value. Finally, the bending moments and shears in the footing are computed, and the structural design of the footing is carried out.

Design loads. The total effective or *excess load* Q_t transferred to the subgrade may be expressed by the equation,

$$Q_t = [Q - W_s] + Q_l = Q_{dn} + Q_l \qquad (54.5)$$

in which

Q = permanent or *dead load* on the base of the footing, including the weight of the footing and the soil located above the footing. If the water table is higher than the base of the footing, the hydrostatic uplift, Article 12, on the submerged part of the body of soil and concrete should be deducted.

W_s = effective weight of the soil (total weight of soil reduced by hydro-static uplift) that was located above the base of the footing prior to excavation. However, in connection with basement footings such as c and d in Figure 171, the weight of the soil previously located above the basement floor should not be deducted, because the soil was removed not only above the base but also above the area adjoining at least one side of the base.

$Q_{dn} = Q - W_s$ = net dead load

Q_l = live load on footing, including that due to wind and snow

In any discussion of live load, a distinction must be made between the *normal live load* and the *maximum live load*. The normal live load Q_{ln} is that part of the live load which acts on the foundation at least as often as once a year; the maximum live load Q_{lmax} acts only during the simultaneous occurrence of several exceptional events. For instance, the normal live load in a tall office building includes only the weight of the equipment and furniture, of the persons who normally occupy the building on weekdays, and of a normal snow load. The maximum live load is the sum of the weights of the furniture and equipment, of the maximum number of persons who may crowd into the building on exceptional occasions, combined with the maximum snow and wind load. The total excess load on a footing at normal live load will be indicated by the symbol,

$$Q_{tn} = Q_{dn} + Q_{ln} \qquad (54.6)$$

and at maximum live load by

$$Q_{t\max} = Q_{dn} + Q_{l\max} \qquad (54.7)$$

Because of the exceptional character of the maximum live load and the low probability that the foundation will ever be called on to sustain it, it is customary to design footings in such a manner that the soil pressure produced by the normal total load Q_{tn} is the same for all the footings. However, sound engineering also requires that even the maximum load $Q_{t\max}$ should not cause irreparable damage to the structure. The procedure for complying with this requirement without excessive expenditure depends on the type of subsoil.

If the footings rest on sand, an increase of load produces an almost simultaneous increase of settlement, but it can be assumed that the factor of safety with respect to a foundation failure remains adequate. In order to eliminate the possibility of serious damage due to the maximum live load, the designer should estimate the greatest differential settlement ΔS in excess of the normal value of $\frac{3}{4}$ in. that, in his judgment, the structure can stand without serious injury. An additional differential settlement of ΔS would correspond to a maximum settlement of 1.33 ΔS plus the normal maximum value of 1 in.

If all of the footings were designed on the basis of a maximum settlement of 1 in. at normal live load, the maximum live load would increase the maximum settlement to

$$S_{\max} = 1'' \times \frac{Q_{t\max}}{Q_{tn}} \qquad (54.8)$$

If $S_{\max}$ is smaller than the tolerable maximum of $(1.33\Delta S + 1'')$, the maximum live load can be disregarded. On the other hand, if $S_{\max}$ is larger than $(1.33\Delta S + 1'')$, the footings should be designed so that the soil pressure at normal live load is

$$q_a' = q_a \frac{1.33\Delta S + 1''}{S_{\max}} \qquad (54.9)$$

The value of q_a' is commonly different for different footings. The smallest value should be used for proportioning all the footings; it corresponds to the footing for which the ratio Q_{tmax}/Q_{tn} is greatest.

If the footings of a building rest on clay, the allowable soil pressure is determined by the conditions that under the normal total load the factor of safety against failure should be equal to 3, but under no circumstances should it be less than 2. If the factor of safety G_s at normal total load is equal to 3, the factor of safety G_s' at maximum total load is

$$G_s' = 3\,\frac{Q_{tn}}{Q_{tmax}} \tag{54.10}$$

If G_s' is equal to 2 or more, the maximum live load can be disregarded, and all the footings can be proportioned for normal live load on the basis of $G_s = 3$. On the other hand, if G_s' is less than 2, the allowable soil pressure must be so chosen that the factor of safety at normal live load is equal to $6/G_s'$.

Reduction of settlement by adjusting footing size. In the discussion of allowable soil pressure, it was mentioned that the settlement of loaded areas with similar shape but different size increases at a given intensity of load with increasing width of the area. If the footings of a structure differ greatly in size, the differential settlement due to this cause can be important. In such instances it may be justifiable to adapt the pressure on the base of the footings to some extent to the size of the footings. If the subsoil consists of sand, the differential settlement can be reduced by decreasing the size of the smallest footings, because even after the reduction the factor of safety G_s of these footings with respect to breaking into the ground is likely to be adequate. The application of this procedure to footing foundations on clay would reduce the value of G_s for the smallest footings to less than 3, which is not admissible. Hence, the differential settlement of footing foundations on clay can be reduced only by increasing the size of the largest footings beyond that required by the allowable soil pressure. However, sound judgment is required to make such adjustments with prospects for success, because periodic and exceptional changes in the loading conditions must be considered.

Layout of footings and computation of moments. It is customary to lay out each footing so that the resultant load Q_{tn}, equation 54.6, passes through the centroid of the area covered by the footing. The bending moments are then computed on the assumption that the soil pressure is distributed uniformly over the base. In reality, the contact pressure against footings on sand decreases from the center toward the rim, Figure 96b, and the real bending moments are usually less than the computed ones. On the other hand, if the footings are very rigid, and they rest on soft or medium clay, the contact pressure may increase toward the rim, Figure 96a, and the real moments may exceed the computed ones. However, the difference is amply covered by the margin of safety customarily provided in structural design.

The columns that support crane runways in industrial buildings are subject to large eccentric loads whenever the crane operates near by, but during the rest of the time they carry ordinary dead and live loads. It is customary to design the connections between the columns and the footings for the eccentric loads. As a consequence, the moments are transmitted to the base of the footings. If the footings rest on clay, the allowable soil pressure q_a should not be exceeded under the toe of any footing when all the loads, including that due to the crane, are acting. The centroid of the base of every footing should be made to coincide with the resultant of the net dead load, the normal live load, and a small fraction, such as 25 per cent, of the crane load; and all of the footings should be proportioned for the same soil pressure under this resultant load. On the other hand, if the footings rest on sand, they should be laid out so that the soil pressure is uniform and equal to q_a under the net dead load, the normal live load, and the maximum crane load that can be expected under ordinary operating conditions. Under no conceivable combination of loads should the pressure $1.5q_a$ be exceeded.

Precautions during construction. All footing foundations are inevitably designed on the assumption that the soil beneath the footings is in approximately the same state as that disclosed by whatever borings or load tests were made. If the soil contains soft pockets not encountered by the borings, or if the soil structure is disturbed during excavation, the settlement will be larger and more unequal than the designer anticipated. To avoid such a risk a simple penetration test should be made at the site of each footing after the excavation is completed. One of several practicable methods is merely to count the number of blows per foot required for driving a sounding rod into the ground by means of a drop weight. If exceptionally soft spots are encountered within the seat of settlement of any one footing, this footing should be redesigned. Such a procedure is more economical than subsequent repair.

Disturbance of the structure of the subsoil during construction is especially likely to occur under two conditions commonly encountered in the field. If the subsoil consists chiefly of silt or fine sand, it can be radically disturbed by pumping from open sumps. The disturbance is likely to be associated with serious damage to adjoining property due to loss of ground. Hence, if footings on such soils require excavation below the water table, the site should be drained by pumping from well points and not from open sumps, Article 47. Pumping from well points occasionally causes a noticeable settlement of the adjoining ground surface. However, if this does occur, it is certain that the detrimental effects of pumping from open sumps would have been far greater.

If the subsoil consists of clay, the top layer of the exposed clay is likely to become soft because of the absorption of moisture from puddles and the kneading effect of walking on it. Therefore, footings on clay should be concreted and backfilled immediately after the excavation is completed. If this cannot be done, the last 4 to 6 in. of clay should not be removed until preparations for placing the concrete are complete.

REFERENCES

54.1. K. Terzaghi, The Actual Factor of Safety of Foundations, *Structural Eng.*, Vol 13 (1935), pp 126–160. Discussion of effect of settlement on buildings.

54.2. A. W. Skempton, An Investigation of the Bearing Capacity of a Soft Clay Soil, *J. Inst. Civil Engrs.* (*London*), Vol 18 (1942), pp 307–321, discussions, pp 567–576. Analysis of failure of a large footing on clay.

54.3. A. Scheidig, *Loess* (in German), T. Steinkopff, 1934, pp 125–142. Records of experiences with foundations on loess.

54.4. K. Terzaghi, Settlement of Structures in Europe and Methods of Observation, *Trans. ASCE*, Vol 103 (1938), pp 1432–1448.

54.5. W. L. Hanna and G. Tschebotareff, Settlement Observations of Buildings in Egypt, *Proc. Intern. Conf. Soil Mech.*, Cambridge, Mass. (1936), Vol I, pp 71–77. Comparison between observed and computed settlements.

54.6. W. E. Simpson, Foundation Experiences with Clay in Texas, *Civil Eng.*, Vol 4 (1934), pp 581–584. Discussion of swelling of clays within zone of seasonal variations in moisture and temperature in semiarid climate.

ART. 55. RAFT FOUNDATIONS

Comparison between Raft and Footing Foundations

If the sum of the base areas of the footings required to support a structure exceeds about half the total building area, it is usually preferable to combine the footings into a single mat or raft. Such a raft is only a large footing, and, like a footing, it must satisfy the requirements that the factor of safety with respect to a base failure should be not less than 3 and that the settlement should not exceed an amount acceptable to the designer of the superstructure.

The factor of safety of raft foundations depends on the nature of the subsoil. If the soil consists of very loose sand in a saturated state, it should be compacted by artificial means before the raft is constructed (see Article 50). If the sand is medium or dense, the factor of safety of a raft is considerably greater than that of footings, and its adequacy can be taken for granted without any computation.

The factor of safety of raft foundations on clay is practically independent of the size of the loaded area. It is commonly very low, and several failures have occurred. One of these is illustrated by Figure 182. The structure, a grain elevator near Winnipeg, Canada, was 77 by 190 ft in plan and 102 ft high. It rested on a stratum of "firm" clay overlying rock. On the basis of the results of load tests it was estimated that the ultimate bearing capacity of the clay was between 4 and 5 tons per sq ft, and the design was based on an allowable soil pressure of 2.5 tons per sq ft. When the load on the raft approached this value, one side of the structure settled 29 ft, whereas the opposite side rose 5 ft. The movements took place within less than 24 hr.[55.1] To avoid the risk of such a failure, a raft foundation on clay soil should be designed so that the excess load divided by the loaded area does not exceed the values given in Table 22.

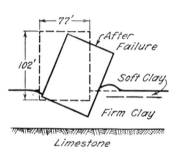

Fig. 182. Diagram illustrating failure of grain elevator near Winnipeg, Canada, by breaking into clay stratum.

The excess load on the base of a raft is computed in the same manner as that on the base of a spread footing, Article 54. If the raft is located beneath a basement, Figure 184, it constitutes with the basement walls a large hollow footing. Since the loaded soil can rise, as indicated by an arrow, only outside the area occupied by the raft, the depth of the overburden is equal to D_f, measured from the ground surface, and not to D_{fs} as for spread footings below basements, Figure 171c and d. Hence, the excess load Q_t on the base of the raft is equal to the difference between the total effective load $Q + Q_l$ at the base of the raft, reduced by the total effective weight W_s of the soil replaced by the basement, or

$$Q_t = (Q + Q_l) - W_s \qquad (55.1)$$

If q_a is the allowable pressure on the subsoil, and A the area covered by the raft, the foundation must satisfy the condition,

$$\frac{Q_t}{A} \lessgtr q_a \qquad (55.2)$$

The relation expressed by equation 55.1 indicates that the excess load on the base of a raft can be reduced by increasing the depth of the basement. This reduction increases the factor of safety of the foundation with respect to breaking into the ground and reduces the settlement. The existence of such a relation was recognized by a few engineers over a century ago, and they used it to advantage in establishing heavy structures on soft ground without the use of piles.

Although the rules governing the factor of safety of rafts and footings are quite similar, the general character of the settlement of these two types of foundations is very different. The causes of the difference are illustrated in Figure 183. This figure represents a vertical section through each of two structures, one of which rests on footings and the other on a raft. The footings and the raft both exert on the subsoil the same load per unit of area, as indicated by the rectangular diagrams at the base of

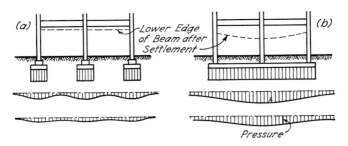

FIG. 183. Distribution of pressure in soil beneath buildings supported by (*a*) widely spaced spread footings and (*b*) concrete mat. The load per unit of area is the same beneath the footings and the mat.

the foundations. In addition, the figure shows the intensity and the distribution of the vertical pressure at different depths below the base level of each foundation.

The footings shown in Figure 183*a* are so far apart that each one settles much as if the others did not exist. If the soil were homogeneous, the footings would settle almost equally; in reality, they settle by different amounts because no natural soil stratum is homogeneous. Since the seat of settlement is located within the uppermost soil stratum, the distribution of the settlement reflects the variations in the compressibility of the soil located within this stratum (see Figure 175). It is always erratic and cannot be predicted by any practicable means. This fact determined the rules that were established for evaluating the allowable soil pressures for footing foundations, Article 54.

The seat of settlement of the raft foundation, Figure 183*b*, extends to a very much greater depth than that of the footing foundation. Within this depth weak spots are scattered at random, as shown in Figure 184, and their effects on the settlement of a loaded area partly cancel each other. Therefore, the area settles as if the loaded soil were more or less homogeneous. The settlement is not necessarily uniform, but it follows a fairly definite instead of an erratic pattern. The pattern differs, however, depending on whether the soil located within the seat of settlement consists of sand or clay.

Settlement of Raft Foundations

Both theory and experience indicate that the settlement of a uniformly loaded area on sand is fairly uniform, provided the area is located at a depth of more than about 8 ft below the adjacent ground surface. If the depth is smaller, the outer parts of the loaded area are likely to settle somewhat more than the central part unless lateral yield of the sand is prevented within a depth of 8 or 10 ft from the ground surface.

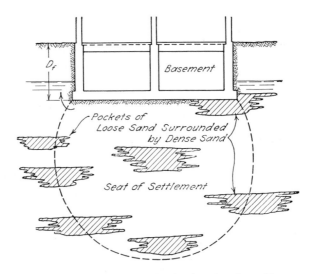

Fig. 184.   Diagram representing erratic distribution of pockets of loose sand throughout a stratum of dense sand located beneath base of a building.

The differential settlement of the area covered by the raft reflects in a general way the variations in the compressibility of the subsoil. However, because of the random distribution of compressible zones in the subsoil, Figure 184, combined with the stiffening effect of the raft and building frame, it can safely be assumed that the differential settlement of a raft foundation per inch of maximum settlement is not more than one half the corresponding value for buildings on footings. Hence, if a differential settlement of $\frac{3}{4}$ in. can be tolerated, the allowable soil pressure can be so chosen that the maximum settlement is 2 in. instead of 1 in. as specified for spread footings. The width B of rafts commonly lies between 40 and 120 ft. Within this range the value of B has very little influence on the maximum settlement (see Figure 176). Therefore, the width can be disregarded in selecting the allowable soil pressure. Finally, at least the major part of the sand located within the seat of settlement is likely to be saturated, because the vertical distance between the base of the raft and the water table is commonly small compared to the width of the raft.

The preceding conditions determine the allowable soil pressure, provided the relative density of the sand is also taken into account. At present, the most expedient method for evaluating the relative density

TABLE 23

PROPOSED ALLOWABLE BEARING VALUES FOR RAFTS ON SAND

N = number of blows per foot in standard penetration test
q_a = proposed allowable bearing value in tons per square foot

Relative Density of Sand	Loose	Medium	Dense	Very Dense
N	Less than 10	10–30	30–50	Over 50
q_a	Requires compaction	0.7–2.5	2.5–4.5	Over 4.5

Values are based on maximum settlement of 2 in.

Depth of sand stratum is presumed to be greater than the width B of the raft, and water table to be close to or above base of raft. If depth to bedrock is much less than $B/2$, or if water table is at depth greater than $B/2$, the allowable bearing values can be increased.

The loads are presumed to be distributed fairly uniformly over the base of the building. If different parts of a large raft on sand carry very different loads per unit of area, it is advisable to establish construction joints at the boundaries between these parts.

is the standard penetration test, Article 44. One test should be made for every $2\frac{1}{2}$ ft of the depth of the drill hole from the level of the base of the raft to a depth B below this level. The N-value for the hole is equal to the average of all the N-values within this depth. At least 6 drill holes are required, and the allowable soil pressure should be chosen on the basis of the smallest N-value furnished by the tests.

Allowable soil pressures corresponding to different N-values are given in Table 23. The values are based on the assumption that the allowable soil pressure on the base of a raft is twice the bearing value for saturated sand obtained by extrapolation from the chart, Figure 177. This assumption is based on the conclusion that the tolerable maximum settlement of rafts is 2 in., in contrast to 1 in. for buildings on spread footings. A more accurate evaluation of the soil pressure would require several sets of load tests, performed at different levels within the seat of settlement. Such a procedure is commonly impracticable.

If the subsoil contains gravel or if it consists of very fine or silty sand, appropriate check tests or corrections are required (see Article 54) which may lead to lower values than those given in Table 23. On the other hand, if the sand rests at a depth less than $B/2$ on sound rock, or if the water table is located permanently below this depth, somewhat higher pressures can be tolerated.

All the preceding recommendations are based on the tacit assumption that the distribution of the loads over the raft is fairly uniform. If the structure supported by the raft consists of several parts with very different heights, it may be advisable to provide construction joints at the boundaries between these parts.

The maximum permissible value for the soil pressure beneath rafts on clay, like that beneath footings on clay, is given in Table 22, page 430, in the column headed q_a. However, on account of the large dimensions of the area covered by a raft and the rapid increase of settlement of clay with increasing size of the loaded area (Figure 179), it is always necessary to find out, at least by a crude estimate, whether the settlement will be tolerable. The computation can be based on the assumption that the loaded clay is laterally confined. The results of the computations show, in accordance with experience, that the base of a uniformly loaded area on clay assumes the shape of a shallow bowl, because the consolidation pressure decreases from the center toward the edges, Figure 183b. However, the slopes of the bowl are so gentle that the difference between the settlement of two adjacent columns never exceeds a small fraction of the difference between the maximum and minimum settlement. For rafts on sand the differences can be almost equal. Therefore, the tolerable differential settlement for rafts on clay is very much greater than that for rafts on sand.

DESIGN OF RAFT FOUNDATIONS

The average gross load per unit of area on the base of a raft is equal to the total effective weight of the building, $Q + Q_l$, divided by the total area A of the base. Since the area occupied by the raft can only be equal to or slightly greater than the area occupied by the building, the designer has no opportunity to change the soil pressure by adjusting the size of the raft. Hence, to satisfy equation 55.2 he is compelled to increase W_s, equation 55.1. This can be done only by providing the structure with one or more basements with adequate depth. The required depth can be computed by trial.

After the depth of basement has been determined, the next step in the design is to compute the forces that act on the raft. In this operation, the designer must depend to a large extent on the soundness of his judgment.

The factors and conditions that need to be considered are illustrated by Figure 185.

Figure 185a shows a vertical section through a structure consisting of a heavy tower and two wings. The water table is located below the base of the raft. On this assumption the total soil reaction is equal to the full weight $Q + Q_l$ of the building including the weight of the raft, whereas the excess load Q_t, equation 55.1, which determines the settlement is equal to the difference between the weight of the structure and the

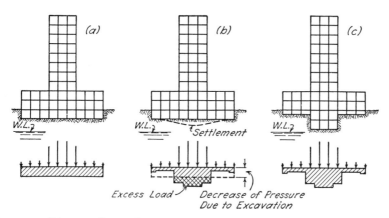

Fɪɢ. 185. Diagram illustrating three different methods for the design of raft foundations on very compressible subsoil. (a) Rigid superstructure, capable of enforcing uniform settlement; (b) flexible superstructure, capable of sustaining large deflections without damage; (c) flexible superstructure, uniform settlement produced by adapting depths of basements to weight of structure located above them.

weight W_s of the soil that has been excavated. If the excess load Q_t is zero, and if, in addition, the structure is rigid, there will be practically no settlement even if the soil reaction is very large. As a rough approximation the soil reaction on the base of a rigid structure may be considered uniform, as indicated by the shaded rectangle in Figure 185a. Yet, the loads are concentrated on the central part of the base of the building. Therefore, the frame of the structure is acted on by very severe bending moments. The cost of the reinforcement required to carry these moments may be prohibitive.

If the building is flexible, the soil reaction on every part of the raft is roughly equal to the load that acts on it, Figure 185b. The corresponding bending moments are relatively small. However, on account of the heavy concentration of loads on the middle part of the raft, this part carries an excess load whereas the excess load on the outer parts is negative. As a consequence, the tower will settle more than the wings, as shown in the figure. A difference in settlement is inevitable even if the total excess load on the subsoil is zero. If the building rests on sand, the difference between the settlements of the tower and the wings is likely to be too small to have an injurious effect on the superstructure, and the raft can be designed as if it were acted on by the forces shown in Figure 185b. On the other hand, if the raft rests on clay, the differential settlement due to the nonuniform pressure distribution may be very large. Construction joints between the tower and the wings may slightly improve the stress conditions in the members of the superstructure, but they cannot prevent the settlement of both wings from increasing toward the tower. Hence, it is necessary to make a settlement computation to determine whether the differential settlement is likely to exceed what the structure can stand without injury. If it is, the designer must choose between two alternatives. Either he specifies a pile or a pier foundation for the structure, or else he provides the tower and the wings with basements of different depth, Figure 185c. The depth of each basement must be determined in such a manner that the settlement of the tower and the wings would theoretically be equal. If this condition is satisfied, the designer can be fairly certain that the differential settlement will be tolerable.

In computing the thickness of the raft and the amount of reinforcement, it is commonly assumed that the raft is a continuous slab freely supported at every point and along every line at which load is transferred onto the slab from above. A distributed load acts on the slab from below. It is equal to the total soil reaction which, in turn, is equal to the full weight of the building without any deduction for hydrostatic uplift or basement excavation. Since the difference between the theoretical and the real distribution of the bending moments in the raft can be very large, it is commonly advisable to provide the raft with twice the theoretical amount of reinforcement.

In the preceding discussion, it has been tacitly assumed that a rigid raft does not settle until the load on the raft becomes equal to the weight of the excavated soil. In many instances, the error due to this assumption can safely be ignored. However, if the subsoil is soft, and the excavation is deep, the settlement that occurs before the effective load on the raft becomes equal to the effective weight of the excavated soil may be large enough to require consideration. The cause of this settlement is discussed under the following subheading.

Heave during Basement Excavation

The excavation for a basement or a subbasement involves the complete removal of the pressure originally exerted against the soil at the base level of the raft. As a consequence, the bottom of the excavation rises. During the subsequent period of construction, the weight of the building becomes equal to and generally exceeds the original overburden pressure; hence, the heave disappears, and the building settles. If the building has a greater weight than the excavated soil, the settlement passes through two stages. The first lasts until the load per unit of area at the base of the raft becomes equal to the original overburden pressure, and the second begins when this pressure is exceeded. The characteristics of the settlement during the second stage have already been described. Those of the first stage may be very different.

At the end of the first stage, when the building load becomes equal to the weight of excavated material, the settlement is equal to or slightly greater than the preceding heave, which is commonly very small. If the building load is not further increased, the settlement stops shortly after construction is finished. It has been mentioned that this fact was utilized long ago, in the design of buildings on soft soils, but it is not generally realized that the progressive settlement of buildings on stiffer soils can also be eliminated by excavating enough soil to compensate for the weight of the building. As a matter of fact, some buildings with basements deep enough to satisfy this requirement have actually been provided with expensive pile support; it is obvious that the money spent for the piles was wasted.

The amount of the heave and subsequent settlement depends on the nature of the subsoil and the dimensions of the excavation. It can seldom be predicted on the basis of soil tests and theory. If the excavation is made in sand above the water table, the heave is so small that it can usually be disregarded. A soft clay subsoil deforms at practically constant water content like an incompressible elastically isotropic material. Hence, the heave could be computed by means of the theory of elasticity if the modulus of elasticity of the clay could be determined by means of soil tests. However, the results of such computations, based on the value of the initial tangent modulus (see Article 18) of undisturbed specimens indicate that the real heave is always much smaller than the computed value. Furthermore, the magnitude of the error cannot be predicted. The following histories of two excavations illustrate the uncertainty associated with estimates of the heave. In both instances, the stresses caused by the excavation were well below the failure load for the clay.

The first excavation was made for a subbasement with an average depth of 35 ft. The building covered an area 200 by 340 ft. The subsoil consisted of a layer of soft glacial clay almost 100 ft thick, with a stiff crust. The clay was buried beneath a thick layer of artificial fill and soft organic silt, and it rested on a layer of gravel and hardpan. The bottom of the excavation was located within the stiff crust, close to its former upper surface. The modulus of elasticity of the clay, determined on the basis of unconfined compression tests on undisturbed samples, had an average value of 100 tons per sq ft. Based on this value, it was estimated that the maximum heave would be about 5 in. The actual maximum heave was 3.5 in.[55.6] In this case, the forecast was relatively accurate.

The second excavation is shown in Figure 186. It covered an area of 60 by 110 ft. The bottom of the excavation was located 30 ft below the surface in a bed of sand that extended for an additional depth of 14 ft. Below the sand was a bed of soft clay 120 ft thick. The average modulus of elasticity of the clay, according to the results of laboratory tests, was

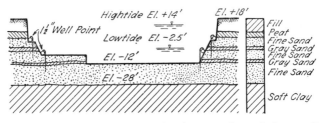

Fig. 186.   Cross section through excavation in strata located above soft clay bed 120 ft thick.

60 tons per sq ft, and the computed heave, based on this value, was 14 in. In order to observe the real heave, an underground reference point was established in the sand, 6 ft above the surface of the clay. Since any heave in excess of 0.02 ft would have been noticed, it may be concluded that the clay behaved during excavation like an almost rigid material with a modulus of elasticity of several thousand tons per square foot. Some clays exhibit a similar rigidity during tunneling and other types of construction operations. However, the rigid state seems to be only temporary. Because of this fact, construction in connection with the excavation shown in Figure 186 was carried on as rapidly as possible, and the loads were applied before any movements started. In order to prevent disturbance of the sand by seepage pressures, excavation was not started until the water table was lowered by pumping from well points, as indicated in the figure. The weight of the finished structure was approximately equal to the weight of the soil removed, and the ensuing settlement was too small to be measured.

If the clay beneath an excavation contains a great number of continuous layers or seams of coarse silt or sand, the water content of the clay may increase to such an extent that the major part of the heave is caused by swelling. Predictions of the rate of swelling, based on the results of laboratory consolidation tests, are likely to be very inaccurate, because the degree of continuity of the pervious strata cannot be learned by sampling in advance of construction.

If the depth of the basement is increased by open excavation beyond a certain value, the bottom of the excavation becomes unstable and fails by heaving, regardless of the strength and nature of the lateral support for the sides, Article 32. However, the critical depth can be almost doubled by performing the excavation under compressed air. In excessively soft ground, raft foundations have been successfully established by constructing the side walls and floor of the basement as a unit near the surface of the ground and lowering the entire unit to grade by washing or pumping through holes in the floor.

Footing Foundations on Natural Rafts

If the footings of a building rest on a thick firm stratum underlain by considerably more compressible ones, the firm stratum acts like a natural raft that distributes the weight of the building over the soft layers. The footings are designed as if the soft strata did not exist, because the settlement due to consolidation of the soft strata is practically independent of the pressure on the base of the footing.

The load responsible for the settlement due to consolidation is equal to the total effective weight of the building reduced by the effective weight of the excavated soil. In the computation of the magnitude and distribution of the consolidation pressure within the soft layers, the weight of the excavated soil is assumed to represent a negative load uniformly distributed over the bottom of the basement. The weight of the building is a positive load that acts on the bases of the footings. At any point in the soft layers the consolidation pressure is equal to the difference between the pressures produced by these two loads. The settlement due to consolidation is estimated on the assumption that the soft soil is laterally confined. The importance of the settlement that may ensue is illustrated by Figure 181.

If the computation shows that the settlement conditions are unacceptable, the design of the foundation must be changed. This can be done, for instance, by providing the different parts of the building with basements of different depths, Figure 185c, or by supporting the structure on piles or piers.

Footings on Sand in Basements below the Water Table

A basement located below the water table must be provided with a watertight floor slab interconnecting the footings. If the load on the footings is applied after the slab is concreted, the footings together with the slab constitute a raft whose base is acted on not only by the water pressure but also by a more or less uniformly distributed soil reaction.

In order to avoid the necessity for making the floor slab strong enough to withstand both pressures, the slab between the footings should not be concreted until the footings carry the full dead load. The load on the base of the footings will then be equal to the full weight of the building reduced by the full hydrostatic uplift on the cellar floor, and the interconnecting slab will be acted on by water pressure only. However, the footings must be designed on the assumption that the hydrostatic uplift

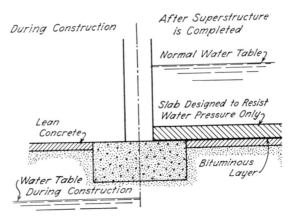

FIG. 187. Details of footing on sand in basement located below water table.

is inactive, because the water table is not allowed to rise above the cellar floor until the footings carry the full dead weight of the structure. The postponement of the construction of the floor slab requires the continuation of pumping until the superstructure is completed. The sequence of operations is shown in Figure 187. To prevent the floor slab from floating, it must be anchored either to the columns or, preferably, to the footings.

Summary of Rules for the Design of Raft Foundations

(1) If a structure resting on a sand stratum can stand a differential settlement of $\frac{3}{4}$ in. between adjacent columns without injury, a maximum settlement of 2 in. can be tolerated. The corresponding allowable soil pressures are given in Table 23.

(2) The allowable soil pressure for rafts with a width B cannot be determined reliably by means of load tests unless several sets of tests are made, at several depths within a distance B below the base of the raft. Such tests are economically justified only under exceptional conditions.

(3) If different parts of a large raft on sand carry very different loads per unit of area, it is advisable to establish construction joints at the boundaries between these parts.

(4) A raft foundation on clay should satisfy the conditions that the factor of safety with respect to a failure of the loaded clay should not be less than 3 and that the differential settlement should not be large enough to damage the superstructure. Both the factor of safety and the settlement depend not on the total weight of the structure but on the difference between the weight of the structure and that of the excavated soil. Therefore, the design requirements can usually be met by appropriate selection of the depth of the basement.

(5) The differential settlement of a uniformly loaded flexible raft on clay is chiefly due to dishing. It is roughly equal to one-half the maximum settlement. If the building itself is flexible, the differential settlement can be eliminated by providing the building with a very stiff substructure. If different parts of a large raft on clay carry very different loads, the bending moments in a stiff substructure are so great that the cost of the substructure is likely to be prohibitive. Another alternative is to vary the depths of the basements in accordance with the loads in such a manner that the difference between the building load and the weight of the excavated soil per unit of area has approximately the same value for every part of the raft. Whichever alternative is adopted, the design requires at least a rough settlement computation.

(6) Layers of stiff clay or of dense sand located above layers of soft clay act like natural rafts. The footings of buildings resting on such layers are designed as if the soft layers did not exist. Since the settlement due to the consolidation of the soft layers may be very large, a settlement computation is required. The means for reducing the settlement due to consolidation are the same as those described in connection with rafts on homogeneous beds of clay.

REFERENCES

55.1. Failure of Transcona Grain-Elevator, *Eng. News*, Vol 70 (1913), pp 944–1107. The elevator rested on soft clay.

55.2. A Remarkable Test of Reinforced Concrete Construction, *Eng. News*, Vol 57 (1907), p 458. Complete failure of foundation of a mill building on soft clay in Tunis, North Africa.

55.3. W. E. Simpson, Foundation Experiences with Clay in Texas, *Civil Eng.*, Vol 4 (1934), pp 581–584. Results of settlement observations on a building with raft foundation on precompressed clay.

55.4. Jose A. Cuevas, The Floating Foundation of the New Building for the National Lottery of Mexico, *Proc. Intern. Conf. Soil Mech.*, Cambridge, Mass. (1936), Vol I, pp 294–301. Description of an attempt to prevent settlement of raft foundation on very soft clay by deep subbasement. Record of heave observations.

55.5. A. CASAGRANDE AND R. E. FADUM, Application of Soil Mechanics in Designing Building Foundations, *Trans. ASCE*, Vol 109 (1944), pp 383–416, discussion, pp 417–490. Description of two building foundations resting on natural raft consisting of stiff clay.

55.6. R. E. FADUM, *Observations and Analysis of Building Settlements in Boston*, doctor's thesis, Graduate School of Engineering, Harvard University, 1941. Record of heave observation on the two buildings referred to in 55.5.

55.7. K. TERZAGHI, Recording Results of Field Tests on Soils, *Civil Eng.*, Vol 13 (1943), pp 585–587. Records of settlement observations on raft foundation supported by precompressed plastic silt.

ART. 56. PILE FOUNDATIONS

FUNCTION OF PILES

A structure is founded on piles if the soil immediately below its base does not have adequate bearing capacity or if an estimate of costs indicates that a pile foundation may be cheaper than any other.

Piles are made in many forms and of a variety of materials. A description of the principal types and of the methods for installing them can be found in reference 56.1. In this discussion we shall consider only piles of the more common types that are driven into the ground by a mechanical device known as a pile driver. However, the general principles are applicable, with minor modifications, to the design of foundations on other types of piles, installed in a different manner. Furthermore, we shall assume that the piles carry only static loads, because the effect of pulsating loads and of vibrations on pile foundations has not yet been adequately investigated.

With respect to the manner in which they function, piles may be divided into three categories:

1. *Friction piles in coarse-grained very permeable soil.* These piles transfer most of their load to the soil through skin friction. The process of driving such piles close to each other in groups greatly reduces the porosity and compressibility of the soil within and around the groups. Therefore, piles of this category are sometimes called *compaction piles*.

2. *Friction piles in very fine-grained soils of low permeability.* These piles also transfer their load to the soil through skin friction, but they do not compact the soil appreciably. Foundations supported by piles of this type are commonly known as *floating pile foundations*.

3. *Point-bearing piles.* These piles transfer their load onto a firm stratum located at a considerable depth below the base of the structure.

In nature, homogeneous soil strata are very rare. Therefore, no sharp boundaries can be established between the three principal categories of piles. The same pile may displace part of the mass of soil through which it is driven without changing the relative density, whereas the remainder of the soil may undergo compaction. The point of a pile may be embedded in a firm sand stratum capable of supporting the pile by point bearing, but, nevertheless, a considerable part of the load is likely to be carried by skin friction. Because of the wide variety of soil conditions encountered in practice, any attempt to establish rules for the design of pile foundations necessarily involves radical simplifications, and the rules themselves are useful only as guides to judgment. For the same reason, theoretical refinements in dealing with pile problems, such as attempts to compute the failure load on pile groups by means of the theory of elasticity, are completely out of place and can safely be ignored. Even conclusions based on the results of small-scale model tests may be far from reliable.

Design of Pile Foundations

Historical development. Before the 19th century almost all buildings were established on continuous footings. Piles were used as a means of support wherever the ground appeared incapable of sustaining the pressure exerted by the footings. Since timber was abundant and labor cheap, as many piles were driven as the ground would take. Settlement caused no concern, because the prevalent type of structures could stand a considerable amount of unequal settlement without injury.

In the 19th century, when industrial development created a demand for heavy but inexpensive structures in locations underlain by soft ground, the cost of pile foundations became an item of consequence, and engineers were expected to specify no more piles than were necessary to provide adequate support for the buildings. This could not be done without at least some knowledge of the ultimate load that an individual pile could carry. Efforts to obtain the necessary information at a minimum expenditure of money and labor led to theoretical speculations that resulted in an impressive assortment of pile formulas. However, the realization slowly grew that the pile formulas had inherent shortcomings, and it became more and more customary to determine the allowable load per pile on all but the smallest jobs by making load tests on test piles.

The number of piles required to support a given structure was determined by the simple procedure of dividing the total load by the allowable load per pile. Many foundations designed in this manner were satisfactory, but now and then excessive and unexpected settlements occurred. These incidents indicated that the settlement of an entire pile foundation was not necessarily related to the settlement of a single test pile, even at the same load per pile.[56.2] They led to the obvious conclusion that a knowledge of the bearing capacity of a single pile constitutes only part of the information necessary for the design of a satisfactory pile foundation. To find out whether the settlement of a pile foundation will remain within tolerable limits, the designer must consider the stresses produced in the soil by the entire load assigned to the foundation, and he must estimate the settlement produced by these stresses. This estimate requires a knowledge of the fundamental principles of soil mechanics. If the results of the investigation show that the settlement may exceed an acceptable value, the design must be changed.

Steps in design of a pile foundation. The first requirement for the preliminary design of a pile foundation is a soil profile representing the results of exploratory borings. The factors that determine the depth to which the subsoil should be explored were discussed in Article 45. Usually, the soil profile provides all the information required to decide whether the foundation can be supported by friction piles entirely embedded in sand, by point-bearing piles driven through soft strata into a firm one, or by a floating pile foundation.

The next step in the preliminary design is to select the length and type of pile. If point-bearing piles are appropriate, it may be possible to judge the required length with reasonable accuracy on the basis of the soil profile. The length of friction piles in sand, however, can be determined only by driving test piles, and that of friction piles in soft clay by making an estimate of the factor of safety of the pile groups against complete failure (see page 468). The selection of the type of pile is governed at least partly by practical considerations.[56.1, 56.3]

After the length and type of pile have been tentatively chosen, the ultimate bearing capacity of a single pile is either estimated or else determined by means of load tests. This value is divided by an appropriate factor of safety to obtain the "safe design load" per pile. The total number of piles required to support the structure is determined by dividing the total weight of the structure by the "safe design load" per pile.

After the number of piles has been determined, the next step is to choose their spacing. It is generally agreed that the distance D between the centers of piles with a top diameter d should not be less than $2.5d$. This rule is based on practical considerations. If the spacing is less than $2.5d$, the heave of the soil is likely to be excessive, and the driving of each new pile may displace or lift the adjacent ones. On the other hand, a spacing of more than $4d$ is uneconomical, because it increases the cost of the footings without materially benefiting the foundation. The most suitable value of D between these limits must be selected in accordance with the soil conditions, as explained subsequently.

When the spacing has been decided on, the piles are laid out in either a square or a triangular pattern. By multiplying the number of piles by D^2 (square pattern) or by $\frac{1}{2}D^2\sqrt{3}$ (triangular pattern), the total area required for the pile-supported parts of the foundation is obtained. If this area is considerably smaller than half the total area covered by the structure, the structure is established on pile-supported footings; if it is considerably greater, the structure is founded on a pile-supported raft, and the spacing of the piles is increased so that the pile layout forms a continuous pattern. If the intensity of loading on different parts of the raft is very different, the spacing between piles is adapted to the intensity on each of the parts. Finally, if it is doubtful whether the structure should be established on footings or on a raft, the decision is made after a comparison of the costs of the two alternatives.

If the foundation is supported by friction piles in soft clay or plastic silt, an estimate must be made of the ultimate bearing capacity of the pile groups, and the load on the groups must not be allowed to exceed one half, or preferably one third of the ultimate value. The consequences of ignoring this condition can be catastrophic. In several instances, structures together with the supporting piles and the soil located between the piles have sunk suddenly into the ground, although the load per pile did not exceed the "safe design load." The procedure for estimating the bearing capacity of pile groups is described subsequently.

If the load per pile is such that the bearing capacity of the pile groups is not exceeded, the foundation will not fail suddenly by sinking into the ground. However, adequate bearing capacity does not exclude the possibility of excessive settlement, because the settlement of an entire pile foundation has no relation whatsoever to the settlement of a single pile under the load per pile assigned to the foundation. The settlement of the foundation may range between a fraction of an inch and several feet, depending on the soil conditions, the number of piles, and the area covered by the structure. Settlements of less than about 2 in. are commonly not harmful, but settlements of 6 in. or more may have very undesirable effects on the superstructure. Hence, if a foundation rests on friction piles driven into soft clay, or if the points of point-bearing piles are located above soft strata, the need for a settlement computation is imperative. Failure to make such a computation has been responsible for many unsatisfactory pile foundations.

The final step in the design of the foundation is the structural design of the pile-supported footings or raft. The computations of bending moments and shears are commonly based on the assumption that each pile carries the same load. Theoretical considerations and the results of field tests [56.4] both lead to the conclusion that this assumption is usually far from correct. If the substrata are fairly horizontal, and the points of the piles do not rest on bedrock, the load per pile in a group supporting a rigid footing increases from the center piles toward the edges. The error involved in the commonly accepted assumption, however, is well within the customary margin of safety for reinforced-concrete design.

The details of the successive steps in the design of pile foundations are presented under the following subheadings.

Ultimate Loads and "Safe Design Loads" for Single Piles

Skin friction and point resistance. The term *ultimate load* or *bearing capacity* of a single pile indicates the load at which the settlement of the pile exceeds any reasonable value, such as $\frac{1}{2}$ ft. Whatever the load may be, it is carried partly by skin friction and partly by the resistance of the soil directly beneath the point, as indicated in Figure 188a. Therefore, the ultimate bearing capacity Q_d can be resolved into two parts: Q_f which is due to skin friction, and Q_p which is due to point resistance. Hence,

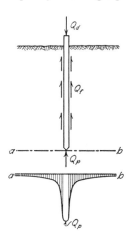

$$Q_d = Q_f + Q_p \tag{56.1}$$

FIG. 188. (a) Loaded friction pile in soft clay; (b) distribution of pressure on horizontal section through point of pile.

In Figure 188b, *ab* represents a horizontal section through the point of the pile, and the shaded areas indicate the pressure on this section. The total pressure is obviously equal to Q_d. Various refined theoretical methods have been used to compute the distribution of this pressure, but the results of the computations cannot be relied on, because all the methods are based on the assumptions that the soil is perfectly homogeneous and elastic. Authoritative information on the pressure distribution can be obtained only by direct measurements, and so far no such measurements have been made. However, there is no doubt that the distribution depends not only on the dimensions of the pile, but also on the load, the nature of the soil, and the conditions of stratification. It is also likely to change appreciably with time.

Skin friction on single pile in sand. When a pile is driven into very dense sand, refusal against further penetration is met at a depth of a very few feet, whereas in very loose sand piles can be driven to great depth without encountering appreciable resistance. In every sand both the average skin friction per unit of area of contact and the point resistance increase with increasing depth. The total skin friction that resists further penetration of a cylindrical or prismatic pile into a homogeneous stratum of sand is considerably greater than one-half the total ultimate bearing capacity Q_d of the pile, but the resistance against pulling is considerably less than half of Q_d. The difference between the two values of skin friction is due to the fact that a downward movement of the pile increases the pressure against its sides, whereas an upward movement decreases it.

After the pile is driven to refusal, the average skin friction resisting further penetration under static load is of the order of 500 lb per sq ft for loose sand (long piles), and 2000 lb per sq ft for very dense sand (short piles).

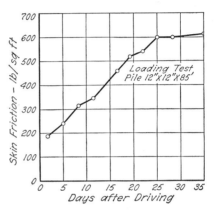

FIG. 189. Diagram illustrating increase of ultimate bearing capacity of friction pile with time.

Occasionally, it has been observed that the bearing capacity of piles in sand decreases conspicuously during the first 2 or 3 days after driving. Although this phenomenon is rather exceptional, the possibility of its occurrence should never be ignored. It is probable, but not certain, that the high initial bearing capacity is due to a temporary state of stress that develops in the sand surrounding the point of the pile during driving. This state of stress is associated with a temporary excess point resistance.

Skin friction of piles in soft clay. The point resistance of friction piles embedded in soft clay is negligible compared to the skin friction. The skin friction per unit of contact area is more or less independent of the depth of penetration and the method of installing the pile. It depends almost entirely on the properties of the clay. The resistance against pulling is commonly, but not always, nearly equal to the resistance against further penetration under load. All these relations are much simpler than the corresponding ones for friction piles in sand. However, by contrast, the relations between skin friction and time are much more complex and as yet are unpredictable. The skin friction usually increases during the first month after the pile is driven, but the amount of increase varies considerably with the nature of the soil.

The curve in Figure 189 represents the increase in bearing capacity of a friction pile with time. The pile was driven into soft brown clay with streaks of silt. The liquid limit of the clay was between 37 and 45 per cent, the plastic limit between 20 and 22 per cent, and the natural water content slightly below the liquid limit. During the pile-driving operations the soil turned almost liquid, and the skin friction had a very small value. Although the piles penetrated 12 in. under a single blow, they rose 10 in. when the hammer was lifted, and a special device had to be used to prevent the piles from rising. Yet, within a month the skin friction increased to more than three times its initial value.

On the other hand, the bearing capacity of piles driven into some silty clays decreases during the first few days after driving. Such a decrease was observed after piles 80 ft long were driven through 40 to 50 ft of soft silt into an underlying stratum of "compact blue clay" at Balboa, Canal Zone. The decrease of the resistance against further penetration took place within one day. A similar phenomenon occurred during the construction of the Navy Yard at Charleston, S. C.,[56.5] when timber piles were driven through 10 ft of silt into "stiff blue mud."

When piles are driven into soft clay, the clay located in the path of the penetrating pile is displaced and becomes severely distorted. After the pile is driven, the disturbed clay surrounds it like a shell a few inches thick. However, beyond the outer boundaries of this shell the disturbance of the soil structure is very moderate. Experience indicates that the shell of badly disturbed clay rapidly consolidates and becomes stiffer than the undisturbed clay and that it is likely to adhere to the pile if the pile is pulled.

Driving piles into saturated silt may temporarily liquefy the silt for a considerable distance. What little is known about the consequences of the liquefaction seems to indicate that the volume of the silt remains practically unchanged. Yet, within a few days or weeks the silt appears to become as solid and stable as it was originally. Hence, it is rather unlikely that the effect of pile driving on either soft clays or silts is detrimental, and in the following discussions it is assumed that the physical properties of the soils do not experience significant permanent alteration.

In spite of the influence of disturbance and the diverse time effects that take place immediately after a pile is driven into soft clay or soft plastic silt, the ultimate value of the skin friction is commonly equal to about one-half the unconfined compressive strength of the clay. Table 24 gives the range of ultimate values of the skin friction likely to develop in the principal types of cohesive soils. It may be emphasized that this as well as more elaborate tables serves only as a guide for making preliminary estimates. Reliable information cannot be obtained without performing loading and pulling tests on full-sized piles in the field.

Action of point-bearing piles. In contrast to friction piles, point-bearing piles are assumed to transfer the load through their points onto a firm stratum. Nevertheless, a considerable part of the load is carried at least temporarily by skin friction. This has been demonstrated by load tests in both the laboratory and the field.[56.6] However, if the pile passes through a very compressible soil such as soft silt or clay, the pressure transferred to this soil by skin friction gradually consolidates it, and, as a consequence, the pile tends to settle. The settlement is resisted only by the soil in which the point is embedded, and, as time goes on, the pressure on the point increases. This process continues until the major part of the load on the pile is carried by the point. If the load assigned to the pile in the foundation exceeds the point resistance, the resulting settle-

TABLE 24

ULTIMATE VALUES OF SKIN FRICTION ON
PILES EMBEDDED IN COHESIVE SOILS

lb per sq ft of contact area

Soft clay and silt	200–600
Sandy silt	400–1000
Stiff clay	800–2000

ment can be very large. Yet, the danger is not revealed by the results of a load test on a single pile, even if the load test is applied for several weeks. Hence, it is more important to know the point resistance than the total bearing capacity of a point-bearing pile.

Relations between driving resistance and depth.   If the depth to which a pile has penetrated is plotted against the number of hammer blows per inch of penetration, a resistance diagram is obtained. Typical diagrams are shown in Figure 190. The shape of the penetration curve indicates almost unmistakably into which of the three main categories the pile belongs. Figure 190a shows curves typical for piles driven into loose and into dense sand. In both types of sand the penetration resistance increases with depth. On the other hand, the pile represented by Figure 190d was driven through soft clay, and the penetration resistance became practically constant. The sharp break in the curve in Figure 190c indicates that the pile point passed from soft silt into a fairly dense sand. Such a break is typical for point-bearing piles. By correlating the resistance diagrams with the soil profile on a given job, the engineer can usually obtain a reliable conception of the material in which each pile is embedded. In particular, he can determine whether the point of the pile has reached a suitable bearing stratum.

Use of pile formulas for estimating ultimate bearing capacity.   When a point-bearing pile encounters a firm stratum, the penetration resistance increases sharply, Figure 190c. In a general way, the greater this increase, the greater is likely to be the point resistance of the pile. This observation has led to various attempts to express the relationship between the bearing capacity of a pile and the penetration resistance under the last few blows of the hammer. The results are known as pile formulas. In the United States the most popular expression is the Engineering News formula, according to which the ultimate bearing capacity of a pile should be

$$Q_{dy} = 6\,\frac{2W_H H}{S + c} \tag{56.2}$$

where Q_{dy} (lb) = ultimate bearing capacity of pile
$\quad\;\; W_H$ (lb) = weight of hammer
$\quad\;\;\; H$ (ft) = fall of hammer
$\quad\;\;\; S$ (in.) = penetration under last blow
$\quad\;\;\; c$ (in.) = empirical constant, taken as 1.0 for drop hammers and
$\qquad\qquad\qquad$ 0.1 for steam hammers

According to Figure 190d, the value of S that appears in the formulas is, for friction piles in clay, practically independent of depth. As a consequence, equation 56.2 leads to the conclusion that the ultimate

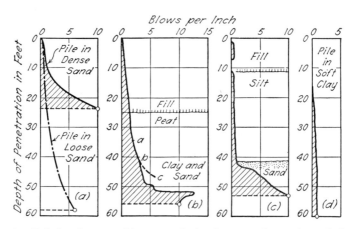

Fig. 190. Relation between blows per inch of penetration and total depth of penetration for wood piles driven into subsoils of various characteristics.

bearing capacity of such piles is also independent of depth. However, experience has shown that the ultimate bearing capacity of friction piles increases approximately in direct proportion to the length of the piles. This fact strictly excludes the application of the Engineering News formula or any other pile formula to friction piles in soft silt or clay. As a matter of fact, in several cities, including Shanghai and New Orleans, where the prevalence of thick deposits of soft soil calls for extensive use of friction piles, [no experienced engineer would even consider using a pile formula. [On small jobs the bearing capacity is estimated on the basis of empirical values for the average skin friction per unit of area, and the point resistance is disregarded. On large jobs load tests are made.]

However, even for point-bearing piles and other piles for which the penetration resistance increases with depth, the agreement between the real ultimate bearing capacity and that computed on the basis of the Engineering News formula is hardly satisfactory. The reasons are explained in Article 30. By correlating a considerable number of real values of Q_d, selected at random, with the corresponding values Q_{dy} computed by means of equation 56.2, it was found that the real values were, on the average, only 0.7 of the computed ones. Of greater significance, however, was the fact that individual values of the real bearing capacity ranged from 0.3 to 2.8 times the computed values. Therefore, if the bearing capacity of a pile is estimated by means of equation 56.2, the uncertainty in the estimate calls for a very liberal factor of safety. The Engineering News formula is used with a theoretical factor of safety of 6. Hence, the real factor of safety, according to the values given here, is likely to range between about 2 and 17.

The practical implications of these facts are illustrated by the following example. A building is to be constructed on pile-supported footings, each of which must support a load of 160 tons. Test piles are driven, and the penetration under the final blows is measured. According to the Engineering News formula, the ultimate bearing capacity Q_{dy}, equation 56.2, is 60 tons, and the safe load is 10 tons per pile. Hence, the designer will establish each footing on 16 piles. If the pile spacing is 3 ft, the footing will be about 12 ft square. However, according to the preceding paragraph, if a load test were made on the test pile, it might furnish any value for Q_d between $0.3 \times 60 = 18$ tons and $2.8 \times 60 = 168$ tons. If the real bearing capacity happens to be 20 tons, the design is satisfactory. But, if it is actually 110 tons, each pile could be assigned a load of as much as 40 tons, and only four piles would be required to support the footing. Furthermore, the footing could be reduced to 6 ft square. Hence, the owner would not only save 12 piles per footing, but the footings themselves would be much cheaper. Thus, the use of the Engineering News formula may involve a considerable waste of time and capital.

The Engineering News formula contains no terms that express the properties of the pile, although it is certain that some of these properties have a large influence on the effect of the hammer blow. Since other more elaborate formulas, such as Redtenbacher's or Hiley's, contain factors representing the weight, dimensions, modulus of elasticity, and coefficient of restitution of the pile, they convey the impression of greater reliability. [However, experience has shown that they are almost as inaccurate as the simpler Engineering News formula. Hence, on large jobs good engineering practice calls for determining the ultimate bearing capacity by means of load tests on full-sized piles.]

Load tests on piles. It has been pointed out that the bearing capacity of all piles except those driven to bedrock does not reach its ultimate value until a certain time has elapsed. Hence, the results of load tests are not conclusive unless the tests are made after the period of adjustment. For piles in permeable ground this period amounts to 2 or 3 days, and for piles partly or wholly surrounded by silt or clay to about a month.

Pile load tests are commonly made by constructing a platform on top of the pile, loading it with sand or pig iron, and observing the settlement of the pile by means of a level. This procedure is cumbersome because of the large weights to be handled and the time required. A more expedient procedure is known as a *bootstrap test.* In preparation for such a test three piles are driven in line at a spacing of 5 ft. The upper ends of the outer piles are connected by a strong and stiff yoke. The middle pile is the test pile, and it is loaded by jacking against the yoke. The pull on the anchor piles slightly reduces the settlement of the test pile, but this disadvantage is more than offset by the ease with which the process of loading can be repeated once every few days. The curve shown in Figure 189 was obtained by means of such a test.

In order to design foundations on point-bearing piles driven through clay strata into sand, information is needed concerning the bearing capacity of that part of the pile located in the sand. For the sake of brevity this is referred to as the point resistance, although it includes the skin friction at the surface of contact between the pile and the sand. Unless it is absolutely certain that the "safe design load" is considerably less than the point resistance, the latter should be determined by load tests in the field. For this purpose two test piles may be driven at a distance of about 5 ft from each other. One of them is driven to refusal within the bearing stratum. The other is driven until its point is about 3 ft above the surface of the bearing stratum. Since the point resistance of a pile embedded in sand approaches its ultimate value quite rapidly, the load tests can be made as soon as 3 days after driving the test piles. The effect of time on the skin friction can be eliminated by loading both piles simultaneously and at equal rates. The point resistance is equal to the difference between the ultimate bearing capacity of the two piles.

Evaluation of "safe design load." The term *"safe design load"* Q_a indicates the load at which the factor of safety with respect to a downward plunging or sinking of a single pile has a value consistent with the customary safety requirements.

If the "safe design load" for the pile is estimated by means of the Engineering News formula,

$$Q_a = \frac{2W_H H}{S + c} = \frac{1}{6} Q_{dy} \qquad (30.4)$$

the theoretical factor of safety is 6. The reason for using such a large value has already been explained. An equally large factor of safety is required with any other pile formula.

If the ultimate bearing capacity is determined by means of a load test, the customary factors of safety range between 2.5 and 3. Even the smaller value is fully adequate. [The principal uncertainties in the load-test method lie in the assignment of a value for the ultimate bearing capacity based on an interpretation of the load-settlement curve.]

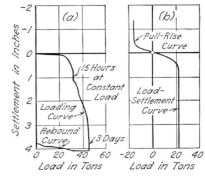

FIG. 191. Typical load-settlement curve for (*a*) point-bearing pile; (*b*) friction pile.

The general character of load-settlement curves ranges between the two extremes shown in Figure 191. The curve in Figure 191*a* is typical for friction piles embedded in coarse-grained soils and for point-bearing piles that transfer their load onto sand strata. Since the settlement curve gradually approaches an inclined tangent as the load on the pile increases, no definite value can be assigned to the ultimate bearing capacity. The safe design load on such piles should not exceed one-half the load required to produce a penetration of 2 in.

The load-settlement curves for friction piles differ considerably from each other in character. An extreme possibility is represented in Figure 191*b*. The test pile was driven 37 ft through soft silt and clay with layers of peat. The point did not reach a firm stratum. Under loads of less than 22 tons the settlement of the pile was insignificant, but, when the load became equal to this value, the pile suddenly sank several feet and did not stop until the loading platform hit the ground. The pull–rise curve, also shown in the figure, is similar to the load-settlement curve. The safe design load for such piles can be considered equal to the ultimate bearing capacity Q_d divided by a factor of safety of 2.5.

Ultimate Bearing Capacity of Pile Groups

Both theory and experience have shown that pile groups may fail as units by breaking into the ground before the load per pile becomes equal to the "safe design load." Such a failure is illustrated in Figure 192. Hence, the computation of the safe design load must be supplemented by a computation of the ultimate bearing capacity of the entire group. Let

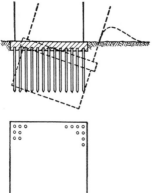

D_f = depth of penetration of the piles

r = radius of periphery of pile group

s = average shearing resistance of soil, per unit of area, between surface and depth D_f

Q_{dr} = ultimate bearing capacity of the base of a cylindrical pier with radius r and depth D_f. This quantity may be estimated by means of equation 29.8.

If the piles and the confined mass of soil sink as a unit like a pier, the ultimate bearing capacity Q_c of the cluster is approximately determined by the equation,

Fig. 192. Diagram illustrating failure due to breaking into ground of entire pile cluster, including the soil located between the piles.

$$Q_c = Q_{dr} + 2\pi r D_f s \qquad (56.3)$$

Computations based on this equation have shown that a base failure can hardly occur unless the pile group consists of a large number of friction piles embedded in silt or soft clay, as shown in Figure 192, or else of point-bearing piles that transfer their load onto a firm but thin stratum underlain by a thick deposit of silt or soft clay. A pile group can be considered safe against such a failure if the total design load (number of piles times the "safe design load" per pile) does not exceed $Q_c/3$. If this condition is not satisfied, the design of the foundation must be changed.

Settlement of Friction Pile Foundations in Sand

Dense sand is an excellent subsoil that does not need any reinforcement by piles. If piles have to be installed in dense sand for some purpose such as to transfer the weight of a bridge pier to a level below that of the deepest scour, it is usually necessary to aid the penetration of the pile by jetting. Hence, in the following paragraphs, we consider only piles driven into loose sand. Furthermore, we assume that the sand within which the piles are driven is not underlain by any material more compressible than the sand itself.

If all other conditions are the same, the skin friction against the piles increases with increasing relative density of the sand. While a pile is being driven, the density of the surrounding sand increases. Large-scale experiments have shown that the compaction caused by driving one pile influences the bearing capacity of any other pile located within a distance equal at least to five times the diameter of the pile.[56.7] As a consequence, if only one pile in a group is loaded, its settlement under a given load will be less if the number of piles in the group is large than if it is small. Nevertheless, if all the piles are loaded, the settlement of the group under a given load per pile increases with the number of piles.

The ultimate bearing capacity of piles in sand increases roughly with the square of the depth of penetration, whereas the cost of the piles increases with depth at a much smaller rate. Therefore, it is economical to drive piles in sand to such a depth that further penetration becomes difficult and slow. The number of blows per inch at which driving must be discontinued, regardless of other considerations, is determined by the condition that the pile should not be injured by the process of driving.[56 8]

The most suitable spacing D between the centers of piles with a top diameter d appears to be $3d$. In clusters each pile should be driven until the number of blows per inch becomes equal to that at which the driving of the test pile was discontinued. Driving should proceed outward from the center of the cluster; otherwise, the inner piles cannot be driven to as great a depth as the others.

After the piles have been installed, each cluster constitutes the core of a column of compacted sand embedded in loose sand. If the load per pile of such a foundation does not exceed the "safe design load," the settlement will not be greater than that of a similar structure supported by footings on dense sand. However, if the sand stratum containing the piles is interspersed with pockets or layers of silt or clay, the settlement may be almost as large as that of a floating pile foundation, because the pressure transmitted through the skin of the piles onto these layers causes them to consolidate.

Settlement of Point-Bearing Pile Foundations

Introduction. Point-bearing pile foundations may be divided into five principal categories, depending on the nature of the bearing stratum. The following possibilities are considered under separate subheadings:

1. The points rest on sound bedrock.
2. The points have been driven into decomposed bedrock.

3. The points are embedded in dense sand underlain by equally incompressible strata.

4. The points are embedded in stiff clay underlain by even more incompressible strata.

5. The points are embedded in a stratum of dense sand or stiff clay located above a stratum of soft clay.

Points resting on sound bedrock.   Under ideal conditions piles driven to sound bedrock act like piers, and the settlement does not exceed the elastic shortening of the piles. However, unless the points of wood piles are adequately protected, they are likely to be injured by brooming, whereupon the beneficial effect of the rigid point support is lost. If the points encounter a smooth but inclined rock surface, they may travel down the slope without giving any visible indication of their progressive deflection. When the weight of the building is added, the deflection may increase still further, and the foundation may fail. Under such conditions wood piles should not be used. Even reinforced-concrete piles may break.

Points driven into decomposed bedrock.   Decomposed rocks, particularly of metamorphic origin, may be as compressible as medium clay. Yet, they usually contain fragments of fairly intact rock that interfere with driving the piles through the compressible zone. Under these circumstances reliable information on the probable settlement can be obtained only by securing undisturbed cores of the decomposed material and making a settlement forecast on the basis of the results of consolidation tests. If the settlement may conceivably exceed the tolerable value, some method must be used for punching through the zone of decomposed rock.

Points driven through compressible strata into sand.   In the preceding discussion of the ultimate bearing capacity of a single pile of this type it was shown that the settlement of the pile depends primarily on the ratio between the point resistance and the pile load. The same general statement can be made with regard to the settlement of the entire foundation. If the load per pile is equal to or less than the point resistance, the settlement is likely to be of no consequence. On the other hand, if it is greater, the settlement may be large and detrimental. However, in any event, the average settlement of the foundation will be many times greater than the settlement of a single pile acted on by the "safe design load." These statements are illustrated by the following example.

An apartment house in Vienna, Austria, was constructed on continuous footings 40 in. wide, supported by cast-in-place concrete piles driven through about 20 ft of loose fill into fairly dense gravel. Each pile carried a load of 24 tons. In Figure 193b, curve C_0 shows the result of a load test on a single pile, and C the load-settlement curve for the same pile during construction. When the load due to the weight of the building reached its ultimate value of 24 tons, the settlement of the pile was very much greater than that of the same pile during the load test. Curves of equal settlement for the entire foundation 11 weeks after the building was completed are shown in Figure 193a. Their complete lack of symmetry suggests that the seat of settlement was in the upper part of the firm

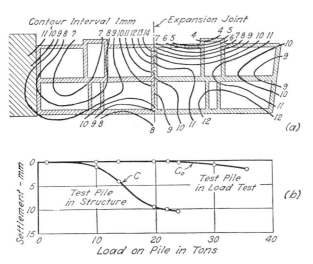

Fig. 193.   (a) Settlement contours one year after construction of brick buildings supported by continuous footings on conical piles bearing on dense gravel stratum; (b) load–settlement relations for single pile under test load and under same load beneath structure.

stratum and that the settlement reflected primarily the local variations in compressibility of this stratum. If the walls had been perfectly flexible, the curves of equal settlement would extend without any break across the expansion joint at mid-length of the building. The discontinuities indicate that the walls acted as semirigid beams that bridged the weakest spots in the supporting stratum. However, from a practical point of view the settlement was irrelevant, because the maximum differential settlement did not exceed $\frac{1}{2}$ in. The success of the foundation was due to the fact that the load per pile was smaller than the point resistance.

In the example referred to in the preceding paragraph the point resistance was large, because only a small amount of energy was consumed by the soft upper strata during driving. On the other hand, if some of the top strata are very firm, most of the driving energy is used in overcoming the side friction in the upper strata, and the resistance against further penetration becomes excessive while the point resistance is still very low. Reliable information on the point resistance of such piles can be obtained only by making load tests on two piles of different length, as described on page 466. More expedient but less reliable is the method of estimating the point resistance on the basis of the pile-driving record. According to this procedure, a pile formula is used to compute the ultimate bearing capacity of the pile from the penetration under the last blow and from the penetration per blow just before the point entered the bearing stratum. The point resistance is equal to the difference between the two values thus computed. However, the error associated with this procedure may be very large, because both of the computed values involve all of the uncertainties inherent in the use of a pile formula.

If the investigations show that the point resistance is inadequate, it can be increased by *spudding*. This term indicates punching or drilling a hole down to the surface of a satisfactory bearing stratum. After the hole is made, the pile is inserted and driven. Thus the energy available for driving the point into the bearing stratum is increased, and, as a consequence, the point resistance is also increased.

If the load per pile does not exceed two thirds of the point resistance, the settlement of the foundation will be unimportant, regardless of the spacing of the piles. A spacing of $3d$ satisfies all practical requirements. The center piles in a cluster should be driven first to insure that their points will have adequate penetration into the bearing stratum.

In some localities the bedrock is covered by a composite stratum consisting of irregular pockets of sand or sand and gravel alternating with pockets of more compressible material such as clay, or rock fragments embedded in clay. This composite base is buried beneath soft sediments. The conventional exploratory borings do not necessarily reveal its composite character. However, while a test pile is being driven, the variations in the character of the subsoil come into prominence. For example, Figure 190b represents the depth-resistance curve for a pile driven through fill and peat into a sand stratum containing layers and pockets of clay. The curve consists of inclined sections such as *ab* followed by vertical ones. These abrupt transitions may indicate the passage of the point of the pile from a firm soil into soft silt or clay; if the soil below the level of point *b* had been similar to that above it, the curve would have continued as indicated by the dash line *bc*. Since the depth-resistance curve has several steps, the point of the pile evidently passed through several firm strata alternating with soft ones. However, quite similar abrupt transitions may be caused by the passage of the point of the pile from a dense layer of sand into a loose one. This possibility is illustrated by Figure 120. In any event, the individual piles of a cluster driven into a subsoil with an erratic soil profile are likely to meet refusal at very different depths. For instance, one of two adjacent piles driven at a distance of 2.5 ft from each other into the subsoil shown in Figure 120 met refusal at a depth of 60 ft, whereas the other penetrated to a depth of 85 ft. If the soil located between the points of piles with very different length consists only of loose sand, the performance of the cluster under load may be perfectly satisfactory. On the other hand, if it contains pockets of soft clay or silt, the settlement of the pile-supported footing may be excessive. Hence, if adjacent foundation piles meet refusal at very different depths, a boring should be made near by to determine the cause of the difference. If the boring shows that the soil contains pockets of highly compressible material below the level of the shortest piles, it is necessary to enforce the penetration of all the piles to a level below the bottom of the zone that contains the pockets. If this cannot be done by jetting, spudding may be required. All those piles that met refusal above the level of the lowest soft pockets should be pulled, or disregarded and replaced by piles with adequate length.

On flood plains and along the seacoast the construction of pile foundations is often preceded by placing a fill over the site of the proposed structure. If the subsoil consists of loose sand or other highly permeable and relatively incompressible soils, the effect of the fill on the piles can be disregarded. On the other hand, if the subsoil contains layers of soft silt or clay, the presence of the fill considerably increases the load on the piles and, as a consequence, also causes an increase in settlement. This fact was first recognized in Holland, where many buildings located in the coastal plains rest on point-bearing piles driven through about 60 ft of very soft strata to refusal in a bed of sand. Wherever the site was covered by a thick layer of fill shortly before the piles were driven, it was found that the buildings supported by the piles settled excessively. Once this fact was noticed, the cause of the settlement became obvious.

Before such piles are driven, the compressible strata gradually consolidate under the weight of the newly applied fill, and the fill settles. As soon as the piles are installed, the fill material located in the upper part of the pile clusters can no longer settle freely because its downward movement is resisted by skin friction between the fill and the piles. An imperceptible downward movement of the fill with respect to the piles is sufficient to transfer onto the piles the weight of all the fill located within the cluster. If A represents the area of a horizontal section included within the boundaries of a cluster, n the number of piles, H the thickness of the fill, and γ its unit weight, the load Q' which acts on each pile due to the weight of the fill within the cluster is

$$Q' = \frac{A}{n} \gamma H \qquad (56.4)$$

In the spaces between clusters, the weight of the fill causes progressive settlement. If the clusters consist of point-bearing piles, the piles do not participate in the downward movement, and, as a consequence, the soil that surrounds the clusters moves down with reference to the clusters. It tends to drag each cluster down.

The drag increases as the consolidation of the clay surrounding the cluster proceeds. The minimum value depends on the distance through which the surface of the clay subsides. It is almost zero for very small subsidences, and it increases with increasing subsidence. It cannot become greater than the product of the thickness H of the clay stratum, the circumference L of the cluster, and the average shearing resistance s of the clay. If n is the number of piles in the cluster, the maximum value of the drag is

$$Q_{max}'' = \frac{LHs}{n} \qquad (56.5)$$

The real value Q'' ranges between zero and Q_{max}''. At the present state of our knowledge it can be evaluated only by judgment.

The forces that produce the loads Q' and Q'' are known as *negative skin friction*. With increasing spacing between piles both Q' and Q'' increase. Hence, to reduce the effects of negative skin friction the spacing between piles should be reduced to $2.5d$, the minimum compatible with practical requirements.

If Q is the load per pile exerted by a building on piles driven through new fill and soft clay into a sand stratum, the lower ends of the piles will ultimately receive a load

$$Q_t = Q + Q' + Q'' \qquad (56.6)$$

If this load is greater than the point resistance of the pile, the settlement of the foundation will be excessive, regardless of what ultimate bearing capacity a load test may indicate. Hence, if a foundation on point-bearing piles is to be established at the site of a recent fill, both the point resistance and the value of Q_t, equation 56.6, should be determined.

Points driven through compressible strata into stiff clay. Under these conditions most of the load on the piles is ultimately carried by the points. This produces a large concentration of stress in the clay near the point of each pile. The results of a load test on a single pile may be perfectly reassuring, because, first of all, the major part of the load during the test is carried by skin friction, and, second, the consolidation of the clay near the pile points develops very slowly. However, as time goes on, the settlement due to this consolidation may become very large. To obtain reliable information concerning this possibility, it is advisable to drive a steel pipe with a conical loosely attached point through the soft strata into the stiff clay and to make a load test by inserting a column in the pipe to transfer the load directly to the point. The diameter of the pipe should be roughly equal to that of the tip of the proposed piles. The point should preferably be made of a permeable material such as artificial porous stone. The load should be left on the point for at least a month. The settlement should be measured once a day during the first week and twice a week thereafter. The shape of the time–settlement curve obtained by plotting the settlement data permits at least a crude estimate of the ultimate settlement of the pile.

The spacing of the piles should not be less than $3d$, to reduce the disturbance of the clay constituting the bearing stratum as much as possible. A spacing of $3.5d$ is preferable. The difference between the ultimate settlement of the single test pile and of the entire foundation is likely to be unimportant.

If the area to be occupied by the foundation has been covered by a recent fill, the foundation should be designed for a load Q_t per pile, equation 56.6, on account of the negative skin friction.

Points embedded in firm stratum underlain by soft clay. If the bearing stratum, such as a thick layer of dense sand, is located above a layer of soft clay, the settlement of the pile foundation is the sum of two independent items. The first part is equal to the settlement that would take place if the sand stratum were not underlain by compressible material. The factors that determine this part of the settlement are discussed under the preceding subheadings. The second part is due to the gradual consolidation of the compressible layer located beneath the stratum in which the points of the piles are embedded. Whereas the first part is negligible if the foundation is properly designed, the second may be very large and detrimental. This possibility has often been overlooked even in recent years.

In one instance about 5000 wood piles 80 ft long were driven to firm bearing in dense sand through fill and through 50 to 65 ft of loose fine sand containing thin layers of silt and soft clay. The piles were arranged in clusters and capped by footings. The load per pile was about 16 tons, less than one quarter of the ultimate bearing capacity as determined by load tests, and no measurable settlement was anticipated. Yet, the foundation actually settled more than 2 ft. The seat of settlement was a layer of clay 30 ft thick, located 25 ft below the points of the longest piles. The water content of the clay was close to the liquid limit.

The settlement of a pile foundation due to the consolidation of a soft layer below the bearing stratum can be computed by the procedures given in Articles 13 and 36, on the assumption that the structure is perfectly flexible and that the loads act directly on the surface of the bearing stratum. The total load that produces the consolidation is equal to the difference between the total effective weight of the building and

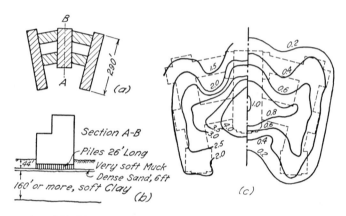

Fig. 194. (*a* and *b*) Plan and cross section of structure supported by piles driven into dense sand layer above deep clay deposit; (*c*) settlement contours for structure. Contours on left side represent observed settlement in inches at completion of structure; contours on right side represent lines of equal relative settlement based on computation and results of consolidation tests.

the effective weight of the excavated soil (see Article 55). The reliability of this procedure is illustrated by Figure 194. Figures 194*a* and *b* represent, respectively, a simplified plan and vertical section through a steel frame building with cut-stone facing. The structure rests on about 10,000 wood piles 26 ft long, driven so that their points came to bearing in the upper part of a layer of dense sand. The load per pile is 15 tons. Since the average settlement of the test pile was only $\frac{1}{4}$ in. under 30 tons, the designers did not expect that the maximum settlement of the entire foundation would exceed this value. The real maximum settlement, however, had already exceeded 1 ft within 2 years after construction. The contours of observed settlement, in inches, at the end of the construction period are shown on the left side of Figure 194*c*. The right side shows curves of equal computed settlement, plotted as a fraction of the maximum settlement. In spite of the simplifying assumptions made in the calculations, the computed differential settlement is in good agreement with the actual settlement. According to the results of the settlement analysis, the ultimate maximum settlement will be about 18 in., but the real settlement will be considerably greater because of the secondary time effect, Article 14.

In order to get information about the magnitude of the settlement due to consolidation of compressible strata located beneath the pile points, the exploratory borings must be supplemented at least by several tube-sample borings from which continuous samples of all the highly compressible strata are secured. If an accurate settlement forecast is called for, an undisturbed sample boring must also be made. The program for testing the samples and the method of computation is identical with that prescribed for the settlement of raft foundations located above soft clay strata, Article 55. If the computation indicates that the settlement may exceed a tolerable value, other methods for constructing the foundation must be considered.

If the computation indicates that the settlement will be tolerable, the spacing between piles may be determined by means of the same rules that are used for foundations on point-bearing piles embedded in sand.

Redriving of point-bearing piles. If a pile is driven through silt or clay, the neighboring piles may rise as much as several inches, and their points lose contact with the point-supporting soil. Subsequent application of a load on these piles causes a settlement equal to the preceding rise. Hence, if the soil conditions are conducive to a rise, reference points should be established on the heads of the piles and observed by means of a level from time to time. If a rise is observed, the piles must be redriven before the footings are constructed.

Settlement of Floating Pile Foundations

In some types of soft ground piles of any kind can be driven to great depth without appreciable resistance against further penetration. The depth-penetration diagrams for such piles resemble that shown in Figure 190d. These conditions call for a floating pile foundation, wherein the minimum length of the piles is determined not by a specified resistance against further penetration under the blows of a hammer, but by the requirement that the factor of safety of the pile groups with respect to a base failure should be equal to at least 2 or 3. The ultimate bearing capacity Q_c of each group can be estimated by means of equation 56.3. The value of s in this equation can best be determined by loading to failure several test piles of different length. However, before the computation can be made, the spacing between piles must be decided on.

According to equation 56.3, the ultimate bearing capacity of a friction pile group increases with increasing spacing. Furthermore, at a given load per pile the settlement of a cluster consisting of a given number of piles decreases as the spacing increases. Hence, it would appear that a fairly large spacing is advantageous. However, as yet, empirical data concerning the effect of spacing on the settlement are very scarce. In 1915 two groups of friction piles embedded in soft silty clay were loaded with 240 tons per group.[56.9] Each group contained 16 piles 77 ft long. In one the piles were spaced at $2\frac{1}{2}$ ft, and in the other at $3\frac{1}{2}$ ft. After 40 days both groups had settled $4\frac{1}{2}$ in. but after 270 days the settlement of

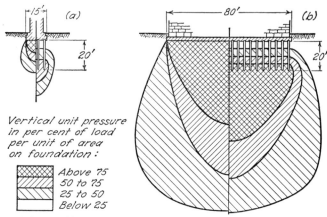

FIG. 195. Diagram illustrating increase of vertical pressure in soil beneath friction pile foundations having piles of equal lengths carrying equal loads. In (*a*) width of foundation is small compared to pile length; in (*b*) width of foundation is large compared to pile length.

the group with the closer spacing was 11 in., and that of the other group only 8 in. Inasmuch as such an advantage must be paid for by constructing very much larger footings, it is doubtful that a spacing in excess of 3.5*d* is economical.

If the number of piles in a group is increased at a given spacing and at a given load per pile, both the intensity of the greatest stress in the soil and the depth of the highly stressed zone increase. This can be seen by comparing the right-hand sides of the diagrams in Figures 195*a* and *b*. As a consequence the settlement of a pile-supported foundation covering a large area is greater than that of a smaller foundation supported by equally loaded piles of the same length and driven at the same spacing. Similarly, the settlement of a foundation covering a given area and supporting a given total load decreases with increasing length of the piles, in spite of the fact that fewer piles are needed to carry the load. These conclusions are confirmed by experience in every city where the soil conditions call for floating pile foundations.[56.10]

On the left sides of Figures 195a and b are shown the intensity and the distribution of the stresses in the soil computed on the assumption that no piles are present. The ultimate settlement of the pile foundations shown on the right side of the diagrams can be roughly estimated on the following simplifying assumption. Above the level of the lower third-point of the length of the piles the water content of the clay remains unchanged, and below this level consolidation proceeds as if the building were supported on a flexible raft located at that level. The presence of the piles is disregarded. According to this assumption, the benefit derived from the piles is equivalent to replacing the subsoil by a practically incompressible material that extends from the base of the foundation to a depth equal to two thirds of the length of the piles. If this depth is several times greater than the width of the footings, and the footings are widely spaced, the settlement of the pile foundation will be small, no matter how bad the subsoil may be. On the other hand, if this depth is considerably smaller than the width of the loaded area, and the loaded area is large, the ultimate settlement may be excessive even under a moderate load. These conclusions have been consistently confirmed by experience. Both experience and theory have also shown that raft foundations supported by uniformly loaded and equally spaced friction piles, like simple raft foundations, always tend to assume the shape of a shallow bowl.

If the structure contains a basement, the load that produces consolidation is equal to the difference between the effective weight of the building and the effective weight of the soil that was excavated to form the basement (see Article 55).

EFFICIENCY EQUATIONS

The preceding discussions have demonstrated that the settlement of a pile foundation has no relation whatsoever to the settlement of a single pile under a load equal to the load per pile in the foundation. The growing realization of this fact has led to various attempts to express the influence of the number and spacing of the piles on the settlement of the foundation by so-called *efficiency equations.*[56.4], [56.11], [56.12] However, the extraordinary variety of soils encountered in piling practice excludes the possibility of establishing a limited number of sufficiently accurate efficiency equations of general validity. The effect of the number and spacing of the piles on the ratio between the settlement of a single pile under a given load and that of a group under the same load per pile depends to a large extent on the sequence and properties of the soil strata. Furthermore, at a given length and spacing of the piles the ratio changes to a considerable extent with the load per pile. Nevertheless, in none of the existing efficiency theories are these vital facts given adequate consideration. Because of the great number and diversity of the factors involved, it seems very doubtful, to say the least, whether the efficiency equations represent a step in the right direction.

At the present state of knowledge and for many years to come it seems preferable to consider every case individually and to evaluate the probable settlement of a proposed pile foundation on the basis of the physical properties of the soils onto which the load is transmitted by the piles. Examples of the use of this procedure have been given under the preceding subheadings. If the probable settlement exceeds the tolerable maximum, the design must be modified. The maximum tolerable settlement of pile foundations is determined by the same factors as those that govern the permissible settlement of footing and raft foundations, Articles 54 and 55.

If the distribution of the loads over the area to be occupied by a structure is very uneven, the secondary stresses in the structure due to unequal settlement can be appreciably relieved by dividing the structure into blocks separated from each other by continuous vertical joints.

Selection of Type of Pile

The designer of a pile foundation can choose among several different types of piles, any one of which may provide adequate support for the proposed foundation. The final choice is governed by economic considerations and by conditions imposed by the character of the job.

Until the end of the last century untreated timber piles were used almost exclusively. This type of pile is relatively cheap, but it has two major disadvantages. First, a wood pile must be cut off below the lowest water table; if the water table is subsequently lowered on account of a permanent change in ground-water conditions, the uppermost parts of the pile disintegrate within a relatively short time. Second, a wood pile may break if it is driven too hard, although the foreman may not detect anything unusual.[56.8] The risk of deterioration may be reduced by impregnation with wood preservatives, but the risk of breakage can be reduced only by stopping the driving of the pile while its bearing capacity is still relatively low. Since concrete or steel piles can be driven harder than wood piles without risk of damage, the safe design load for such piles is considerably greater than that for wood piles. Recognition of this fact in practice is exemplified by the values that represent the loads commonly assigned to piles of various types. These values are given in Table 25.

Although the "safe design loads" for piles of different types are different, the spacing between piles of all types is practically the same.

Therefore, the footings required to transfer a given load onto wood piles are considerably larger and more expensive than footings with equal bearing capacities supported by concrete or steel piles. Furthermore, the bases of footings resting on concrete or steel piles can be established at any convenient elevation, whereas those of footings on wood piles must be located below the lowest position of the water table. These advantages in many instances compensate for the fact that the cost of a concrete or steel pile is several times that of a wood pile.

Before the beginning of the 20th century all concrete piles were of the precast reinforced type. During the following decade cast-in-place piles became widely used, and the manufacture of concrete piles developed

TABLE 25

CUSTOMARY DESIGN LOADS FOR PILES

Type of Pile	Allowable Load (tons)
Wood	15–25
Composite	20–30
Cast-in-place concrete	30–40
Precast reinforced concrete	30–45
Steel H-section	30–45

into a highly specialized industry. More recently structural steel has also entered the field. The piles from which the designer may choose differ in their method of installation, their shape, the texture of their surface, and several other aspects. Almost every type of pile has features that make it exceptionally suitable under certain soil conditions and less suitable or inapplicable under others. For example, if piles are expected to carry their load by skin friction, conical types are preferable to prismatic ones, and bulb piles are not applicable at all. On the other hand, if the piles are expected to derive their support by point bearing, conical piles offer no advantage, and bulb piles may be the best choice, unless other types are more economical. In order to meet the wide variety of soil conditions encountered in practice, every large pile company offers its clients several very different types of piles.

The choice of the type of pile may also be influenced by special requirements imposed on the designer by the character of the job.[56.4] Precast reinforced-concrete piles require heavy pile drivers with leads high enough to handle the longest piles on the job. They also require a large vacant space to serve as a casting yard. If these requirements are not met, precast piles cannot be used. If vibrations due to pile driving cannot be tolerated for some reason, a pile must be adopted which can be jacked down or else installed in a drill hole.

These and similar factors must be considered by the designer in connection with every pile job. Proper choice of a pile type requires judgment, experience in pile driving, and thorough grounding in the principles discussed in this article.

SUMMARY OF PRINCIPLES IN DESIGN AND CONSTRUCTION OF PILE FOUNDATIONS

Design of a pile foundation requires first the selection of the type, length, and spacing of the piles, and the "safe design load" per pile.

Selection of the type of pile is governed chiefly by economic and practical considerations. The choice among point-bearing piles of different types should be based on point resistance, not on total ultimate bearing capacity.

The length of point-bearing piles is determined by the location of the bearing stratum. Friction piles in any type of soil should be made as long as economically possible. By increasing the length of friction piles, the number of piles required to carry a given load is reduced, the ultimate bearing capacity of the entire pile foundation is increased, and the settlement is decreased.

The spacing D between the centers of wood piles with a butt diameter d should conform roughly to the following rules: For point-bearing piles driven to rock, or driven through soft clay strata to sand a short time after the ground surface has been covered by a fill, $D = 2.5d$. For point-bearing piles driven through less compressible strata into dense sand and for friction piles in loose sand, $D = 3d$. For point-bearing piles driven to bearing in stiff clay, and for friction piles in soft clay, $D = 3d$ to $3.5d$.

The "safe design load" can be determined either by means of a pile formula or a load test. The load-test method is more accurate. However, a pile foundation is not necessarily satisfactory even if the load per pile is less than the "safe design load." It may settle excessively, or if it is a floating pile foundation it may fail completely. To avoid these risks the group action of the piles must be considered.

Attempts to evaluate the group action by efficiency equations are likely to be misleading. All of the existing equations claim a wide range of validity, whereas the variety of actual soil conditions precludes the possibility that any such equation could have more than a very limited range of applicability. Therefore, efficiency equations should not be used. General instructions for judging group action on the basis of soil profiles have been given in the text.

Point-bearing piles driven through highly compressible strata into sand may settle excessively unless the load per pile is considerably smaller than the point resistance. If a large part of the energy of the blows of the hammer is consumed by the skin friction in the uppermost strata, the point resistance may be smaller than the "safe design load." In case of doubt the point resistance should be determined. If the individual piles in clusters of point-bearing piles meet refusal at very different depths, a boring should be made near the cluster to determine the cause of the variation. If the boring shows that the soil located between the levels of the shortest and the longest piles contains pockets or layers of soft clay or silt, only those piles should be considered satisfactory that extend below the level of the lowest pockets. The others should be disregarded and replaced by substitute piles that should be driven to the necessary depth with the aid of jetting or spudding.

Clusters of point-bearing piles driven through clay strata supporting newly deposited fill will be acted on not only by the weight of the structure but also by the weight of the new fill located between the piles in each cluster, and by the negative skin friction along the vertical boundaries of the clusters.

If the points of the piles in large clusters are driven into a sand stratum located above soft clay layers, or if such clusters are entirely embedded in soft clay, appreciable progressive settlement is inevitable and should be estimated in advance of construction.

Large clusters of friction piles embedded in soft clay may not have adequate safety with respect to a base failure of the group as a whole. Hence, the factor of safety with respect to such a failure should always be estimated.

If piles are driven into sand without the aid of a water jet, driving should proceed from the centers of the clusters toward the edges. Friction piles in soft silt or clay should be driven to the same depth, regardless of the number of blows for the last foot. Piles of any other category should be driven until the number of blows for the last inch becomes equal to that of the test piles that furnished the information for evaluating the design load. If point-bearing piles are to be driven through firm strata underlain by or alternating with soft compressible ones jetting or spudding may be required.

REFERENCES

56.1. R. D. CHELLIS, *Pile-Driving Handbook*, Pitman Publishing Corp., New York, 1944. See Chapter IV, Selection of Driving Equipment, and Chapter V, Selection of Type of Pile and Methods of Driving. In this book as in many others on piles, the pile formulas receive far more attention than they deserve. The catalogues of the different companies listed on page 268 should be consulted.

56.2. K. TERZAGHI, The Actual Factor of Safety in Foundations, *Structural*

Eng. Vol 13 (1935), pp 126–160. Results of settlement observations on pile foundations.

56.3. A. E. Cummings, Pile Foundations, *Proc. Purdue Conf. Soil Mech.*, Lafayette, Ind., Sept. 1940, pp 320–338. (Reprints issued by Raymond Concrete Pile Co., New York.) Summary of practical considerations that enter into the selection of the type of pile.

56.4. W. F. Swiger, Foundation Tests for Los Angeles Steam Plant, *Civil Eng.*, Vol 11 (1941), pp 711–714. Results of loading tests on pile groups in fine sand and discussion of the California efficiency formula.

56.5. R. M. Miller, Soil Reactions in Relation to Foundations on Piles, *Trans. ASCE*, Vol 103 (1938), pp 1193–1236. Review of the variety of soil conditions that may be encountered in connection with pile foundations.

56.6. V. Hansen and F. N. Kneas, Static Load Tests for Bearing Piles, *Civil Eng.*, Vol 12 (1942), pp 545–547. Field tests to determine total load carried by point-bearing pile at different depths below its top.

56.7. H. Press, The Bearing Capacity of Pile Groups in Relation to that of Single Piles (in German), *Bautechnik*, Vol 11 (1933), pp 625–627. Large-scale tests in loose sand to determine influence of number of piles in a cluster on the bearing capacity of an individual pile in the group.

56.8. T. C. Bruns, Don't Hit Timber Piles Too Hard, *Civil Eng.*, Vol 11 (1941), pp 726–728. Discussion of damage to timber piles due to overdriving.

56.9. C. W. Staniford, Loading Tests of Lagged Piles, *Eng. News*, Vol 74 (1915), pp 76–77. Results of tests on two groups of friction piles with different spacing.

56.10. N. W. B. Clarke and J. B. Watson, Settlement Records and Loading Data for Various Buildings Erected by the Public Works Department, Municipal Council, Shanghai, and J. A. Favret, Foundation Data, *Proc. Intern. Conf. Soil Mech.*, Cambridge, Mass. (1936), Vol II, pp 174–186. Data concerning settlement of floating pile foundations in Shanghai, China. Discussion by K. Terzaghi, Vol III, pp 92–96.

56.11. F. M. Masters, Timber Friction Pile Foundations, *Trans. ASCE*, Vol 108 (1943), pp 115–140. Load tests on several groups of friction piles and theoretical interpretations of the test results. Results concerning influence of spacing on ultimate bearing capacity of groups are inconclusive because of lack of adequate data concerning characteristics of the soil. Concerning the theoretical aspects of the theory, consult discussions by R. D. Mindlin, pp 147–149, and A. E. Cummings, pp 162–169.

56.12. *Uniform Building Code*, Pacific Coast Building Officials Conference, Los Angeles, 1940, pp 206–207. Typical efficiency formula.

ART. 57. PIER FOUNDATIONS

Function of Piers

Piers are prismatic or cylindrical columns that have essentially the same function as piles or pile clusters. If piers are constructed to support a bridge, their sole purpose may be to transfer the loads to a level below that of the deepest scour. In some semiarid regions piers are used to transfer the loads to a level below the zone of periodic desiccation of highly plastic clays, Article 21. However, in all other instances, piers serve, like point-bearing piles, to transfer the loads onto a firm stratum located beneath softer ones.

The principal difference between piers and piles lies in the method of installation and in the influence of this method on the load that can be assigned to the foundation without risk of excessive settlement. In Article 56 it is explained that the design load on a point-bearing pile should not exceed the point resistance, regardless of what the skin friction may be. Point-bearing piles are driven with a hammer. This method is very expedient, but driving must be discontinued as soon as the number of blows per inch exceeds a certain value. At this stage the point resistance may be greater than the customary design load, but it can also be very much smaller, depending on the amount of driving energy consumed by the skin friction. Piers are commonly installed by some process of excavation that is slow compared to pile driving, but that can always be continued until the bottom of the excavation arrives at the level called for by the construction drawings. Therefore, the relative merits of piers in comparison with piles depend primarily on the soil conditions. This fact is shown by the following examples.

If a pile is driven through soft ground into a stratum of dense sand, the point of the pile displaces and compacts the sand. The point resistance of such a pile is likely to be many times greater than that of a cylindrical pier with equal diameter, because the process of installing the pier does not compact the sand but, instead, gives it an opportunity to expand. On the other hand, if the layer of dense sand is located beneath a sequence of thin layers of soft clay and thick layers of sand, most of the energy of pile driving is likely to be used up by skin friction, and driving must be discontinued while the point resistance is still very small. Under such conditions piers would probably be safer and more economical than point-bearing piles.

If it is intended to transfer the weight of a structure onto sound bedrock overlain by a thick layer of decomposed rock which, in turn, is buried beneath soft sediments, piers may be preferable for the following reason. Some decomposed rocks are as compressible as medium or even soft clay. Yet they commonly contain large fragments of less decomposed material. These fragments prevent the points of piles from being driven into sound rock, whereas they can easily be removed from the excavation for a pier.

TYPES OF PIERS

Since piles and piers serve the same purposes, no sharp distinction can be made between the two. Cast-in-place piles installed in drill holes could as well be called piers of small diameter, because, at least theoretically, the drill holes can be made to any depth. Drilled-in caissons are made by driving a heavy steel pipe with a cutting shoe down to bedrock and as far into the rock as it will go. In this respect the caissons are piles. After refusal is met, the soil encased in the pipe is removed, a hole is drilled through the decomposed top layer into sound rock by means of a churn drill, and the hole and the pipe are filled with concrete. These procedures are characteristic for piers.

The great variety of types intermediate between typical piles and typical piers involves a similar diversity in the methods of installation. If the diameter of a pier is small enough to justify the use of well-drilling methods, the pier can be installed in almost any type of soil. On the other hand, the most suitable method for constructing piers of large diameter is chiefly determined by the soil conditions. If an attempt is made to build such a pier by a method that is not practicable under the given soil conditions, the contractor will be compelled to change the method during construction. An emergency change of procedure always involves a considerable loss of time and money. Therefore, the engineer who chooses the method for constructing piers of large diameter should be familiar with the prerequisites for success. The most common methods of construction are discussed under the following subheading.

Methods for Constructing Large-Diameter Piers

The methods for constructing piers of large diameter can be divided into two general classes, the sinking of caissons, and the excavation of open shafts. Strictly speaking, a caisson is a shell within which the excavation is made. The shell descends into the ground to the level of the base of the foundation and eventually becomes an integral part of the pier. The oldest type of caisson is the drop shaft or open caisson, Figures 196a to c. The shell sinks under its own weight as the soil at the bottom of the caisson is excavated. If the bottom is located above the water table, or if the water is removed by pumping from an open sump, the excavation can be made by hand, Figure 196a; otherwise, the soil must be removed by dredging, Figures 196b and c, and the bottom of the caisson sealed with underwater concrete when grade is reached. Obstacles in the path of the cutting edge, such as buried logs or boulders, may delay the sinking of the caisson by several days or weeks. If they cannot be removed within a reasonable length of time, the work must be continued by the compressed-air method, Figure 196d. As the caisson descends, air pressure is maintained in the working chamber at the value of the hydrostatic pressure in the pore water at the level of the cutting edge. For physiological reasons the use of air pressure is limited to a depth of about 120 ft below the water table. Beyond a depth of 40 ft the cost increases rapidly. The compressed-air method must also be used as a substitute for pumping if the specifications call for cleaning the bottom of the pier excavation before placing the concrete.

Two commonly used open-shaft methods for establishing piers are the *Gow method*, Figure 196e, and the *Chicago method*, Figure 196f. Neither procedure can be used unless the water can be removed by pumping or

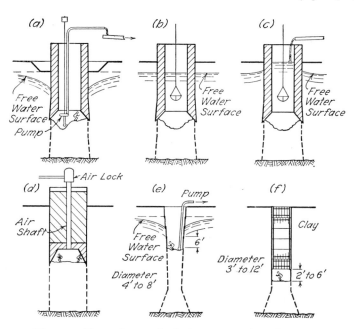

FIG. 196. Diagrams illustrating methods for constructing piers. (*a* to *c*) Open-caisson method; (*d*) compressed-air caisson; (*e*) open shaft with telescoping steel-shell lining (Gow method); (*f*) open shaft lined with wood lagging and steel rings (Chicago method).

bailing. In the Gow method the sides of the excavation are supported by a series of steel cylinders, each of which is 2 in. smaller in diameter than the one above. The cylinders are driven with a light hammer while the soil is being excavated by hand. The lowest part of the shaft is usually belled out. After the excavation has been completed, the shaft is filled with concrete, and the cylinders are recovered one by one.

The Chicago method is used exclusively in clay. A cylindrical hole is dug by hand for a depth which varies from as little as 2 ft in soft clay to 6 ft in stiff clay. The sides of the excavation are accurately trimmed and lined with vertical boards held against the clay by two or more steel rings. The hole is then deepened for several more feet and lined in the same manner. When the bottom reaches final elevation, the hole is filled with concrete. In homogeneous clay, water causes no difficulty, but, if water-bearing strata of sand or silt are encountered, special construction expedients may be required.

STABILITY OF BOTTOM DURING OPEN EXCAVATION

The stability of the bottom of a pier excavation is determined by the same factors that govern that of the bottom of open cuts, Articles 47 and 48. In very dense sand it may be possible to pump water from the caisson or open shaft without destroying the stability of the material below the bottom, because the deformation produced by the seepage pressure does not cause an increase in the neutral stress. In loose sand, however, the deformation causes an excess hydrostatic pressure that tends to liquefy the sand. In one instance the Gow method, Figure 196e, was used successfully to establish the first members of a group of piers. The excavations were carried through a stratum of fine dense sand to rock located about 10 ft below the water table. However, beneath one part of the building site a mixture of sand and water rose into the shafts as soon as the excavation was carried to a depth of a few feet below the water table. All efforts to stop the flow failed, and the remaining piers had to be constructed by a method that did not require pumping. The most probable reason for this unexpected development is that the latter shafts happened to penetrate a large pocket of loose sand. The occurrence of such pockets surrounded by dense sand with essentially the same grain-size characteristics is by no means uncommon.

If pumping from sumps seems impracticable, the alternative methods are predrainage of the soil by pumping from well points, excavation under compressed air, or dredging. Well points cannot be used unless the base of the proposed piers is located less than about 20 ft below the level at which the header pipe can be established, Article 47. If the soil consists of fine silt, even the vacuum method may fail to stabilize the soil (see Article 47). Because of the expense and other limitations of the compressed-air method (see page 486) the most common alternative for pumping is dredging.

Dredging in sand usually removes a volume of sand greater than the volume of the caisson. If the sand is loose, the quantity excavated may be twice that displaced by the caisson. The excess excavation is associated with loss of ground and settlement of the near-by ground surface. However, the loss can be almost entirely prevented by maintaining the water level within the caisson several feet above the water table, as shown in Figure 196c. The excess head produces a flow of water from the caisson into the sand located below the bottom of the excavation, and the corresponding seepage pressure counteracts the tendency of the sand to rise. To maintain the flow, the excavating tools must be hoisted out of the caisson slowly.

The soil investigations required to learn whether a given method of unwatering is practicable on a given job are described in the discussions of the methods for unwatering open cuts, Article 47.

In choosing between the dredging and compressed-air methods for sinking a caisson, several factors should be considered. If obstacles in the soil are encountered when the dredging method is being used, they may cause unpredictable delays. The compressed-air method avoids this risk, because the workmen have access to the obstacle. It has the added advantage that the base for the pier can be prepared carefully, and all loose material removed. On the other hand, the use of compressed air is inherently much more expensive.

Evaluation of Skin Friction

While excavation is being carried on within a caisson of the drop-shaft type, the soil adjoining the caisson is supported by the walls of the shaft. Sections are added to the shaft above the ground surface, and, as excavation proceeds, the caisson slides down. The downward movement is resisted by skin friction. In order to overcome the skin friction, light-weight drop shafts, such as those of steel, must be loaded with dead weights. On the other hand, heavy caissons, such as those of reinforced concrete, may descend under their own weight.

Adding weights to the top of a caisson is a cumbersome procedure that considerably increases the cost of construction. Therefore, concrete caissons are commonly designed in such a manner that their weight exceeds the skin friction at every stage of construction. Hence, the design requires evaluation of the skin friction. Experience has demonstrated that theoretical methods for evaluating the skin friction on the basis of soil tests are entirely unreliable (see Article 30). The principal source of existing information regarding skin friction is the record of loads required to start caissons that had become stuck. These records suggest that for a given soil the skin friction per unit of contact area reaches a fairly constant value below a depth of about 25 ft. Table 26 gives the values that have been obtained for caissons ranging in depth from 25 to 125 ft. For each material the range of values is fairly close to that for skin friction on piles in the same material. However, no perfect agreement should be expected, because in a given material f_s depends on the shape of the lowest part of the caisson, on the method of excavation, and on the diameter of the caisson. Values from other jobs in the vicinity should not be relied on unless all of the circumstances attending the caisson sinking are known. In clay the skin friction is likely to increase with time.

The friction between the walls of concrete caissons and fine-grained soils such as silt or clay can be considerably reduced by providing the outside of the caissons with a coating that has a smooth oily surface and that, in addition, is tough enough not to be rubbed off while the caisson descends. Such a coating was used on the caissons for the piers of the

TABLE 26

VALUES OF SKIN FRICTION FOR CAISSONS

Type of Soil	Skin Friction f_s (lb/sq ft)
Silt and soft clay	150–600
Very stiff clay	1000–4000
Loose sand	250–700
Dense sand	700–1400
Dense gravel	1000–2000

San Francisco–Oakland Bay bridge. The results of friction tests made prior to construction indicated that it reduced the friction between the concrete and a fairly stiff clay by roughly 40 per cent.

ALLOWABLE SOIL PRESSURE FOR PIERS RESTING ON SAND

Piers commonly serve to transfer the weight of a structure onto a firm stratum covered by soft and compressible soil. If piles are driven into such a stratum, almost the entire load on the pile is ultimately carried by the point resistance (see Article 56). For similar reasons practically the entire load on a pier is ultimately carried only by its base. Hence, the allowable load on piers surrounded by relatively compressible soil should not include any allowance for skin friction.

The buried part of a bridge pier may be completely surrounded by sand that has a low compressibility and is capable of carrying a considerable part of the load on the pier by skin friction. However, the base of such a pier is commonly located at a moderate depth below the maximum depth of scour, Article 53. During exceptionally high water, most of the sand surrounding the pier is temporarily removed. Hence, even in connection with bridge piers entirely surrounded by sand, it should be assumed that the entire load on the pier is carried by the base.

The factor of safety against failure of a pier on sand would commonly be adequate, even if the soil surrounding the pier were removed. Since the factor of safety actually increases rapidly with increasing depth of foundation, it can be taken for granted that the pier will not experience a base failure. Therefore, the allowable bearing value is determined exclusively by settlement considerations.

The settlement of a loaded area on sand depends to a large extent on the stress conditions that exist in the sand before the load is applied. The construction of a pier is always preceded by the excavation of a shaft. This process is associated with a relaxation of all the stresses in the sand adjoining the walls and the bottom of the shaft. If the depth of the shaft exceeds four or five times the diameter, the state of stress in the sand near the bottom of the shaft is practically independent of the depth of the shaft. Therefore, it is to be expected that the influence of the depth of foundation on the settlement of the piers will be relatively small compared to its influence on the ultimate bearing capacity. This conclusion is corroborated by the following observations.

Load tests were made at the same depth on two circular bearing plates each covering an area of 1 sq ft. One plate was located on the bottom of a large open shaft, and the other on the bottom of a drill hole with a diameter of 1.15 ft. At a load of 2 tons per sq ft, the settlement of the plate in the shaft was 0.90 in., and that in the drill hole was 0.52 in.

Similar experiments were made in the shaft to which Figure 124 refers. After the shaft was excavated to a depth of about 50 ft, a load test was made on a bearing plate 1 ft square. The settlement under a load of 2 tons per sq ft was 0.25 in. A second bearing plate 3.3 by 3.3 ft was installed on the bottom of the shaft, and the narrow space between the edges of the plate and the sides of the shaft was filled with concrete to prevent even a local heave of the loaded sand. The settlement of the plate at a load of 2 tons per sq ft was 0.47 in.[57.1] According to equation 54.1, the settlement of a plate of the same size on the surface of a similar sand deposit with no confinement or surcharge would be 0.59 in.

These and various other observations indicate that the settlement of the base of a pier on sand at any depth is likely to be about one-half the settlement of an equally loaded footing covering the same area on sand of the same characteristics. Therefore, the allowable bearing values for piers on sand can be assumed to equal twice the value that would be admissible for footings resting on the same sand in the same state, Article 54. If the excess unit pressure on the base of the piers does not exceed this value, the maximum settlement will not exceed 1 in. Furthermore, if the bases of all the piers have approximately the same width, the differential settlement between piers will not exceed $\frac{1}{2}$ in. If the designer feels that he can tolerate larger settlements, he may increase the bearing values accordingly.

A modification of this procedure may be required if the base of a bridge pier is located fairly close to the level to which scour may remove

the sand. The scour temporarily reduces the depth of foundation of the
pier to much less than 4 or 5 times the width of the base. Hence, the
pressure on the base of such piers should not exceed that appropriate
for footings of the same area resting on the same sand in a saturated
condition.

PIERS ON CLAY

The allowable pressure on the base of a pier resting on stiff clay is
determined by the rules governing the allowable load for footings on
clay (Table 22, page 430), regardless of the depth at which the base of
the pier is located. The use of these rules is conservative, because the
shearing stresses f_s and t, Figure 77, increase the ultimate bearing
capacity of the pier to some extent.

The total load that can safely be applied to the clay beneath the pier
is equal to the sum of the allowable load on the base of the pier and the
effective weight of the soil excavated during construction. Hence, the
design load on large piers, at a given allowable load on the base, can be
considerably increased by making the piers hollow. This fact has been
utilized many times in the design of bridge piers.

On clay the settlement of piers, like that of footings, depends to a
large extent on the load history of the clay. Pier foundations on normally
loaded clay are uneconomical, and their settlement is prohibitive.
Therefore, piers are established only on precompressed clay. Yet, if the
area covered by a pier is large, the precompressed state of the underlying
clay does not necessarily preclude important settlement. This statement
is illustrated by the following observation. Near the end of the last
century bridge piers were established by the compressed-air method on a
thick stratum of very stiff precompressed clay beneath the Danube
River. The base of each pier was 75 ft long and 20 ft wide. The effective
load on the bases of the piers ranged between 3.3 and 4.8 tons per sq ft.
For a very stiff clay this load is well below the critical value for a base
failure. Yet within half a century the difference between the settlement
of the piers became equal to 3 in. The value of the maximum settlement
could not be ascertained, but there is no doubt that it was much greater
than the differential settlement. Hence, if the base of a pier on stiff clays
covers a large area, a settlement computation should be made. The
uncertainties involved in the determination of the settlement of loaded
areas on precompressed clay are discussed in Article 13.

PIER FOUNDATIONS ON NATURAL RAFTS

Pier foundations on natural rafts differ in no essential way from footing
foundations on such rafts. The piers are designed as if the raft rested on a

rigid base, but the design must be supplemented by a settlement computation (see Article 55).

SUMMARY OF RULES FOR ESTIMATING ALLOWABLE BEARING VALUE FOR BASES OF PIERS

1. The allowable bearing value for the base of a pier on sand is equal to twice the allowable bearing value for footings covering the same area on sand of the same characteristics (see Article 54). The settlement of piers designed on the basis of these values is unlikely to exceed 1 in. If larger settlements are acceptable, the bearing values can be increased accordingly. If the piers are surrounded by sand that may be removed by scour during high water, the allowable bearing value should be taken equal to that for footings of the same size resting on sand of the same characteristics.

2. If the excavation for a pier is made by dredging, the water level within the dredging shaft should be maintained several feet above the outside water level. This procedure reduces the tendency of the sand to flow toward the bottom of the excavation. Yet, even if the flow is prevented, the bottom of the excavation will be very uneven and partly covered with a layer of loose sand. Hence, if the sand is excavated by dredging, an allowance must be made for the unavoidable disturbance of the sand. No such allowance is required if the excavation is made under compressed air.

3. Normally loaded clay is unsuitable for sustaining loaded piers. The allowable bearing values for piers on precompressed clay can be selected on the basis of Table 22. If the width of the area covered by the base of each pier exceeds 10 ft, a settlement computation should be made.

4. Pier foundations on natural rafts call for the same investigations as footing foundations on such rafts.

REFERENCES

57.1. See Ref. 44.9. Results of loading tests on the bottom of a shaft at different depths below the ground surface.

57.2. E. L. CORTHELL, *Allowable Pressures on Deep Foundations*, John Wiley & Sons, New York, 1907. Compilation of data concerning skin friction on caissons and the pressure on the base of existing piers.

57.3. H. L. WILEY, The Sinking of the Piers for the Grand Trunk Pacific Bridge at Fort William, Ontario, Canada, *Trans. ASCE*, Vol 62 (1909), pp 113–134. Data on skin friction.

57.4. Load Tests on Piers for Chicago New Union Station, *Eng. News-Record*,

Vol 88 (1922), pp 822–824. Large-scale tests for determining skin friction on pier built by the Chicago method.

57.5. H. S. JACOBY AND R. P. DAVIS, *Foundations of Bridges and Buildings*, third edition, McGraw-Hill Book Company, New York, 1941. Chapters IX to XI contain a general description of the common methods for constructing large piers. Chapter X also contains data on skin friction.

ART. 58. DAM FOUNDATIONS

GENERAL CONSIDERATIONS

Storage dams with a height of more than about 200 ft are commonly considered impracticable, unless they can be built on rock foundations. Therefore, this article deals only with the foundations for dams of lesser height.

In general, the foundation for a dam must satisfy part or all of the following requirements: The differential settlement must not be excessive; there must be no danger of failure by sliding and no danger of damage or failure by spreading of the base; and the leakage out of the reservoir must be tolerable. The relative importance of these requirements depends on several factors. For instance, a plain or reinforced-concrete dam is so rigid that large differential settlements cause serious damage, unless water-tight joints are provided that permit relative movement between different parts of the structure. Rock-fill and earth dams, on the other hand, are insensitive to deformations of their base unless they contain concrete cutoff walls or are connected to such fairly rigid auxiliary structures as concrete outlet conduits. The loss of water by percolation through the subsoil may be a matter of no consequence whatsoever in a flood-control structure. Because of the complexity of the problems involved, the design of dam foundations is far more difficult than the design of building foundations. Mature judgment and broad experience are essential. Hence, in this book only the fundamental principles and general procedures are presented.

SETTLEMENT OF DAM FOUNDATIONS

If a dam is of a rigid type or contains rigid elements, a settlement forecast is needed in advance of construction to determine whether joints are required between various parts of the structure, and, if so, how much movement should be anticipated. The methods for making the forecasts are no different from those that have been described for estimating the settlement of buildings (see Article 36). To supplement the available information concerning the future settlement the observational method can often be used to advantage (see page xviii). The following history of a dam across the Svir River in Russia will serve as an example.

The dam includes a reinforced-concrete powerhouse section, Figure 197, and a plain concrete overflow section, Figure 198. It rests on a deposit of stratified heavily precompressed clay at least 300 ft thick. According to Article 13, forecasts of settlement due to consolidation of

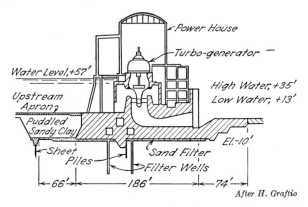

FIG. 197.   Section through powerhouse portion of dam resting on thick deposit of stratified clay. Svir III, USSR.

precompressed clay are always very unreliable. Furthermore, the schedule of operations precluded the possibility of making elaborate soil investigations before construction. Therefore, it was decided to base the preliminary settlement computations on the results of tests of a few

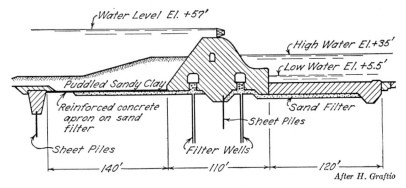

FIG. 198.   Section through dam resting on thick deposit of clay.   Stability against sliding increased by weighted concrete apron on upstream side.   Svir III, USSR.

representative samples obtained from a test shaft. The forecast showed that a joint was necessary between the powerhouse and the adjacent overflow section and that no rigid connection could be tolerated between the body of the dam and the adjoining aprons.

The preliminary settlement computations also indicated that filling the reservoir would cause the powerhouse to tilt upstream about 1°. Since the turbines had to be installed before the reservoir was filled, and the computed tilt was far in excess of the value considered admissible by the turbine designers, it was decided to install the turbine shafts out of plumb in such a manner that they would become vertical when the reservoir was filled. In order to secure a more accurate value for the tilt, the results of the preliminary soil tests were used as a basis for computing the displacement of many points on and beneath the ground surface at different stages of construction. As construction proceeded, the displacements were measured. It was found that the real displacements were consistently equal to 0.35 times the computed displacements. Therefore, the turbine shafts were mounted with a downstream tilt of 0.35°, and, when the reservoir was filled, the shafts were practically vertical.[58.1]

Safety of Concrete Dams with Respect to Sliding

The potential surface of sliding in the subsoil of a concrete dam may be located in very permeable material such as clean sand, in a soil of intermediate permeability such as silt, or else in clay which is practically impermeable. In the following discussion, only the two extreme possibilities are considered.

If the surface of sliding is located in sand, the total sliding resistance S (pounds) per lineal foot of the dam is

$$S = (P - U) \tan \phi$$

in which

P = total vertical pressure on base of dam due to weight of dam and vertical component of water pressure on the inclined faces of the dam (lb per lin ft)

U = total neutral pressure on base of dam (lb per lin ft)

ϕ = angle of friction between concrete and sand

Since the value of $\tan \phi$ is always at least 0.6, and since the neutral pressure U can usually be reduced to a very small value by means of suitable drainage provisions, it is seldom difficult to eliminate the danger of sliding.

On the other hand, if the substrata contain horizontal layers of soft clay, or if the dam rests on a thick clay stratum, it may be very difficult to establish adequate resistance against sliding. After the clay beneath a dam becomes consolidated, sliding is resisted both by cohesion and by friction. However, because of the low permeability of the clay, consolidation proceeds very slowly, and, furthermore, the rate of consolidation can seldom be reliably forecast. Therefore, it is commonly advisable to assume that the frictional resistance is still negligible at the end of the period of construction and to depend only on the cohesion.

In order to make the dam shown in Figure 198 safe against sliding before the underlying clay consolidated, its base width was increased from 110 to 250 ft by a reinforced concrete apron on the upstream side. Since the apron was an integral part of the dam, sliding was resisted by cohesion over the full length of 250 ft. The factor of safety increased steadily because of consolidation of the clay under the weight of the dam itself as well as the weight of the water above the apron. To make the weight of the water effective the under side of the apron was drained.

Damage or Failure Due to Spreading

Figure 199a is a vertical section through a rock-fill dam. The line ab is the trace of a vertical plane oriented parallel to the axis of the dam. This plane is acted on by the lateral earth pressure P_A exerted by the material in the central part of the fill. The force P_A tends to push the fill located between ab and the toe C of the dam in an outward direction. This statement applies to every vertical plane parallel to the axis of the dam. Hence, the soil located beneath the dam is acted on by horizontal shearing stresses. The effect of these stresses depends on the shearing resistance of the soil at and immediately below the base of the dam.

If the dam rests on sand, the resistance against a shear failure at or below the base is always considerably greater than the shearing stresses due to the tendency of the fill to spread. Therefore, the forces P_A, Figure 199a, produce merely a slight increase of the width of the base of the dam. Yet, the increase can be great enough to damage relatively rigid parts of the dam construction. The history of the dam shown in Figure 199a serves as an example. The dam has a reinforced-concrete skin on the upstream face, connected to the uppermost widened part of the cutoff wall. Since the cutoff wall has a thickness of 13 ft, it is very rigid. As the rock fill was placed, the upstream toe moved outward about 11 in., and the downstream toe about 1 in. Compared to the height of the dam these movements were very small. Nevertheless, they were large enough to fracture the upper 40 ft of the cutoff wall. Since the open cracks established free communication between the reservoir and the downstream side of the cutoff wall, it was necessary to grout the cracks before filling the reservoir.

Figure 199b shows the distribution of the horizontal strain over the base of the dam. The data were obtained by measuring the clearance at the joints between individual sections of drainage conduits that were tightly fitted before the rock fill was placed. Since the upstream slope of the rock fill was much steeper than the downstream slope, the shearing stresses and the resulting strains beneath the upstream slope were much greater than below the downstream slope. The amount of stretching of

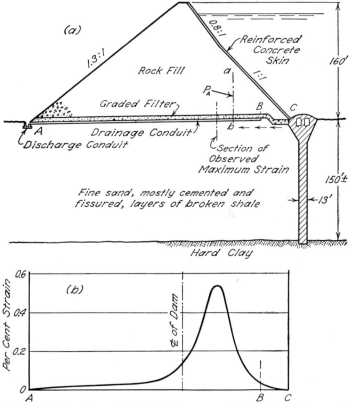

Fig. 199.   (*a*) Section through rock-fill dam on sand, friable sandstone, and shale; (*b*) diagram showing distribution of horizontal strain due to tendency of fill to spread.

the base of a fill cannot be predicted reliably on the basis of soil tests. Therefore, the only source of information is the results of field observations, such as those represented in Figure 199*b*.

If the subsoil of a rock-fill or earth dam contains a stratum of soft clay at shallow depth, the shearing stresses caused by the tendency to spread may be great enough to cause failure of the fill by spreading along a plane of sliding located within the clay (see Figure 200). The mechanics of failures of this type and the means for preventing them are discussed in Article 52. All of the major failures of this type have occurred during the construction period. As time goes on, the shearing resistance of the clay increases, and, as a consequence, the factor of safety against spreading also increases.

Losses Due to Seepage

If a dam serves to store water for power, water supply, or irrigation, safety is not the only requirement. The foundation must be designed in such a manner that the loss of water by seepage does not exceed a certain maximum specified in advance by the owners or the engineers in charge of the project.

The loss of water may occur partly through the body of the dam and partly through the natural soil that constitutes the sides and bottom of

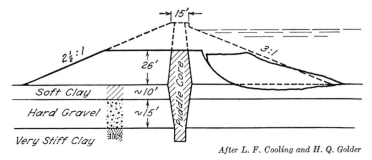

After L. F. Cooling and H. Q. Golder

Fig. 200.   Diagram showing failure during construction of dam, due to spreading in layer of clay between base of fill and underlying stratum of gravel.

the reservoir. Since seepage through the dam can be reduced at moderate cost to a very small quantity, only the losses through the natural soil located beneath and beside the dam are likely to constitute a serious problem.

If the dam is located on a permeable stratum that rests at a moderate depth on an impermeable layer, the seepage beneath the dam may be intercepted by a cutoff that extends from the base of the dam to the tight stratum. In the dam shown in Figure 200 the cutoff consists of a puddled clay core. If the impervious base is at a relatively great depth (see Figure 199a), the expense of a complete cutoff wall for the entire length of the dam may be prohibitive, and only the middle part of the cutoff is carried to the impermeable stratum. If the impervious stratum is located at such a depth that it is impracticable to reach it, the cutoff is carried only as deep as is necessary to keep the losses within the specified limits (see Figure 201a). In any event, the cutoff must be carried for some distance into the slopes beyond the ends of the dam in order to reduce the loss by horizontal flow around the ends of the structure.

In order to check whether the design of a given dam satisfies the requirements stipulated by the owners, the seepage losses must be estimated in advance of construction. The estimate of seepage through natural ground can be made only on the basis of a permeability profile such as that shown in Figure 126. The essential features of the same

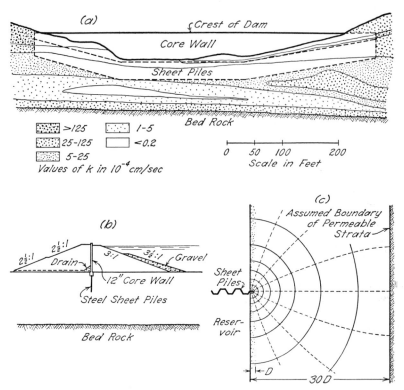

FIG. 201. (a) Permeability profile of dam located in relatively pervious glacial deposit; (b) cross section through dam and foundation; (c) flow net for estimating seepage losses around end of dam through horizontal pervious layers.

profile are shown to an undistorted scale in Figure 201a, and a section through the dam is shown in Figure 201b. Seepage through the dam is intercepted by a 12-in. reinforced-concrete core wall that rests at the base of the dam on the sheet-pile cutoff. The lower edge of the cutoff, represented by a dash line in Figure 201a, is located at a considerable distance above bedrock because the permeability profile indicates that the permeability decreases in a general way with depth. The highly permeable layer located immediately above the rock surface has no effect on the seepage losses because it is practically sealed by the more impermeable layers above it. This fact was recognized early in the test-boring operations, because it was found that the layer contained artesian water under considerable pressure.

It can be seen from Figure 201a without any computation that the loss of water by nearly horizontal flow around the ends of the dam would be much greater than that due to flow beneath the cutoff wall, because of the relatively high permeability of the soil in which the ends of the cutoff wall are embedded. Therefore, in estimating the seepage losses, the flow under the wall was disregarded, and a flow net was constructed that represented the horizontal flow of the water around each of the two ends of the cutoff wall. In drawing the flow net, Figure 201c, it was assumed arbitrarily that the permeable layers did not extend into the mountain more than 30 times the horizontal distance D between the end of the cutoff wall and the edge of the reservoir, because the quantity of percolation beyond this distance would be negligible. It was further assumed that all of the soil strata were continuous. Therefore, the computation furnished an upper limiting value for the seepage losses. Since even the computed losses were within the specified limits, the sheet-pile cutoff shown in Figure 201 was considered adequate. As a matter of fact, the real seepage losses were much smaller than those computed.[58.2]

A similar but more elaborate seepage computation was made for the dam shown in Figure 199a. The crest of the structure had a length of 1500 ft. Since the complete cutoff was practicable only beneath the highest part of the dam, seepage losses were expected under the rest of the structure because of flow in both vertical and horizontal planes. On the basis of the results of the permeability survey, the values of k in the horizontal and vertical directions were estimated. However, the magnitude of the project and the severity of the specifications made it imperative to check the estimated values in advance of construction. This was done by excavating a shaft to a depth of 170 ft below the valley floor and measuring the inflow. It amounted to 190 gal per min, in comparison with 285 computed on the basis of the values of k obtained from the permeability survey. Data regarding the seepage from the finished structure are not yet available.[58.3]

If the estimated losses are excessive, there are two means for reducing them. The depth and width of the cutoff may be increased, or the permeability of the soil may be reduced by injection of cement, chemicals, or bentonite slurries. References describing the various injection procedures are given in the Appendix. In general, medium to coarse clean sands can be injected successfully, but very fine or silty sands cannot.

The flow of water out of the ground on the downstream side of the cutoff represents a potential source of failure by piping. The mechanics of these failures are discussed in the following article.

REFERENCES

58.1. H. Graftio, Some Features in Connection with the Foundation of Svir 3 Hydro-electric Power Development, *Proc. Intern. Conf. Soil Mech.*, Cambridge, Mass. (1936), Vol I, pp 284–290.

58.2. K. Terzaghi, Soil Studies for the Granville Dam at Westfield, Mass., *J. New Engl. Water Works Assoc.*, Vol 43 (1929), pp 191–223. Permeability survey of the subsoil of an earth dam, located above strata with variable permeability. The capillary-rise method used in this study has been superseded by other methods.

58.3. I. Gutmann, Algerian Rockfill Dam Substructures, *Eng. News-Record*, Vol 120, No. 21, May 26, 1938, pp 749–751.

58.4. T. T. Knappen and R. R. Philippe, Practical Soil Mechanics at Muskingum-III, *Eng. News-Record*, Vol 116, Apr. 23, 1936, p 595. Description of early application of soil mechanics to design of dam foundations.

58.5. F. S. Brown, Foundation Investigation for the Franklin Falls Dam, *J. Boston Soc. Civil Engrs.*, Vol 28 (1941), pp 126–143. Abstract of results of permeability survey.

ART. 59. SAFEGUARDS AGAINST PIPING

General Characteristics of Piping Failures

Unless the foundation of a dam is provided with a perfectly watertight cutoff, water percolates through the subsoil from the reservoir to the downstream side, where it may emerge in the form of springs. Under certain conditions discussed in the following paragraphs, the percolating water may produce one of two phenomena. Either the seepage pressure may lift the entire body of soil located along the downstream toe, or else the water that comes out of the ground at the downstream toe may start a

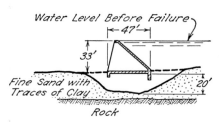

Fig. 202.   Diagram illustrating failure of dam foundation due to piping.

process of erosion that culminates in the formation of a tunnel-shaped passage or *pipe* beneath the structure. A mixture of soil and water then rushes through the passage, undermining the structure and flooding the channel below the dam. Failures of either type are known as *failures due to piping*. The first type has been referred to as failure by *heave*, and the second as failure by *subsurface erosion*.

The failure of a dam by piping ranks among the most serious accidents in civil engineering. It is likely to include not only failure of the structure but also extensive damage to the subsoil for a considerable depth. Furthermore, it not infrequently happens without warning and causes loss of life and damage to property located in the lower reaches of the valley. Therefore, the conditions that lead to failure by piping and the means for avoiding the danger deserve special attention.

Figure 202 illustrates a typical failure caused by piping. The dam, of the slab and buttress type, rested on a reinforced-concrete base slab provided with an upstream cutoff wall 9 ft deep and a downstream cutoff 7 ft deep. Failure occurred suddenly by a rush of water beneath the dam. A 52-ft gap was left in the subsoil and was bridged over by the structure.

Causes and Mechanics of Piping

Until the beginning of the 20th century the causes of piping remained unknown, in spite of the fact that piping failures were not uncommon. Designers realized the value of sheet-pile cutoffs but no rules were available for determining the proper depth to which the piles should be driven or for estimating the factor of safety against failure of the completed structure. However, after the catastrophic failure in 1898 of Narora Dam on the Ganges River in India, attention was drawn to the problem, and the first serious effort was made to analyze accumulated experience and to establish a set of rules for the design of dam foundations on permeable strata. These rules were based on the assumption that the sole cause of piping was erosion along the surface of contact between the soil and the base of the dam. The path that a water particle followed along this surface was called the *line of creep*. If the length L of the line of creep was such that the average hydraulic gradient $i = h/L$ was less than a certain critical value for the foundation material, the dam was believed to be safe. The quantity,

$$C_c = \frac{L}{h_{cr}} \tag{59.1}$$

was called the *creep ratio*. The value h_{cr} represented the greatest height to which the water level in the reservoir could rise with reference to tailwater level without producing failure by piping. The available failure records indicated that the ratio C_c increased with increasing fineness of soil from about 4 for gravel to about 18 for fine sand and silt.

The first step in designing a dam on the basis of equation 59.1 was to estimate the creep ratio C_c of the subsoil. This was done by means of a table containing the values of C_c for the principal types of soil. The required length L of the creep line was then obtained by multiplying the creep ratio C_c by the hydraulic head h_{cr} created by the dam. The foundation was laid out in such a manner that the length of the creep line was at least equal to L. For example, the length of the line of creep for the dam shown in Figure 203 is

$$L = t_1 + t_2 + B + t_3 + t_4 = B + \Sigma t$$

and this distance must be at least as great as $C_c h_{cr}$.

During the next 30 years it was gradually recognized that vertical sections of the line of creep contribute more toward reducing the danger of piping than horizontal sections of equal length. The difference is due to the fact that the subsoil of dams is commonly of sedimentary origin, and

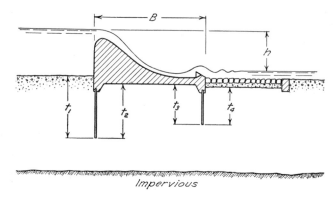

Fɪɢ. 203.　Diagram indicating dimensions used for computation of length of line of creep.

sedimentary deposits are always much less permeable in the vertical direction than in the horizontal directions (see Article 11). If k_h and k_v are, respectively, the coefficients of permeability in the horizontal and vertical directions, the loss in head per unit of length of vertical sections of the line of creep is roughly equal to the ratio k_h/k_v times that of horizontal sections. The value of the ratio ranges between 2 or 3 and almost infinity, depending on the details of stratification and the importance of the variations of the permeability in the vertical direction.

To take account of the greater efficiency of vertical sections of the line of creep, the original procedure was modified by the assumption that every horizontal section of the line of creep was only one third as effective as a vertical section of the same length. On this assumption, the equation,

$$C_w = \frac{\frac{1}{3}B + \Sigma t}{h_{cr}} \tag{59.2}$$

was obtained. The value C_w is known as the *weighted creep ratio*. Since equation 59.2 corresponds approximately to the ratio $k_h/k_v = 3$, it is obvious that it does not take into account the wide range of values that this ratio can have in the field.

Table 27 is an abstract of a list of safe values for C_w, based on a digest of about 280 dam foundations of which 24 had failed.[59.1]

The line-of-creep approach to the problem is purely empirical. Like every other procedure based solely on statistical data, it leads to design with an unknown factor of safety. Experience and experiments have shown that the values of C_w, equation 59.2, are widely scattered from the statistical average for a given soil. The values of C_w contained in Table 27 represent maximum rather than average values, and the values of h_{cr}

TABLE 27

WEIGHTED CREEP VALUES C_w (EQ. 59.2)

Very fine sand or silt	8.5
Fine sand	7.0
Medium sand	6.0
Coarse sand	5.0
Fine gravel	4.0
Medium gravel	3.5
Coarse gravel including cobbles	3.0
Boulders with some cobbles and gravel	2.5

From E. W. LANE, Security from Underseepage—Masonry Dams on Earth Foundations, *Trans. ASCE*, Vol 100 (1935), p 1257.

obtained by means of equation 59.2 and Table 27 represent the smallest heads at which piping ever occurred. Therefore, the wide scattering of the values of C_w from the statistical average implies that as a rule the factor of safety of dams designed on the basis of equation 59.2 and Table 27 is very high. The factor of safety of some of the dams must be excessive; that of others may be barely tolerable, and an unprecedented coincidence of several unfavorable circumstances may even lead to failure. Similar situations have been noted in the discussions of pile formulas, Articles 30 and 56, and of footing design on the basis of tabulated values for the allowable soil pressure, Article 54. Such situations call for theoretical and experimental investigations to supplement the existing empirical knowledge.

The theoretical evaluation of the factor of safety of dams with respect to piping is based exclusively on the theory of piping by heave, Article 40. To verify this theory the tests illustrated by Figure 204 were performed.[59.2] The weighted creep ratio for the finest sand used in the tests was $C_w = 7$. The measured critical heads h_c at which piping occurred, the heads h_c' computed by means of the theory of piping, and the heads

h_{cr} computed by means of equation 59.2 are given in Table 28. This table shows that the agreement between the values of h_c observed in the tests and those computed according to the theory of piping, Article 40, is very satisfactory, whereas the values h_{cr} are far too low. If the discharge area is covered with a heavy filter, as in tests b and d, design on the basis of equation 59.2 would appear to be grossly wasteful. However, it would be dangerous to base the design of a dam foundation on the results of the theory of piping and the laboratory tests without first considering the purely empirical aspects of the process.

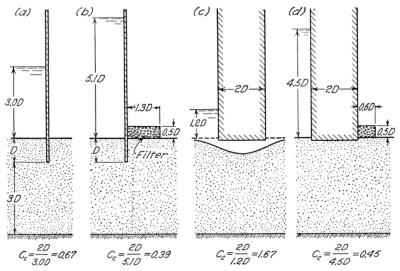

Fig. 204.   Diagram showing results of laboratory experiments to determine critical head with respect to piping under different conditions. Corresponding values of creep ratio C_c indicated for each condition.

Both the theory and the tests lead to the conclusion that the factor of safety against piping by heave is practically independent of grain size. Furthermore, the conditions that determine the factor of safety with respect to failure by heave are independent of time. Hence, piping by heave should occur either during the first filling of the reservoir or else not at all. In striking contrast to these characteristics of piping failures by heave, construction experience leaves no doubt that the grain size does have a considerable influence on the critical head. Furthermore, the majority of piping failures have occurred several months or even years after the ill-fated dams were put into operation. Hence, it appears that most if not all piping failures of actual dams were caused by subsurface erosion and not by heave. The frequency of piping failures due to subsurface erosion is obviously due to the fact that all natural soil strata are more or less nonhomogeneous. When water percolates through such strata, it follows the most permeable zones, and it leaves the ground in the form of springs. If the discharge of a spring is great enough, and the soil conditions favor underground erosion, the spring may gradually create a tunnel by cutting backward along a line of maximum hydraulic gradient. As soon as the intake end of this natural tunnel arrives near the bottom of the reservoir, the water breaks into the tunnel, and the dam fails by piping.

TABLE 28

COMPARISON BETWEEN MEASURED AND COMPUTED CRITICAL HEADS
TEST ARRANGEMENT SHOWN IN FIGURE 204

Test Arrangement	Sheet Piles		Flat-Bottom Weir	
	Test a, No Filter	Test b, with Filter	Test c, No Filter	Test d, with Filter
h_c observed in test	3.0D	5.1D	1.2D	4.5D
h_c' computed by theory, Article 40	2.9D	4.8D	1.0D	4.6D
h_{cr} computed by means of equation 59.2	0.3D	0.3D	0.14D	0.14D
Value of ratio h_c/h_c'	1.0	1.1	1.2	0.97
Value of ratio h_c/h_{cr}	10	17	8	32

Erosion tunnels with unsupported roofs are conceivable only in soils with at least a trace of cohesion, Article 33. The greater the cohesion, the wider are the spaces that can be bridged by the soil. In a general way, the cohesion of soils increases with decreasing grain size. Therefore, the danger of a piping failure due to subsurface erosion increases with decreasing grain size, and the corresponding values of the creep ratio also increase.

The head required to produce failure of a dam by piping due to sub-surface erosion can be very much smaller than the critical head for piping by heave. Therefore, the foundation for a dam cannot safely be designed on the basis of the theory of piping by heave, Article 40, unless the possibility of a failure due to subsurface erosion is eliminated by covering all the areas where springs may develop with inverted filters, Article 11. The design of such filters requires thorough familiarity with all the circumstances attending subsurface erosion in the field.

SUBSURFACE EROSION

The destruction of dams by piping is usually so complete that the sequence of events can seldom be reconstructed. However, subsurface erosion can also be induced by careless pumping from open sumps or by natural events such as the tapping of bodies of ground water by the erosion of river banks. These processes commonly leave evidence that remains open to inspection. Therefore, they constitute the principal sources of our knowledge of the characteristics of subsurface erosion. The following paragraphs contain abstracts of the records of pertinent observations.

Figure 205 represents a cross section through a gently inclined blanket of gravel that rests on a deep bed of very fine uniform loose sand. At *A* a pit was dug for the foundation of a new machine. Although the pit was surrounded by sheet piles that extended to a considerable depth below

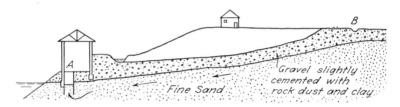

Fig. 205.   Diagram illustrating underground erosion produced by pumping mixture of sand and water from sump *A*.   Sinkhole at *B* 300 ft distant from *A*.

final grade, the pump discharged a mixture of sand and water. The quantity of sand removed was far in excess of the volume of the pit. Before final grade was reached, the building collapsed. At the same time a sink hole, 3 ft deep and 20 ft in diameter appeared at *B*, at a distance 300 ft from the pit. Between *A* and *B* the ground surface was intact. Hence, the loss of ground can be accounted for only by soil transportation in a relatively narrow subterranean conduit. It is most likely that the conduit was located immediately below the gravel blanket, because the slightly cemented gravel was capable of forming an unsupported roof.

In the Rhineland pumping was kept up for 13 years in a sand pit. The bottom of the pit was located between 16 and 20 ft below the original water table. During this period three of the springs that discharged into the sump cut backward and eroded tunnels in the slightly cohesive sand. Each tunnel terminated in a sink hole on the ground surface. The largest tunnel was 3 to 6 ft wide and in its length of 170 ft had an average grade of only 6 per cent. The sink hole above the end of this tunnel was 8 ft deep and 35 ft in diameter.

In another instance an open cut was excavated for the construction of a sewer. The excavation passed through fairly stiff clay into fine sand that was drained by pumping from an open sump. While pumping proceeded, a narrow strip of the ground surface subsided about 1 ft. The formation of the trough started at the sump and gradually proceeded to a distance of about 600 ft. The width of the trough increased from a few feet at the sump to more than 10 ft at the farther end.

Examples of underground erosion due to natural causes are also not uncommon. On the east bank of the Mississippi River near Memphis a large-scale subsidence occurred after the high water of 1927. At this location the river bank rises in a bluff about 100 ft high. Without any warning a strip at the top of the bluff about 700 ft long and 100 ft wide started to subside at the rate of 1 ft per hr. The pavement that covered

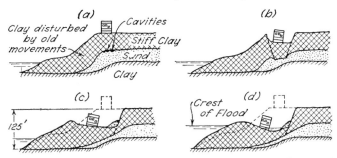

Fig. 206.   Diagrams illustrating large-scale subsidence due to underground erosion (*a*) Incipient state; (*b*), (*c*), and (*d*) subsidence after 24 hr, two months, and one year, respectively.

the ground surface remained horizontal and fairly intact for a period of about 30 hr. During the following two months the subsidence increased to as much as 60 ft, and the subsided surface broke up, as shown in Figure 206. The trough-like depression was caused by the failure of the roof above the intake section of an underground sand flow.[59.3]

Although the piping phenomena described in the preceding paragraphs took place in very different soil formations, they all had one important feature in common. The subsidence of the roof always occurred at a great distance from the discharge end of the tunnel. This fact indicates that the erosive capacity of a spring increases as the length of the tunnel increases. The reason is illustrated by the flow nets in Figure 207. The thin dash curves indicate equipotential lines, or contour lines of the water table, whereas the solid curves represent the flow lines. The dash-dotted lines indicate the boundary of the intake area. With increasing length of the tunnel, the number of diverted flow lines increases. Thus, the discharge from the spring becomes greater, and the rate of erosion increases.

Progressive subsurface erosion starting at springs near the toe of a dam also proceeds as shown in Figure 207, along lines leading toward the reservoir. The frequent occurrence of springs at the downstream edge is known to everyone who has had experience with dams. If a spring is powerful enough to start erosion in the first place, the erosion will almost certainly become more serious as time goes on, because the flow from a given spring increases with the length of the eroded tunnel, Figure 207. Finally, the dam will fail by piping.

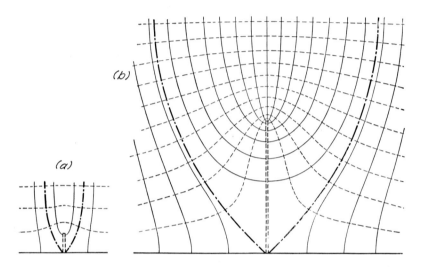

FIG. 207.   Flow nets illustrating increase of intake area of spring as length of eroded channel increases.   (a) Incipient state; (b) after erosion has proceeded to considerable distance from spring.

MEANS FOR AVOIDING PIPING

In discussing the means for avoiding piping we must make a distinction between small and large jobs. A similar distinction was made between small and large retaining walls and between shallow and deep cuts.

The design of short and low dams is a routine procedure, because the structures are not important enough to justify elaborate preliminary investigations. Dams of this category are protected against piping by making the designs in accordance with the line-of-creep rule expressed by equation 59.2.

A dam designed on the basis of equation 59.2 will be safe, unless poor design or construction combine with exceptionally unfavorable foundation conditions. In addition to compliance with equation 59.2, sound engineering merely requires the avoidance of an unnecessary concentration of flow lines beneath unprotected areas on the downstream side of the dam. The consequences of disregarding this fundamental requirement are illustrated in Figure 208a, which represents a section through Hauser Lake Dam in Montana. The subsoil consisted of 66 ft of gravel. The water was retained by a skin of steel plates supported by a steel framework that rested on large footings. The presence of the footings produced a local concentration of flow lines, as shown in the figure. The dam failed in 1908, one year after the first filling. Since it did not fail immediately, the cause was undoubtedly spring erosion. A second example is shown in Figure 208b, which represents a section through a dam across the Elwha River in Washington. The structure rested on gravel and coarse sand underlain by bedrock. While the reservoir was

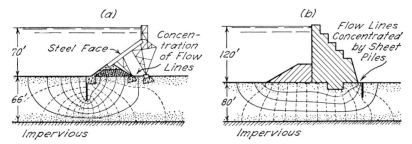

FIG. 208.   Flow nets showing concentration of flow lines responsible for failure by piping of two dams; (a) Hauser Lake Dam, Mont. (b) Elwha River Dam, Wash.

being filled, large springs developed at the downstream toe. In order to reduce the flow, a row of sheet piles was driven to a depth between 30 and 40 ft, at a distance of 8 ft from the toe. This obstruction caused a concentration of flow lines, as shown in the figure, and subsurface erosion occurred. The dam failed before the sheet-pile wall was completed.

Routine design on the basis of equation 59.2 is adequately safe provided the most primitive precautions are taken to avoid local concentration of flow lines. However, when practiced in connection with large dams it is certain to be uneconomical. In order to depart without risk from the routine method of design it is necessary, first of all, to make a thorough soil exploration, including the preparation of permeability profiles such as the one shown in Figure 201a. These profiles furnish the data required for establishing a working hypothesis regarding the trend of the flow of seepage out of the reservoir. All those areas where subsurface erosion may conceivably start must be covered by graded inverted filters. The presence of the filters prevents even incipient erosion at all points of the protected area and increases the critical head from the value required to produce erosion to the much larger value required to produce failure by heave. Rules for the design of filters are given in Article 11.

Seepage computations must always be based on simplifying assumptions regarding the permeability pattern of the subsoil, and the difference between the predicted and the real flow of seepage can be very great, irrespective of the thoroughness with which the subsoil has been explored.[59.2] Therefore, it is necessary to find out by means of observation wells whether and to what extent the theoretical and the actual flow of seepage are in agreement. If the observations disclose a strong flow of seepage toward unprotected areas, these areas must also be covered with filters, or else the seepage must be diverted into filter wells or drainage tunnels. Experience has shown that the hydraulic pressure conditions in the subsoil of storage dams may change progressively for many years after construction.[59.4] Hence, supervision of these conditions must be continued until the effects of the fluctuations of the water level in the reservoir become reversible.

EXAMPLES OF FILTER PROTECTION

The rock-fill dam shown in Figure 199a rests on a stratum of sand and cemented sand with an erratic permeability profile. Only the middle part of the cutoff wall extends down to the impermeable base, and the impounded water enters the subsoil of the dam by flowing beneath the shallower side portions of the wall. Therefore, springs could emerge at almost any point of the base. After construction the base of the dam would be inaccessible, and subsurface erosion could proceed without being noticed. To eliminate this danger the entire base of the dam except at the two ends was covered with an inverted filter that occupies an area of about 400,000 sq ft. The water that enters the filter is collected in large-diameter open-joint drain pipes that discharge into an open drainage ditch following the toe of the rock fill. The soil conditions are such that clogging of the filter is almost unconceivable. Yet, even if it should occur, it would be without serious practical consequence, because the only function of the filter is to prevent soil particles from being washed into the interstices of the rock fill. Even a completely clogged filter would serve this purpose. Any spring that might develop at a later date beyond the boundaries of the protected area would be located outside the area occupied by the rock fill. It would be plainly visible, and underground erosion by the water vein feeding the spring could easily be stopped by means of a filter plug while erosion was still in an incipient state.

Piping beneath masonry dams is most likely to start just below the downstream toe (see Figure 208b). Therefore, this region should be protected by a filter. However, if the dam is of the overflow type, solid matter carried by floods may clog the filter. In such instances it may be preferable to install the filter beneath the middle of the dam, as shown in Figure 209. This dam, of the bear-trap type, rests on fine sand containing some silt and streaks and layers of gravel. The seepage water drains from the filter into a drain pipe that is embedded in the concrete and discharges into the tail water. According to Table 27, a dam on such soil should have a weighted creep ratio at least equal to 6 or 7. The ratio for the dam as designed and built is only 4.0. Yet, in spite of the low creep

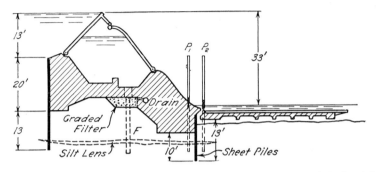

Fig. 209. Overflow dam of bear-trap type with graded filter beneath body of dam. If piezometric observations indicate ineffectiveness of filter due to obstruction of flow by silt or clay seams, bleeder wells F are required.

ratio, the dam satisfies all legitimate safety requirements, because the graded filter shown in the figure excludes the possibility of failure due to underground erosion.

Figure 209 also demonstrates the necessity for ascertaining the piezometric levels in the subsoil of the dam at least during the first filling of the reservoir. The design of the filter shown in the figure and the estimate of the factor of safety of the dam with respect to piping were based on the assumption that the subsoil is more or less homogeneous. This assumption seemed justified on the basis of the results of the test borings. However, the sand that constitutes the subsoil might have contained a few undetected thin layers of silt or clay. Discontinuous layers of this kind are harmless, but, if one of them is continuous over the entire area between the upper and lower row of sheet piles, as indicated by the thin dash lines in Figure 209, its presence has two very detrimental consequences. It considerably reduces the effective length of the line of creep, and, in addition, it prevents the flow of seepage toward the filter. Therefore, it is necessary to provide the concrete floor located above the filter area with plugged holes and, during the first filling of the reservoir, to observe the water level in piezometric tubes such as P_1 and P_2. If the water level in these tubes remains close to the tail water, it can be assumed that the filter serves its purpose. On the other hand, if the water level rises perceptibly when the level in the reservoir goes up, the efficacy of the filter is doubtful, and it becomes necessary to tap the permeable soil located below the lower edge of the sheet piles by means of filter wells F. It is very unlikely that such a necessity will arise. However, failures due to piping also occur without being anticipated, and sound engineering requires the elimination of even remote possibilities of failure.

REFERENCES

59.1. E. W. Lane, Security from Under-Seepage Masonry Dams on Earth Foundations, *Trans. ASCE*, Vol 100 (1935), pp 1235–1351. Digest of data on which the weighted creep equation is based. A planographed supplement, P-2 (1934), contains the cross-sections of dams referred to in the paper and a bibliography of dam failures due to piping.

59.2. K. Terzaghi, Effect of Minor Geologic Details on the Safety of Dams, *Bull. AIME, Tech. Pub.* 215 (1929), Class I, Mining Geology, No. 26, pp 31–46. Record of model test demonstrating piping by heave and discussion of influence of details of stratification on factor of safety.

59.3. K. Terzaghi, Underground Erosion and the Corpus Christi Dam Failure, *Eng. News-Record*, Vol 107 (1931), pp 90–92. Review of piping phenomena due to subsurface erosion.

59.4. J. Hinds, Upward Pressures under Dams, *Trans. ASCE*, Vol 93 (1929), pp 1527–1582. Results of measurements of hydraulic head in subsoil of several dams of the U. S. Bureau of Reclamation.

CHAPTER X

SETTLEMENT DUE TO EXCEPTIONAL CAUSES

ART. 60. SETTLEMENT DUE TO CONSTRUCTION OPERATIONS

EXTRANEOUS CAUSES OF SETTLEMENT

In Chapter IX we have discussed the settlement of buildings and other structures under the influence of their own weight. Although this is the most common type of settlement, other types are important enough to deserve consideration. They include settlement due to increasing the load on the surrounding soil, to excavation in the vicinity, to lowering the ground water table, and to vibrations. In this article we shall consider only the first two categories.

SETTLEMENT DUE TO INCREASING LOAD ON SURROUNDING SOIL

The application of a load to one portion of the ground surface above any type of soil causes the surface of the adjacent soil to tilt (see Figure 210a). The distance within which the tilt is of any practical importance depends, however, on the soil profile as well as the dimensions of the loaded area. If the subsoil contains soft clay, the magnitude and distribution of the settlement can be roughly estimated on the basis of the results of soil tests. If the subsoil is sand, the settlement cannot be computed and estimates can be based only on the records of precedents.

If rafts on sand are designed in accordance with the rules contained in municipal building codes, they are likely to settle as much as 2 in. Exceptionally, they may settle even more (see Article 55). Since the greatest part of this settlement occurs during construction, the structure itself will not be damaged unless it is very sensitive. However, the tilt of the adjoining ground surface toward the loaded area may be great enough to damage neighboring structures. In New York, for example, a 20-story building was constructed on a lot between two 7-story buildings supported by spread footings on a deposit of fine sand. The new building rested on a raft at a depth of 20 ft below the ground surface. The soil pressure was 2 tons per sq ft in excess of the weight of soil removed. Since the building itself settled only 1.8 in., and the settlement was fairly uniform, the building remained intact. Yet, the neighboring buildings

515

were damaged by shear cracks and by distortion of door and window frames (see also reference 60.1).

If the subsoil consists of soft clay, the effect of the weight of a new building on its neighbors can be much greater, although not necessarily more detrimental. In Istanbul a tall building was erected on a site separated from that of its equally tall neighbor by a narrow alley. The

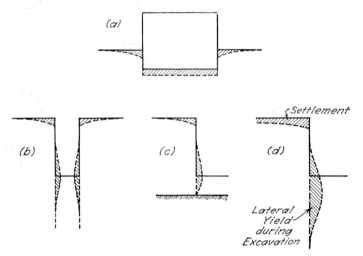

Fig. 210.   Diagrams indicating settlement of ground surface adjacent to areas in which construction operations are carried out.   (a) Settlement due to weight of structure; (b) settlement due to lateral yield of clay beside narrow deep cut; (c) settlement due to lateral yield of clay beside wide deep cut above stiffer soil; (d) settlement due to lateral yield of clay beside and below wide deep cut in soft clay of great depth.

new structure caused such a large tilt of the old one that the cornices of the two structures came into contact with each other. Yet, neither structure was damaged.

Settlement Due to Excavation

Forecast of settlement due to excavation.   If all other conditions are the same, settlement due to excavation depends to a large extent on the type of bracing used to support the adjoining soil and on the care with which the bracing is installed. Therefore, the magnitude of the settlement cannot be computed. A forecast can be based only on reliable well-documented case records.

The most common types of large excavations are open cuts, in which entire structures or basements can be built, and individual shafts, in which single piers are constructed. Tunnels constitute a third type which, however, are beyond the scope of this book.

Open cuts in sand. Even if the ground surface adjacent to an open cut in sand carries shallow heavily loaded footings, the settlement due to excavating the cut does not extend beyond a distance equal to the depth of the cut. If the adjacent ground surface carries no load, the settlement does not extend beyond half this distance. If the cut is properly braced, the maximum settlement is not likely to exceed about 0.5 per cent of the depth of the cut. However, even this amount may be enough to cause damage, as shown in Figure 211. The excavation responsible for the

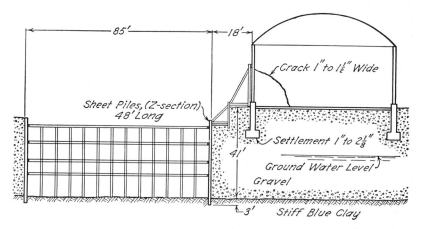

Fig. 211. Cross section through open cut in gravel, showing method of bracing and damage to adjacent structure due to settlement.

settlement was made in water-bearing gravel. The bracing was carefully placed, according to the method illustrated by Figure 147c, and the sheet piles were driven through the gravel into a stratum of stiff clay. This made pumping unnecessary. Nevertheless, the footings of the adjacent building settled 1 to 2 in., and cracks developed in the walls as indicated in the figure. Part of the settlement occurred while the sheet piles were being driven.

Open cuts in soft clay. When an open cut is excavated in soft clay, the clay located at the sides of the cut acts like a surcharge. Under this surcharge the clay near the bottom of the cut yields laterally toward the excavation, and the bottom of the cut rises. As a consequence of these movements, the ground surface located above the yielding clay settles. An additional lateral yield occurs above the bottom of the cut during the intermission between excavation and installation of the struts. The magnitude of these lateral movements and of the corresponding settlement depends primarily on the width–depth ratio of the cut, on the construction procedure, and on the depth of the soft clay beneath the bottom of the cut.

If the cut is very narrow, Figure 210b, or if the bottom of the cut is located close to the surface of a firm stratum, Figure 210c, the lateral yield spreads only a short distance from the sides of the cut. Therefore, the settlement of the ground surface is restricted to relatively narrow belts located on each side of the cut. The width of these belts does not exceed the depth of the cut. Beyond this distance the settlement is inconsequential. By careful bracing the inward yield of the clay can be kept within 0.5 per cent of the depth of the cut, and the greatest surface settlement is of the same order of magnitude. Appreciably greater settlements are usually due to poor workmanship.

The soil deformations that lead to the settlement of the surface adjoining a wide cut in a relatively shallow stratum of soft clay, Figure 210c, have actually been observed and measured.[60.2] The soft clay in which the cut was made was underlain by moderately stiff clay at a depth of about 14 ft below final grade. The sides of the cut were supported by sheet piles that were driven through the soft clay into the stiff stratum before excavation was started. The curves on the left side of Figure 212 represent successive positions of the sheet-pile wall on the dates shown. On the right side of the figure are inscribed the dates at which the struts were placed. The dash lines indicate the corresponding positions of the bottom of the cut. The diagram shows that the lateral yield spread to the base of the soft clay layer at an early stage of the excavation. Since the sheet piles penetrated into the stiff clay, the inward movement of the buried section decreased toward the lower ends of the piles. As a consequence the heave of the bottom was unimportant, and the small tunnel shown in the figure rose only 1 in. The exceptionally great movement of the sheeting at a depth of 10 ft below the ground surface was caused by a delay in installing the top strut; otherwise it would not have occurred. At a distance from the edge of the cut equal to its final depth, the settlement amounted to 0.7 in., but settlement was noticeable up to distances of 86 ft.

If the cut is wide, and the clay is soft to a great depth below the bottom, the lateral yield involves a wide and deep body of clay, Figure 210d. The corresponding settlement may extend to a distance considerably greater than the depth of the cut. As soon as the depth of excavation exceeds about one-half the critical height of the clay, Article 24, the settlement begins to increase rapidly and spreads to a great distance from the edge of the cut, regardless of the care with which the sides are braced. When the depth becomes equal to the critical height, base failure becomes inevitable, and the bottom of the cut rises (see Article 31).

The cut illustrated in Figure 213a was excavated in varved clay to a depth of 20 ft. It was located at a distance of 30 ft from a building. In spite of the very careful workmanship in placing the shoring, the walls

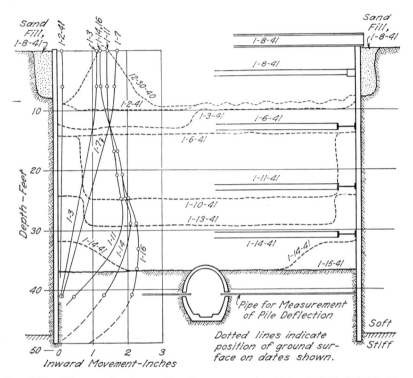

FIG. 212. Diagram showing results of measurements of lateral yield of sheet piling at side of open cut in soft clay underlain at shallow depth by stiff clay. Positions of deflected sheeting shown at left side of diagram. Dash lines indicate stage of excavation on dates shown. Dates shown on struts indicate time of placement.

of the building were cracked as indicated in the figure. The open cut shown in Figure 213b was excavated in very soft clay with layers of sand and silt. The soil profile is represented in Figure 134, page 307. Sheet-pile walls were driven all around the boundaries of the cut to a depth of 4 ft below final grade. While the cut was being excavated, a crack appeared in a concrete floor 70 ft away. In this instance, the settlement could have been somewhat reduced, but not avoided, by increasing the depth of penetration of the sheet piles from 4 to about 15 ft.

Open shafts or caissons in soft clay.   During the excavation of an open shaft or the sinking of an open caisson in soft clay, the clay beneath the bottom also heaves. Furthermore, if the lower parts of the walls of the shaft are unsupported, as in shafts excavated by the Chicago method, Figure 196*f*, the lateral squeeze can be appreciable. Because of these movements the volume of excavated soil is greater than that of the shaft

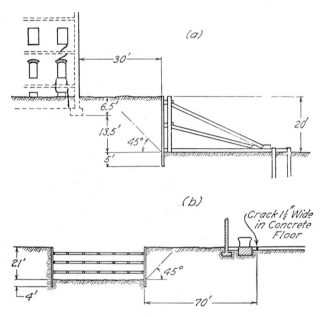

Fig. 213.   Cross sections through wide open cuts in soft clay of great depth. Damage to adjacent structures due to settlement shown by cracks in masonry.

or caisson. The difference is known as *lost ground;* loss of ground always involves settlement of the ground surface.

The physical processes associated with the lateral squeeze are represented in Figure 214*b*. The figure shows a vertical section through a shaft being excavated according to the Chicago method. Installation of each new set of lagging with height *h* is preceded by excavation to depth *h* below the lower edge of the lined section. Figure 214*a* represents a horizontal section through the unlined part of the shaft. Prior to excavation, the cylindrical surface with diameter d_0 is acted on by a radial pressure p_0. Excavation reduces this pressure to zero, whereupon the cylindrical shell of clay surrounding the shaft is acted on by an unbalanced external radial pressure. This pressure reduces the inner diameter of the shell, and the clay advances toward the shaft, as indicated by shaded areas along the walls of the excavation in Figure 214b. Because of the squeeze, every wedge-shaped element *abcd*, Figure 214a, is compressed circumferentially and stretched radially. For similar reasons the bottom of the shaft heaves, as indicated in Figure 214b. The entire shaded area represents the ground lost during the excavation of one section. The total volume of lost ground is roughly equal to the entire area of the walls of the shaft times the width Δd of the squeeze area adjoining the walls in Figure 214b. This loss causes a settlement of the ground surface surrounding the top of the shaft.

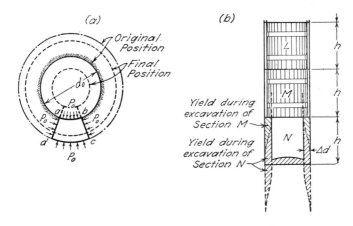

FIG. 214.   (a) Diagram illustrating cause of loss of ground during excavation by Chicago method; (b) lost ground associated with excavation.

When a single shaft is excavated, the effect of the loss of ground may not be noticeable at the ground surface. However, if many shafts are sunk close to each other, the subsidences accumulate and affect the entire vicinity. Such a subsidence occurred on the job illustrated by Figure 215. On a building lot 190 by 150 ft, 120 shafts with diameters ranging from 5 to 8 ft were excavated through soft glacial clay to hardpan. Sinking of the shafts required 3 months and involved the removal of 17,000 cu yd of clay. Immediately after the excavation was started, the area surrounding the lot started to subside and finally settled to the position indicated in Figure 215b. The adjoining buildings had to be provided with temporary shoring and underpinning to maintain them at their original elevation. Figure 215c shows the progress of the excavation of the shafts with time, and also the corresponding settlements of two reference points P_1 and P_2 located, respectively, at mid-length of one side and at the corner of the lot. The similarity between the curves shows very clearly that the settlement was due chiefly to the loss of ground associated with the excavation of the shafts.

Several means are available for reducing the settlement caused by excavating shafts for piers in soft clay. The following procedures are listed in approximate order of increasing efficacy and cost.

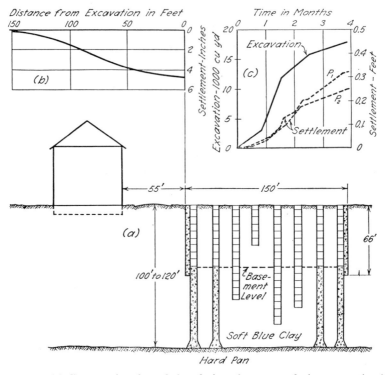

Fig. 215. (a) Cross section through foundation of structure during excavation for piers by Chicago method; (b) relation between settlement of ground surface and distance from edge of foundation area; (c) relation between quantity of soil excavated from shafts, settlement of ground surface, and time.

(a) Use of sheet piles or cylindrical shells that eliminate the vertical part of the working face. One such method is illustrated in Figure 196e.

(b) Use of the heavy liquid method. According to this procedure, a hole is churned into the ground by means of a large rotating bit. The hole is not cased, but is kept filled with the slurry produced by the churning operations. Thus, the tendency for the sides and the bottom to squeeze is opposed by the weight of the fluid, which is heavier than water because it contains clay in suspension. After the hole has been drilled, a light steel shell is inserted to serve as a lining, the slurry is pumped out, and the bottom of the hole is cleaned off and inspected. Concrete is then placed, and the shell withdrawn as the level of the concrete rises.

(c) Use of compressed air. Since the air pressure compensates only for the water pressure at the level of the working face, some loss of ground is inevitable. However, the settlement is reduced to a small fraction of that associated with the Chicago method, Figure 196f.

(d) Use of heavy steel shells driven to final grade and left in the ground. After a shell is driven, the soil is removed by dredging or by means of an air or water jet, and the shell is cleaned with suitable tools, such as a mechanically operated brush, and is filled with concrete. This method has frequently been used with success for the construction of cylindrical piers in very soft soils. It may be less expensive than the compressed-air method.

Practical value of settlement observations during excavation period. The preceding review of the various causes of the settlement of the area surrounding an excavation leaves no doubt that a certain amount of settlement is inevitable. For example, nothing can be done to prevent the settlement due to the lateral yield of the soil toward the zone of heave below the bottom of an open cut. Neither can the bulging of the sides of the cut be prevented during the process of excavating from the level of one set of struts to that of the next set. However, in contrast to the yield that occurs below the bottom, the amount of inward yield of the sides depends to a large extent on the vertical spacing between struts, on the speed of excavation, and on various details of the construction procedure. Hence the corresponding settlement can be considerably reduced by appropriate modifications of the construction procedure.

On a given job reliable information on the relative importance of the lateral yield below and above the bottom of the excavation can be obtained only by measuring the settlement and keeping a record of all the circumstances that might have influenced it. References 60.2, 60.3, and 60.4 contain the results of such investigations. On the basis of the results, the engineer is able to decide whether or not the settlement can be reduced substantially by practicable changes in the procedure. In addition to serving their purpose on the job, the settlement records are of great assistance in planning the construction procedure for other excavations to be made in similar soils, and in predicting the effects of the excavation on structures and public utilities located near the site.

REFERENCES

60.1. K. Terzaghi, Settlement of Structures in Europe and Methods of Observation, *Trans. ASCE*, Vol 103 (1938), Paper 2008, pp 1432–1448. Effect of filling of oil tanks on settlement of neighboring tanks.

60.2. R. B. Peck, Earth-Pressure Measurements in Open Cuts, Chicago Subway, *Trans. ASCE*, Vol 108 (1943), Paper 2200, pp 1008–1036. Record of settlements due to excavation of open cuts in soft clay.

60.3. K. Terzaghi, Linerplate Tunnels on the Chicago Subway, *Trans. ASCE*, Vol 108 (1943), pp 970–1007. Record of settlements caused by the construction of liner-plate tunnels in soft clay.

60.4. K. Terzaghi, Shield Tunnels of the Chicago Subway, *J. Boston Soc. Civil Engrs.*, Vol 29 (1942), pp 163–210. Record of heave and settlement due to shoving a shield through soft clay.

ART. 61. SETTLEMENT DUE TO LOWERING THE WATER TABLE

Causes of Settlement

Whenever a large open excavation is to be made below the water table by any process other than dredging or the sinking of a caisson by the compressed-air method, the water table must be temporarily lowered by pumping, Article 47. By lowering the water table the effective load on the subsoil is increased by an amount equal to the difference between the drained weight (solid and soil moisture combined) and the submerged weight of the entire mass of soil located between the original and the lowered water table. The increase of the effective overburden pressure causes additional compression. This, in turn, produces a settlement that at every point is roughly proportional to the descent of the piezometric level at that point. For a given descent the settlement depends on the compressibility of the subsoil.

Effect of Lowering the Water Table in Sand Strata

Pumping from sand that does not contain any clay strata increases the effective pressure, but the corresponding settlement is usually small unless the sand is very loose. However, if the water table is raised and lowered periodically, the settlement may become important, because every temporary increase of effective pressure increases the settlement by a certain amount. This fact can be demonstrated by means of laboratory tests on laterally confined sand. The magnitude of the increment of settlement decreases with increasing number of cycles and approaches zero, but the final total settlement is many times greater than the settlement produced by the first cycle. The looser the sand, the greater is the settlement.

During construction in an open excavation fluctuations of the lowered water table are usually insignificant. Therefore, if pumping causes large settlements in any but very loose sand, the settlements are probably due to causes other than the increase of the effective weight of the drained portion of the sand. The most common cause is careless pumping from an open sump, Article 47. Several instances of settlement due to this cause are described in Article 59. In all these instances one or more subsurface conduits were formed by backward erosion from springs that discharged into a pit. The settlement produced by the erosion led to the formation of shallow and narrow troughs located above the conduits. The width and depth of the troughs increased with increasing distance from the springs, and the troughs terminated in sink holes. Settlement of this type can be avoided by pumping from well points or by providing the sump with a filter lining.

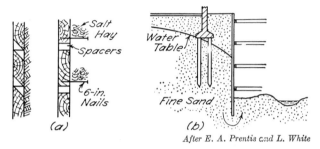

After E. A. Prentis and L. White

Fig. 216. (a) Louvre-type sheeting successfully used in part of open cut in water-bearing sand to prevent loss of ground; (b) continuous steel sheeting used in other sections of the same cut.   Adjacent foundations settled on account of loss of ground by erosive action of rising water veins.

Loss of ground can also occur on one or both sides of an open cut lined by watertight sheet piles. The loss is caused by the erosive action of water as it rises toward the bottom of the cut along the inner face of the sheet piles. It can be avoided by providing the sides of the cut with a permeable instead of an impermeable lining. The following observation demonstrates the efficacy of this procedure. A subway cut was made in New York through fine sand and coarse silt close to buildings founded on pile-supported footings. The points of the piles did not rest on a hard stratum. In one section of the cut the bracing was of the type shown in Figure 147b. The sheeting consisted of boards placed horizontally with spaces between them, as shown in Figure 216a. The spaces were packed with marsh hay to permit free flow of water into the cut without allowing sand to enter. In a second section the sheeting consisted of steel sheet piling driven along the sides of the cut. The sheeting compelled the water to enter the cut by percolating under the sheet piles, as indicated in Figure 216b. Therefore, conditions were favorable for the development of erosion by springs, and the footings of the adjacent buildings settled about 6 in. Excavation of the section with permeable sheeting, on the other hand, produced no noticeable settlement.

Effect of Pumping on Clay Strata

If the subsoil contains layers of soft clay, silt, or peat, lowering of the ground-water table may cause large settlements. In Mexico City, for example, where the subsoil consists of soft bentonitic clays with horizontal layers of water-bearing sand, the withdrawal of water by pumping from sand layers has been accompanied by a general irregular subsidence of the whole area. In some places, the surface has settled more than 5 ft.[61.1] Similarly, in the Santa Clara Valley in California, the operation of 2000 wells to provide water for irrigation initiated a process of progressive settlement. The floor of this valley is underlain by a thick bed of

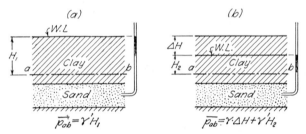

Fig. 217.   Diagrams illustrating cause of settlement of clay surface due to pumping from underlying water-bearing sand.

marine clay that contains layers of water-bearing sand and gravel at a depth of 100 to 200 ft. In 1920 the withdrawal of water began to exceed the natural supply, and the piezometric levels began to descend. By 1933 the corresponding settlement had reached locally as much as 4 ft.[61.2]

The physical causes of this phenomenon are illustrated in Figure 217, which represents a section through a bed of saturated clay overlying a pervious sand layer. In Figure 217a the piezometric level is assumed to be at the ground surface; in b it has been lowered through the distance ΔH by pumping from the layer of sand. Before pumping, the effective pressure on a section ab is

$$\bar{p}_{ab} = \gamma' H_1$$

where γ' is the submerged unit weight of the clay (see Article 12). During and after pumping the effective pressure gradually increases and approaches a final value.

$$\bar{p}_{ab} = \gamma \Delta H + \gamma' H_2$$

where γ is the unit weight, soil plus water, of the saturated clay. The change in effective pressure due to the lowering of the piezometric level is

$$\gamma \Delta H + \gamma' H_2 - \gamma' H_1 = \Delta H(\gamma - \gamma') = \gamma_w \Delta H$$

Therefore, lowering the water table by a distance ΔH ultimately increases the effective pressure on a horizontal section through the clay by an amount equal to the weight of a column of water ΔH in height. This increase involves a progressive settlement of the surface of the clay due to consolidation. The rate and magnitude of the settlement can be computed on the basis of the theory of consolidation and the results of soil tests, Article 41.

If the clay strata are soft and thick, and if the water table is lowered through a considerable distance, the settlement due to pumping is likely to be very great and to spread over a large area. A record of settle-

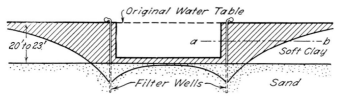

FIG. 218.   Simplified cross section through excavation for Vreeswijk Locks, Holland, showing position of water table lowered by filter wells during excavation (vertical scale greatly exaggerated).

ment of this type was obtained during the construction of the Vreeswijk locks in Holland. At the site of the locks the subsoil consisted of 20 to 23 ft of clay and peat underlain by a thick layer of water-bearing sand. The bottom of the pit was 21 ft below the ground surface and covered an area 170 ft wide by 900 ft long.

Before construction the water level was 8 in. above the ground. During excavation it was lowered, by pumping from filter wells that extended into the sand, to the position indicated in Figure 218. As a result of the pumping, the total effective vertical pressure on any horizontal section such as ab was gradually increased by an amount equal to the height of the shaded area above ab times the unit weight of water. Since the total height of the shaded area was a maximum adjacent to the excavation, the settlement was greatest at the edge of the cut. Even at a distance of 130 ft, the settlement amounted to 2 ft, and it was noticeable as far as 2500 ft.[61.3]

REFERENCES

61.1. José A. Cuevas, Foundation Conditions in Mexico City, *Proc. Intern. Conf. Soil Mech.*, Cambridge, Mass. (1936), Vol III, pp 233–237. Description of the general subsidence of the area covered by the city due to pumping from wells.

61.2. F. H. Tibbetts, Areal Subsidence (letter to the editor), *Eng. News-Record*, Vol 111 (1933), p 204. Brief description of the subsidence of the floor of the Santa

Clara Valley, Calif., due to pumping from irrigation wells. See also *Eng. News-Record*, Vol 118 (1937), pp 479–480.

61.3. W. H. Brinkhorst, Settlement of Soil Surface around Foundation Pit, *Proc. Intern. Conf. Soil Mech.*, Cambridge, Mass. (1936), Vol I, pp 115–119. Record of settlements due to pumping from foundation pit for the locks at Vreeswijk, Holland.

ART. 62. SETTLEMENT CAUSED BY VIBRATIONS

Factors Determining Magnitude of Settlement

Any structure founded on cohesionless soil is likely to settle excessively if the soil is subject to vibrations from such sources as moving machinery, traffic, pile driving, blasting, or earthquakes. On the other hand, the settlement caused by vibration of a foundation on clay is usually so small that it is unlikely to cause serious damage under any circumstances. This conspicuous difference between the effect of vibrations on sand and on clay has already been emphasized in the discussion of the methods for the compaction of fills, Article 50. On account of its sensitivity to vibrations, sand can most effectively be compacted by vibratory equipment, whereas clay can be compacted only by static forces. So far no important settlements of clay foundations due to vibrations have been brought to public attention. Therefore, only the effects of vibrations on sand will be considered.

In Article 19 it is shown that the settlement of the surface of sand due to a pulsating load is many times greater than that produced by static action of the peak value of the load. At a given peak value the settlement depends on the frequency of the pulsations. The greatest settlements occur within a range of about 500 to 2500 impulses per min. This is referred to as the *optimum range*. Since the number of revolutions of steam turbines and turbogenerators lies within this range, the effect of the operation of these machines on settlement is particularly conspicuous.

Examples of Settlement Due to Vibrations

The following examples demonstrate the magnitude of the settlements that may be caused by the vibration of machinery. In Germany a coal-handling plant, 170 by 66 ft in plan, contained coal crushers mounted on concrete blocks 10 ft square. The building rested on footings supported by a bed of fairly dense sand 60 to 130 ft deep. Although the allowable soil pressure of 1.4 tons per sq ft was very conservative, the unequal settlement assumed such proportions that the building was severely damaged and had to be underpinned. In another locality turbogenerators were installed in a powerhouse founded on fairly dense sand and gravel.

The number of revolutions, 1500 per min, was within the optimum range. As a consequence, the maximum settlement of the foundations exceeded 1 ft within a year after the power plant started to operate.

The frequency of traffic vibrations is not necessarily within the optimum range. Nevertheless, experience has shown that continued exposure to such vibrations is likely to produce considerable settlement. In Holland it has been observed that new buildings adjoining old main highways commonly tilt away from the highways. The cause of the tilt is the fact that traffic vibrations had compacted the subsoil beneath and next to the highway, whereas the sand supporting the rear part of the buildings was still in its original condition. In Berlin some of the foundations of the elevated railway settled as much as 14 in. during 40 years of operation. They rested on fairly dense sand and were designed on the basis of an allowable soil pressure of 3.5 tons per sq ft. In Munich where most buildings rest on 20 ft of dense sand and gravel overlying rock, truck traffic of increasing intensity caused settlements of such magnitude that several streets had to be entirely closed to trucking. Within a 10-year period, the damage to adjacent structures rose to about $1,500,000.

Reliable information concerning the settlement caused by pile driving is rather scarce. In one instance about 100 piles were driven into a deposit of sand and gravel so loose that piles as long as 50 ft could be driven without jetting. Within the area occupied by the piles the ground surface settled 6 in. The settlement decreased with increasing distance from the edge of the area to a value of $\frac{1}{8}$ in. at a distance of 50 ft.

No quantitative data are available regarding the settlement due to blasting, but it is probable that the effect is similar to that produced by a mild earthquake. The intensity of earthquakes is usually expressed by the ratio n_g between the greatest acceleration associated with the earthquake and the acceleration g of gravity. For fairly strong earthquakes $n_g = 0.1$. During a very mild earthquake in Vienna, with an intensity $n_g = 0.003$, it was observed that a grain bin with a width of 50 ft and a height of 80 ft settled 1.7 in. more on one side than on the other. The absolute maximum settlement is unknown. The bin was supported by short conical piles embedded in very fine fairly dense water-bearing sand. The load was 4 tons per sq ft over the total area. When the bin was filled for the first time, the settlement was practically uniform and amounted only to about 0.2 in.

Occasionally, pile driving and blasting give rise to complaints or suits for damage, whereupon the engineer may be called on to determine whether or not the complaints are justified. One method of investigation that eliminates the personal equation is illustrated by the following examples.

In the first instance the owner of a house complained that vibrations due to pile driving were causing damage to his structure. To check the validity of his complaint, a fully loaded truck of the heaviest type was driven past the house at maximum legal speed, while seismographic observations were made in the house at points where the owner claimed the vibrations were strongest. During pile-driving operations the seismic observations were repeated. The results indicated that the vibrations caused by pile driving were milder than those caused by the truck. Since the owner was not justified in objecting to vibrations smaller than those caused by trucks passing his house at the maximum legal speed, his claim to damages was disallowed.

In the second instance an owner also protested against blasting in the vicinity of his house, whereupon a similar truck experiment was made. After the experiment charges differing in size were fired, and the corresponding vibrations were observed in the house. The contractor was given permission to blast with charges not greater than those that caused vibrations equivalent to the ones produced by the truck.

Only one satisfactory method is known for protecting a building against vibrations transmitted to it through the soil. It consists of surrounding the structure with a ditch at least 12 ft deep. The sides of the ditch should preferably be unsupported. If space is so limited that the ditch must be provided with vertical sides braced against each other, the bracing must be designed so that it does not transmit the vibrations from one side of the ditch to the other. Observations suggest that protective ditches are most effective if the frequency of vibration is high.

ART. 63. SETTLEMENT DUE TO DETERIORATION OF FOUNDATION CONCRETE

CHARACTERISTICS OF SETTLEMENT DUE TO DETERIORATION OF CONCRETE

If a structure on a concrete foundation begins to develop cracks or to show other signs of differential movement some time after construction, in spite of the fact that the subsoil has not been affected by excavation in the vicinity or by lowering the water table, the defects may be due to one of three causes. These include an increase of the stresses in the structure to the point of failure as a result of increasing differential settlement, a deterioration of the concrete in the foundation, or the development of defects in the superstructure.

If settlement observations have been carried on since the end of the construction period, the shape of the settlement curves seldom leaves any doubt regarding the cause of the settlement. Curves representing the relation between time and the settlement caused by a fairly constant load are smooth, and their slope either decreases with time or becomes constant. Unmotivated departure from this trend demonstrates almost beyond a doubt that the settlement is caused by gradually developing defects of the foundation.

If no settlement observations have been made, it is advisable to determine without delay the elevation of several points whose original position is at least approximately known, to establish a reliable bench mark, and to start settlement observations. By extrapolation from the settlement curves obtained by means of these observations it is usually possible to determine whether the movements started during construction or at a later date. It is not uncommon for concrete deterioration to cause a temporary rise of the structure. This facilitates the diagnosis. If the results leave any doubt regarding the causes of the movements, cores of the foundation concrete should be secured, examined, and tested.

The danger of concrete disintegration is often ignored. When the movements due to disintegration start and cause the first cracks, the cracks are commonly ascribed to unequal settlement, and the real cause is not recognized until the deterioration has advanced so far that it can no longer fail to attract attention. Therefore, the manifestations of concrete disintegration and the conditions leading to chemical attack deserve careful consideration.

Causes and Effects of Concrete Disintegration

Sulphates and carbon dioxide are the substances which most commonly attack concrete structures exposed to groundwater, lake or sea water.

Sulphates are found in sea water, in saline lakes, and in the pore water of so-called "alkali" soils and of rocks and sediments containing gypsum. Sulphides may also be harmful, because they may react with atmospheric oxygen to form sulphates or sulphuric acid. The most common sulphides are FeS_2 (marcasite or pyrite) occurring in marsh deposits and in many rocks, and hydrogen sulphide, H_2S. The latter is likely to be encountered in sewage, in decaying organic matter, and in some regions of relatively recent volcanic activity.

The incidents described in the following paragraphs illustrate the effects of such deleterious substances.

The piers for a bridge across the Neckar river in Germany were constructed on precast reinforced concrete point-bearing piles driven through 33 ft of sand and gravel into shale. A few months after construction the piers settled badly. It was found that the piles had become soft because of attack by water containing CO_2 gas that seeped out of the shale.

The foundations of a bridge across the Elbe river consisted of concrete piers 30 by 65 ft in plan. They extended 35 ft below mean low water to shale buried beneath sand and clay. The excavation was made under compressed air. In spite of their massive character, the piers heaved and cracked so badly that the superstructure could not be erected. The water seeping from the shale was colorless and odorless. Therefore, during construction it was considered nonaggressive. Yet, it contained a quantity of SO_3 equivalent to 1.7 gm of H_2SO_4 per liter, and the presence of this substance caused the concrete to swell intensely. The deterioration was so great that the piers had to be completely reconstructed.

In Seewen, Switzerland, a building was founded on concrete piers about 1 sq yd in cross section. Thirty years after construction the concrete of some of the piers had disintegrated completely. The aggregate was embedded in a white slimy mass that consisted chiefly of calcium carbonate. Disintegration was evidently caused by carbonic acid contained in the ground water.

A sewer canal 7600 ft in length was constructed in sand with layers of peat containing pyrite (FeS_2). A few months after construction longitudinal cracks appeared. The concrete along the cracks was so soft that it could be cut with a knife.

In many of the semiarid regions of the western United States the soil is highly alkaline and contains a sufficient quantity of sulphates to cause relatively rapid deterioration of ordinary concrete. The condition is so widespread and of such importance that many studies have been made by state and Federal agencies to determine the causes of deterioration and the means for reducing the undesirable effects.

METHODS OF DETECTING DELETERIOUS WATER

In order to detect the presence of substances that may cause the disintegration of concrete it is necessary to secure 1 gal samples of the water to which the concrete will be exposed and to have them analyzed. Water analyses should be made, even if there is no reason to suspect the presence of deleterious substances, because contamination may take place at some later date. If there is documentary proof that the water was safe at the time of construction, suit for damage can be filed against the party responsible for the contamination. To be adequate the record of the investigation should contain the following data:

Minimum and mean annual temperature of the water in situ.
pH of water and temperature at which it was determined.
Total dissolved solids.
Methyl orange alkalinity.

Content of calcium (Ca) and sulphate (SO_4).

Content of chlorine (Cl), for sea water and brackish water only.

If there is any reason to suspect the presence of sulphates or sulphides in the soil, representative soil samples should also be analyzed.

Samples of ground water should be taken at different depths from each of several borings, because it has been observed repeatedly that the aggressiveness of ground water may vary considerably from place to place within a small area. If samples are procured from relief pipes, shafts, or open sumps, they should be taken from near the bottom. Samples of water from lakes or other bodies of standing water should likewise be collected at the bottom. This precaution is necessary, because the concentration of dissolved gases such as carbon dioxide or hydrogen sulphide is likely to decrease from the bottom toward the surface. The corresponding difference between the pH value of the water at or near the surface and that of the water at the bottom may be as high as one unit.

Under normal conditions a routine chemical analysis, made by a commercial laboratory, provides sufficient information to indicate whether or not the water is likely to be deleterious. However, if there is any evidence to suggest the presence of a notable concentration of dissolved gas, such as the evolution of bubbles from the water, an odor of H_2S or an abnormally low pH as determined in the laboratory (less than 7 for fresh water, or less than 8 for sea or brackish water), the following precautions are called for. The samples should be taken under the supervision of a sanitary engineer or a chemist familiar with the technique of sampling gas-bearing water, and a pH determination should be made at the site immediately after collection of the sample, because the concentration of acid-forming gaseous constituents is likely to decrease during transportation of samples to the laboratory. If the gases include H_2S, it is advisable to supplement the routine water analysis by a determination of the H_2S concentration.

CONDITIONS LEADING TO CHEMICAL ALTERATION

The maximum concentration of deleterious substances that can safely be disregarded depends not only on the quality of the concrete, the composition of the cement and the degree of exposure, but also on the nature of the other substances dissolved in the water.

In general, water or soil containing more than 0.1 per cent of sulphates is likely to attack concrete.

Hydrogen sulphide is also likely to attack concrete, but the conditions under which it produces deterioration are not yet clearly understood.

If hydrogen sulphide or any other sulphide has an opportunity to oxidize, a sulphate is formed. The effect of the sulphates has been mentioned before.

The presence of carbon dioxide in fresh water may lead to serious deterioration of concrete exposed to it, if the concentration is sufficient to render the water acid, that is, if the pH-value of the water is less than 7. However, not all fresh water characterized by a pH-value of less than 7 is aggressive. Sea water may probably be considered as potentially dangerous if its pH is less than about 7.3. Doubtful or border-line cases may require the advice of an expert.

Means of Delaying Chemical Alteration of Concrete

In some districts the water is so intensely deleterious that concrete exposed to it is likely to disintegrate within a relatively short time. In such districts the base of the concrete foundation should, if possible, be established well above the highest ground-water level. If this cannot be done, every precaution should be taken to render the concrete as impervious as possible. The mix should be rich, and the lowest water–cement ratio consistent with suitable workability should be used. Special care should be taken in selecting aggregate and in handling, placing, and curing the concrete. In mass concrete, where stresses due to volume changes of thermal origin are likely to be large, cracking may be reduced or entirely eliminated by the use of low heat or of modified cement. It is also advantageous to place mass concrete at a time of the year when the minimum daily temperature is below the mean annual temperature. If this is not practicable, or if the body of concrete is very large, artificial cooling may be advisable.

For structures exposed to sulphates, the designer should specify a sulphate-resistant cement characterized by low tricalcium aluminate and low tetracalcium aluminoferrate in preference to low heat or modified cement. Standard Portland cement should not be used in any structure exposed to sulphates.

For structures exposed to natural acidic water, such as water containing carbonic or sulphuric acid, reliance must be placed chiefly on low permeability of the concrete and freedom from cracks, because no type of Portland cement is acid-resistant. Since low permeability can only delay but not prevent deterioration, concrete exposed to water containing an appreciable quantity of free acid will ultimately be destroyed. Small concrete members may disintegrate within one year and large bodies within about 30 years.

REFERENCES

63.1. F. M. LEA AND C. H. DESCH, *The Chemistry of Cement and Concrete*, Arnold, London, 1935. This book contains three chapters devoted to the reaction between hydrated cement and deleterious substances present in water. The discussion is based on the results of tests and, to a lesser extent, on case records. The discussion of the effect of carbonic acid on concrete is correct in principle, but the quantitative criteria that these authors give for determining the aggressiveness of water containing CO_2 are subject to qualification in the light of present-day knowledge of the solubility of $CaCO_3$ in natural waters.

63.2. A. KLEINLOGEL, *Influences on Concrete* (in German), third edition, Berlin, 1930.

MISCELLANEOUS PROBLEMS OF DESIGN AND CONSTRUCTION

SCOPE OF APPENDIX

The following review provides the reader with comments and selected references concerning topics that belong in Part C but have not been considered there because of lack of space. These topics include subgrade studies for highways and airports, the design of sheet-pile bulkheads, the design of cofferdams, earth tunneling, the design of culverts, and methods of grouting soils with cement and chemicals.

SUBGRADE STUDIES FOR HIGHWAYS AND AIRPORTS

The rapid extension of the systems of hard-surfaced roads in the United States and abroad provided the incentive for thorough subgrade investigations prior to the design of the roadways and for improved methods of subgrade treatment. Thus originated a highly specialized branch of soil mechanics known as *highway soils engineering*. The heavy demands for military air transportation in World War II led to the development of an allied branch known as *airport soils engineering*.

In contrast to the performance of the subsoils of foundations, that of the subgrades of highway and airport pavements is decisively influenced by climatic conditions. On account of this fact, general conclusions based on the results of laboratory tests and maintenance experience in geographically limited districts can be very misleading.

A review of current American highway practice in subgrade surveys, soil testing, soil classification, and subgrade and base-course treatment can be found in L. I. Hewes, *American Highway Practice*, Wiley, New York, 1942, Vol. 1, Chapters III and V and Appendix IV. Similar information pertaining to civilian airport design is given in Glidden, Law, and Cowles, *Airports*, McGraw-Hill, New York, 1946, Chapters IV and VII, and sample specifications in the Appendix. Procedures for military airports are described by Middlebrooks and Bertram in "Soil Tests for Design of Runway Pavements," *Proc. Highway Research*

Board, Vol. 22, 1942, pp. 144–173. The relative merits of rigid and flexible pavements for runways are still a matter of controversy.

SHEET-PILE BULKHEADS

Sheet-pile bulkheads serve the same purpose as retaining walls, but, since they consist of single rows of sheet piles, they require external support. The lower ends of the piles are buried in the ground, whereas the upper ends are anchored to anchor plates, anchor walls, or clusters of anchor piles. Until quite recently it was generally believed that the earth pressure against sheet-pile bulkheads was determined by the same laws that applied to retaining walls. Even today the customary methods of bulkhead design are based on this assumption. However, experience, experiments, and theoretical investigations indicate that the maximum bending moment in the sheet piles may be considerably smaller than that computed on the basis of the customary methods. On the other hand the real anchor pull seems to exceed the computed value, and most bulkhead failures occur on account of a failure of the anchorage.

The theoretical principles of bulkhead design are stated in K. Terzaghi, *Theoretical Soil Mechanics*, Wiley, New York, 1943, pp. 216–234, with references. See also J. P. R. N. Stroyer, "Earth Pressure on Flexible Walls," paper 5024, *J. Inst. Civil Engrs. (London)*, Vol. 1, 1935–36, pp. 94, 139; discussions pp. 550–557. This paper deals with the results of model tests that demonstrate the importance of the influence of the outward deflection of the bulkhead on the maximum bending moment.

STABILITY AND STIFFNESS OF COFFERDAMS

Cofferdams are dams with a brief service period. They are built around the site of construction operations to be performed in the dry below the level of rivers or bodies of standing water. In the design of a cofferdam consideration must be given to the head of water that will act against the dam, the dimensions of the area to be drained, the subsoil conditions, the fluctuations of the outside water level, and the possibility of erosion along the outer face of the cofferdam. An analysis of the conditions that determine the stability and stiffness of cofferdams is contained in the paper "Stability and Stiffness of Cellular Cofferdams," by K. Terzaghi, *Trans. ASCE*, paper 2253, Vol. 110, 1945, pp. 1083–1119; discussions pp. 1120 to 1202. A comprehensive review of practical experiences with different types of cofferdams can be found in the book, *Cofferdams*, by L. White and E. A. Prentis, Columbia University Press, New York, 1940, pp. 93–253. Some of the statements and views expressed in the theoretical part of the book, pp. 1–92, are controversial,

and the practical value of model studies appears to be overemphasized. The results of model studies are no more reliable than those obtained by the flow-net method, Article 39.

EARTH TUNNELING

A distinction must be made between the earth pressure on temporary and on permanent tunnel supports. The temporary lining supports the roof and the walls of the tunnel until the permanent lining can be conveniently constructed. While a tunnel or shaft is being excavated and the temporary lining is being installed, the shearing resistance of the surrounding soil is likely to be fully active. At this stage the pressure on the tunnel lining is governed primarily by the laws of arch action (see K. Terzaghi, *Theoretical Soil Mechanics*, pp. 66–76 and 194–215). After the permanent tunnel lining is constructed, the pressure on the tunnel increases for some time. In sands above the water table the increase is only moderate, but in stiff swelling clays it is very large.

The earth-pressure phenomena encountered in earth tunnels and the means for coping with the difficulties that arise from the tendency of the soil to invade the tunnel are described in *Earth Tunneling with Steel Supports* by R. V. Proctor and T. L. White, The Commercial Shearing and Stamping Co., Youngstown, Ohio, 1948, Section I: *Principles of Earth Tunneling*, by K. Terzaghi.

The results of experimental investigations of arch action in sand above yielding roof supports are described in the paper "Stress Distribution in Dry and in Saturated Sand above a Yielding Trap-Door," by K. Terzaghi, *Proc. Intern. Conf. Soil Mech.*, Cambridge, Mass., 1936, Vol. I, pp. 307–311. Results of the measurements of pressures on the temporary and permanent lining of tunnels through soft silt and soft clay are recorded in the papers, "The Measurement of Soil Pressures on the Lining of the Midtown Hudson Tunnel," by G. M. Rapp and A. H. Baker, *Proc. Intern. Conf. Soil Mech.*, Cambridge, Mass., 1936, Vol. II, pp. 150–156; "Liner-Plate Tunnels on the Chicago, (Ill.) Subway," by K. Terzaghi, *Trans. ASCE*, Paper 2200, Vol. 108, 1943, pp. 970–1007; "Earth Pressure on Tunnels," by W. S. Housel, *Trans. ASCE*, Paper 2200, Vol. 108, 1943, pp. 1037–1058; and "Shield Tunnels of the Chicago Subway," by K. Terzaghi, *J. Eoston Soc. Civil Engrs.*, Vol. 29, 1942, pp. 163–210.

Opinions are divided concerning the assumptions on which the design of the permanent linings of earth tunnels should be based. In this connection the two last-mentioned papers by K. Terzaghi may be consulted. See also G. L. Groves, "Tunnel Linings with Special Reference to a New Form of Reinforced Concrete Lining," *J. Inst. Civil Engrs. (London)*,

Paper 5304, March 1943, pp. 29–64; discussions, October 1943, pp. 357–365.

CULVERT DESIGN

Culverts are tunnel-like water conduits constructed in open cuts and subsequently buried. If a culvert is located on a nonrigid base, it is acted upon not only by earth pressure but also by bending in a vertical plane through its longitudinal axis, on account of the trough-shaped settlement of the base of the fill. It is also subjected to axial tension because of the shearing stresses that increase the width of the base of the fill. The failure of culverts by axial tension is not uncommon.

The distribution of the earth pressure on the outside of culverts depends to a large extent on the stiffness of the culvert walls and the compressibility of the backfill on the sides of the culvert. In the existing methods of culvert design, this important fact has not yet been adequately considered. Most of the methods are based on the assumption that the culvert is rigid. As consequence, the real bending moments in the walls of culverts with a rectangular cross section or in the shells of culverts with a circular cross section are likely to be very much smaller than the computed ones. When the references are consulted, this fact should be kept in mind.

A review of present American practice in culvert design can be found in L. I. Hewes, *American Highway Practice*, Wiley, New York, 1942, Vol. II, Appendixes I and II. See also *Handbook of Culvert and Drainage Practice*, Armco International Corporation, Middletown, Ohio, 1938, pp. 11–118. The results of measurements of the earth pressure on a cut-and-cover conduit in service were published in "Achieving Strength and Tightness in Cut-and-Cover Conduit" by D. B. Gumensky, *Eng. News-Record*, Vol. 117, 1936, pp. 633–635. Under different conditions of backfill and culvert rigidity entirely different results would have been obtained.

GROUTING WITH CEMENT AND CHEMICALS

Grouting serves either to reduce the quantity of water that percolates into an excavation or else to increase the bearing capacity of the soil. If the effective size of a sand or a sand–gravel mixture is greater than about 1 mm, the soil can be transformed into concrete by injecting cement grout into its interstices under pressure. Fine and very fine sands have been solidified by the successive injection of two different chemicals that react in the voids to form a hard and fairly impermeable binder. Reduction of the permeability of fine and very fine sands without appreciable increase in strength can be achieved by injecting a single solution that precipitates a gel one or several hours after injection. Neither method can be used with any prospect for success in fine silt or clay, because the low permeability of these soils prevents impregnation within a reasonable length of time.

A review of the principal methods of grouting and of the conditions for their successful application can be found in "Opening Discussion M-6" by K. Terzaghi, *Proc. Intern. Conf. Soil Mech.* Cambridge, Mass., 1936, Vol. III, pp. 180–182. The same *Proceedings* contain the articles, "A New Method of Impermeabilizing and Improving the Physical Properties of Pervious Subsoils by Injecting Bituminous Emulsions," by J. H. Pfeiffer, Vol. I, pp. 263–266; and "The Foundation of the Building La Baloise in Lugano, Switzerland, Involving Modern Methods in Deep Foundation Technique," by G. D. Rodio, Vol. III, pp. 215–226. Some practical applications of the two-chemical method for grouting fine sand are described in "Use of Silification for Construction in Running Ground, Process of H. Joosten" (in French), by K. Pohl, *Genie Civil* (Paris), Vol. C, Jan. 2, 1932, pp. 14–17.

Occasionally coarse-grained soils have been grouted with clay or bentonite suspensions, but the published data do not yet permit defining the conditions for successful application of this method.

AUTHOR INDEX

SUBJECT INDEX

UPHEAVAL

$$\gamma H - \frac{C_{FRIC} H}{.707 B} \le \frac{5.7 c}{1.5} + \left(\gamma z - \frac{c z}{.707 B}\right) \quad \gamma H \downarrow \begin{array}{c} c \uparrow \\ c \uparrow \end{array}$$

$$C \times z + \left(C \times (y+z)\right) = (x+y+z) \cdot \underline{\frac{WT}{FT \text{ of CAISSON}}}$$

CAISSON SINKING SCHEDULE

Depth of Point	Depth of Soil Inside	Height of Caisson Above Ground
$y + z$	z	x

483